The Nature
and Properties
of Soils

SIXTH EDITION

The Nature and Properties of Soils

A COLLEGE TEXT OF EDAPHOLOGY

HARRY O. BUCKMAN
PROFESSOR OF SOIL TECHNOLOGY
EMERITUS, CORNELL UNIVERSITY

NYLE C. BRADY
PROFESSOR OF SOIL SCIENCE
AND HEAD, DEPARTMENT OF AGRONOMY
CORNELL UNIVERSITY

Revised by
NYLE C. BRADY

THE MACMILLAN COMPANY—*New York*

6/1969

Eleventh Printing, 1968

Library of Congress catalog card number: 60–5682

The Macmillan Company, New York
Collier-Macmillan Canada, Ltd., Toronto, Ontario

Printed in the United States of America

Previous editions, entitled THE NATURE AND PROPERTIES OF SOILS by T. Lyttleton Lyon, Harry O. Buckman, and Nyle C. Brady © copyright 1922, 1929, 1937, 1943 and 1952 by The Macmillan Company. Copyrights renewed 1950 by Bertha C. Lyon and Harry O. Buckman and 1957 by Harry O. Buckman.

Preface

The author of an elementary book in an applied science is faced with two major problems. He must attempt to be scientifically correct in presenting the subject. At the same time his presentation must be such that the student maintains an interest in the subject and has no difficulty in understanding it. With advancing scientific knowledge and less than adequate preparation of many college students, these problems have become increasingly critical.

The changes which have been made in the sixth edition of this text are all related to these two major problems. For example, the chapters dealing with clay minerals, soil water, soil pH, weathering and soil nitrogen have been revised to incorporate new concepts resulting from research. In all other chapters less extensive modifications have been made to bring the subject matter up to date. Throughout the text new photographs, diagrams, and figures have been used to present the subjects of soil science in a more simplified manner. In the interest of clarity, the subject matter presentation may have been oversimplified in some cases. However, in general the concepts presented are based on sound research data and the terminology used is of the same level as that found in an elementary college chemistry text. The assumption has been made that the students using this text have a sufficient knowledge of elementary chemistry, physics, and geology to understand simple chemical formulae and equations.

Two subjects—micronutrients and soil survey interpretation—are given somewhat more attention than was the case in the fifth edition. The almost universal recognition of the significance of micronutrients justifies a separate chapter of these essential elements. There is also a need for a better understanding of the use that can be made of soil survey information in determining the best land-use patterns.

The authors express their appreciation to the many soil scientists whose helpful suggestions and criticisms were invaluable in revising this text. Especial thanks are due Dr. T. R. Nielsen, Cornell University, whose critical review of the fifth edition was the basis for some of the changes and improvements made herein. The junior author is also indebted to his wife, Martha, whose encouragement and unselfish assistance in typing and proofreading the manuscript were invaluable.

Contents

Chapter 16.   *The Nitrogen Economy of Soils*   409

The Soil in Perspective

CHAPTER 1

Man is dependent on soils—and to a certain extent good soils are dependent upon man and the use he makes of them. Soils are the natural bodies on which plants grow. Man enjoys and uses these plants either because of their beauty or their ability to supply fiber and food for himself and his animals. His very living standard is often determined by the quality of his soils and the kinds and quality of plants and animals grown on them.

Great civilizations have almost invariably had good soils as one of their chief natural resources. Furthermore, these civilizations have remained great only so long as they properly cared for their soils. The downfall of great nations utilizing the Tigris, Euphrates, and Nile River Valleys coincided with a deterioration of soil and water management and conservation practices. Even in our own country unwise exploitation and misuse has badly damaged some soils and has called our attention to the need for stringent measures to conserve and improve this valuable resource.

1:1. WHAT IS SOIL?

The commonplace features of nature are often not well understood or appreciated. For many of us, the soil is such a feature. It can be found most everywhere and has seemingly always been with us. Because of this, the majority of us have never taken the trouble to find out what the soil is, where it comes from, and what its basic properties are. We may not have observed how different the soil is in one place as compared to another. Certainly few of us know the reasons for these differences.

Concepts of soil. Part of our lack of concern with the soil may be due to our different concepts and viewpoints concerning this important prod-

1

uct of nature. For example, to a mining engineer the soil is the debris covering the rocks or minerals which he must quarry. It is a nuisance and must be disposed of. To the highway engineer it may be the material on which a road bed is to be placed. If its properties are suitable it is useful. If its properties are unsuitable it must be removed and rock and gravel put in its place.

The average homeowner has a concept of soil. It is a pleasant one if as he says "the ground is nice and mellow or loamy." The opposite viewpoint is associated with "hard clay" which resists being spaded up into a good seedbed for a flower garden. The housewife can differentiate between variations in the soil, especially those relating to its stickiness or tendency to cling to shoe soles and eventually to carpets.

The farmer, along with the homeowner, looks upon the soil as a habitat for plants. He makes a living from the soil and is thereby forced to pay more attention to its characteristics. To him the soil is more than useful—it is indispensable.

In order to learn more about the soil we must have a common concept as to what it is. Furthermore, our concept must encompass the viewpoints of the engineer, the homeowner and his wife, and by all means, the farmer. In developing this concept let us first consider soil as it is found in nature.

Soil vs. regolith.   Every one has seen views such as that shown in Figure 1:1 in which unconsolidated materials are found on underlying rocks. Above bedrock some unconsolidated debris such as that shown in the photograph is present almost universally. This material, known as *regolith,* may be nebligibly shallow or it may be hundreds of feet in thickness. It may be material which has weathered from the underlying rock or it may have been transported by the action of wind, water, or ice and deposited upon the bedrock. In any case, the regolith is apt to be variable in composition from place to place.

If one were to examine the upper 3 to 6 feet of the regolith he would often find that it differed from the material below. Being nearer to the atmosphere, this upper zone has been more subject to the weathering action of wind, water, and heat. Furthermore, it is the zone in which most of the plant roots are found. Plant residues, deposited originally on the surface, have become incorporated by earthworms into the surface layers and have been disintegrated and partially decomposed by microorganisms.

The presence of some undecomposed organic matter along with weathering of minerals in the soil have often resulted in the formation of characteristic horizontal layering. This upper and biochemically weathered portion of the regolith, which is generally considered to be the soil, may be distinguished from the material below [1] by: (1) a relatively high organic matter content; (2) an abundance of the roots of higher plants and of soil organisms; (3) more intense weathering; and (4) the presence of characteristic horizontal layers.

Figure 1:1. Diagram showing the relative positions of the regolith, its soil and the underlying country rock. Sometimes the regolith is so thin that it has been changed entirely to soil, which, in such a case, rests directly on bed rock. *(Photo courtesy Tennessee Valley Authority.)*

The scientist considers the soil to be a *natural body* having both depth and surface area. He also looks upon the soil as a product of nature resulting from both destructive and synthetic forces. Weathering and microbial decay of organic residues are examples of destructive processes, while the formation of new minerals, such as certain clays, and the development of characteristic layer patterns are synthetic in nature. Last, but not least,

[1] In cases where the regolith was relatively uniform originally, the material below the soil is considered as having composition similar to the *parent material* from which the soil formed.

the scientist considers the soil as a habitat for plants. He recognizes the contributions which plants have made to soil development and realizes that the most important practical use of soils is in crop production.

The soil vs. a soil. Man has found that characteristics of the soil vary widely from place to place. For example, on steep slopes the soil is generally not as deep and productive as is the case when it is formed on gentle slopes. Where it has developed from sandstone it tends to be more sandy and less fertile than where it has formed from rocks such as shale. Its properties are quite different when it has developed under tropical climates as compared to temperate or arctic conditions.

Scientists have recognized these soil variations from place to place and have set up classification systems in which the soil is considered as composed of a large number of individual soils, each having its distinguishing characteristics. Therefore, *a soil,* as distinguished from *the soil,* is merely a well-defined subdivision having recognized limits in its characteristics and properties. Thus, a sandy soil, a clay soil, and a loam soil are examples of specific soils which collectively make up the over-all *soil* which covers land areas.

1:2. THE SOIL PROFILE

Let us examine in somewhat greater detail the characteristics of a representative soil as found in the field. If we were to cut a section downward through this soil, the horizontal layers previously referred to would be found. Such a section is called a *profile* and the individual layers are regarded as *horizons.* These horizons above the parent material are collectively referred to as the *solum.*[2] Every well-developed, undisturbed soil has its own distinctive profile characteristics. They are made use of in soil classification and survey and are of great practical importance. In judging a soil its whole profile should be taken into consideration.

The upper layers of a soil profile generally contain considerable amounts of organic matter and are usually darkened appreciably because of such an accumulation. Layers thus characterized are conveniently referred to as the major zone of organic-matter accumulation. When a soil is plowed and cultivated, they include the familiar *surface soil* or *furrow-slice.* The underlying *subsoil,* also markedly weathered, contains comparatively less organic matter. The various subsoil layers, especially in mature, humid-region soils, often present two very general belts: (1) an

---

[2] *Solum*—a latin legal term meaning soil, land, or parcel of land.

upper zone of transition; and (2) a lower zone of accumulation. In the
latter, iron and aluminum oxides, clay, and even calcium carbonate may
gradually concentrate. (See Fig. 1:2.)

SURFACE SOIL
Zone of maximum organic
accumulation. Coincides
more or less closely with
furrow-slice

SUBSOIL
Character is determined
to a considerable degree
by nature of soil
forming forces

SUBSTRATUM
Usually more or
less weathered

Figure 1:2. A representative soil profile. The surface horizons are relatively high in organic matter and become the furrow-slice when the land is plowed. The subsoil, while markedly weathered, usually contains but little organic matter. At variable depths it merges more or less gradually into the substratum (parent material). All of the layers above the substratum are spoken of collectively as the *solum*.

The solum thus described extends an indefinite but moderate depth
below the surface. A depth of 3 or 4 feet is representative for temperate-
region soils. Here, the noticeably modified lower subsoil gradually merges
with the less weathered portion of the regolith. This part of the regolith
is called the *parent material* to distinguish it from the soil just above. It is
usually weathered, and its upper portion is geologically on the point of
becoming a part of the lower subsoil and hence of the solum.

It is not to be inferred that the various layers comprising a soil profile
are always distinct and well defined. In fact, the transition from one to the
other often is so gradual that the establishment of boundaries is rather
difficult. Nevertheless, for any particular soil the various horizons are characteristic and greatly influence the growth of higher plants.

1:3. SUBSOIL vs. SURFACE SOIL

The productivity of a soil is determined in no small degree by the nature of its subsoil. The practical importance of this fact is seen when we consider that the subsoil normally is subject to little field alteration except by drainage. Even when roots do not penetrate deeply into the subsoil, its permeability and its chemical nature still may favorably or unfavorably influence the surface soil as a medium for plant growth. (See Fig. 1:3.)

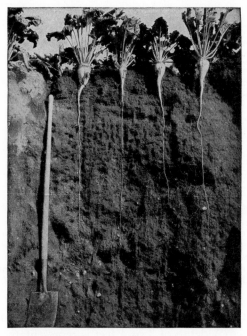

Figure 1:3. Deep rooting plants such as sugar beets must have a porous subsoil for most satisfactory growth. In the case pictured the crop undoubtedly is obtaining large amounts of mineral nutrients as well as water from the subsoil or even from the substratum. A fairly permeable subsoil is especially desirable where irrigation is practiced. *(The Great Western Sugar Company Photo.)*

The situation in respect to the surface soil is somewhat different. In the first place, it is the major zone of root development, it carries much of the nutrients available to plants, and it supplies a large share of the water used by crops. *Second,* as the layer which is plowed and cultivated, it is subject to manipulation and management. By proper cultivation and by the incorporation of organic residues, its physical condition may be modified. It can be fertilized, limed, and drained. In short, its fertility and to a lesser degree its productivity,[3] may be raised, or lowered, or satisfactorily stabilized at levels consistent with economic crop production.

This explains why much of the soil investigation and research has been expended upon the surface layer. It also explains why most of the discussion and explanation that follows, the data quoted, and the conclusions drawn concern themselves with surface soils. Plowing, cultivation, liming, and fertilization are essentially furrow-slice considerations. In fact, the term "soil," unmodified, will from here on be taken as reference to the surface layer, the so-called topsoil, or in practical terms, the furrow-slice.

1:4. MINERAL (INORGANIC) vs. ORGANIC SOILS

The profile generalizations presented above show the organic matter to be largely in the surface horizon. However, even in this zone the amounts are always comparatively low, ranging in general from 1 to 5 or 6 per cent. Because of the predominance of inorganic constituents that necessarily results, such soils are conveniently referred to as *mineral* or *inorganic soils*. Most soils are of this nature and are so common that a person involuntarily thinks of this type when the term soil is mentioned.

But in swamps, bogs, and marshes, conditions often encourage the accumulation of much organic matter. This gives rise to peat deposits and muck soils in which the organic content may range as high as 95 per cent. Perhaps 80 per cent of organic matter and 20 per cent of minerals are reliable representative figures for the organic deposits now being cultivated. A high organic content characterizes the whole profile, quite in contrast with the mineral soil sections already described. (See Fig. 13:1.) As such they are referred to as *organic* or *muck soils*.

As might be expected, muck soils are markedly different from mineral soils in many important respects and their practical handling presents problems that are both distinctive and unique. In spite of their smaller area, these soils are very important for certain crops, especially those, such as vegetables, which respond to intensive culture.

Not only are mineral soils of wider area and better known than are organic soils, but also they are in general more important agriculturally. Consequently, mineral soils deservedly receive the major attention in

[3] The term *fertility* refers to the inherent capacity of a soil to supply nutrients to plants in adequate amounts and in suitable proportions. *Productivity* is related to the ability of a soil to yield crops. Productivity is the broader term since fertility is only one of a number of factors that determine the magnitude of crop yields.

this text, the origin, character, and agricultural use of organic soils being considered as a unit in Chapter 13. Until then the discussion will concern itself almost exclusively with mineral soils.

1:5. THE APPROACH—EDAPHOLOGICAL vs. PEDOLOGICAL

Now that a general concept of soils has been presented, we recognize that a soil can be considered (1) as a biochemically weathered product of nature, and (2) as a habitat for the growth of plants. These conceptions illustrate the two paths of approach that can be used in studying soils— that of the *pedologist* in the one case and that of the *edaphologist* in the other.

Certain phases such as the origin of the soil, its classification and description, are embraced in what is designated as pedology.[4] *Pedology* considers the soil purely as a natural body and lays minor emphasis on its immediate practical utilization. The pedologist studies, examines and classifies soils as they occur in their natural environment. His findings may be as useful to highway and construction engineers as to the farmer.

Edaphology[5] is the study of the soil from the standpoint of higher plants. It considers the various properties of soils as they relate to plant production. The edaphologist is a practical man since he has the production of food and fiber as an ultimate goal. At the same time, he must be a scientist in order to determine reasons for variation in the productivity of soils and to find means of conserving and improving this productivity.

In this textbook our dominant viewpoint shall be that of the edaphologist. Pedology will be used only to the extent that it gives us a general understanding of soils as they occur in nature and as they are classified.

1:6. AN EDAPHOLOGICAL CHARACTERIZATION
OF MINERAL SOILS

Mineral soils have already been designated as the "upper and biologically weathered portion of the regolith." When expanded by profile and horizon study, this statement presents a pedological concept of soil origin and characterization. If, however, the production of higher plants is to be a part of the picture, a broader and more inclusive statement must be offered. In the light of the ideas already presented respecting the general function of the soil, the following edaphological definition is suggested:

[4] Pedology from *pedon* meaning soil or earth.
[5] Edaphology from *edaphos* also meaning soil or ground. The term *edaphology* was suggested by Dr. Horace L. Jones, Professor of the Classics, Emeritus, Cornell University. Its meaning was formulated by the authors of this text.

The soil may be defined as a natural body, synthesized in profile form from a variable mixture of broken and weathered minerals and decaying organic matter, which covers the earth in a thin layer and which supplies, when containing the proper amounts of air and water, mechanical support and, in part, sustenance for plants.

1:7. FOUR MAJOR COMPONENTS OF SOILS

The definition just cited leads logically to an inquiry as to soil composition. This will be dealt with here in a very general way. Mineral soils consist of four major components: *mineral materials, organic matter, water,* and *air*. These, in the main, are in a rather fine state of subdivision and are intimately mixed. In fact, the contact is often so close as to render satisfactory separation rather difficult.

Volume composition of mineral soils. In Figure 1:4 is shown the approximate volume composition of a representative silt loam surface soil in optimum condition for plant growth. Note that it contains about 50 per cent pore space (air and water). The solid space is made up by volume of about 45 per cent mineral matter and 5 per cent organic matter. At optimum moisture for plant growth, the 50 per cent of pore space possessed by this representative silt loam is divided roughly in half—25 per cent of water space and 25 per cent of air. The proportion of air and water is, of course,

Figure 1:4. Volume composition of a silt loam surface soil when in good condition for plant growth. The air and water in a soil are extremely variable, and their proportion determines in large degree its suitability for plant growth.

subject to great fluctuations under natural conditions, depending on the weather and other factors. (See Fig. 1:4.)

In presenting such an arbitrary volume representation of a surface mineral soil, it must be emphasized that the four main components of the normal soil exist for the most part in an intimately mixed condition. This encourages both simple and complex reactions within and between the groups and permits an ideal environment for the growth of plants.

As might be expected, the volume composition of subsoils is somewhat different from that just described. Compared to topsoils they are lower in organic matter content, and have a tendency to be somewhat more compact and to contain a higher percentage of small pores. This means a higher percentage of minerals and water and a considerable lower content of organic matter and air.

1:8. THE MINERAL (INORGANIC) CONSTITUENTS IN SOILS

A casual examination of a sample of soil illustrates that the inorganic portion is variable in size and in composition. It is normally composed of small *rock* fragments and of *minerals* [6] of various kinds. The rock fragments are remnants of massive rocks from which the regolith and in turn the soil has been formed by weathering. They are usually quite coarse. (See Table 1:1.) The minerals, on the other hand, are extremely variable

TABLE 1:1

Four Major Size Classes of Inorganic Particles and Their General Properties

Size Fraction	Common Name	Visible Using	Dominant Composition
1. Very coarse	Stone, gravel	Naked eye	Rock fragments
2. Coarse	Sands	Naked eye	Primary minerals
3. Fine	Silt	Microscope	Primary and secondary minerals
4. Very fine	Clay	Electron microscope	Mostly secondary minerals

in size. Some are as large as the smaller rock fragments; others, such as colloidal clay particles, are so small that they cannot be seen even with the aid of an ordinary microscope. An electron microscope must be used.

Minerals such as quartz and other so-called *primary* minerals have persisted more or less unchanged in composition from the original country rock. Other minerals such as the silicate clays and iron oxides have been formed by the weathering of less resistant minerals as the regolith developed and soil formation progressed. These minerals are called *secondary* minerals. In general, the primary minerals tend to dominate the coarser fractions of soil while secondary minerals are most prominent in the fine materials and especially in clays. It is obvious, therefore, that mineral particle size will have much to do with the properties of soils in

[6] The word *mineral* is used in this text in two ways: first, as a general term to describe soils which are dominated by inorganic constituents, and second, as a more specific term to describe distinct minerals found in nature such as *quartz, feldspars,* etc. A more detailed discussion of the common soil-forming minerals and the rocks in which they are found is given in Chapter 11.

the field. This will be further emphasized in a later section in which the chemical properties of clay, the finest of the mineral fractions, are considered.

1:9. THE SOIL ORGANIC MATTER

Soil organic matter represents an accumulation of partially decayed and partially resynthesized plant and animal residues. Such material is in an active state of decay, being subject to attack by soil microorganisms. Consequently, it is a rather transitory soil constituent and must be renewed constantly by the addition of higher plant residues.

The organic matter content of a soil is small—only about 3 to 5 per cent by weight in the case of a representative mineral topsoil. Its influence on soil properties and consequently on plant growth, however, is far greater than this low content would lead one to believe. In the first place, organic matter functions as a "granulator" of the mineral particles, being largely responsible for the loose, friable condition of productive soils. Also, organic matter is a major soil source of two important mineral elements, phosphorus and sulfur, and essentially the sole source of nitrogen. Through its effect on the physical condition of soils, organic matter also tends to increase the amounts of water a soil can hold and the proportion of this water that is available for plant growth. Last, organic matter is the main source of energy for soil microorganisms. Without it, biochemical activity would come practically to a standstill.

For convenience, the soil organic matter may be considered to consist of two general groups: (1) orginal tissue and its partially decomposed equivalents; and (2) the humus. The original tissue includes the more or less undecomposed additions that are constantly being made—the roots and the tops of higher plants. These materials are subject to vigorous attack by soil organisms, both plant and animal, which use them as sources of energy and as tissue-building material.

The gelatinous, more resistant products of this decomposition, both those synthesized by the microorganisms and those modified from the original plant tissue, are collectively known as *humus*. This material, usually black or brown in color, is colloidal in nature. Its capacity to hold water and nutrient ions greatly exceeds that of clay, its inorganic counterpart. Small amounts of humus thus augment tremendously the soil's capacity to promote plant production.

The nonsolid or pore spaces in the soil are occupied by either water or air. Consequently the content of these two important components in a given soil are interrelated; as one increases, the other decreases and vice versa. An optimum balance between water and air must be maintained for best plant growth. This concept should be kept in mind as these two components are discussed in the next two sections.

1:10. SOIL WATER—A DYNAMIC SOLUTION

Two major concepts concerning soil water are necessary in order to obtain a general idea of the significance of this major component of the soil. These are: (1) water is held within the soil pores with varying degrees of tenacity depending on the amount of water present; and (2) together with its dissolved salts, soil water makes up the so-called *soil solution* which is so important as a medium for supplying nutrients to growing plants. The significance of these two facts in relation to plant growth is great.

The tenacity with which water is held by soil solids determines to a marked degree the movement of water in soils and its use by plants. An example of the latter relationship will be cited. When the moisture content of a soil is optimum for plant growth (see Fig. 1:4), plants can readily assimilate the soil water, much of which is present in pores of intermediate size. As some of the moisture is removed by the growing plants, that which remains is present in only the tiny pores and as thin films around the soil particles. The attraction of the soil solids for this water is great, and they can compete successfully with higher plants for it. Consequently, not all the water that soils can hold is available to plants. Much of it remains in the soil after plants have used some water and have wilted or even died as a consequence of water shortage. The practical significance of this available water limitation will of course be determined by the kind of soils and by the supply of rain or irrigation water.

The soil solution contains small but significant quantities of dissolved salts, many of which are essential for plant growth. There is an exchange of nutrients between the solids and the soil solution and, in turn, between the soil solution and plants. These exchanges are influenced to a degree by the concentration of salts in the solution which in turn is determined by the total salts in the soil and by the content of soil water. Thus, we can see the dynamic nature of this solute-bearing water and its importance to plant life.

1:11. THE SOIL AIR—ALSO A CHANGEABLE CONSTITUENT

Soil air differs from that of the atmosphere in several respects. First, the soil air is not continuous, being located in the maze of soil pores separated by soil solids. This fact accounts for its variation in composition from place to place in the soil. In local pockets, reactions involving the gases can greatly modify the composition of the soil air. Second, soil air generally has a higher moisture content than the atmosphere, the relative humidity approaching 100 per cent when soil moisture is optimum. Third, the content of carbon dioxide is generally higher and that of oxygen lower than that found in the atmosphere. Carbon dioxide is often several hundred times more concentrated than the 0.03 per cent commonly found in the atmosphere. Oxygen decreases accordingly, and in extreme cases may be no more than 10 to 12 per cent as compared to about 20 per cent for normal atmosphere.

The content and composition of soil air is determined to a large degree by the soil-water relationships. Being a mixture of gases, the air simply moves into those soil pores not occupied by water. Following a rain, the pores first vacated by the soil water are the large pores, followed by medium sized pores as water is removed by evaporation and plant utilization. Thus, the soil air generally occupies the large pores and, as the soil dries out those intermediate in size.

This explains the tendency for soils with a high proportion of tiny pores to be poorly aerated. In such soils, water tends to dominate and the soil-air content and composition is unsatisfactory for best plant growth.

The dynamic nature of soil air is seen from the above discussion. The tendency for rapid changes in air content and composition has marked effects not only on the growth of economic plants but also upon the soil organisms, plant and animal, which occupy the soil. We shall now turn briefly to the part which these organisms play in soil reactions.

1:12. THE SOIL—A TREMENDOUS BIOLOGICAL LABORATORY

The representative mineral soil, bearing as it does so much available energy in organic form, harbors a varied population of living organisms. Indeed, the *life* of the soil plays such a prominent and indispensable role in the changes constantly occurring, that no discussion of the soil is complete without its consideration.

Representatives of both animals and plants are abundant in soils. The whole range in size from the larger rodents, worms, and insects to the tiniest bacteria commonly occurs in normal soils. Moreover, most organisms vary so much both in numbers and amounts as to make precise statements impossible. For example, the number of bacteria alone in 1 gram of soil may range from 100,000 to several billion, depending on conditions.

The total weight of living matter, including plant roots, in an acre-furrow-slice of a representative mineral soil may be placed at 5,000 pounds at least, while 10,000 or 20,000 pounds may be more nearly correct for many soils. In any case, the quantity of living organic matter is sufficient to influence profoundly the physical and chemical trend of soil changes. Indeed it can even be said that "practically all natural soil reactions are directly or indirectly biochemical in nature."

Activities of soil organisms vary from the largely physical disintegration of plant residues by insects and earthworms to the eventual complete decomposition of these residues by smaller organisms such as bacteria, fungi, and actinomycetes. Accompanying these decaying processes is the release of several nutrient elements from organic combination. Nitrogen, phosphorus, and sulfur are examples. By contrast, conditions in nature are such that organisms need these elements for their growth and a reversal occurs, i.e., the elements are converted again into organic combinations not available to higher plants.

Humus synthesis, exclusively a biochemical phenomenon, results from soil-organism activity. This material is certainly one of the most useful of the products of microbial action. We shall now turn our attention to some of the chemical properties of humus and its inorganic counterpart, clay.

1:13. CLAY AND HUMUS—THE SEAT OF SOIL ACTIVITY

In the previous sections, attention was called to the dynamic nature of the finer portions of the soil—clay and humus. Both these constituents exist in the so-called colloidal state wherein the individual particles are characterized by extremely small size, large surface area per unit weight, and the presence of surface charges to which ions and water are attracted.

The chemical and physical properties of soils are controlled largely by clay and humus. They act as centers of activity around which chemical reactions, and nutrient exchanges occur. Furthermore, by attracting ions to their surfaces, they temporarily protect essential nutrients from leaching and then release them slowly for plant use. Because of their surface charges they are also thought to act as "contact bridges" between larger particles, thus helping to maintain stable granular structure so desirable in a porous, easily worked soil.

On a weight basis, the humus colloids have greater nutrient- and water-holding capacity than does clay. The latter is generally present in larger amounts, however, and so its total contribution to the chemical and physical properties will generally equal that of humus. The best agricultural soils contain a good balance of these two important soil constituents.

1:14. THE VIEWPOINT—A COLLOIDO-BIOLOGICAL CONCEPT

In this chapter an attempt has been made to give a very general picture of the soil in relation to its environment. A general viewpoint has been presented concerning the four major components of soil. An edaphological approach has been used since plant production is still the major function of soils.

Two major concepts presented herein should be emphasized before we move into more detailed study of soil components in succeeding chapters. First, most of the chemical activity in soils is associated with a relatively small proportion of the total soil components—the clay and humus. The soil may be visualized as possessing a basic mineral framework made up mostly of inert materials, but the physical and chemical properties are controlled to a large degree by the colloidal and extremely active fractions.

The second fact which should be emphasized is that there is a vigorous soil organism population associated with humus and plant residues. They are responsible for a continuous turnover of organic materials including humus. Furthermore, they control, to a considerable extent, the supply of nutrient elements—both by releasing them through decomposition, and under different circumstances by competing with higher plants for them.

These two ideas lead logically to the statement that a study of soils from the standpoint of plants can best be approached from a *colloido-biological* viewpoint. This approach will be used in the chapters which follow.

The Supply and Availability of Plant Nutrients in Mineral Soils

CHAPTER 2

The capacity of soils to supply higher plants with certain essential elements is a fundamental problem in crop production. In this chapter we will deal with these elements as they exist and function in soils. More detailed consideration will be reserved for later chapters as will the means of supplementing the soil's supply of these necessary nutrients.[1]

2:1. FACTORS CONTROLLING THE GROWTH OF HIGHER PLANTS

Before discussing the essential elements specifically it should be pointed out that collectively they are only one of the environmental factors influencing the growth of plants. Six such external factors are generally recognized: (1) light; (2) mechanical support; (3) heat; (4) air; (5) water; and (6) nutrients. With the exception of light, the soil is an agent in supplying, either wholly or in part, all of these external factors.[2]

It is well to remember that plant growth is dependent upon a favorable combination of these factors and that any one of them, if out of balance with the others, can reduce or even entirely prevent the growth of plants. Furthermore, the factor which is *least* optimum will determine the level of crop production (see Fig. 2:1). This principle, sometimes called the *principle of limiting factors,* may be stated as follows:

The level of crop production can be no greater than that allowed by the most limiting of the essential plant growth factors.

[1] Chapters 14 through 21 deal in more detail with these subjects.
[2] Absence of disease and lack of serious insect pests are often mentioned as negative factors in this connection.

16

This concept is a most important one and must be taken into consideration when dealing with nutrient elements. We must be concerned not only with the supply of a given element but also with its supply in relation to all other factors which may affect plant growth.

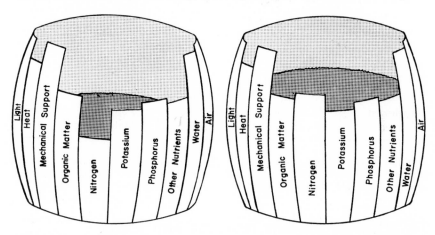

Figure 2:1. Simplified diagrams to illustrate the principle of limiting factors. The level of water in the barrels above represents the level of crop production. On the left, nitrogen is represented as being the factor that is most limiting. Even though the other elements are present in more adequate amounts, crop production can be no higher than that allowed by the nitrogen. When nitrogen fertilizer is added (right) the level of crop production is raised until it is controlled by the next most limiting factor, in this case, potassium.

2:2. THE ESSENTIAL ELEMENTS

Research has shown that certain elements are necessary for the normal growth of plants. These *essential elements* must be present in forms usable by plants and in concentrations optimum for plant growth. Furthermore, there must be a proper balance among the concentrations of the various soluble nutrients in the soil.[3]

Sixteen elements have been demonstrated to be essential for plant growth. They are listed in Table 2:1 and are classified according to sources—whether primarily from air and water or from soil solids—and whether used by plants in relatively large or small amounts.[4]

[3] Too much calcium, for example, may interfere with phosphorus and boron nutrition or may encourage chlorosis due to a reduction in the availability of the soil iron, zinc, or manganese.

[4] For instance, it is not uncommon for a crop such as corn to remove 100 pounds of nitrogen an acre. The amount of boron carried away by the same crop might be as little as 10 or 15 grams.

TABLE 2:1

Essential Nutrient Elements and Their Sources

			Essential Elements Used in Relatively Small Amounts [a]	
Essential Elements Used in Relatively Large Amounts				
Mostly from Air and Water	*From Soil Solids*		*From Soil Solids*	
			Iron	Copper
Carbon	Nitrogen	Calcium	Manganese	Zinc
Hydrogen	Phosphorus	Magnesium	Boron	Chlorine
Oxygen	Potassium	Sulfur	Molybdenum	

[a] Other minor elements such as sodium, fluorine, iodine, silicon, cobalt, strontium, and barium do not seem to be universally essential, as are the sixteen already cited, although the soluble compounds of some may increase crop growth.

2:3. ESSENTIAL ELEMENTS FROM AIR AND WATER

Higher plants obtain most of their carbon and oxygen directly from the air by photosynthesis.[5] The hydrogen is derived, either directly or indirectly, from the water of the soil. All of the other essential elements, except certain supplies of the nitrogen acquired from the soil air indirectly by legumes, are obtained from the soil solids.

It must not be inferred from this that the bulk of the plant tissue is synthesized from the soil nutrients. Quite the reverse is true. Ordinarily from 94 to 99.5 per cent of fresh plant tissue is made up of carbon, hydrogen, and oxygen, and only from 0.5 to perhaps 5 or 6 per cent is from soil constituents. In spite of this, it is the nutrient elements obtained from the soil that usually limit crop development. Plant growth, except in cases of drought, cold weather, poor drainage, or disease, is not seriously retarded by a lack of carbon, hydrogen, and oxygen.[6] Hence, there is justification for the nutrient emphasis that is placed on the soil and the thirteen elements that it supplies.

[5] In the process of photosynthesis, energy from the sun in the presence of chlorophyll, facilitates the synthesis of sugar from CO_2 and water, the former entering the plant through the stomata, the latter being absorbed from the soil.

[6] It is well to remember, however, that a serious lack of oxygen for roots may occur in heavy soils, especially if drainage is poor. This is an important factor in respect to the location of orchards, and is more critical than generally supposed (see p. 249).

2:4. ESSENTIAL ELEMENTS FROM THE SOIL [7]

Macronutrients. Of the thirteen essential elements obtained from the soil by plants, six are used in relatively large quantities and consequently receive first attention. They are *nitrogen, phosphorus, potassium, calcium, magnesium,* and *sulfur.* Because they are used by plants in relatively large amounts they are designated for convenience as *macronutrients.* Plant growth may be retarded because these elements are actually lacking in the soil, because they become available too slowly, or because they are not adequately balanced by other nutrients. Sometimes all three of these limitations are operative. This is often true in respect to nitrogen.

Nitrogen, phosphorus, and potassium are commonly supplied to the soil as farm manure and as commercial fertilizers. Therefore, they are often called *fertilizer* elements. In the same way calcium and magnesium are commonly applied as lime and are styled *lime* elements. Sulfur, other than that present in rain water, usually goes into the soil as an incidental ingredient of such fertilizers as farm manure, superphosphate, and sulfate of ammonia. In special cases, sulfur is applied alone as flowers of sulfur, either to correct nutritional deficiencies or to adjust the reaction of the soil.[8]

Micronutrients.[9] The other nutrient elements (*iron, manganese, copper, zinc, boron, molybdenum,* and *chlorine*) are used by higher plants in very small amounts and as a consequence are called *micronutrients.* Such a designation does not mean that they are less essential than the so-called macronutrients. In fact, such elements are fundamentally just as important (see Fig. 2:2).

Except for iron, trace elements are found sparingly in most soils (see Table 2:2) and their availability to plants is often very low. Consequently, even though the removal by plants is small for any given season, the cumulative effects of crop production over a period of years may rapidly

---

[7] The terms *primary* and *secondary* elements are sometimes used to refer to the macronutrients. Likewise micronutrients are sometimes referred to as *trace, minor,* or *rare* elements.

[8] Certain regions in eastern Washington and Oregon are notably deficient in sulfur for alfalfa production. Sulfur-deficient areas also occur in Minnesota and elsewhere in the United States.

[9] Even under natural conditions these elements sometimes occur in toxic amounts as is the case of manganese in some Hawaiian soils and zinc in New York woody peats. Zinc from smelter smoke is a good example of commercial contamination.

reduce the limited stores originally present. The three general soil situations where micronutrients are most apt to be a problem are: (1) sandy
soils, (2) organic soils, and (3) very alkaline soils. This is due to the
relatively small quantities of micronutrients in sands and organic soils
and to the low availability of most of these elements under very alkaline
conditions.

The deficiencies of micronutrients discovered in many of our soils in

Figure 2:2. Trace elements are just as necessary for normal plant growth as are
nitrogen, phosphorus, and potassium. Note the influence of boron on sunflowers growing on a sand originally deficient in this constituent. The soil at the left received no
boron. The progressive increase in plant growth to the right is in response to increasing
increments of this element. Yet the maximum amount of boron applied was at the
rate of only 2.4 pounds per acre-furrow-slice. *(Photo courtesy J. E. Dawson and Collin
McClung.)*

recent years have highlighted the practical significance of these elements.
Because macronutrient fertility problems are more widespread, however,
they will be given our first attention. Micronutrients will be considered in
more detail later (Chapter 18).

Four nutrient questions. In order to arrive at a logical conclusion
as to why nutrient deficiencies often occur in soils, four phases of great
importance must be examined. They are: (1) the amounts of the various
macronutrients present in mineral soils; (2) their forms of combination;
(3) the processes by which these elements become available to plants;
and (4) the soil solution and its pH. These phases will be considered in
order.

TABLE 2:2

**The Range in Micronutrient Content Commonly Found in Soils and a
Suggested Analysis of a Representative Surface Soil**

Nutrient	Normal Range		Suggested Analysis of a Representative Surface Soil
	Percentage	*p.p.m.*[a]	*p.p.m.*
Iron	.500–5.000	5000–50,000	25,000
Manganese	.020–1.000	200–10,000	2,500
Zinc	.001– .025	10– 250	100
Boron	.0005– .015	5– 150	50
Copper	.0005– .015	5– 150	50
Molybdenum	.00002– .0005	0.2– 5	2
Chlorine	.001–0.1	10– 1,000	50

[a] p.p.m. = parts per million. These estimates are based on published data from a number of sources, especially R. L. Mitchell, "Trace Elements," in F. E. Bear, *Chemistry of the Soil* (New York: Reinhold, 1955), chap. 9.

2:5. AMOUNTS OF THE MACRONUTRIENTS PRESENT IN MINERAL SOILS

Although soils vary greatly in chemical composition, it is possible to indicate the percentage range within which the macronutrients are ordinarily found when a number of surface soils are considered. Also, analyses are suggested for representative surface soils of humid-temperate and arid-temperate regions respectively. (See Table 2:3 and Fig. 2:3.)

It must be remembered, however, that such figures do not fit any particular soil, but present a very rough average of the data available. Also, it should be pointed out that the percentage values given are for topsoils only. These figures show that soils of arid regions are, in general, higher in all of the important constituents except organic matter and nitrogen. (See Fig. 2:3.) An exception, even to this, is found in the black earth soils (chernozems) of subhumid regions which sometimes may range as high as 16 per cent of organic matter and 0.70 to 0.80 per cent of nitrogen. (See p. 314.)

Organic matter, nitrogen and phosphorus. The percentage of organic matter exceeds that of any other constituent listed in Table 2:3. Yet its amount in most surface soils usually is critical. It is of prime importance in keeping the soil loose and open and is an essential source of several nutrient elements. The addition and subsequent decay of organic matter in the soil is thus highly significant both physically and chemically.

Total Amounts of Organic Matter and Primary Nutrients Present in Temperate-region Mineral Surface Soils [a]

Constituents	Ranges in Percentages that Ordinarily May be Expected	Representative Analyses			
		Humid Region Soil		Arid Region Soil	
		Percentage	Lb. to Acre Furrow-Slice	Percentage	Lb. to Acre Furrow-Slice [b]
Organic matter	0.40–10.00	4.00	80,000	3.25	65,000
Nitrogen (N)	0.02– 0.50	.15	3,000	.12	2,400
Phosphoric acid (P₂O₅)	0.02– 0.40	.10	2,000	.15	3,000
Potash (K₂O)	0.20– 4.00	2.00	40,000	2.40	48,000
Lime (CaO)	0.10– 5.00	.60	12,000	1.50	30,000
Magnesia (MgO)	0.20– 2.50	.50	10,000	1.00	20,000
Sulfur trioxide (SO₃)	0.02– 0.50	.10	2,000	.20	4,000

[a] As a supplement to the generalized figures of Table 2:2, the analyses of eight representative United States surface soils are presented below as published by C. F. Marbut. For the complete set, see "Soils of the United States," *Atlas of American Agriculture,* Part 3, U.S. Dept. of Agri., 1935.

Constituents	Norfolk Fine Sand, Florida	Sassafras Sandy Loam, Virginia	Ontario Loam, New York	Loam from Ely, Nevada	Hagerstown Silt Loam, Tennessee	Cascade Silt Loam, Oregon	Marshall Silt Loam, Iowa	Summit Clay from Kansas
	%	%	%	%	%	%	%	%
SiO₂	91.49	85.96	76.54	61.69	73.11	70.40	72.63	71.60
TiO₂	0.50	0.59	0.64	0.47	1.05	1.08	0.63	0.81
Fe₂O₃	1.75	1.74	3.43	3.87	6.12	3.90	3.14	3.56
Al₂O₃	4.51	6.26	9.38	13.77	8.30	13.14	12.03	11.45
MnO	0.007	0.04	0.08	0.12	0.44	0.07	0.10	0.06
CaO	0.01	0.40	0.80	5.48	0.37	1.78	0.79	0.97
MgO	0.02	0.36	0.75	2.60	0.45	0.97	0.82	0.86
K₂O	0.16	1.54	1.95	2.90	0.91	2.11	2.23	2.42
Na₂O	Trace	0.58	1.04	1.47	0.20	1.98	1.36	1.04
P₂O₅	0.05	0.02	0.10	0.18	0.16	0.16	0.12	0.09
SO₃	0.05	0.07	0.08	0.12	0.07	0.21	0.12	0.11
Ignition	1.83	1.91	5.30	7.62	8.82	4.25	6.01	6.60
Nitrogen	0.02	0.02	0.16	0.10	0.27	0.08	0.17	0.09

[b] The furrow-slice of a representative mineral soil is considered to contain approximately 2,000,000 pounds of dry earth to the acre.

Nitrogen and phosphorus are almost always present in comparatively small amounts in mineral soils. Moreover, a large proportion of these elements at any one time is held in combinations unavailable to plants. For

Figure 2:3. Chemical analyses of a representative humid-region surface soil and a brown, arid-region surface soil respectively. Note in each case the relatively large amounts of organic matter and potash, the low percentages of nitrogen, phosphoric acid, and sulfur, and the intermediate rating of the lime and magnesia. Typical soils of arid regions seem in general to be higher in all of the constituents cited except organic matter and nitrogen.

example, even the more simple compounds of phosphorus are relatively insoluble in many soils. As a result, this element is doubly critical—low total amounts and very low availability to plants.

Potassium, calcium, and magnesium. The total quantity of potassium, in marked contrast to the phosphorus, is usually plentiful except in sandy soils. The main problem is one of availability. Calcium shows great variation but it is generally present in lesser amounts than is potash. When it is lacking, soils tend to be acid. Calcium compounds, therefore, generally are added to correct this condition, although the direct nutrient influence of calcium cannot be disregarded.

Magnesium, besides its importance as a nutrient, functions in the soil much as does calcium. Its deficiency in some soils has long been suspected.

Until recently, however, it has not been considered especially critical since it is carried by most limestones, sometimes in large amounts. Where liming is practiced, therefore, its lack often is automatically rectified. In spite of this, however, magnesium deficiency is a major problem in many areas in eastern United States.

Sulfur. While usually no more plentiful than phosphorus, sulfur is more readily available. This is because its simple inorganic compounds are not rendered insoluble by reacting with certain other soil constituents as is the case with phosphorus. As already suggested, the addition of sulfur in farm manure, rain water, and fertilizers tends in an automatic way to relieve a possible deficiency in humid-temperate regions. In certain areas of the West, however, specific additions of sulfur-containing compounds are required.

Critical constituents. The above discussion seems to indicate that three constituents are likely to be critical in almost all mineral soils. Two— *organic matter* and *nitrogen*—merit particular attention because of the small amounts originally present and because of their ready loss through oxidation, leaching, or crop removal. The third, *phosphorus,* faces a double handicap as already explained—an exceptionally small amount present and a low availability to higher plants.

Under humid conditions *calcium* by all means must be included in the list above since it is sure to be much depleted by leaching. Consequently, it is needed not only as a nutrient but also as a means of controlling soil acidity. In arid regions, however, the leaching of calcium usually is negligible. Consequently, this nutrient is likely to be present in abundance, especially in the subsoil.

It is not to be inferred from the preceding generalizations, however, that *potassium, magnesium,* and *sulfur* may not be lacking in certain soils or that the problem of their supply may not at times be critical. The ever increasing use of potash fertilizers, the demand for dolomitic limestone, and the emphasis placed on sulfur additions are evidence of this.

2:6. FORMS IN WHICH THE MACRONUTRIENTS OCCUR IN SOILS

An examination of representative soils will reveal that, in general, the nutrient elements exist in two conditions: (1) complex and rather insoluble compounds; and (2) simple forms usually soluble in the soil water and rather readily available to higher plants. Due to the chemical and biochemical processes at work the general trend of the elements in the soil is from the complex to the simpler forms. (See Table 2:4.) The reverse process—that of synthesis and increased complexity—does occur, however. The building of proteins from simple nitrogen salts and the reversion of soluble phosphates to complex and insoluble compounds are examples.

TABLE 2:4

Forms in Which the Macronutrients Occur in Mineral Soils

Group 1 *The More Complex and Less Active* *Forms*	Group 2 *Some of the Simpler and More* *Available Forms and Their Ionic* *Equivalents*	
Nitrogen		
Organic combinations: proteins, amino acids, and similar forms; colloidal and subject to decomposition.	Ammonium salts. .... NH_4^+ Nitrite salts. .... NO_2^- Nitrate salts. .... NO_3^-	
Phosphorus		
Apatite, an original source. Secondary Ca, Fe, Al phosphates. Organic; phytin, nucleic acid, and other combinations.	Phosphate of Ca, K, Mg, etc. $\rbrace$ $HPO_4^=$ Soluble organic forms. $\quad$ $H_2PO_4^-$	
Potassium		
Original minerals such as feldspars and mica. Complex secondary aluminum silicates such as clays, especially illite.	Potassium ions adsorbed by colloidal complex. Potassium salts, such as sulfates, carbonates, etc. $\Big\rbrace$ K^+	
Calcium		
Minerals such as feldspars, hornblende, calcite and dolomite.	Calcium ions adsorbed by colloidal complex. A variety of simple calcium salts. $\Big\rbrace$ Ca^{++}	
Magnesium		
Minerals such as mica, hornblende, dolomite, and serpentine. Secondary aluminum silicates, such as clays, especially montmorillonite.	Magnesium ions adsorbed by colloidal complex. Numerous simple salts of magnesium. $\Big\rbrace$ Mg^{++}	
Sulfur		
Mineral combinations such as pyrite and gypsum. Organic forms; colloidal and subject to decomposition.	Various sulfites .... $SO_3^=$ and sulfates .... $SO_4^=$ of Ca, K, Mg, etc.	

Simple available forms.   The simpler and more soluble constituents of soils, especially those of humid regions, tend to disappear in drainage or are used by microorganisms and higher plants. Consequently, the greater proportion of the macronutrients exists in the soil in complex conditions. From thence they gradually become available through various processes of simplification. As a result, the productive capacity of a soil depends not so much upon the total amounts of the various nutrients present as upon the ease with which transfer is made to simple and available forms. Such a situation indicates why a *total* chemical analysis is likely to be of uncertain value in deciding the fertilizer needs of a soil. This is rather discouraging, since the total amount of a nutrient may be determined with great accuracy while its *availability* ordinarily is susceptible to little more than a rough approximation.

Organic combination.   The decomposition of soil organic matter allows nutrients held in this complex form to be released and simple compounds appear which are more or less available to higher plants. Practically all of the nitrogen and much of the sulfur and the phosphorus are held in organic combinations. (See Table 2:4.) Since phosphorus in complex mineral forms usually is very slowly available, there is some advantage of the organic association. Even so, however, organic phosphorus does not become available as easily and quickly as do organic sulfur and nitrogen.

Inorganic combinations.   Most of the potassium, calcium, and magnesium exists in the soil in strictly inorganic forms. There is quite a difference, however, in the degree of availability of the three elements. For example, a much larger amount of calcium is held in an easily replaceable exchangeable condition by the colloidal fractions of the soil. (See Fig. 2:4.) In this form it is quite readily available to plants. The quantity of this element in a replaceable or available form far exceeds that of any other macronutrient in the soil. This is reflected in humid regions in the significant losses of calcium in drainage water and the consequent need for its replacement by liming.

The situation in respect to potassium, and to a lesser extent for magnesium, is quite different. A very high percentage of the total quantities of these elements are held in the less available forms. (See Fig. 2:4.) The exchangeable or readily available potassium, for example, usually makes up less than 1 per cent of the total quantity of this element in the soil. Although the relative content of exchangeable magnesium is usually somewhat higher, it is still lower than that of calcium.

While sulfur is held in both mineral and organic forms (see Table 2:4), the latter combinations tend to predominate in humid-region surface soils. The availability of sulfur depends on the rate of organic decomposition. Its transfer from organic forms to inorganic salts which can be used by

Figure 2:4. Diagram showing the percentages of total and exchangeable (replaceable) K, Ca, and Mg respectively present in the representative humid-temperate region mineral soil. Note that the amount of exchangeable Ca is approximately 10 times greater than the exchangeable K and 5 times that of the exchangeable Mg. About 25 per cent of the total Ca is represented as exchangeable, the corresponding figures for K and Mg are .50 per cent and 6.50 per cent, respectively.

plants seldom gives trouble. In soils of arid regions, considerable sulfur may occur in the sulfate form as well as in organic combination. Gypsum is a common carrier of inorganic sulfur in such soils. The presence of calcium sulfate in the lower horizons of the chestnut soils of the Dakotas is an example. (See p. 315.)

The quantity of simple inorganic salts such as KCl, NaCl, and Na_2SO_4 in humid region soils is generally quite small. As one moves into more arid climates these salts are present in a somewhat higher concentration, especially in the lower horizons. Where drainage and leaching is restricted and rainfall is low, salts may be found in the plow layer in quantities sufficiently large enough to hinder or even prevent crop production.

2:7. THE TRANSFER OF PLANT NUTRIENTS
TO AVAILABLE FORMS

The soil is such a complex body that it is impractical at this point to present in any detail the various changes that normally occur. The discussion that follows can only indicate in a very general way some of the more important transformations which affect the availability of the essential elements.

Nitrogen.   Since most of the soil nitrogen is found in the organic matter, the decomposition of the latter must take place if the nitrogen is to appear in simple forms. This decomposition is a very complex, biochemical process, and is accompanied by the evolution of much carbon dioxide. The nitrogen finally emerges as an ammonium compound and, if conditions are favorable, it is oxidized to the nitrite and then to the nitrate form. The two latter changes are spoken of as *nitrification* and are brought about by two special-purpose bacterial groups. Since most of the nitrogen utilized by higher plants is absorbed in the ammonium and nitrate forms, the importance of these processes is obvious. The transformations may be outlined in a simple way as follows:

$$\text{Organic nitrogen} \longrightarrow \text{Ammonium} \longrightarrow \text{Nitrite} \longrightarrow \text{Nitrate}$$

Organic nitrogen	$\longrightarrow$	Ammonium	$\longrightarrow$	Nitrite	$\longrightarrow$	Nitrate
(proteins, amino		Salts		Salts		Salts
acids, etc.)		$NH_4{}^+$		$NO_2{}^-$		$NO_3{}^-$

Decomposition and Ammonification   Nitrification

Since the above transformations result largely from the activity of the soil organisms (microflora), they are influenced profoundly by soil conditions. When the soil is cold, waterlogged or excessively acid, these biochemical changes do not progress rapidly. The nitrifying organisms are especially sensitive to these conditions.

When organic matter containing a large amount of carbon compared to nitrogen is added to a soil, the above processes may be reversed temporarily. The soil microorganisms, having large amounts of energy-producing materials at their disposal, multiply rapidly and use the nitrogen themselves, thus interfering with its simplification and appearance as ammonium and nitrates. In such cases, the soil organisms are competing directly with the higher plants. It must be concluded, therefore, that the simplification of the nitrogen is not always easy, rapid, or in proportion to the amounts present. This must, of course, be taken into consideration in the practical management of any soil.

Phosphorus. When the soil phosphorus is held in organic combination, decay will encourage its simplification. The mineral phosphorus, however, presents a much more difficult problem. The various native soil phosphates are present in small quantities and are usually rather insoluble in water. Even when plant rootlets, aided by CO_2 and other root exudates, are in intimate contact with the mineral phosphates the rate of solution still is slow. A simple example illustrative of the solvent influence of carbon dioxide and water is given below, tricalcium phosphate [10] tentatively representing the various insoluble soil phosphates:

$$Ca_3(PO_4)_2 + 4H_2O + 4CO_2 \rightarrow Ca(H_2PO_4)_2 + 2Ca(HCO_3)_2$$

Insoluble   Water-soluble   Soluble calcium
phosphate   phosphate   bicarbonate

By this means growing plants encourage an availability that might otherwise be almost negligible. Thus, a soil may supply a crop with appreciable quantities of phosphorus, and yet the soil solution and drainage water may contain very small amounts of this element. (See Fig. 2:5.)

Figure 2:5. A photomicrograph of dicalcium phosphate dihydrate crystals bonded to a root hair. This illustrates the intimate relationship between plant roots and some chemical fertilizers. *(Photo courtesy J. R. Lehr, Tennessee Valley Authority.)*

[10] It is questionable whether the simple tricalcium phosphate $[Ca_3(PO_4)_2]$ actually exists in soils. It is used here merely in an illustrative way.

It should also be emphasized that simplification of phosphorus, like that of the nitrogen, may be reversed. Microorganisms readily appropriate simple and soluble phosphorus compounds and build them up into complex organic forms. Also such soluble fertilizer compounds as $Ca(H_2PO_4)_2$ and $NH_4H_2PO_4$ may be changed to insoluble calcium phosphates or to the equally complex and insoluble iron and aluminum combinations. Such forms liberate their phosphorus very reluctantly indeed.

Potassium and calcium.   It will be remembered that some of the calcium and most all the potassium occur as components of complex soil minerals. These forms slowly succumb through the years to the solvent action of water charged with carbonic and other acids. The ease with which the essential elements are rendered soluble depends upon the complexity of the soil minerals and on the intensity of weathering. The general reaction may be illustrated as follows, allowing the potash feldspar microcline to represent the complex minerals and carbonic acid the soil acids:

$$2KAlSi_3O_8 + H_2CO_3 + H_2O \rightarrow H_4Al_2Si_2O_9 + K_2CO_3 + 4SiO_2$$

| Microcline feldspar | Hydrated silicate | Soluble carbonate |

The potassium released through such a reaction may be taken up by plants, lost in drainage, or held by the negatively charged soil colloids. The latter form of nutrient combination will now receive our attention.

A small proportion of the potassium and much of the calcium present in soils is held on the surfaces of the colloids as *adsorbed* [11] cations. These cations are easily released to the soil solution by exchanging with other cations. The general reaction may be shown as follows, assuming that hydrogen from an acid such as H_2CO_3 replaces calcium from the soil colloids:

$$Ca \,\boxed{\begin{array}{c}\text{Colloidal}\\\text{Surface}\end{array}} + 2H_2CO_3 \rightarrow \begin{array}{c}H\\H\end{array}\boxed{\begin{array}{c}\text{Colloidal}\\\text{Surface}\end{array}} + Ca(HCO_3)_2$$

| Adsorbed calcium | Carbonic acid | Adsorbed hydrogen | Soluble bicarbonate |

A great deal of the calcium becomes mobile by this type of reaction. The replacement, or *ionic exchange* as it is called, takes place with surprising

---

[11] *Adsorption* refers to the adhesion of substances to the surfaces of solids. In soils it has to do with the attraction of ions and of water molecules to colloidal particles. The ions are not too tightly held, being replaceable by or exchangeable with ions of a like charge.

Absorption in contrast refers to surface penetration such as takes place when nutrients and water enter plant roots. Thus Ca ions, for instance, are absorbed as they are taken in by plant roots but adsorbed by soil colloids.

ease and rapidity, and undoubtedly is one of the most important types of reactions occurring in soils. Because of this situation, soils, although containing in general considerably more total potassium than total calcium (see Fig. 2:4), release the latter element to the soil solution and to leaching much more lavishly. This has a direct bearing on calcium nutrition, soil acidity, liming, and other practical considerations.[12]

Magnesium. Since magnesium is held in the soil in much the same condition as is calcium, the exchange reaction cited for the latter shows how the magnesium may be released to the soil solution. However, some of the magnesium comes directly from the soil minerals by weathering, much as does the potassium. Hence, the illustrations cited for the transfer of potassium and calcium will serve for magnesium also. It is only necessary to visualize the formation and solution of magnesium bicarbonate by the breakdown of minerals in one case and by ionic exchange in the other.

Just as in the case of nitrogen and phosphorus, the release of potassium, calcium, and magnesium to the soil solution may easily be reversed. Thus, when soluble compounds of potassium, calcium, or magnesium are added to a soil, the colloidal matter adsorbs large quantities of the metallic ions. Indeed, they may be even more firmly fixed as a molecular part of the mineral colloids. This is especially true for potassium.

Sulfur. As in the case of the nitrogen, the sulfur transformations are largely biological. They go on readily in most soils and while probably subject to marked retardation at times, such influences are apparently not as serious as in the case of the nitrogen. The transformations may be indicated in a general way as follows:

The last stage, sulfur oxidation, is, like nitrification, brought about largely by certain types of bacteria. The sulfate compounds that result (see Table 2:4) are the source of most of the sulfur acquired by higher plants.

---

[12] It should be mentioned at this point that the colloidal complex of the soil carries other cations besides calcium and hydrogen in a replaceable condition. Magnesium, potassium, ammonium, sodium, and other ions are present in minor amounts.

Again, soil organisms, especially bacteria and fungi, utilize sulfur as well as the metals already mentioned. Their synthetic activities are excellent examples of a practical reversal of the simplifying processes. While such transpositions temporarily compete with higher plants, they tend to conserve nutrients by reducing the loss of valuable constituents in drainage water.

2:8. MORE ABOUT THE SOIL SOLUTION—ITS pH

It has already been emphasized that because of its segregation in the large and small pore spaces of the soil, the soil solution is not always continuous. (See Section 1:10.) As a result, not all of the water can move freely. Also, the soil solution is exceedingly changeable, varying as to the gross amount present in any soil, as well as to the amount and proportion of its soluble constituents.

Concentration of soil solution. It is agreed, in general, that as the soil moisture is reduced in amount, especially by evaporation, the concentration of soluble salts in the soil solution rises rapidly. Hence, if the moisture fluctuation in a humid-region mineral soil is of sufficient range, a variation in the concentration of the soil solution from a few parts per million, say 100, to possible 30,000 parts per million is quite possible. It is suggested that under ordinary conditions the acre-furrow-slice of an arable humid-region mineral soil contains from 500 to 1,000 pounds of soluble salts.

In arid and semiarid regions, the soil solution is usually somewhat more concentrated than where the rainfall is heavier. Under conditions of low rainfall and restricted drainage, salt concentrations are so high as to interfere at times with the growth of plants. The presence of even 0.5 per cent of total soluble salts is considered serious. This would mean about 10,000 pounds to an acre-furrow-slice.

Reaction of the soil solution. Another point of importance in respect to the soil solution is its reaction—that is, whether it is *acid, neutral,* or *alkaline*. Without considering at this time the conditions controlling soil reaction (see p. 358), it suffices to say that some soil solutions possess a preponderance of H over OH ions and, therefore, are acid. Some, on the other hand, show the reverse and are alkaline, while others having an equal concentration of H and OH ions, are neutral. (See Fig. 2:6.)

The exact relationship in any particular case is usually evaluated in terms of H ion concentration which is usually expressed in terms of pH. A soil is said to be *acid* if the pH is less than 7, *neutral* if at 7, and *alkaline* if the pH is above 7. Thus, as the H ions of the soil solution increase, the pH decreases and vice versa. On the other hand, as the OH ion concentration increases, the pH of the solution goes up accordingly.[13]

| ACID | NEUTRAL | ALKALINE |
| $pH = 6.0$ | $pH = 7.0$ | $pH = 8.0$ |

Figure 2:6. Diagramatic representation of neutrality, acidity, and alkalinity. At neutrality the H ions and OH ions of a solution are balanced, their respective numbers being the same (pH 7).

At pH 6, the H ions are dominant, being 10 times greater while the OH ions have decreased proportionately being only 1/10 as numerous. The solution, therefore, is acid, there being 100 times more H ions than OH ions present.

At pH 8, the exact reverse is true, the OH ions being 100 times more numerous than the H ions. Hence the solution is alkaline. This mutually inverse relationship must always be kept in mind in using pH data. See note at bottom of page.

It is not to be inferred that we are dealing with a homogeneous distribution of the H and OH ions in the soil solution. Hydrogen ions usually are adsorbed by soils to a much greater degree than are the OH ions. Consequently, one is prepared to visualize the H ions (1) as being especially concentrated at and near the colloidal interfaces, and (2) as becoming less numerous as the outer portions of the water films are approached.

---

[13] If the reader is not definitely familiar with pH values, it would be well to consult a good textbook on chemistry. It may be pointed out here, however, that the pH value of a solution is the logarithm of the reciprocal of the H ion concentration. It may be stated conveniently as follows:

$$pH = \log \frac{1}{[H^+]}$$

Also, it should be noted that the concentration of the H ion (and consequently the pH) is related mathematically to the concentration of the OH ion. In any solution in which water is the solvent the product of the concentration of these two ions is approximately 10^{-14}. Thus:

$$\text{Conc. } H^+ \times \text{Conc. } OH^- = 10^{-14}$$

If, for example, the pH = 6 the H ion concentration is 10^{-6} equivalents per liter and the OH ion concentration is

$$\frac{10^{-14}}{10^{-6}} = 10^{-8} \text{ equivalents per liter.}$$

(See Fig. 14:1.) Since the OH ions vary in numbers inversely with H ions, this makes for a higher pH in the outer moisture zones. Such a situation has many nutritional consequences in respect to both micro-organisms and higher plants and will receive more attention later (pp. 371 and 372).

Ranges in pH. In Figure 2:7 are shown the ranges in soil pH encountered as well as the relationship between pH values and terms commonly used to describe soil reaction. Two types of pH ranges are shown, *extreme* and *common*. For mineral soils the extreme range in pH extends from near 3.5 to perhaps 10 or above. It is to be noted in this connection that certain peat soils may show a pH of less than 3. At the other extreme are alkali soils, some of which may reach a pH near 11.

Figure 2:7. Diagram showing the extreme range in pH for most mineral soils and the range commonly found in humid-region and arid-region soils respectively. The maximum alkalinity for alkali soils is also indicated, as well as the minimum pH likely to be encountered in very acid peat soils.

The common ranges in pH shown by soils of humid regions and arid regions, respectively, are sharply in contrast with the extreme spread noted above. That for soils of humid regions extends roughly from somewhat below 5 to above 7. It is to be noted that the latter figure overlaps the range common to soils of arid regions whose usual pH spread is from a little below 7 to approximately 9.

2:9. THE NUTRITIONAL IMPORTANCE OF SOIL pH

The soil pH may influence nutrient absorption and plant growth in two ways: (1) through the *direct* effect of the hydrogen ion; or (2) *indirectly,* through its influence on nutrient availability and the presence of toxic ions. In most soils the latter effect is of greatest significance. Although at extreme pH values the direct toxic effect of the hydrogen ion can be demonstrated, most plants are able to tolerate a wide range in the concentration of this ion as long as a proper balance of the other elements is maintained. Unfortunately, the availability of several of the essential nutrients is drastically affected by soil pH as is the solubility of certain elements that are toxic to plant growth. Examples of these effects will be cited.

Several essential elements tend to become less available as the pH is raised from say 5.0 to 7.5 or 8.0. Iron, manganese, and zinc are good examples. Molybdenum availability, on the other hand, is affected in the opposite way, being higher at the higher pH levels. The case of phosphorus in respect to pH is especially interesting. While this nutrient is never readily soluble in the soil, it seems to be held with less tenacity in a pH range centering around 6.5. (See p. 439 and Fig. 17:2.) Here, most plants seem to be able to extract it from the soil with least difficulty.

At pH values below 5.0 to 5.5, aluminum, iron, and manganese are often soluble in sufficient quantities to be toxic to the growth of some plants. At very high pH values, the bicarbonate ion is sometimes present in sufficient quantities to interfere with the normal uptake of other ions and thus is detrimental to optimum growth. These few examples of the indirect effects of soil pH show why much importance must be placed on this characteristic in the diagnosis of fertility problems.

2:10. FORMS OF ELEMENTS USED BY PLANTS

There are two general sources of readily available nutrients in the soil. These are: (1) nutrients adsorbed on the colloids; and (2) salts in the soil solution. In both cases the essential elements are present as ions [14] such as K^+, Ca^{++}, Cl^-, $SO_4^=$. The positively charged ions (cations) such as K^+ are mostly adsorbed by the colloids, whereas the negatively charged ions (anions) and a small fraction of the cations are found in the soil solution. The more important ions present in the soil solution or on the soil colloids may be tabulated as follows:

---

[14] Inorganic salts exist largely as electrically charged units called ions. For instance, KCl is in reality a combination of K^+ and Cl^- ions while $NaNO_3$ is made up of Na^+ and NO_3^- ions. In solution these ions tend to dissociate from each other, the dissociation being essentially 100 per cent if the solution is dilute.

Nitrogen	NH_4^+,	NO_2^-, NO_3^-	Calcium	Ca^{++}
Phosphorus	$HPO_4^=$,	$H_2PO_4^-$	Magnesium	Mg^{++}
Potassium	K^+		Sulfur	$SO_3^=$, $SO_4^=$
Iron	Fe^{++},	Fe^{+++}	Zinc	Zn^{++}
Molybdenum	$MoO_4^=$		Boron	$BO_3^{\equiv}$
Manganese	Mn^{++},	Mn^{++++}	Chlorine	Cl^-
Copper	Cu^+,	Cu^{++}	Water	H^+, OH^-
Carbon	$CO_3^=$,	HCO_3^-		

Nitrogen, phosphorus, and sulfur. An explanation should be made regarding the use by plants of certain ions. Most of the nitrogen, for example, is absorbed in either the ammoniacal or nitrate forms, depending on the conditions of the soil, the kind of plant, and its stage of growth. In general, the presence of both ions seems most favorable. The nitrite ion is generally present in small quantities only since it is so readily oxidized to the nitrate form. This is fortunate as any concentration of nitrite nitrogen is likely to be toxic to plants.

The particular phosphate ion presented to higher plants seems to be determined to a considerable extent by the pH of the soil. When the latter is distinctly alkaline, the $HPO_4^=$ ion is the form in which soluble phosphorus occurs. As the pH is lowered and the soil becomes slightly to moderately acid, both $HPO_4^=$ and $H_2PO_4^-$ ions prevail, while at high acidities the phosphorus is present largely as $H_2PO_4^-$ ion. Both these forms are considered to be absorbed by higher plants. It is well to note that soluble organic forms of phosphorus cannot be used to any extent directly by higher plants but must undergo mineralization and appear in the mineral forms before appreciable utilization takes place.

The intake of sulfur by higher plants apparently is largely as the $SO_4^=$ ion. This is the final product of oxidation and if the sulfur organisms are vigorous, little $SO_3^=$ ions can accumulate. The situation in some respects resembles that already cited regarding nitrite oxidation.

Other elements. Little need be said at this point regarding potassium, calcium, magnesium, zinc, boron, and chlorine as they occur in the soil solution in only one ionic form respectively. But iron, manganese, and copper are in a little different category. The oxidation-reduction condition of the soil is a factor here. If the soil is well aerated, the ion of higher valence in each case tends to predominate. But if drainage is poor, reduction may occur and the lower-valent forms will be present. Thus, aeration, especially in the subsoil, is of tremendous nutritive importance.

The carbon dioxide of the atmosphere in its photosynthetic role is the direct source of most of the carbon acquired by higher plants, but not necessarily of all. In the soil solution carbonate and bicarbonate ions occur and there is some evidence that these may be adsorbed by higher plants. In fact, at times a considerable amount of carbon probably enters the plant directly from the soil.[15]

2:11. SOIL AND PLANT INTERRELATIONS

It might hastily be assumed from what has been said regarding the transfer of nutrients that their solubility and availability result entirely from a series of soil phenomena, the plant simply absorbing in a passive sort of way that which is presented. Such, however, is certainly not the case. The rootlets and root hairs are in most instances in very intimate contact with the soil colloidal surfaces. (See Fig. 2:8.) In fact, the relationship is so close that nutrients are thought by some authorities to pass from the soil solids to the plant without leaving the sphere of colloidal influence.[16] The nutrients thus appropriated are soluble but have not appeared in the soil solution as free, unadsorbed, migrating ions or molecules. Whether such a root-soil exchange occurs or whether nutrients are absorbed from the soil solution, intimate soil-plant contacts encourage nutrient uptake. (See Fig. 2:8.)

This effect of intimate root-soil association apparently is much accentuated by: (1) root exudates, and (2) microbial

Figure 2:8. Diagram suggestive of the (1) interchange between the soil solids (colloidal and noncolloidal) and the soil solution proper; (2) movements of constituents to and from the plant root surfaces within the zone of colloidal influence (contact zone); and (3) interchange between the free soil solution and the absorbing surfaces of plant root systems. The loss of nutrients in drainage (4) is from the free portion of the soil solution.

activity in the immediate neighborhood of the absorbing surfaces. Plant roots give off large amounts of CO_2 and other acid-forming substances as well. These, no doubt, speed up interchange to a remarkable degree. Also,

---

[15] B. E. Livingston and R. Beal, "The Soil as a Direct Source of Carbon Dioxide," *Plant Physiol.,* 9: 237–59, 1934. The authors estimate that at times plants may obtain as much as 5 per cent of their carbon from the soil.

[16] See H. Jenny and R. Overstreet, "Cation Interchange between Plant Roots and Soil Colloids," *Soil Sci.,* 47: 257–72, 1939; and D. E. Williams and N. T. Coleman, "Cation Exchange Properties of Plant Root Surfaces," *Plant and Soil,* 2: 243–56, 1950.

organic excretions from plant roots provide food and energy for micro-organisms. The concentration of microbial activity within the plant-root zone (rhizosphere) is ample proof of this.[17] Such biochemical phenomena cannot fail to increase greatly the rate and ease of transfer of nutrients from soil to plant.

2:12. SOIL FERTILITY INFERENCES

Certain practical conclusions are inescapable in respect to the plant-nutrient relationships just presented. An adequate supply of each nutrient must be maintained in the soil. In addition, provision must be made for a rate of availability suitable to normal crop growth. This involves a more or less complex transfer to the soil solution and to the plant, the latter seeming to participate in ways other than those of mere absorption.

Moreover, an adequate nutrient proportion is requisite, the total concentration of available nutrients being vital. Such a balance tends to insure the desirable physiological conditions necessary for successful plant production. The pH of the soil solution, since it influences profoundly many of the important soil and plant processes, plays a critical role in such an adjustment. Soil management, to be successful, must encompass all of these phases.

---

[17] The localization of microorganisms around living rootlets and root hairs has been demonstrated. A discussion of the significance of these rhizosphere organisms is given by F. E. Clark in "Soil Microorganisms and Plant Roots," *Advances in Agronomy* (1:242–82, 1949).

Some Important Physical Properties of Mineral Soils

CHAPTER 3

Physically, a mineral soil is a porous mixture of inorganic particles, decaying organic matter, and air and water. The larger mineral fragments usually are imbedded in and coated over with colloidal and other materials in a fine state of subdivision. In some cases, the larger mineral particles predominate and a gravelly or sandy soil results. In other cases, the mineral colloids are more prevalent giving the soil clayey characteristics. All gradations between these extremes are found in nature. Organic matter acts as a binding agent to encourage the individual particles to cluster into clumps or aggregates.

Two very important physical properties of soils will be considered in this chapter. These are: *soil texture* and *soil structure*. Soil texture is concerned with the size of mineral particles. Specifically it refers to the relative proportion of the various size-groups in a given soil. No less important is soil structure, which is the arrangement of soil particles into groups or aggregates. Together, these properties help determine, not only the nutrient-supplying ability of soil solids but also the supply of water and air, so important to plant life. We shall start our consideration of these properties with a brief discussion of soil particle-size and its significance.

3:1. CLASSIFICATION OF SOIL PARTICLES AND MECHANICAL ANALYSIS

In the time covered by a generation of man, the soil processes, while surprisingly active, usually do not alter appreciably the size of the individual mineral particles. Thus, a sandy soil remains sandy and a clay soil remains a clay. For this reason the proportion of various size-groups in a given soil (the texture) assumes added significance. It cannot be altered

39

and thus is considered a basic property of a soil which to an appreciable extent determines the economic value of the area.

In order to study successfully the mineral particles of a soil, scientists usually separate them into convenient groups according to size. The various groups are spoken of as *separates*. The analytical procedure by which the particles are thus separated is called a *mechanical analysis*. It is a determination of the particle-size distribution.

As might be expected, a number of different classifications have been devised. Two of the most important will be cited, that established by the United States Department of Agriculture and that later advanced by the International Society of Soil Science. They will be found in Table 3:1.

TABLE 3:1

The Classification of Soil Particles According to Two Systems (U.S. and International) and the Mechanical Analyses of Two Soils Using the U.S. System

| Soil Separate | United States Department of Agriculture System [a] | | | International System [b] |
	Diameter Limits (*mm.*)	*Analyses of Two Typical Soils* sandy loam (*Percentage*)	clay loam (*Percentage*)	Diameter Limits (*mm.*)
Very coarse sand	2.00–1.00[c]	3.1	2.2	
Coarse sand	1.00–0.50	10.5	4.0	2.00–0.20
Medium sand	0.50–0.25	8.2	6.3	
Fine sand	0.25–0.10	25.3	8.4	0.20–0.02
Very fine sand	0.10–0.05	22.0	9.6	
Silt	0.05–0.002[d]	21.1	37.2	0.02–0.002
Clay	below 0.002	9.8	32.3	below 0.002

[a] L. J. Briggs, *et al.*, *The Centrifugal Method of Soil Analysis*, Bulletin 24, Bureau of Soils, U.S. Dept. of Agric., 1904.

[b] System established by the International Soil Science Society, based on A. Atterberg, "Die Mechanische Bodenanalyse und die Klassifikation der Mineralboden Schwedens," *Inter. Mitt. fur Bodenkunde*, 2:312–42, 1912. And F. Schusct, "Uber die Sitzung der Internationalen Kommission fur die Mechanische und Physikalische Bodenundersuchung in Berlin am 31, October, 1913," *Internat. Mitt. fur Bodenkunde*, 4:1–31, 1914.

[c] Originally this separate was spoken of as *fine gravel*. The present designation is more appropriate because it avoids confusion with the larger and more typical gravel particles.

[d] Previous to 1938, the silt range was set at 0.05–0.005. This must be kept in mind in dealing with mechanical analyses made before that date.

In the first column is given the names of the various separates, and in the second the range in size of each group according to the United States system. Columns three and four show the percentages of each separate in two very different specimen soils, a sandy loam and a clay loam. In order to obtain such figures, a sample of soil is broken up and the very fine sand and larger fractions are separated into the arbitrary groups by sieving. The silt and clay percentages are then determined by methods which depend upon the rate of settling of these two separates from suspension. This combined operation is the mechanical analysis already mentioned.[1] In the fifth column, the range in size of the four separates used in the international system is given.

Stone and gravel, while they figure in the practical examination and evaluation of a field soil, do not enter into the analysis of the fine earth. Their amounts are usually rated separately. The organic matter, ordinarily comparatively small in quantity, either is allowed to distribute itself through the various mineral groups or more often is removed by oxidation previous to the mechanical separation. The percentage of total organic matter, however, is generally quoted separately as it throws additional light on the probable physical nature of the soil in question. The percentage of calcium carbonate, if it is present, may also be given.

Sand, when dominant, yields a coarse-textured soil, which has properties known to everyone as *sandy* or *light* since such a soil is easily worked. On the other hand, a fine-textured soil is made up largely of silt and clay, and its plasticity and stickiness indicate that it is likely to be difficult to work or *heavy*. The use of the terms "light" and "heavy" refer to ease of working and not to soil weight. As we shall see later, the weight of a cubic foot of dry sand is actually greater in most cases than that of clay.

Not only is a mechanical analysis valuable in picturing in a general way the physical properties of a soil but it is also of use in deciding as to the textural name—that is, whether a soil is a sand, sandy loam, loam, etc. This phase is considered in Section 3:5.

3:2. THE PHYSICAL NATURE OF THE SOIL SEPARATES

The coarse separates. Stone, gravel, and sand, because of their sizes, function as separate particles. The first two range in size from 2 mm.

---

[1] The principle involved in the method is simple. When soil particles are suspended in water, they tend to sink and rapidity of settling is roughly proportional to their size. The suspension of a sample of soil is, therefore, the first step; the second step is that of settling and the withdrawal by some means of successive grades; and the third step is the determination of the percentage of each group of particles based on the original sample. The apparatus and techniques are rather complicated. For an over-all discussion consult: V. J. Kilmer and L. T. Alexander, "Methods of Making Mechanical Analyses of Soils," *Soil Sci.*, 68: 15–24, 1949.

upward and may be more or less rounded, irregularly angular, or even flat as the case may be.[2] Sand grains also may be rounded or quite irregular, depending on the amount of abrasion that they have received. (See Fig. 3:1.) When not coated with clay and silt, such particles exhibit practically no plasticity[3] and stickiness, and as a consequence, are little influenced by changes in moisture content. Their water-holding capacity is low, and because of the large size of the spaces between the separate particles, the passage of percolating water is rapid. They, therefore, facilitate drainage and encourage good air movement. Soils dominated by sand or gravel, therefore, are of open character, possess good drainage and aeration, and are usually in a loose friable condition.

Figure 3:1. Sand grains from soil. Note that the particles are irregular as to size and shape. While quartz usually predominates, other minerals may also occur. Silt particles have about the same shape and composition, differing only in size.

Clay and silt. The clay particles commonly are mica-like in shape and when moist are highly plastic. When clay is wetted with a suitable amount of water, it expands and becomes sticky. On drying, it shrinks (see Fig. 4:8) with absorption of considerable energy. On wetting again, swelling occurs with the evolution of heat. This is called the *heat of wetting*. The adsorptive capacity of clays for water, gases, and soluble salts is very high. The diagram in Figure 3:2 shows how these properties increase as the particle size becomes smaller.

In contrast with the platelike clay, silt particles tend to be irregularly fragmental, diverse in shape, and seldom smooth or flat. (See Fig. 3:1.) In fact, they really are microsand particles, quartz being the dominant mineral. The silt separate possesses some plasticity, cohesion (stickiness), and adsorption due to an adhering film of clay but, of course, to a much lesser degree than the clay separate itself. In fact, the influence of silt is

---

[2] The distinction between gravel and stone is now technically based on size. Gravel, chert, and slate are considered to range from 2 mm. up to 3 inches along their greatest diameter. Stone, cobbles, and boulders, on the other hand, exceed 3 inches in respect to their greatest dimension. Note that these differentiations are not in line with the popular concept that all gravels are rounded and smooth and that all stones are roughly irregular.

[3] *Plasticity* is the property of a material which allows one to mold it when moist into various forms by applying pressure. When the pressure is released the material will maintain its molded form.

such as to make it a rather unsatisfactory soil constituent physically unless supplemented by adequate amounts of sand, clay, and organic matter.

The presence of silt and especially clay in a soil imparts to it a *fine texture,* and a slow water and air movement. Such a soil is highly plastic, becoming sticky when too wet, and hard and cloddy when dry unless properly handled. The expansion and contraction on wetting and drying usually are great. And the water-holding capacity of clayey and silty soils generally is high. As already mentioned, such soils are spoken of as *heavy* because of their difficult working qualities, markedly in contrast with *light,* easily tilled sandy and gravelly surface soils.

Figure 3:2. The finer the texture of a soil, the greater is the effective surface exposed by its particles. Note that adsorption, swelling, and the other physical properties cited follow the same trend and that their intensities go up rapidly as the colloidal size is approached.

3:3. THE MINERALOGICAL AND CHEMICAL COMPOSITIONS OF SOIL SEPARATES

Although at this point our interest in soil particles is largely a physical one, a glance at their mineralogical make-up and chemical composition may not be amiss.

Mineralogical characteristics. As already suggested, the coarsest sand particles often are fragments of rock as well as of quartz, the most prevalent mineral in this separate. Quartz also commonly dominates the finer grades of sand as well as the silt separate. (See Fig. 3:1.) In addition, variable quantities of other primary minerals usually occur, such as the various feldspars and micas. (See Fig. 3:3.) Gibbsite, hematite, and limonite minerals also are found, usually as coatings on the sand grains. The latter two impart various shades of red and yellow if present in sufficient quantities. The soils of our Piedmont plateau and well-oxidized tropical earths are good examples.

Some of the clay particles, especially those in the coarser clay fractions, are composed of the minerals already cited as quartz, hematite, and gibbsite. An even more important group, however, is the complex aluminosilicates. Three main mineral types are at present recognized although others are known to occur in significant quantities—*kaolinite, illite,* and *montmorillonite.* It will suffice at this time to say that these groups vary markedly in plasticity, cohesion, and adsorption, kaolinite being lowest in each case and montmorillonite highest. It is, therefore, of considerable importance as to which clay type dominates or codominates any particular soil.

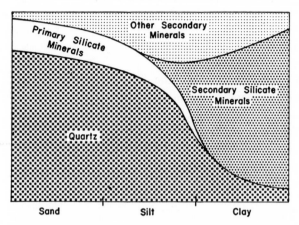

Figure 3:3. Diagram showing the general relationship between particle size and kinds of minerals present. Quartz dominates the sand and coarse silt fractions. Primary silicates such as the feldspars, hornblende, and micas are present in the sands but tend to disappear as one moves to the silt fraction. Secondary silicates dominate the fine colloidal clay. Other secondary minerals such as the oxides of iron and aluminum are prominant in the fine silt and coarse clay fractions.

Chemical make-up. Since sand and silt are dominantly quartz (SiO_2), these two fractions are generally quite inactive chemically. Even the primary minerals which may contain nutrient elements in their chemical make-up are generally so insoluble as to make their nutrient supplying ability essentially nil. An exception to this general rule is the silt fraction of certain potassium-bearing minerals such as the micas which have been known to release this element at a sufficiently rapid rate to supply, at least in part, plant requirements.

Chemically, kaolinite and the other members of that particular group are aluminum silicates. The same is true for montmorillonite and other clays of that same crystal pattern, but they also carry in addition sodium, iron, or magnesium as the case may be. Illite, often referred to as hydrous mica, is a potassium aluminum silicate. Its high potash content gives it a special nutrient significance. Obviously, the word "clay," as now understood, is a term covering substances differing widely, not only mineralogically and chemically, but physically as well.

If the various soil separates, ranging as they do from very coarse sand to ultrafine clay, differ so markedly in crystal form and chemical composition, will they not also show a like contrast in respect to mineral nutrients? Logically we would expect the sands, being mostly quartz, to be lowest and the clay separate to be highest. This inference is substantiated by the data in Table 3:2. The general relationships shown by these data hold true for most soils, although some exceptions may occur.

TABLE 3:2

Composition of Separates from Various United States Surface Soils [a]

| Separate | Soils Developed from Indicated Materials | | | | |
	Crystalline Residual	Limestone Residual	Coastal Plain	Glacial and Loessial	Arid
			per cent P_2O_5		
Sand	0.07	0.28	0.03	0.15	0.19
Silt	0.22	0.23	0.10	0.23	0.24
Clay	0.70	0.37	0.34	0.86	0.45
			per cent K_2O		
Sand	1.60	1.46	0.37	1.72	3.05
Silt	2.37	1.83	1.33	2.30	4.15
Clay	2.86	2.62	1.62	3.07	5.06
			per cent CaO		
Sand	0.50	12.26	0.07	1.28	4.09
Silt	0.82	10.96	0.19	1.30	9.22
Clay	0.94	9.92	0.55	2.69	8.03

[a] G. H. Failyer, *et al.*, *The Mineral Composition of Soil Particles*, Bulletin 54, Bureau of Soils, U.S. Dept. of Agric., 1908.

Data in respect to the distribution of silicon, iron, aluminum, titanium, calcium, and magnesium through the various separates as reported by Joffe and Kunin are given below. The soil fractionated was a Montalto silt loam of New Jersey, a residual product from basalt. The figures quoted are for the surface eight inch layer only.

Chemical Composition of Montalto Silt Loam Fractions †

Separate	SiO_2 %	Fe_2O_3 %	Al_2O_3 %	TiO_2 %	CaO %	MgO %
Sand	86.3	5.19	6.77	1.05	.37	1.02
Coarse silt	81.3	3.11	7.21	1.05	.41	.82
Fine silt	64.0	9.42	12.00	1.05	.32	2.22
Coarser clay	45.1	13.50	21.10	.96	.38	2.09
Finer clay	30.2	17.10	22.80	.88	.08	1.77

† J. S. Joffe and R. Kunin, "Mechanical Separates and Their Fraction in the Soil Profile: I. Variability in Chemical Composition and Its Pedogenic and Agropedogenic Implications," *Proc. Soil Sci. Soc. Amer.*, 7:187–93, 1942.

3:4. SOIL CLASS—THE TEXTURAL NAMES OF SOILS

As soils are composed of particles varying greatly as to size and shape, specific terms are needed which will convey some idea of their textural make-up and give some indication of their physical properties. For this, *class* names are used, such as sand, sandy loam, silt loam, and the like.

These class names have originated through years of soil study and classification and gradually have been more or less standardized. Three broad yet fundamental groups of soils are recognized: *sands, loams,* and *clays.* On the basis of these, additional class names have been devised.

Sands.   The *sand* group includes all soils of which the sand separates make up 70 per cent or more of the material by weight. The properties of such soils are, therefore, characteristically sandy in contrast with the stickier and more clayey nature of the heavier groups of soil. Two specific classes are recognized—*sand* and *loamy sand.*

Clays.   A soil to be designated as a clay must carry at least 35 per cent of the clay separate and in most cases not less than 40 per cent. So long as the percentage of clay is 40 or above, the characteristics of this separate are distinctly dominant and the class name is *sandy clay, silty clay,* or which is commonest of all, simply *clay.* It is well to note that sandy clays often contain more sand than clay. Likewise, the silt content of silty clays usually exceeds that of the clay fraction itself.

Loams.   The *loam* group, which contains many subdivisions, is more difficult to explain. An ideal loam may be defined as a mixture of sand, silt, and clay particles which exhibit light and heavy properties in about equal proportions. Roughly it is a half-and-half mixture on the basis of properties.

Usually, loams possess the desirable qualities both of sand and clay without exhibiting those undesirable properties, such as extreme looseness and low water capacity on the one hand, and stickiness, compactness, and slow air and water movement on the other.

Most soils of agricultural importance are some type of loam. They may possess the ideal make-up described above and be classed simply as *loam.* In most cases, however, the quantities of sand, silt, or clay present are such as to require a modified class name. Thus, a loam in which sand is dominant is classified as a *sandy loam* of some kind; in the same way there may occur *silt loams, silty clay loams,* and *clay loams.*

Variations in the field.   It readily can be seen that the textural names already established—*sand, loamy sand, sandy loam, loam, silt loam, silty* *clay loam, clay loam, sandy clay, silty clay,* and *clay*—form a more or less graduated sequence from soils that are coarse in texture and easy to handle to those, the heavy clays, that are very fine and difficult to manage. It is also obvious that these class names are a reflection not only of particle-size distribution but also of tillage characteristics and other physical properties. Soil-minded persons should be fully familiar with the concept underlying the nomenclature employed. A study of Figure 3:4 will aid in its visualization.

Figure 3:4. Graphic representation of the mechanical analyses of representative mineral soils.

It is well to point out that for some soils qualifying factors such as stone, gravel and the various grades of sand must be descriptively taken into consideration. Even silt and clay become qualifying terms in practice. All this will be obvious when the lists below are examined.

Sandy soils	Loam Soils	Clayey Soils
Gravelly sands	Stony-sandy loams	Stony clays
Coarse sands	Gravelly-sandy loams	Gravelly clays
Medium sands	Coarse-sandy loams	Sandy clays
Fine sands	Medium-sandy loams	Silty clays
Very fine sands	Fine-sandy loams	Clays
Loamy sands	Very-fine-sandy loams	
Sands	Loams, gravelly loams, and stony loams	
	Silt loams and stony-silt loams	
	Silty-clay loams	
	Clay loams and stony-clay loams	

3:5. THE DETERMINATION OF SOIL CLASS

Field method.   The common field method of determining the class name of a soil is by its *feel*. Probably as much can be judged about the texture and hence the class name of a soil merely by rubbing it between the thumb and fingers as by any other superficial means. Usually it is helpful to wet the sample in order to estimate plasticity more accurately. The way a wet soil "slicks out" gives a good idea as to the amount of clay present. The sand particles are gritty, the silt has a floury or talcum-powder feel when dry, and is only moderately plastic and sticky when wet. Persistent cloddiness generally is imparted by silt and clay.

The method as outlined is used in field operations such as soil survey, land classification, and the like. Accuracy in such a determination is of great practical value and depends largely on experience. Facility in class determination is one of the first things a field man should develop.

Laboratory method.   A more accurate and fundamental method has been devised by the United States Department of Agriculture for the naming of soils based on a mechanical analysis. This method of identification is shown diagrammatically in Figure 3:5. The diagram re-emphasizes that a soil is a mixture of different sizes of particles and that a close correlation exists between particle size distribution and the properties of soils. Obviously, when mechanical analysis of the field soils that he has been working with are available to a surveyor, he can readily check on the accuracy of his class designations. A working knowledge of this method of naming soils is, of course, very essential. The legend explains the use of the triangular chart devised for this purpose. (See Fig. 3:5.)

As a means of emphasizing still further the relationships between textural make-up and class names, apply the data appearing in Figure 3:4 to the triangular chart. If your name-designations check with those of the figure, your handling of the chart is correct.

3:6. THE PARTICLE DENSITY [4] OF MINERAL SOILS

One means of expressing soil weight is in terms of the density of the solid particles making up the soil. It is usually defined as the mass (or

---

[4] The weight of soil solids has often been expressed in terms of their *specific gravity*. This is simply the weight of soil solids compared to the weight of an equal volume of water. Since one cubic centimeter of water weighs approximately one gram, there is little difference between *density* and specific gravity values. Because of the insignificant differences in actual density and specific gravity values, specific gravity data will be used in most cases interchangeably with density data. See *Proc. Soil Sci. Soc. Amer.*, 13: 573, 1948.

weight) of a unit volume of soil solids and is called the *particle density*. In the metric system, particle density is usually expressed in terms of grams per cubic centimeter. Thus, if 1 cubic centimeter of soil solids weighs 2.6 grams, the particle density is 2.6 grams per cc.

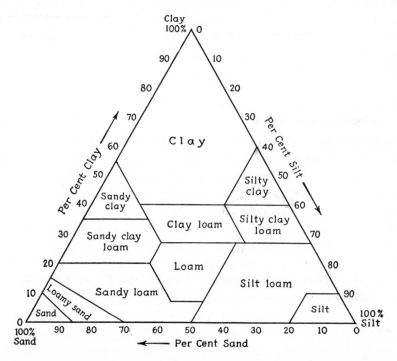

Figure 3:5. Diagram by means of which the textural name of a soil may be determined from a mechanical analysis. In using the diagram, the points corresponding to the percentages of silt and clay present in the soil under consideration are located on the silt and clay lines respectively. Lines are then projected inward, parallel in the first case to the clay side of the triangle and in the second case parallel to the sand side. The name of the compartment in which the two lines intersect is the class name of the soil in question.

Although considerable range may be observed in the density of the individual soil minerals, the figures for most mineral soils usually vary within the narrow limits of 2.60 and 2.75. This occurs because quartz, feldspar, and the colloidal silicates, with densities within this range, usually make up the major portion of mineral soils. Occasionally, however, when unusual amounts of heavy minerals such as magnetite, garnet, epidote, zircon, tourmaline, and hornblende are present, the particle density may exceed 2.75. It should be pointed out that the *fineness* of the particles of a given mineral and the arrangement of the soil solids have nothing to do with the particle density.

Since organic matter weighs much less than does an equal volume of the mineral solids, the amount of this constituent in a soil markedly affects the particle density. As a consequence, surface soils usually possess lower particle densities than do subsoils. Some highly organic mineral top soils may drop as low as 2.4, or even below, in particle density. Nevertheless, for general calculations, the average arable surface soil may be considered as having a particle density of about 2.65.[5]

3:7. THE BULK DENSITY (VOLUME WEIGHT)[6] OF MINERAL SOILS

Bulk density.   This is a second and different method of expressing soil weight. In this case the *total soil space* (space occupied by solids and pore spaces combined) is taken into consideration. Bulk density is defined as the mass (weight) of a unit volume of dry soil. This volume would, of course, include both solids and pores. The comparative calculations of bulk density and particle density are shown diagrammatically in Figure 3:6. A careful study of this figure should make clear the distinction between these two methods of expressing soil weight.

Factors affecting bulk density.   Bulk density is a weight measurement by which the entire soil volume is taken into consideration. Unlike particle density, which is concerned with the solid particles only, bulk density is determined by the quantity of pore spaces as well as the soil solids. Thus, soils that are loose and porous will have low weights per unit volume (bulk densities) and those that are more compact will have high values. Since the particles of sandy soils generally tend to lie in close contact, such soils have high bulk densities. The low organic matter content of sandy soils further encourages this. The particles of the finer surface soils, such as silt loams, clay loams, and clays, on the other hand, ordinarily do not rest so close together. This results from the fact that these

[5] For methods of density determination and for data in respect to certain representative American soils see: W. O. Smith, "Density of Soil Solids and Their Genetic Relations," *Soil Sci.,* 56: 263–72, 1943.

[6] Volume weight is defined as the weight of a given volume of soil compared to the weight of an equal volume of water. Thus, like specific gravity, it is a comparative figure. Bulk density and volume weight values are almost identical and for practical purposes can be used interchangeably. The terminology *bulk density* will be used in this text, however.

Methods for determining bulk density have been reviewed recently by J. A. Vomocil, in "Measurement of Soil Bulk Density and Penetrability: A Review of Methods," *Advances in Agronomy* 9: 159–76, 1957.

surface soils are comparatively well granulated, a condition encouraged by their relatively high organic matter contents. Granulation encourages a fluffy, porous condition which results in low bulk-density values. Consequently, the bulk density of a well granulated silt loam surface soil is sure to be lower than that of a representative sandy loam.

In the field, one cubic centimeter of a certain soil appears as below:

If all the solids were compressed to the bottom, the cube would look like this:

solids and pore spaces — 1.33 gms.

½ pore spaces

½ solids — 1.33 gms.

To calculate bulk density of the soil:

Volume = 1 cc.   Weight = 1.33 gms.

Bulk density = $\dfrac{\text{Weight of soil}}{\text{Volume of soil}}$

To calculate solid particle density:

Volume = 0.5 cc.   Weight = 1.33 gms.

Solid particle density = $\dfrac{\text{Weight of solids}}{\text{Volume of solids}}$

Therefore:

Bulk density = $\dfrac{1.33}{1}$ = 1.33 gms./cc.

Therefore:

Solid particle density = $\dfrac{1.33}{0.5}$ = 2.66 gms./cc.

Figure 3:6. A diagramatic representation of bulk density and particle density of soil. Follow the calculations through carefully and the terminology should be clear. In this particular case the bulk density is one half that of the particle density and the percentage pore space is 50.

The bulk densities of clay, clay loam, and silt loam surface soils normally may range from 1.00 to as high as 1.60 grams per cc. depending on their condition. A variation from 1.20 to 1.80 may be found in sands and sandy loams. Very compact subsoils regardless of texture may have bulk densities as high as 2.0 grams per cc. or even greater.

Even in soils of the same surface texture, great differences in bulk density are to be expected when similar horizon levels are compared. This is clearly shown by data in Table 3:3 respecting Wisconsin silt and clay loams. Moreover, there is a distinct tendency for the bulk density to rise as the profile is penetrated. This apparently results from a lower content of organic matter, less aggregation and root penetration, and a compaction caused by the weight of the overlying layers.

The system of crop and soil management employed on a given soil is likely to influence its bulk density, especially of the surface layers. The addition of farm manure in large amounts tends to lower the weight figure of surface soils as does also a bluegrass sod. Intensive cultivation, on the other hand, operates in the opposite direction.

TABLE 3:3

Bulk Density Data for Certain Wisconsin Profiles [a]

Horizon	Marathon Silt Loam	Miami Silt Loam	Spencer Silt Loam	Superior Clay Loam
Plow layer	1.34	1.28	1.38	1.46
Upper subsoil	1.49	1.41	1.55	—
Lower subsoil	1.59	1.43	1.66	1.66
Parent material	1.72	1.49	1.63	—

[a] L. B. Nelson and R. J. Muckenhirn, "Field Percolation Rates of Four Wisconsin Soils Having Different Drainage Characteristics," *Jour. Amer. Soc. Agron.*, 33:1028–36, 1941.

Data presented in Table 3:4 show this relationship very well. These data are from long-time experiments in four different states, the soils having been under cultivation for from 40 to 150 years. Cropping increased the bulk density of the topsoils in all cases.

TABLE 3:4

The Bulk Density and Per Cent Pore Space of Certain Cultivated Topsoils and of Nearby Uncropped Areas [a]

Soil Type	Years Cropped	Bulk Density Cropped Soil	Uncropped Soil	Per Cent Pore Space Cropped Soil	Uncropped Soil
Hagerstown loam (Penn.)	58	1.25	1.07	50.0	57.2
Marshall silt loam (Iowa)	50+	1.13	0.93	56.2	62.7
Nappanee silt loam (Ohio)	40	1.31	1.05	50.5	60.3
Ave. 19 Georgia soils	45–150	1.45	1.14	45.1	57.1

[a] The above data were obtained from several sources. See T. L. Lyon; H. O. Buckman; and N. C. Brady, *The Nature and Properties of Soils* (New York: Macmillan, 1952), p. 60.

Other weight figures.   When the bulk density of a soil is known in terms of grams per cc., its dry weight in pounds per cubic foot may be found approximately by multiplying by 62.42, the standard weight of a cubic foot of water. Clayey and silty surface soils may vary from 65 to 100 pounds to the cubic foot, while sands and sandy loams may show a variation of 75 to 110 pounds. The greater the organic content, the less is this weight. Very compact subsoils, regardless of texture, may weigh as much as 125 pounds per cubic foot. The figures quoted are for the absolutely dry soil and do not include the water present.

The actual weight of a soil also may be expressed in terms of an acre-foot, referring to a volume of soil 1 acre in extent and 1 foot deep. The weight of an acre-foot of surface mineral soil commonly ranges from 3,000,000 to 4,500,000 pounds of dry substance. The figure most commonly used, however, is 2,000,000 or sometimes 2,500,000 pounds as the weight of average surface soil to a depth of 6 or 7 inches. This is considered as an *acre-furrow-slice*.

3:8. THE PORE SPACE OF MINERAL SOILS

The pore space of a soil is that portion occupied by air and water. The amount of this pore space is determined largely by the arrangement of the solid particles. If they tend to lie close together, as in sands or compact subsoils, the total porosity is low. If they are arranged in porous aggregates, as is often the case in medium textured soils high in organic matter, the pore space per unit volume will be high.

The validity of the above generalizations may readily be substantiated by the use of a very simple formula [7] involving particle density and bulk density figures. A sandy soil having a bulk density of 1.50 and a particle density of 2.65 will be found to have, when these figures are properly applied to the formula below, 43.4 per cent of pore space. A silt loam in which the corresponding values are 1.30 and 2.65 respectively, possesses 50.9 per cent of air and water space. This latter value is close to the pore capacity of a normally granulated silt loam or clay loam surface soil.

Factors influencing total pore space. As might be expected, considerable difference in the total pore space of various soils occurs depend-

[7] The derivation of the formula used to calculate the percentage of total pore space in soil is as follows:

$$\% \text{ solid space} = \frac{\text{Bulk density}}{\text{Particle density}} \times 100$$

Since,

$$\% \text{ pore space} + \% \text{ solid space} = 100$$

then

$$\% \text{ pore space} = 100 - \% \text{ solid space}$$

and

$$\% \text{ pore space} = 100 - \frac{\text{Bulk density}}{\text{Particle density}} \times 100.$$

ing upon conditions. Sandy surface soils show a range of from 35 to 50 per cent while heavy soils vary from 40 to 60 per cent or perhaps even more in cases of high organic matter and marked granulation. Pore space also varies with depth, some compact subsoils dropping as low as 25 or 30 per cent. This accounts in part for the inadequate aeration of such horizons.

The handling of a soil exerts a marked influence upon the pore space of the furrow-slice. For instance, the continuous bluegrass sod of the Hagerstown loam of Pennsylvania cited in Table 3:4 had a total porosity of 57.2 per cent while the comparable rotation plot showed only 50 per cent. Additional data presented in this table from three other states show that cropping tends to lower the total pore space below that of the virgin or uncropped soils. This reduction usually is associated with a decrease in organic matter content and a consequent lowering of granulation. Pore space in the subsoil has been found to decrease with cropping, although to a somewhat lesser degree.

Size of pores.   Two types of individual pore spaces in general occur in soils—*macro-* and *micro-*. While no sharp line of demarcation occurs, the macropores characteristically allow the ready movement of air and percolating water. In contrast, in the microtype of pore, air movement is greatly impeded while water movement is restricted largely to slow capillary movement. Thus, in a sandy soil, in spite of the low total porosity, the movement of air and water is surprisingly rapid because of the dominance of the macrospaces.

Fine textured soils allow relatively slow gas and water movement in spite of the unusually large amount of total pore space. Here the dominating micropores often maintain themselves full of water. Aeration, especially in the subsoil, frequently is inadequate for satisfactory root development and desirable microbial activity. Thus, the *size* of the individual pore spaces rather than their combined volume is the important consideration. The loosening and granulating of fine textured soils promotes aeration, not so much by increasing the pore space in total as by raising the proportion of the macrospaces.

It has already been suggested (p. 9 and Fig. 1:4) that in the case of a well-granulated silt loam surface-soil at optimum moisture for plant growth, the total pore space not only may be near 50 per cent; it is also likely to be shared fairly equally by air and water. In such a case, the micropore space is nearly all filled with water and the macropores with air. Soil aeration under such a condition is likely to be fairly satisfactory especially if a similar ratio of air to water extends well into the subsoil.

Cropping and size of pores. Continuous cropping, particularly of soils originally very high in organic matter, often results in a reduction of large or macropore spaces. Data from a Rendzina soil in Texas presented in Table 3:5 show this effect very strikingly.

TABLE 3:5

The Effect of Continuous Cropping for at Least 40–50 Years on the Total
Pore Space and the Macro- and Micropore Spaces in a
Houston Black Clay from Texas [a]

Sampling Depth Inches	Soil Treatment	Organic Matter (%)	Pore Space		
			Total (%)	Macro (%)	Micro (%)
0–6	Virgin	5.6	58.3	32.7	25.6
	Cultivated	2.9	50.2	16.0	34.2
6–12	Virgin	4.2	56.1	27.0	29.1
	Cultivated	2.8	50.7	14.7	36.0

[a] W. D. Laws and D. D. Evans, "The Effects of Long-time Cultivation on Some Physical and Chemical Properties of Two Rendzina Soils," *Proc. Soil Sci. Soc. Amer.*, 14:15–19, 1949.

The amount of macropore space, so necessary for ready air movement, was reduced about one half by cropping the soil. This severe reduction in pore size extended into the 6- to 12-inch layer also. In fact, samples taken as deep as 42 inches showed the same trend.

A further examination of Table 3:5 shows that cultivation and cropping have appreciably reduced the total pore space. This was accompanied by a more or less proportional rise in the space given over to micropores. As would be expected, the decrease in pore size was associated with a corresponding decrease in organic matter content.

3:9. THE STRUCTURE OF MINERAL SOILS [8]

While *texture* undoubtedly is of great importance in determining certain characteristics of a soil, it is evident that the particular type of particle grouping that happens to predominate must exert considerable influence also. The term *structure* is used to refer to such groupings. Structure is

[8] For a consideration of all phases of soil structure, see L. D. Baver, *Soil Physics* (New York: Wiley, 1956), Chap. 5.

strictly a field term descriptive of the gross, over-all aggregation or arrangement of the soil solids.

A profile may be dominated by a single structural pattern. More often, a number of types of aggregation are encountered as progress is made from horizon to horizon. It is at once apparent that soil conditions and characteristics—such as water movement, heat transfer, aeration, bulk density, and porosity—will be much influenced by structure. In fact, the important physical changes imposed by the farmer in plowing, cultivating, draining, liming, and manuring his land are structural rather than textural.

Structural forms under virgin conditions apparently have been developed from one or both of two possible nonstructural states—(1) *single grained,* and (2) *massive.* In the former, the single, solid particles function as individuals. Loose sand is a good example of this. The binding influence of organic matter often modifies this original form to a certain extent by building up a weak aggregation. In the massive nonstructural case, the soil units originally are very large, irregular, and featureless as far as characteristic soil aggregates are concerned.

Types of soil structure.   These two extremes cited above are the theoretical boundaries of the seven structural types commonly recognized in soil profiles. They are as follows: *platy, columnar, prismatic, blocky, nutlike, granular,* and *crumb.*[9] A brief description of each of these structural types with schematic drawings will be found in Figure 3:7. A more detailed description of each follows:

1. Platelike—*Platy*—In this structural type the aggregates or groups are arranged in relatively thin horizontal plates, leaflets, or lenses. If the units are quite thin, the term *laminar* is used. While most noticeable in the surface layers of virgin soils, platy structure may characterize the subsoil horizons as well.

    Although most structural features are usually a product of soil forming forces, the *platy* type is often inherited from the parent materials, especially when the latter have been laid down by water or ice.

2. Prism-like—*Columnar* and *Prismatic*—These types are characterized by vertically oriented aggregates or pillars. These elongated columns vary in length with different soils and may reach a diameter of 6 inches or more. They commonly occur in the subsoil horizons of arid and semiarid region soils and when well developed are a very striking feature of the profile.

    When the tops are rounded, the term *columnar* is used. This may occur when the profile is changing and certain horizons are degrading. When the tops of the prisms are still plane, level, and clean cut, the structural pattern is designated as

[9] For a more complete consideration of classification see: C. C. Nikiforoff, "Morphological Classification of Soil Structure," *Soil Sci.,* 52: 193–207, 1941; and Report of Committee on Soil Structure, *Proc. Soil Sci. Soc. Amer.,* 10: 479–80, 1948.

prismatic. Both the prismatic and columnar types of aggregation are divided into classes depending on the size or horizontal diameter of the prisms.

3. Blocklike—*Blocky* and *Nuciform* or *Subangular blocky*—In this case the original aggregates have been reduced to blocks, irregularly six faced, and with their three dimensions more or less equal. In size these fragments range from a fraction of an inch to 3 or 4 inches in thickness. In general, the design is so individualistic that identification is easy.

When the edges of the cubes are sharp and the rectangular faces distinct, the type is designated as *blocky*. When subrounding has occurred, the aggregates are spoken of as *nuciform* or *subangular blocky*. These types usually are confined to the subsoil and their stage of development and other characteristics have much to do with soil drainage, aeration, and root penetration.

4. Spheroidal—*Granular* and *Crumb*—All rounded aggregates may be placed in this category although the term more properly refers to those not over ½ inch in diameter. These rounded complexes usually lie loosely and are readily shaken apart. When wetted, the intervening spaces generally are not closed so readily by swelling as may be the case with a blocky structural condition. Ordinarily the aggregates are spoken of as granules and the pattern as *granular*. However, when the granules are especially porous, the term *crumb* is significantly applied.

Granular and, less frequently, crumb structures are characteristic of many surface soils, especially those high in organic matter. They are the only types of aggregation that are commonly influenced by practical methods of soil management.

Figure 3:7. Diagramatic representation of the various structural types found in mineral soils. Their location in the profile is suggested. In arable soils, granulation usually receives the most attention. Nuciform structure is sometimes called *subangular blocky*.

As already emphasized, two or more of the structural conditions listed usually occur in the same soil solum. In humid-temperate regions, a granular aggregation in the surface horizon with a blocky, subangular blocky or platy type of some kind in the subsoil is usual, although granular sub-horizons are not uncommon. In soils of arid regions the blocky type in the subsoil may be replaced by a prismatic arrangement.

Genesis of soil structure.   The mechanics of structure formation are exceedingly complicated and rather obscure. The nature and origin of the parent material are important factors as are the physical and biochemical processes of soil formation, particularly those that result in the synthesis of clay and humus. Climate is also a prime consideration. Soluble salts probably play an important role, particularly in the soils of arid regions. Nor should the downward migration of clay, iron oxides, and lime be overlooked. Undoubtedly, the accumulation of organic matter and its type of decay play a major role, especially in the development of the granular structure so common in the surface soils of grasslands. In fact, the preservation and encouragement of this particular structural type becomes one of the most important soil problems of cultivated lands. Let us turn to this phase without further delay.

3:10. GRANULATION AND ITS PROMOTION IN ARABLE SOILS [10]

In a practical sense we are concerned with two sets of factors in dealing with soil aggregation: (1) those responsible for aggregate formation; and (2) those which give the aggregates stability once they are formed. Since both sets of factors are operating simultaneously, it is sometimes difficult to separate their relative effects on stable granule development in soils.

Genesis of Granules.   Although there is some uncertainty as to the exact mechanism by which granules form, several specific factors are known to influence their genesis. These include: (1) wetting and drying; (2) freezing and thawing; (3) the physical activity of roots and soil animals; (4) the influence of decaying organic matter and of the slimes from the microorganisms and other forms of life; (5) the modifying effects of adsorbed cations; and (6) soil tillage.

Obviously, any action that will develop lines of weakness, shift the particles to and fro, and force contacts that otherwise might not occur, should encourage granulation. Consequently, it is not surprising that the alternate wetting and drying, and freezing and thawing, the physical effects of root extension, and the mixing action of soil organisms and of tillage implements tend to encourage aggregate formation. The benefits

---

[10] A review of the theories concerning aggregation will be found in an article by J. P. Martin, *et al.,* "Soil Aggregation," *Advances in Agronomy,* 7: 2–37, 1955.

of fall plowing on certain types of soil and the slaking of clods under the influence of a gentle rain have long been known and taken advantage of in seedbed preparation. And the granulating influences of earthworms and other soil organisms should not be passed unnoticed.

The influence of organic matter. The major agency in the encouragement of granulation probably is organic matter (see Fig. 3:8) which not only binds but also lightens and expands, making possible the porosity so characteristic of individual soil aggregates. Plant roots probably promote granulation as much or more by the decay of the distributed organic matter as by the disruptive action of their ramifications. The electrochemical properties of the humus, as well as of the clay are probably effective in the organization and the later stabilization of the aggregates. Moreover, slime and other viscous microbial products probably encourage crumb development and exert a stabilizing influence as well. Granulation thus assumes a highly biological aspect.

Figure 3:8. A puddled soil (left) and a well-granulated soil (right). Plant roots and especially humus play the major role in soil granulation. For that reason a sod tends to restore the structural condition of cultivated land. *(Photo courtesy U.S. Soil Conservation Service.)*

Organic matter is of much importance in modifying effects of clay. In fact, some suspect that an actual chemical union may at times take place between the decaying organic matter and the silicate molecules. Moreover, the high adsorptive capacity of humus for water tends to intensify the disruptive effects of temperature changes and moisture fluctuations. The granulation of a clay soil apparently cannot be promoted adequately without the presence of a certain amount of humus. The maintenance of organic matter and of its synthesized products, therefore, is of great practical concern, not only chemically and biologically but physically as well (see Fig. 3:8).

The effect of adsorbed cations.   One of the outstanding characteristics of the colloidal substances of the soil, both mineral and organic, is the ability to adsorb cations (see p. 72). The domination or even partial domination of certain of these cations tends to develop more or less definite physical characteristics. For instance when sodium is a prominent adsorbed ion, the particles are dispersed and a very undesirable soil structure results.

The adsorption of calcium by contrast may encourage granulation by a phenomenon called *flocculation*. When this occurs, the colloidal matter is brought together in floccules and tends to encourage a type of structure that is quite desirable. Flocculation in itself, however, is not granulation as it usually does not provide for the *stabilization* of the aggregates. When such means are present and active as often is the case, flocculation assumes considerable practical significance.[11]

While many soils highly charged with native calcium exhibit granulation to a marked degree, it must not be inferred that this effect is due entirely to the direct influence of the adsorbed calcium. Exchangeable cations merely modify the influence of other factors, especially the over-all effects of decaying organic matter. The addition of lime, therefore, is effective as a granulating agency largely through its influence on biotic forces.

Influence of tillage.   Tillage has both favorable and unfavorable effects on granulation. The short-time effect is often favorable since by action of the implements the soil may be loosened and the organic matter incorporated into and mixed with the soil. Tillage under the proper moisture conditions breaks up clods and makes a more favorable seedbed. A minimum amount of tillage is thus considered necessary in normal soil management.

Over longer periods, tillage operations have detrimental effects on surface soil granules. In the first place, tillage generally hastens the oxidation of organic matter from soils. Second, tillage operations, especially those involving heavy equipment, tend to break down the stable soil aggregates. The compaction [12] that soils suffer from repeatedly running over fields with heavy farm equipment is by no means slight. An indication of the effect of such traffic upon bulk density and macropore space is given in

---

[11] The mechanics of flocculation are more fully considered on page 103.

[12] For a recent review of research on soil compaction see: W. A. Raney; T. W. Edminster; and W. H. Allaway, "Current Status of Research in Soil Compaction," *Proc. Soil Sci. Soc. Amer.,* 19: 423–28, 1955.

Table 3:6. These data help explain the increased interest in recent years in techniques of drastically reducing the tillage operations where possible. (See Fig. 3:10.)

TABLE 3:6

The Packing Effect of Tractor and Sprayer Wheels as Measured by Bulk Density and Macropore Space [a]

Implement Wheel	Bulk Density gm/cc	% Macro- pore Space
Check—no packing	1.25	37.6
Tractor (cultivating)	1.32	35.0
Tractor & Potato Sprayer	1.46	27.0

[a] From A. Klute and W. C. Jacob, "Physical Properties of Sassafras Silt Loam as Affected by Long-time Organic Matter Additions," *Proc. Soil Sci. Soc. Amer.*, 14: 24–8, 1949.

Aggregate stability. One structural feature of great practical importance but not as yet adequately stressed, should receive due attention— aggregate stability. Some granules readily succumb to the beating of rain and the rough and tumble of plowing and fitting of the land. Others, in contrast, resist disintegration, thus making the maintenance of a suitable soil structure comparatively easy. Differences in aggregate stability are apparently related to the presence or absence of certain binding agents. Organic compounds of various kinds are known to possess these stabilizing properties. (See Fig. 3:9.) The kind of clay influences aggregate stability,

Before Wetting | After Wetting

High O.M. | Low O.M. | High O.M. | Low O.M.

Figure 3:9. The aggregates of soils high in organic matter are much more stable than are those low in this constituent. The low organic matter soil aggregates fall apart when they are wetted while those high in organic matter maintain their stability.

kaolinite-dominated granules being more stable than those in which mont-morillonite is prominent. Other inorganic compounds, e.g., iron oxides, have a definite cementing or binding effect giving rise to stable granules.

As a general rule, the larger the aggregates present in any particular soil, the lower is their stability. This is why it is difficult to build up soil aggregation beyond a certain size of granule or crumb in cultivated land.

3:11. THE STRUCTURAL MANAGEMENT OF SOILS

Coarse-textured soils.   Looseness, friability, good aeration and drain-age, and easy tillage are characteristic of sandy soils. On the other hand, such soils are often too loose and open, and lack the capacity to adsorb and hold sufficient moisture and nutrients. They are, as a consequence, likely to be droughty and lacking in fertility. They need granulation. There is only one practical method of improving the structure of such a soil—the addition of organic matter. Organic material will not only act as a binding agent for the particles but will also increase the water-holding capacity.

The maintenance of a soil in sod is recognized the world over as a highly effective means of promoting granulation. This method has been used for centuries, unknowingly perhaps, to encourage and maintain a favorable soil structure. Farm manure and green manures, while markedly less effec-tive, tend in the same direction. It should also be remembered that the canopy effects of sod and other crops and of artificial mulches of various kinds shelter the soil from dashing rains. This beating action often seri-ously impairs granulation, not only by carrying the granules away but also by pounding them to pieces (see Fig. 9:8 and p. 227).

Fine-textured soils.   The structural management of a silicate-clay is not such a simple problem as that of a sandy one. In the sands, the plas-ticity and cohesion are never great due to low content of inorganic colloids. In clays and similar soils of temperate regions, however, the potential plas-ticity and cohesion are always high due to the presence of large amounts of colloidal clay. The more plastic such a soil becomes, the more likely it is to *puddle*,[13] especially if worked when wet. A soil of high plasticity is prone to become hard and cloddy when dry, due to the cohesive tendencies of the small platelike, viscous particles. Such soils must be treated very carefully, especially in tillage operations. If plowed too wet, the aggrega-tion of particles is broken down, and an unfavorable structure is sure to

[13] When a surface soil in a wet and plastic condition has been worked until its pore space is much reduced, it becomes practically impervious to air and water, and is said to be *puddled*. When a soil in this condition dries, it usually becomes hard and dense.

result. On the other hand, if plowed too dry, great clods are turned up which are difficult to work down into a good seedbed. In sandy soils and the so-called hydrous-oxide clays of the tropics [14] such difficulties usually are at a minimum.

Not only must tillage operations be carefully timed in a heavy soil but granulation should be encouraged to the fullest degree. As already emphasized, organic matter is a major concern. In this respect sod crops, especially deep-rooted legumes, should be utilized to the fullest extent and the rotation planned to attain their maximum benefits. Most sod crops not only protect the land from dashing rains and erosion but also help maintain the soil organic matter. They therefore encourage granulation. Others, especially intertilled crops such as corn, potatoes, and cotton, have opposite effects. Aggregation is likely to deteriorate under their regime. A good rotation should so balance these opposing influences as to maintain satisfactory soil structure.

TABLE 3:7

Percentage Water-Stable Aggregation of a Marshall Silt Loam near
Clarinda, Iowa, under Different Cropping Systems.
(Samples Were Taken in August) [a]

Crops	Per Cent of the Water-Stable Aggregates Which Were:	
	Large (1 mm. and above)	*Small* (Less than 1 mm.)
Corn continuously	8.8	91.2
Corn in rotation	23.3	76.7
Meadow in rotation	42.2	57.8
Bluegrass continuously	57.0	43.0

[a] H. A. Wilson, Roger Gish, and G. M. Browning, "Cropping Systems and Season as Factors Affecting Aggregate Stability," *Proc. Soil Sci. Soc. Amer.*, 12:36–43, 1947.

The data shown in Table 3:7 confirm the above commonly accepted observations. A Marshall silt loam near Clarinda, Iowa, was used, the

[14] Much less trouble is encountered with the hydrated iron and aluminum oxide clays of the tropics and semitropics as their normal granulation usually is pronounced and rather stable. This is fortunate as it generally is extremely difficult to maintain any amount of organic matter in these soils when they are under cultivation. (See p. 312.)

cropping system employed having been in operation for a sufficient number of years for differences in their effects to develop. The water-stable aggregation under four crops was investigated in midsummer, usually the season of maximum granulation.

A glance at the table will confirm the degranulating influence commonly ascribed to corn, less rapid, of course, when the crop is grown in a suitable rotation. The aggregating tendency of sod whether it is a meadow mixture or a bluegrass sward is likewise obvious. The data also suggest the degrees of soil granulation a person may normally expect and disclose the rapidity with which aggregation may decline. Certainly, granulation is a fluctuating, ever changing property and deserves more attention in practice than it generally receives.

3:12. SOIL CONSISTENCE [15]

Before considering the effect of tillage on soil properties, one more important physical characteristic of soils should receive our attention. This is soil *consistence* which is a term used to describe the physical condition of a soil at various moisture contents as evidenced by the behavior of that soil toward mechanical stresses or manipulations. Soil consistence is considered a combination of soil properties which are dependent upon the forces of attraction between soil particles as influenced by soil moisture. Terms that are commonly used to describe soil consistence are as follows: *loose, friable, firm, soft, harsh, plastic,* and *sticky.*

Perhaps the best way to explain how soil consistence varies with moisture content is to use the above terms in describing how this soil property varies. A heavy clay soil soon after a rain would be quite high in soil moisture and would be *sticky* to feel. It obviously is too wet to work and if manipulated will tend to puddle or run together. Even when this soil is allowed to dry somewhat it may still be slightly sticky and will be *plastic* in nature. It can be molded into various forms by applying pressure to it. Although it can be plowed at this moisture content, the furrow-slice thus turned will likely form clods when the soil is allowed to dry. The consistence of these clods would then be considered as *hard* or *harsh.*

At a moisture content slightly below that required for plastic consistence, a soil is in optimum condition for working. If it has the appropriate properties it then may be termed as *soft* or *friable.* The exact moisture range over which this condition occurs will be different for different soils. In

---

[15] This subject is covered in greater detail by L. D. Baver, *Soil Physics* (New York: Wiley, 1956), pp. 97–9.

general, this range is much wider for medium-textured soils such as loams and some silt loams than is the case for heavier-textured clays.

In using the example of the clay soil, one should not expect all soils to behave in a like manner. Sandy soils, for example, do not become plastic or sticky when wet, or hard or harsh when dry. They have a tendency to stay quite *loose* throughout their normal field moisture range. Loams and silt loams will tend to be intermediate in their behavior between the clays and sands.

Consistence can be seen to be important in determining the practical utilization of soils. The terms used to describe this soil property are meaningful to one concerned with soil tillage, compaction by farm machinery, etc. These subjects are covered in the next section.

3:13. TILTH AND TILLAGE [16]

Although frequent mention has been made of plowing and cultivation in relation to soil structure, something must be said regarding seedbed preparation and the maintenance of its granulation throughout the season. A convenient term—*tilth*—will greatly facilitate such a discussion, which of necessity must be brief.

Tilth defined.   Simply defined, tilth refers to "the physical condition of the soil in its relation to plant growth" and hence must take cognizance of all soil physical conditions that influence crop development.

Tilth depends not only on granulation and its stability, but also on such factors as moisture content, degree of aeration, rate of water infiltration, drainage, and capillary-water capacity. As might be expected, it often changes rapidly and markedly. For instance, the working properties of heavy soils may be altered abruptly by a slight change in moisture.

One of the objectives of plowing and cultivation, supposedly, is the encouragement and maintenance of good tilth. Unfortunately, when improperly administered these operations may seriously impair tilth directly or set the stage for later deterioration. Let us consider the situation briefly.

Tilth and plowing.   The mold-board plow is a tillage implement designed to accentuate the granulation of the soil by its lifting, twisting, and shearing actions. At the same time, it turns under any organic residues that may be on or in the surface. It is a powerful tool *for good* when properly used—for *ill* if it is not well adjusted or if applied under unsatisfactory conditions. Undoubtedly, it is the best implement available for the preparation of sod land for cultivated crops. It cuts through the matted roots,

[16] For a more detailed coverage of these phases see Baver, *op. cit.*, Chap. 11.

turns the sod into the furrow, and exposes the shattered, subsurface layers for further preparation.

On heavy soils, the plow is indispensable if maximum crop yields are to be attained. On light soils, however, the advantage of the mold-board plow is not so obvious, as disking or some other type of cultivation may be as good or even better, especially if a stubble mulch is desired as is often the case in areas of low rainfall.

Undoubtedly, many farmers plow too much and at times when soil aggregation is seriously impaired. (See Fig. 3:10.) This is likely to be the

Figure 3:10. Research has shown that many farmers overtill their soil, breaking down the soil structure. Minimum tillage procedures such as the one shown above (called "plow-plant") are being used to cut operation costs and to prevent the destruction of soil aggregation. In this case corn is planted with no tillage other than plowing. *(Photo courtesy R. B. Musgrave, Cornell University.)*

case when clayey soils are plowed too wet or too dry. Yet in spite of its misuse and the criticism [17] leveled at it, the plow continues to be an important factor in the structural management of land and the maintenance of crop yields. This is clearly shown by the data of Table 3:8. When and

TABLE 3:8

Data Showing the Influence of Various Methods of Seedbed Preparation upon Soil Porosity and Yields of Unfertilized Corn in Ohio [a]

Seedbed Preparation	After Seven Years		Yield of Corn in Bus. per Acre, Average of Eight Years
	Total Porosity %	Air Space Porosity %	
1. Standard	56.3	25.9	46.7
2. Sod plow	56.0	24.9	47.2
3. Rotary tillage	56.9	24.2	42.1
4. Subsurface tillage	54.8	19.2	39.1
5. Surface tillage only	49.1	14.2	34.5
6. Standard plus straw mulch	55.8	26.9	50.5

[a] J. B. Page, C. J. Willard, and G. W. McCuen, "Progress Report on Tillage Methods in Preparing Land for Corn," *Proc. Soil Sci. Soc. Amer.*, 11:77–80, 1945.
1. The usual fitting methods employed for corn in Ohio, that is, plowing and harrowing.
2. Furrow-slice completely inverted with sod-plow.
3. Over-preparation with rotary tiller.
4. Subsurface tillage—corn planted under trash mulch.
5. Very slight surface tillage—enough to kill weeds.
6. Heavy straw mulch applied after first cultivation of corn.

how to plow, in this age of heavy, mechanized farm implements, are more important than ever before.

Tilth and cultivation. Cultivation is often more likely to impair tilth than is plowing. It is employed more frequently during the rotation, is performed by many types of implements, and drastically influences the upper furrow-slice that is so susceptible to degranulation. Hence, in the preparation of a seedbed only the minimum of cultivation should be applied after plowing, leaving the soil with a granular structure suitable for seeding yet coarse enough at the surface to resist erosion and the puddling effects of beating rains. (See Fig. 3:10.)

[17] For a drastic criticism of the plow, with which most agronomists by no means wholly agree, see: E. H. Faulkner, *Plowman's Folly* (Norman, Okla.: Univ. Oklahoma Press, 1943). For a more studied concept, consult R. A. Norton, E. V. Collins, and G. M. Browning, "Present Status of the Plow as a Tillage Implement." *Agr. Eng.*, 25: 7–10, 1944.

In the spring, coarse granules at the soil surface may insure a satisfactory tilth through the critical portion of the growing season. The influence of a seedbed thus prepared usually greatly affects crop yield. Corn, for instance, is a plant that markedly responds to the persistence of good tilth. For the influence of various methods of seedbed preparation upon soil porosity and corn yields, see Table 3:8. The deductions are obvious.

Cultivation during the growing season serves mainly to break up crusts induced by dashing rains, to insure adequate aeration, and to kill weeds. When herbicides are used, the control of weeds by cultivation ceases to be so important. With intertilled crops, cultivation should be kept at a minimum and ordinarily should not extend much beyond midseason. This is because serious root pruning (see Fig. 8:4) may occur as well as a loss of water by evaporation from the exposed surfaces without a compensating improvement in tilth. Directly and indirectly, cultivation may impair soil aggregation. Do not hasten the decline of tilth by too much cultivation.

Soil Colloids: Their Nature
and Practical Significance

CHAPTER 4

It has already been emphasized that the most active portions of the soil are those in the colloidal state [1] and that the two distinct types of colloidal matter, inorganic and organic, exist in intimate intermixture. The former type of colloidal matter is present almost exclusively as clay of various kinds, while the latter is represented by humus.

Both of these groups are the seat of such varied and vigorous changes that they deserve diligent study. In fact, most investigators feel that many problems dealing with the normal functioning of soil will not be fully understood until we know more about the soil colloids. Attention will be focused to begin with on the inorganic colloidal matter, leaving that of organic origin for later consideration (see pp. 141 and 143).

Size of mineral colloidal particles.   Before dealing with the specific properties of mineral colloids, it may be well to define a little more clearly the actual fraction of the soil which is in the colloidal state. The upper limit in size of the mineral colloidal particles is less than 0.001 mm., or one micron (μ), values as low as 0.5 or even 0.2 microns being commonly accepted. Since the maximum size limit of the *clay* fraction of a soil is considered as 0.002 mm., or 2μ, by no means is all of the clay strictly colloidal.

In a broad way, two groups of clays are recognized—the *silicate clays*

---

[1] The colloidal state refers to a two-phase system in which one material (or materials) in a very finely divided state, approaching but not attaining a molecular subdivision, is dispersed through a second. Each of the two phases of a colloidal system may be a solid, liquid, or gas. All combinations are colloidally possible except a gas dispersed in a gas. Good examples of the colloidal state are milk and cheese, clouds and fog, starch, gelatin, rubber, blood, proteins, plant and animal cells, and of course soil. Obviously, the colloidal state in nature is the rule rather than the exception.

so characteristic of temperate regions, and the *iron* and *aluminum hydrous-oxide clays* found in the tropics and semitropics. Our immediate concern will be with the silicates since they are dominant in the most developed agricultural regions of the world.

4:1. THE GENERAL CONSTITUTION OF SILICATE CLAYS [2]

Shape.   Early students of clayey-colloidal matter visualized the individual particles as more or less spherical. However, it is now definitely established that the particles are laminated, that is made up of layers of plates or flakes (see Fig. 4:1). Their individual size and shape depend upon their mineralogical organization and the conditions under which they have developed. Some of these particles are mica-like and definitely hexagonal; others are irregularly plate- or flakelike; while still others seem to be lath-shaped blades or even rods. With some particles, the edges seem to be clean cut while with others the appearance is indistinctly frayed or fluffy. In all cases, however, the horizontal extension of the individual particles greatly exceeds their vertical dimension.[3]

Each clay particle, regardless of its individual shape, is made up of a large number of platelike structural units. The arrangement is very much like that of a piece of mica—the leaves of the latter representing the platelike units of which the clay particles are composed. (See Fig. 4:2.) These units are held together with varying degrees of tenacity, depending on the particular type of colloid. In some cases, expansion between loosely held units occurs upon wetting, causing an over-all swelling of the clay particles. In other clays, the plates are held more rigidly and little expansion occurs.

Surface area.   As is readily anticipated, clay particles, merely because of their fineness of division, must expose a large amount of *external* surface. But this is by no means all. In some clays there are *internal* surfaces as well. This internal interface occurs between the platelike crystal units that make up each particle. (See Fig. 4:2.) Thus, the tremendous surface area that characterizes clay is accounted for not only by fineness of division

[2] The literature dealing with soil colloidal matter is exceedingly voluminous. Perhaps the best beginning can be made with C. E. Marshall, *The Colloidal Chemistry of Silicate Minerals* (New York: Academic Press, 1949) and with R. E. Grim, *Clay Mineralogy* (New York: McGraw-Hill, 1953).

[3] The flat, mica-like shapes that commonly characterize clay particles can be demonstrated in this simple way. By rotating a suitable clay suspension, the particles in motion are oriented temporarily in the same direction and as a result eddies and currents are clearly apparent as the light is reflected from the faces of the symmetrically arranged crystals. When the particles are at rest, they lose this orientation, the reflection becomes uniform and the eddies disappear. A suspension of round particles, of course, will not show the phenomenon just described.

Figure 4:1. Crystals of kaolinite (upper), montmorillonite (center), and hydrous mica (illite), as pictured by the electron microscope. Note their crystalline nature and mica-like shape. The kaolinite crystals are characteristically six-sided, while the others are irregular flakes. Magnification is 38,000 for both kaolinite and montmorillonite, and 45,000 for illite. *(Illite and kaolinite from work of M. L. Jackson and J. A. Kittrick, University of Wisconsin; montmorillonite by B. M. Siegel, Cornell University.)*

71

but also by the platelike structure of the fine particles. As a conservative estimate, it is suggested that the active interface due to the clay fraction of an acre-furrow-slice of a representative silt or clay loam soil probably exceeds the land area of Illinois or Florida at least 40 or 50 times. The external surface area of one gram of colloidal clay is at least 1,000 times that of 1 gram of coarse sand.

Figure 4:2. A generalized representation of a lath-shaped clay crystal showing its platelike structure. Two types of surfaces are evident—*external* and *internal*. The latter is much more extended than the former and, except for kaolinite and similar clays, is much more important in respect to adsorptive capacity than are the external surfaces.

Electronegative charge and adsorbed cations. The minute silicate-clay colloid particles ordinarily carry a *negative* charge. As a consequence, thousands of positively charged ions or *cations* are attracted to each colloidal crystal. This gives rise to what is known as an ionic double layer. (See Fig. 4:3.) The colloidal particle constitutes the *inner* ionic layer, being essentially a huge *anion,* the surfaces of which are highly negative in charge. The *outer* ionic layer is made up of a swarm of rather loosely held cations which surround and in some cases penetrate the particle. Thus, a clay particle is accompanied by a tremendous number of adsorbed cations.

Since the charges on the individual crystals are normally negative,[4] these crystals function somewhat like a simple acid radical such as Cl^- or $SO_4^=$ and will migrate to the positive pole when subjected to an electrical current. For convenience in designation, the individual crystalline particle is spoken of as a *micelle* (microcell) or a nucleus.

Associated with the layer of cations that throng the adsorptive surfaces of clay particles is a large and indefinite amount of water. Part of these water molecules is carried by the adsorbed cations mentioned above since most of them are definitely hydrated.[5] In addition, all silicate clays hold numerous water molecules packed between the plates that make up the

---

[4] Why the crystal usually carries a negative charge is explained later. (See p. 84.)

[5] It is now agreed that cations are commonly surrounded by water molecules. These are held electrostatically and greatly influence the closeness with which the cations may contact surfaces. For ions with a given valence, smaller ions appear to be more highly hydrated than those large in size. Thus Na is more highly hydrated than K and Mg more so than Ca. Also, divalent ions are more highly hydrated than monovalent ions of the same size. See Grim, op. cit., pp. 148 and 171.

clay micelle. These various types of water *in toto* are referred to when the hydration of clays is under consideration.[6]

Figure 4:3. Diagramatic representation of a colloidal clay crystal (micelle) with its sheetlike structure, its innumerable negative charges, and its swarm of adsorbed cations. Note that Ca ions are dominant, but that some H, K, Mg, and Na ions are present. No attempt has been made to show the adsorption of cations within the crystal (that is, between the platelike crystal units) or the numerous molecules of water that are held by the crystal surfaces and by the individual cations (hydrated ions).

4:2. THE ADSORBED [7] CATIONS

It is evident from the foregoing discussion that clay particles present a system composed of two distinct parts: (1) a relatively large insoluble *micelle;* and (2) a loosely held swarm of *cations.* Since these adsorbed cations are usually rather easily displaced, they are also spoken of as *exchangeable ions.* This replacement, called *cation exchange,* is one of the most important of all soil phenomena. It will be considered in detail later (see p. 90).

While all cations may be adsorbed by clay micelles, certain ones are especially prominent under natural conditions. For humid region colloids, these in the order of their numbers are H^+ and Ca^{++} first, Mg^{++} second, and K^+ and Na^+ third. For well-drained arid-region soils, the order of the exchangeable ions is usually Ca^{++} and Mg^{++} first, Na^+ and K^+ next, and H^+ last. The humid region clays are considered as having a calcium-hydrogen complex, while those in arid regions are dominated by calcium and magnesium.[8]

When the drainage of an arid-region soil is impeded and alkaline salts accumulate, adsorbed Na ions are likely to equal or even exceed those of the adsorbed Ca. Here then would be a sodium or a sodium-calcium com-

[6] A small part of the water is held by the colloidal crystal so tightly that it is considered nonliquid and as a part of the crystalline structure of the clay. A larger quantity of oriented water molecules surround the crystal and in certain clays may be found between the plates of a given colloidal particle.

[7] For a definition of adsorption see note on page 30.

[8] Other exchangeable cations that may be present but usually in small amounts are those of iron, aluminum, manganese, zinc, and ammonium.

plex. By the same rule, in humid regions the displacement of the metallic cations by H ions gives a hydrogen or an acid clay. Since the cation, or cations, preponderant in a colloidal system has much to do with its physical and chemical properties as well as its relationship to plants, this phase of the subject is of tremendous practical importance.

As mentioned above, calcium and magnesium are the adsorbed metallic cations held in largest amounts by the siliceous clays of most humid-region soils. Exchangeable potassium is, in most cases, sparingly present. The data

TABLE 4:1

Relative Proportion of Adsorbed Metallic Cations Present in Certain Surface Soils of the United States. (The percentage figures in each case are based on the sum of the metallic cations taken as 100. Note the geographic distribution of the soil samples.) [a]

	Sum of Metallic Cations Taken as 100			
Soils	*Ca*	*Mg*	*K*	*Na*
Penn Loam (N.J.)	60.8	15.8	19.0	4.4
Mardin Silt Loam (N.Y.)	90.7	5.0	3.1	1.2
Webster Series Soil (Ia.)	76.8	20.4	1.2	1.6
Sweeney Clay Loam (Calif.) (prairie)	76.1	21.3	1.3	1.3
Red River Valley Soil (Minn.) (Free of soluble salts)	73.9	21.5	4.2	.4
Keith Silt Loam (Nebr.) (Chestnut)	77.1	13.3	7.1	2.5
Holdrege Silt Loam (Nebr.) (Chernozem)	66.5	20.9	11.1	1.5

[a] These data were compiled from various sources. See T. L. Lyon; H. O. Buckman; and N. C. Brady, *The Nature and Properties of Soils* (New York: Macmillan, 1952), p. 84.

in Table 4:1 are representative of a considerable amount of information available respecting this relationship.

4:3. THE MINERALOGICAL ORGANIZATION [9] OF THE VARIOUS TYPES OF SILICATE CLAYS

For many years, even after its colloidal nature was recognized, clay was thought to be an amorphous body. X-rays as well as electron-microscope

[9] For brief and clear consideration of the subject consult: H. J. Lutz, and R. F. Chandler, Jr., *Forest Soils* (New York: Wiley, 1946).

examinations, however, show definitely that the clay particles, in spite of their inconceivable smallness, are definitely crystalline. On the basis of their crystalline properties, three major groups of silicate clays are now recognized: [10] (1) kaolinite; (2) montmorillonite; and (3) the hydrous micas, of which Illite is representative. Recent studies have shown the importance of other groups such as vermiculite and chlorite, but their nature is not as yet too well understood.

Kaolinite group.   The first group includes a number of clays: *kaolinite, halloysite, anauxite, dickite,* and several others. Of these, kaolinite is of greatest importance in soils. The crystals of this mineral are platelike in nature, being built up of flat crystal *units*. These units in turn are composed of alternate layers of *alumina* and *silica* sheets as shown by the drawing in Figure 4:4. Since every unit contains one each of the silica and alumina sheets, this group of clays are said to have a *1-to-1-type crystal lattice.*

Figure 4:4. A schematic diagram showing the lattice structure characteristic of kaolinite crystals. The section is a vertical one and gives an edge-wise view of two of the innumerable units that make up a crystal of this clay. Each of the crystal units is composed of one silica sheet and one alumina sheet (1 to 1 type of lattice) bonded very tightly by mutually shared oxygen atoms (represented by small circles).

The respective crystal units are, in turn, bound to each other rather tightly by an oxygen-hydroxyl linkage (denoted by dots) thereby giving a restricted and non-expanding lattice. As a result, ions as well as water molecules penetrate the crystals with great difficulty, if at all. The adsorptive capacity of kaolinite is, therefore, limited almost entirely to the external surfaces of its crystals.

The two sheets of each crystal unit of kaolinite are held together by oxygen atoms which are mutually shared by the silicon and aluminum

---

[10] Methods for the identification and quantitative estimations of the various clays are complicated and technical. See C. D. Jeffries and M. L. Jackson, "Mineralogical Analysis of Soils," *Soil Sci.,* 68: 57–73, 1949.

atoms in their respective sheets. These units, in turn, are held together rather rigidly by oxygen-hydroxyl linkages. (See Fig. 4:4.) Consequently, the lattice is *fixed* and no expansion ordinarily occurs between units when the clay is wetted. Cations and water do not enter *between* the structural units of the micelle. The effective surface of kaolinite is thus restricted to its outer faces. This is one reason for its low adsorptive capacity for cations.

Kaolinite crystals usually are hexagonal with clean-cut edges. (See Fig. 4:1.) In comparison with montmorillonite particles, they are large in size, the diameter generally ranging from 0.10 to 5 microns with the majority falling within 0.2 to 2 microns. Because of the tightness with which their structural units are held together, kaolinite particles are not readily broken down into extremely thin sheets.

In contrast with the other silicate groups, the plasticity, cohesion, shrinkage, and swelling properties of kaolinite are very low. Its restricted interface and limited adsorptive capacity for cations and water molecules have already been mentioned. In general, kaolinite does not exhibit colloidal properties of a high order of intensity.

Montmorillonite group. The montmorillonitic group, like the kaolinitic, contains several clays, such as *montmorillonite, beidellite, nontronite,* and *saponite.* Of these the first is easily the most important although the others occur prominently in certain soils. The flakelike crystals of montmorillonite (see Fig. 4:1) are also composed of crystal units. These units are made up of two silica sheets with an alumina sheet tenaciously bound in between by mutually shared oxygen atoms. (See Fig. 4:5.) The crystal lattice is, therefore, a *2 to 1 type.*

The structural units themselves are so loosely held together by very weak oxygen-oxygen linkages that the crystal lattice is bellows-like and *expands* very readily. As a consequence, montmorillonite crystals may be so easily fractured artificially as to give particles that approach the size of single structural units. Normally, however, montmorillonite crystals range in diameter from 0.01 to 1.00 microns. They are thus much smaller than the average kaolinite micelle.

Cations and water molecules are able to move in between the crystal units of montmorillonite because of its easily expanded crystal lattice. Thus, in addition to the surface of the outside of the particle, *internal surfaces* of very much greater total magnitude are presented. This internal surface is also negatively charged. Consequently, this 2 to 1 type of colloid has a high cation-adsorption capacity—perhaps 10 to 15 times that of kaolinite. Moreover, because of the movement of water in between crystal units, the swelling of montmorillonite greatly exceeds that of kaolinite.

Montmorillonite also is noted for its high plasticity and cohesion, its marked shrinkage on drying, and a ready dispersion of its fine, flaky particles. In fact, montmorillonite crystals disperse so easily that a satisfactory tilth of soils dominated by this clay is difficult to maintain.

Figure 4:5. A schematic representation of the lattice structure that characterizes montmorillonite crystals. This is an edge-wise view of two of the innumerable units that make up a crystal of this clay. Each crystal unit is composed of two sheets of silica and one of alumina (2 to 1 type of lattice) tightly bound together by mutually shared oxygen atoms (represented by small circles).

The respective crystal units in turn are loosely bound to one another by weak oxygen linkages (represented by dots) which allow a ready and comparatively wide expansion of the lattice (quite in contrast to kaolinite). This bellows-like spread of the lattice insures a very high internal adsorption of water and cations much greater than that ascribed to the external surfaces.

Illite has the same general structural organization as does montmorillonite except in respect to the linkages between the crystal units. Here potassium atoms supply additional connecting linkages between the crystal units, thus supplementing the oxygen bonding. These potassium linkages lessen sharply the expansion that the illite crystals are able to exhibit. As a result, the adsorptive capacity of this clay is considerably lower than that of montmorillonite. Illite, nevertheless, exceeds kaolinite in this respect.

Hydrous micas.   Often associated with the montmorillonitic clays is a rather indefinite group called the *hydrous micas* of which illite is the most important. Since its lattice is the *2 to 1 type,* illite resembles montmorillonite in its general make-up. (See Fig. 4:5.) However, its particles normally are considerably larger and about 15 per cent of the silicon in the silica sheets has been replaced by aluminum. The valences vacated by this substitution are satisfied largely by potassium. These potassium atoms lie between the structural units and exert a definite stabilizing effect on the crystal lattice. Hence, illite crystals are less expansive than are those of montmorillonite. Such properties as hydration, cation adsorption, swelling, shrinkage, plasticity, and ease of dispersion are less intensely developed in illite. Nevertheless, illite excels kaolinite in respect to these characteristics. As to size, illite crystals are apparently intermediate between those of montmorillonite and kaolinite. (See Table 4:2.) Whenever unfertilized soils show an unusually high content of potassium, it is probable that illite makes up a goodly proportion of the clay present.

TABLE 4:2

Comparative Properties of Three Major Types of Colloids

	Type of Colloid		
Property	*Montmorillonite*	*Illite*	*Kaolinite*
Size (microns)	0.01–1.0	0.1–2.0	0.1–5.0
Shape	irregular flakes	irregular flakes	hexagonal crystals
External surface	high	medium	low
Internal surface	very high	medium	none
Cohesion, plasticity	high	medium	low
Swelling capacity	high	medium	low
Cation exchange capacity (me/100 gm)	80–100	15–40	3–15

Other clay groups.   With more refined research tools and techniques, the soil scientists and mineralogists have demonstrated the presence of other important groups of silicate clays in soils. Two such groups that have been found prominent in certain soils are *chlorite* and *vermiculite*. These minerals apparently contain magnesium as a major constituent of the crystal units. Chlorite, for example, is probably composed of alternating silica and brucite $[(MgOH)_2]$ sheets, a given crystal containing two of each sheet.[11] Although relatively little is known concerning the specific

[11] This mineral is said to have a 2 to 2 type structure. See L. D. Whittig, and M. L. Jackson, "Interstratified-layer Silicates in Some Soils of Northern Wisconsin," *Pro. 3rd. Nat. Conf. on Clays and Clay Minerals,* Edited by W. O. Milligan, National Research Council, 1955, pp. 322–35. See this same publication (pp. 117–45) for a second article on chlorite by R. E. Martin, "Reference Chlorite Characterization for Chlorite Identification in Soil Clays."

properties of these minerals, they are known to have sizable cation-exchange capacities, chlorite equaling illite and vermiculite often exceeding montmorillonite in this respect. As more research is done, we can expect some clarification of the importance of these minerals.

In obtaining a general concept of clay minerals one should recognize that the specific groups do not occur independent of the other. In a given soil, one is apt to find several clay minerals in an intimate mixture. Furthermore, minerals having properties and composition intermediate between those of two well-defined minerals will be found. Such minerals are termed *mixer layer* or interstratified since within a given crystal the individual crystal units may well be of more than one type. Terms such as "chlorite-illite" and "illite-montmorillonite" are used to describe mixed-layer minerals.

4:4. GEOGRAPHIC DISTRIBUTION OF SILICATE CLAYS

The clay of any particular soil is made up, not of one mineral, but of a mixture of different colloidal minerals. In a given soil, the mixture may vary from horizon to horizon. This occurs because the kind of clay that develops depends not only upon climatic influences and profile conditions but also upon the nature of the parent material. The situation may be further complicated by the presence in the parent material itself of clays that were formed under a preceding and perhaps an entirely different type of climatic regime. Nevertheless, some very general deductions seem possible in respect to the soils of the United States.

Regional differences. It would seem, in general, that the clays in our Southern soils are likely to be dominated by kaolinitic minerals.[12] (See Table 4:3.) It should be remembered, however, that montmorillonitic soils in this area are not at all uncommon. In the cool, humid regions to the north, hydrous mica often is prominent, especially if potassium-bearing minerals are present in the parent materials. Nevertheless, kaolinite still is prominent and often dominates such soils.

Shifting to the prairie soils of the Middle West, montmorillonite usually appears conspicuously and, with the hydrous mica, usually exceeds kaolinite. Chernozems with a definitely lower rainfall show less kaolinite

[12] This general statement is substantiated by a recent report of the analyses of a wide variety of Southern soils. However, the prominence of other minerals such as illite, vermiculite, and montmorillonite was demonstrated. See *Certain Properties of Selected Southeastern United States Soils and Mineralogical Procedures for Their Study,* Southern Cooperative Series Bul. 61 for Cooperative Regional Research Project, S-14, 1959.

and much more montmorillonite and hydrous mica, while in desert soils the latter two are definitely dominant.

TABLE 4:3

Relative Amounts of the Three Silicate Clay Groups Present in Certain Representative Soils of the United States (Expressed as Ratios) [a]

No. of Soils	Soils and Areas From Which Clays Were Obtained	Kaolinite	Hydrous Micas	Montmo-rillonite
			Sum of Groups Taken as 100	
	Southern Soils:			
5	Red podzolics, southern states	90	10	0
8	Red podzolics, Ala.	100	0	0
3	Black belt soils, Ala.	47	0	53
	Eastern Soils:			
8	Gray podzolics, eastern U.S.	63	37	0
4	Certain New York soils	0	100	0
	Midwestern Soils:			
5	Iowa soils	11	26	63
3	Midwestern soils	25	63	12
5	Iowa soils	16	3	81
	Western Soils:			
4	Desert soils	22	78	
12	Arizona soils	5	52	43

[a] These data were compiled from various sources throughout the United States. See T. L. Lyon; H. O. Buckman; and N. C. Brady, *The Nature and Properties of Soils* (New York: Macmillan, 1952), p. 90.

While these conclusions are more or less tentative, they suggest that clay mixtures vary widely with different soils and that the type of clay mineral predominating is controlled to a considerable degree by climate and parent material. Nevertheless, it is often difficult to explain just why a particular clay material or mixture of clay minerals occurs in a given soil.

Clays other than silicates. In discussing the distribution of silicate clays in the United States, it must not be forgotten that other colloidal minerals besides the ones mentioned are present. These occur either as mere accessories or as an important part of the colloidal complex. Of the latter, the oxides of silicon, iron, and aluminum should be mentioned. While these occur frequently in temperate-region soils, the latter two are especially important in tropical and semitropical regions, giving rise to what are spoken of as *latosols*. Although these *hydrous oxide clays* will be considered later (p. 86), it is well to note here that, as progress is made from a humid-temperate region to the humid tropics, the silicate clays often contain a larger and larger admixture of colloidal iron and aluminum hydrous oxides. The red and yellow soils of our Southern states (p. 308) provide very good evidence of this transition.

Sections 4:5 to 4:7 inclusive deal with the genesis of silicate clays, the sources of their negative charges, and their chemical composition. The reader who is interested in only the more general consideration of silicate clays may choose to omit these sections and continue with section 4:8, page 86.

4:5. GENESIS OF SILICATE CLAYS [13]

The silicate clays are developed most abundantly from such minerals as the feldspars, micas, amphiboles and pyroxines. Apparently the transformation of these minerals into silicate clays has taken place in soils, and elsewhere, by at least two distinct processes: (1) a comparatively slight physical and chemical *alteration* of the primary minerals; and (2) a *decomposition* of the original minerals, with the subsequent *recrystallization* of certain of their decomposition products into the silicate clays. These processes will each be given brief consideration.

Alteration. Alteration of the minerals may be encouraged by chemical attacks with the consequent removal of certain soluble constituents and the substitution of others within the crystal lattice. The changes which occur as muscovite is altered to hydrous micas may be used as an example. Muscovite is a 2 to 1 type primary mineral with a rigid-lattice structure. As the weathering process begins some potassium is lost from the crystal structure and water molecules enter into the lattice to give a more loose and less rigid crystal. Also, there is a relative increase in the silica content, as compared to aluminum, in the so-called silica sheet. Some of these changes, perhaps oversimplified, can be shown as follows:

$$K_2Al_4(Al_2Si_6)O_{20}(OH)_4 + Si^{+4} \xrightarrow{H_2O} \{K_{0.2}\} \; (K_{0.8})Al_4(AlSi_7)O_{20}(OH)_4 + K^+ + Al^{+3}$$

Muscovite   Illite

(rigid lattice)   (semirigid lattice)

$\{K_{0.2}\}$ represents exchangeable potassium while $(K_{0.8})$ represents potassium held **semirigidly between crystal units.**

There has been a release of potassium and aluminum, a minor change in the chemical make-up, a loosening of crystal lattice and an initiation of exchangeable properties with little basic change in the crystal structure of the original mineral. It is still a 2 to 1 type, only having been *altered* in the process of weathering. Continued removal of potassium and substitution of magnesium for some of the aluminum in

---

[13] This subject is briefly summarized by P. F. Kerr; M. S. Main; and P. K. Hamilton, *Occurrence and Microscopic Examination of Reference-Clay Mineral Specimens,* American Petroleum Institute Project 49, Preliminary Report No. 5, pp. 1–14, 1950.

the alumina sheet would result in the formation of montmorillonite. (See Fig. 4:6.)

These examples illustrate the structural similarity among some of the various clay minerals. They also suggest that there may be a gradual transition from one mineral to another and that there are *intermediate* minerals with properties and characteristics in between those of the distinct groups. In verification of this, recent research has revealed the presence of so-called "mixed layer" minerals with names such as "Illite-montmorillonite," "chlorite-illite," "Illite-vermiculite," etc. These names suggest that a given colloidal crystal may contain crystal units of one mineral in between crystal units of another. Certainly they emphasize the complexity of clay mineralogy and of the soils of which these minerals are a part.

Recrystallization.   The crystallization of silicate clays from soluble weathering products of other minerals is perhaps even more important in clay genesis than is alteration. A good example is the formation of kaolinite from solutions containing soluble aluminum and silicon. This process of recrystallization involves a complete change from the structural make-up of the original minerals and is usually the result of much more intense weathering than that required by the alteration process described above.

Moreover, such crystallization makes possible the formation of more than one kind of clay from a given mineral. The exact silicate colloid which forms apparently depends upon the condition of weathering and the ions present in the weathering solution as crystallization occurs.

Relative stages of weathering.   The more specific conditions resulting in the formation of one or more of the important types of clay are shown in Figure 4:6. Perhaps the first generalization to be drawn from this outline is that there is a difference in the weathering stage of the minerals. The chlorite and hydrous micas apparently represent the younger-weathering stages of the silicates while kaolinite represents the oldest.[14] Montmorillonite is considered to occupy an intermediate stage of weathering. With Figure 4:6 as a guide, let us consider briefly the conditions which might yield each of the three groups of clays.

Genesis of individual clays.[15]   Hydrous micas represented by illite are thought to be formed, if conditions are favorable, by the alteration of the micas. This is postulated because illite is so similar to muscovite in make-up and general characteristics. Apparently, as indicated earlier, only a comparatively slight alteration is necessary to effect the change from one to the other.

In other cases, illite has apparently been formed from original minerals, such as the potash feldspars, by recrystallization under conditions of an abundant potassium supply. In still other instances, illite may be formed from montmorillonite if the latter is in contact with abundant potassium. More common, however, is the reverse reaction by which illite weathers to montmorillonite by the loss of much of its potassium. (See Fig. 4:6.)

Chlorite is apparently formed by the alteration of the magnesium and iron-rich mica, biotite. This change is accompanied by a loss of some magnesium, potassium,

[14] For a discussion of weathering stages see M. L. Jackson, *et al.*, "Weathering Sequence of Clay Size Minerals in Soils and Sediments: I. Fundamental Generalizations," *Journ. Phys. & Coll. Chem.*, 52: 1237–60, 1948.

[15] This discussion is not limited to the changes occurring in soils at the present time. It may also refer to changes which have taken place in the past in the genesis of the parent material or of the soil.

and iron. Further alteration and weathering may yield illite (hydrous micas) or vermiculite, either of which can be altered to form montmorillonite.

Montmorillonite may be formed by recrystallization from a variety of minerals provided conditions are appropriate. Apparently, mild-weathering conditions (usually slightly acid to alkaline), a relative abundance of magnesium, and an absence of excess leaching are all conducive to the formation of this mineral. Alteration of other silicate clays, such as chlorite, illite, and vermiculite, may also yield montmorillonite. (See Fig. 4:6.)

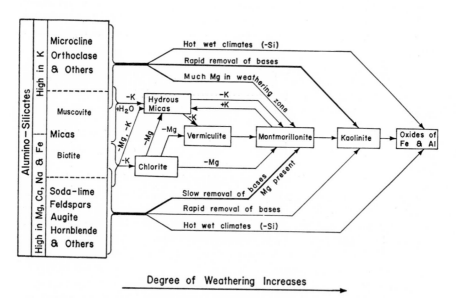

Degree of Weathering Increases

Figure 4:6. Diagram showing the general conditions for the formation of the various silicate clays and the oxides of iron and aluminum. In each case, genesis is accompanied by the removal of soluble elements such as K, Na, Ca, and Mg.

As already stated, kaolinite represents a more advanced stage of weathering than does any of the other major types of silicate clays. It is formed from the decomposition of silicates under conditions of moderately- to strongly-acid weathering which results in the removal of the alkali and alkaline-earth metals. The soluble aluminum and silicon products that are released may recrystallize, under proper conditions, to form kaolinite. This mineral, in turn, is subject to decomposition, especially in the tropics, with the formation of aluminum oxides and soluble silica.

As weathering of primary and secondary minerals occurs, ions of several elements are released. The more soluble ions such as sodium and potassium are usually removed in leaching waters. Others such as aluminum, iron and silicon may either recrystallize into new silicate-clay minerals or, more commonly, may form insoluble minerals such as the hydrous oxides of iron and aluminum. As shown in Figure 4:6, these compounds represent more advanced stages of weathering. They usually dominate soils only under tropical or semitropical conditions where intense weathering has resulted in the removal of most of the silica. (See p. 311.)

4:6. SOURCE OF THE NEGATIVE CHARGE OF SILICATE CLAYS [16]

Exposed crystal edges.   There are at least two ways to account for the negative charges associated with silicate clay particles. The first method involves unsatisfied valences at the broken edges of the silica and alumina sheets. Also, the flat, external surfaces of minerals such as kaolinite have some exposed hydroxyl groups which act as exchange sites. These hydroxyl groups are attached to aluminum atoms within the alumina sheet. The hydrogen of these OH radicals dissociates slightly and the colloidal surface is left with a negative charge carried by the oxygen. The loosely held hydrogen is readily exchangeable. The situation may be represented as follows:

One O Valence is
satisfied within   —O—························H+
the crystal by Al

Negative charged   Loosely held
crystal surface   exchangeable hydrogen

The presence of thousands of such groups gives the clay particles a definite electronegativity. Consequently, they are surrounded by H ions and other cations that may have replaced such hydrogen. This phenomenon apparently accounts for most of the adsorbing capacity of 1 to 1 type of colloidal clays. It also is of some significance with the 2 to 1 types, especially at broken crystal edges.

Ionic substitution.   A second source of the over-all negative charge carried by clay crystals is the substitution of one atom for another within the crystal lattice. For example, in some 2 to 1 type minerals such as montmorillonite, magnesium atoms have substituted for some of the aluminum atoms in the ideal alumina sheet previously described. Furthermore, the substitution is on the basis of one Mg^{++} atom for each Al^{+++} atom replaced. Therefore, each substitution results in an unsatisfied negative valence since a three-valent atom is replaced by a two-valent one. This may be shown as follows if we assume that the three valences of the aluminum atoms were satisfied by an equivalent of one O atom and one OH group:

Alumina Sheet   Alumina Sheet
(no substitution)   (Mg substituted for Al)

| $O= Al+++ OH-$ | | $O=Mg++OH-$ |

No net charge   One excess negative charge

[16] The presence of negative charges on clay particles can be demonstrated in a number of ways. One very simple method is to treat two samples of a clay with water suspensions of gentian violet and eosin red respectively. The particles of the former dye carry a positive charge and since they are markedly adsorbed by the clay, the clay must be negative. Conversely, the eosin particles, which are negatively charged, are only slightly adsorbed, if at all, by the clay.

Similarly, in minerals such as beidellite and illite the substitution of a three-valent atom such as Al for one of the four-valent silicon atoms in the silica sheet leaves an unsatisfied negative valence. This may be represented as follows since each Si is associated with an equivalent of 2 oxygen atoms:

<table>
<tr><td>Silica Sheet
(no substitution)</td><td>Silica Sheet
(Al substituted for Si)</td></tr>
<tr><td>$\boxed{O= Si++++ O=}$</td><td>$\boxed{O= Al+++ O=}$</td></tr>
<tr><td>No charge</td><td>One excess negative charge</td></tr>
</table>

With the 2 to 1 type of colloidal clays, the substitution phenomenon just explained accounts for a major share of their adsorbing abilities. Substitution may have occurred in either or both the alumina and silica sheets. In montmorillonite, most of the substitution has occurred in the alumina sheet, although some may have taken place in the silica sheet as well. Similarly, substitution in both sheets has occurred in illite, although the substitution and the source of charge lie largely in the silica sheet. In addition to the magnesium and aluminum ions, iron, manganese, and other ions may, in a similar way, enter the lattice of certain minerals.

4:7. THE CHEMICAL COMPOSITION OF SILICATE CLAYS

Using purified materials, chemists have long been able to determine the formulas of minerals from accurate quantitative analyses. This was done with kaolinite long before its crystal structure was known. Later such work was verified by means of x-ray diffraction patterns and other clays, hitherto unknown, were thereby discovered and classified. Once the crystal form of any particular clay mineral is known and the position of the various atoms in its lattice ascertained, its ideal formula can be written.

Because of the extensive lattice modifications and ionic substitutions common in clays, there are no chemical formulas which can be used to identify specifically a given mineral group. However, so-called "type" formulas can be used to illustrate differences in composition. Examples are shown in table 4:4.

The $\{Na\}$, $\{K\}$, and $\{Mg\}$ ions are considered as mostly exchangeable while the others are part of the lattice structure. Only the major substitutions have been shown. It will be noted that the differences among the formulas for montmorillonite, illite, chlorite, and vermiculite largely reflect differences in the ions dominant in the silica and alumina sheets. Intercrystal unit molecules are also illustrated.

It has already been strongly emphasized (p. 45) that the clay separate usually is richer in the mineral elements of nutrition than any of the other textural groups. This is, of course, the reason why soils of fine texture are, in general, strong soils agriculturally. However, considering only the formulas of the more common clay types as listed above, one might wonder how this could be true since only potassium, sodium and magnesium are shown as being available. The answer has already been in part suggested. Let us carry it further.

It will be remembered that cations of various kinds— $Ca++$, $Mg++$, $K+$, NH_4+ —are held at the colloidal surfaces. That these are readily available to plants is well

TABLE 4:4

Chemical Formulas of Important Clay Minerals Showing the Most Prominent Substitution in the Al and Si Sheets as Well as the Molecules between Crystal Units.[a] Readily Exchangeable Ions are Shown in Brackets

| *Clay Mineral* | *Dominant Cations in* | | *Nos. of Oxygen and Hydroxyl* | *Between Crystal Units* |
	Al Sheet	*Si Sheet*		
Kaolinite	Al_4	Si_4	$O_{10}(OH)_8$	
Montmorillonite (no ionic substitution)	Al_4	Si_8	$O_{20}(OH)_4$	
Montmorillonite	$Al_{3.5}Mg_{0.5}$ $\{Na_{0.5}\}$	Si_8	$O_{20}(OH)_4$	nH_2O
Vermiculite	Mg_6	Si_7Al $\{Mg_{0.5}\}$	$O_{20}(OH)_4$	XH_2O, Mg^{++}
Chlorite	Mg_6	Si_6Al_2	$O_{20}(OH)_4$	$Mg_4Al_2(OH)_{12}$
Illite	Al_4	Si_7Al $\{K_{0.2}\}$	$O_{20}(OH)_4$	$K_{0.8}$
Muscovite	Al_4	Si_6Al_2	$O_{20}(OH)_4$	K_2

[a] Note that the substitution of Mg for Al or Al for Si is compensated for by either exchangeable or intercrystal unit ions, e.g., $\{Na\}$

The actual formulas of specific minerals are considerably more complicated than those shown. See R. E. Grim, *Clay Mineralogy* (New York: McGraw-Hill, 1953), pp. 43–76.

known. Furthermore, with time there occurs in some instances a gradual release of ions, especially potassium, from the crystal lattice. Also, the hydrous oxides of iron and aluminum adsorb plant nutrients, such as phosphorus, which with time may be used by plants. Thus, colloidal clay, as it normally occurs in field soils, is not made of merely silicon, aluminum, and oxygen but carries also a varied supply of plant nutrients, such as Ca, Mg, K, P, and N, as well as trace elements. Obviously, the nutrient content of the silicate clays is by no means a minor feature of its physicochemical organization.

4:8. HYDROUS OXIDE CLAYS OF IRON AND ALUMINUM

The discussion so far has dealt only with silicate clays. However, hydrous-oxide clays also deserve attention for at least two reasons: (1) they occur in temperate regions intermixed with silicate clays; and (2) this type of colloidal matter is often dominant in the soils of the tropics and semitropics. The red and yellow latosols of these regions are controlled in large degree by iron and aluminum hydrous oxides of various types.

As their name suggests, *hydrous oxides* are oxides containing associated-water molecules. The exact mechanism by means of which these water molecules are held is somewhat uncertain. For simplicity, the hydrous oxides are often shown as actual iron and aluminum hydroxides [Al (OH)$_3$ and Fe (OH)$_3$]. Probably more correct general formulas are as follows: $Fe_2O_3 \cdot XH_2O$ and $Al_2O_3 \cdot XH_2O$. The X indicates that the quantity of associated water of hydration is different for different minerals. In soils, gibbsite ($Al_2O_3 \cdot 3H_2O$) is probably the dominant aluminum oxide while goethite ($Fe_2O_3 \cdot H_2O$) and limonite $Fe_2O_3 \cdot XH_2O$ are the most prominent iron-hydrous oxides.[17]

Although relatively less is known about the hydrous-oxide clays, they seem to have some properties in common with the silicates. For example, they are thought to have definite crystalline structure.[18] The small particles may carry negative charges and thus serve as a central micelle around which a swarm of cations are attracted. The same general constitution as described for the silicates may be visualized. Because of the much smaller number of negative charges per micelle however, cation adsorption is lower than even for kaolinite. Also, most hydrous oxides are not as sticky, plastic, and cohesive as are the silicates. This accounts for the much better physical condition of soils dominated by hydrous oxides.

4:9. ORGANIC SOIL COLLOIDS—HUMUS

Since the clays of surface soils usually carry an appreciable admixture of humus, a brief word is necessary at this point regarding organic colloids. Otherwise the soil significance of the colloidal state of matter cannot be fully visualized.

We shall not concern ourselves here with the origin of humus or with its chemical composition. Those phases are more appropriately considered under soil-organic matter (see p. 141). Moreover, we shall merely mention in passing the color relations, the low plasticity, the low cohesion, and the high-water capacity of the organic colloids. In the present section we shall consider the general colloidal organization of humus in comparison with that of clay.

[17] A very general discussion of these minerals is given by A. F. Frederickson in *Problems of Clay and Laterite Genesis* (York, Pa.: Maple, 1952), pp. 1–11.

[18] Seemingly amorphous hydrous oxides of iron and aluminum are known, although refined techniques may prove them to be crystalline.

Colloidal organization.   Humus may be considered to have a colloidal organization similar to that of clay shown in Figure 4:3. A highly charged anion (micelle) is surrounded by a swarm of adsorbed cations. As later sections will show, the reactions of these cations are essentially the same whether they are adsorbed by clay or by humus.

Some important differences should be noted, however, between humus and the inorganic micelles. First, the complex humus micelle is composed basically of carbon, hydrogen, and oxygen rather than aluminum, silicon, and oxygen, as is the case for silicate clays. Also the cation-adsorptive capacity of humus far exceeds that of even montmorillonite. The humus micelle is not considered crystalline and the size of the individual particles, although extremely variable, may be at least as small as montmorillonite. Last, humus is not as stable as clay and is thus somewhat more dynamic—being formed and destroyed much more rapidly than clay.

The information thus far presented on colloids has emphasized the complexity of the compounds and crystals of which the individual micelles are made. In spite of this complexity, however, the general organization is about the same for each of the colloidal groups. That is, a central, negatively charged micelle is surrounded by a swarm of cations. Let us now consider in somewhat more detail this general organization and the reactions modifying it.

4:10. COLLOIDS—ACID SALTS

Colloidal particles regardless of their composition are made up of a complex negative radical, the micelle, and a miscellany of adsorbed cations. In a humid region, those cations of calcium and hydrogen are by far the most numerous. Consequently, a colloidal complex may be represented in the following simple and convenient way:

$$\begin{matrix} _x\mathrm{Ca} \\ _y\mathrm{H} \\ _z B \end{matrix} \boxed{\quad \text{Micelle} \quad}$$

The significance of the Ca and H of the formula is obvious since in a humid region these cations jointly dominate the complex. The B stands for the small amounts of other so-called base-forming cations Mg, K, Na, etc., that are usually present in the ionic-outer layer. The x, y, and z indicate that the numbers of cations are variable.

The above illustration emphasizes that clays and their associated-exchangeable ions can be considered as *complex-acid salts*. This can be verified by comparing the formula above with that of $CaHPO_4$, a well-known acid salt. In both cases negatively charged radicals (anions) are associated with metallic cations and with hydrogen. The only difference is one of size and charge, the clay anion (micelle) being much larger than the phosphate and, of course, having many more negative charges per anion.

When by the proper laboratory manipulations the metallic cations are replaced entirely by H ions, a clay acid or H $\boxed{\text{Micelle}}$ results. In a like manner Ca ions may be given dominance and a calcium "salt," Ca $\boxed{\text{Micelle}}$, comes into being. It should be noted that several different acids and calcium salts are possible depending upon the nature of the micelle—that is, whether we are dealing with kaolinite, montmorillonite, humus or some other colloid. Of course in nature, soil colloids are very seldom wholly acids or wholly salts. As illustrated by the general formula at the beginning of this section, they are actually mixtures of *complex-acid salts*.

Why adsorbed Ca and H ions are so prominent. The adsorptive surfaces of humid-region colloidal particles usually are dominated by calcium and hydrogen ions. The reason for this can now be explained. In the early stages of clay formation the solution surrounding the decomposing silicates contains calcium, magnesium, potassium, and sodium, which have been liberated by weathering. These ions are not all held with equal tightness by the soil colloids. The order of strength of adsorption when they are present in equivalent quantities is Ca> Mg> K> Na. Consequently, one would expect the quantity of these ions in the exchangeable form to be in the same order, with calcium being the most dominant and sodium the least dominant cation. This is generally the case in most well-drained, humid-region soils.

As organic matter gradually accumulates and soil processes are fully initiated, carbonic and other acids are generated. Hydrogen ions, which are more strongly adsorbed than calcium, gradually enter the cationic swarm by cation exchange, forcing part of the calcium out. In humid regions the replaced calcium is lost by drainage. Consequently, the colloids gradually develop a calcium-hydrogen complex with an acidity in rough proportion to the dominance of the entering hydrogen ions.

In regions of lower rainfall, the calcium and other bases do not leach from the soil and consequently hydrogen does not become dominant. In either case, however, one can visualize, in a general way at least, not only how silicate clays are generated, but why certain cations are so prominent at their colloidal surfaces and at those of humus and hydrous oxides as well.

4:11. CATION EXCHANGE [19]

With the fundamental colloidal conceptions already presented as a background, the exchange of one cation for another on soil colloids may be accounted for very simply. The tendency of hydrogen ions to force such a transfer will be used to illustrate this phenomenon. Cation exchange is one of the commonest and most important of soil reactions.

A simple example.   Consider, to begin with, a representative humid-region mineral surface-soil, rather high in adsorbed calcium, and functioning under optimum conditions of moisture and temperature. A considerable amount of carbonic and other acids is formed as the organic matter decomposes. The H ions thus generated will tend to replace the exchangeable calcium of the colloidal complex. This occurs not only because of mass action effect but also because under comparable conditions ionic hydrogen is adsorbed more strongly than is the ionic calcium. The reaction may be shown simply as follows, only one ion of the copiously-adsorbed calcium being represented as displaced.

$$\text{Ca}\;\boxed{\text{Micelle}}\; + 2\text{H}^+ \rightleftarrows\; \dfrac{\text{H}}{\text{H}}\;\boxed{\text{Micelle}}\; + \text{Ca}^{++}$$

The reaction takes place fairly rapidly and the interchange of calcium and hydrogen is chemically equivalent. Moreover, if the H ion concentration were decreased for any reason or the Ca ions are increased, say by liming, the adjustment would be to the left in response to mass action. Conversely, if the H ions are increased or if the Ca ions are removed by leaching, the adjustment would be to the right. The soil is so dynamic that the equalization is constantly changing, oscillating back and forth as conditions dictate.

Cation exchange under natural conditions.   With these principles in mind, suppose we write the reaction more completely and as it commonly occurs in humid-region surface soils. We shall assume, for the sake of simplicity, that the number of Ca, H, and other metallic cations (B)

---

[19] The term *base exchange* is often used in referring to this phenomenon. *Cation exchange,* however, is preferable because base exchange suggests that only metallic ions are involved in the interchange. This, of course, is incorrect. The term *base* is used to refer to the metallic cations since they are potential base formers.

are in the ratio of 40, 40, and 20 per micelle respectively. The metallic cations (B) are considered monovalent in this case.

$$\begin{array}{c} Ca_{40} \\ H_{40} \\ B_{20} \end{array} \boxed{\text{Micelle}} + 5H_2CO_3 \rightleftarrows \begin{array}{c} Ca_{38} \\ H_{45} \\ B_{19} \end{array} \boxed{\text{Micelle}} \begin{array}{l} 2\ Ca(HCO_3)_2 \\ +\ B(HCO_3) \\ \text{\footnotesize subject to} \\ \text{\footnotesize loss in drainage} \end{array}$$

It is important to note that the reaction tends to go toward the right—that is, H ions are entering and calcium and other bases (B) are being forced out of the exchange complex into the soil solution. This is because the establishment of equilibrium is prevented by the loss of carbonates and bicarbonates in drainage. Obviously, as long as this continues and the H ions concentration is not correspondingly diminished, the adjustment will continue as pictured.

It is to be noted also that one micelle is taken to represent the whole colloidal fraction and that the loss of metallic cations (Ca and B) is just balanced by the gain in H ions. That is, the exchange is in *chemically equivalent amounts.*

Loss of metallic elements. Not only is the above reaction a very excellent illustration of cation exchange but also it is one of the most important and far reaching transfers that occurs in humid-region surface soils. Because of this phenomenon, and the presence in most soils of relatively large amounts of adsorbed calcium, this element is the metallic cation usually most copiously lost in drainage. The fact that magnesium, potassium, and sodium are affected in the same way, but to a lesser degree, serves to emphasize the rapidity with which cation exchange and leaching tend to deplete humid-region surface soils of adsorbed bases.

Moreover, the continual adsorption of H ions by the colloidal micelles at the expense of the calcium and other bases increases the acidic properties of the clay. By equalization, this tends in turn to increase the H ion concentration of the soil solution and pH of the soil is thereby gradually lowered. Thus, cation exchange accounts for the great loss of lime that most humid-region surface soils suffer each season (p. 216) and at the same time indicates why such soils tend to become acid so rapidly.[20]

Influence of lime and fertilizer. Since cation exchange is an equilibrium response, the direction of the movement of any particular ion may readily be reversed. Hence, if lime is applied to an acid soil, the reverse of the replacement just cited occurs. The active calcium ions by mass action

[20] This subject is so important in a practical way that it will receive detailed consideration in later chapters. (See p. 397.)

replace the hydrogen and other cations. As a result, the clay becomes higher in exchangeable calcium and lower in adsorbed hydrogen. And as the soil solution adjusts to this altered proportion of bases and hydrogen, its pH is raised and the whole chemical make-up of the soil is modified.

One more illustration of cation exchange will be offered. A soil fairly high in replaceable calcium is treated with a liberal application of potassium chloride, a common fertilizer salt. The exchange may be represented as follows if we assume that K ions replace one H ion and two each of the other cations associated with a given micelle. (Again *B* is considered as monovalent.)

$$\begin{matrix} Ca_{40} \\ H_{40} \\ B_{20} \end{matrix} \boxed{\text{Micelle}} + 7\ KCl \rightleftarrows \begin{matrix} K_7 \\ Ca_{38} \\ H_{39} \\ B_{18} \end{matrix} \boxed{\text{Micelle}} + \begin{matrix} 2\ CaCl_2 \\ HCl \\ 2\ BCl \end{matrix}$$

The reaction is not difficult to interpret if the previous example was fully understood. Obviously, some of the added potassium pushes its way into the colloidal complex and forces out equivalent quantities of calcium, hydrogen, and other elements which appear in the soil solution.

The adsorption of the added potassium is considered to be of advantage since a nutrient so held remains largely in an available condition but is less subject to leaching than are most fertilizer salts. Hence, cation exchange is an important consideration not only for nutrients already present in soils but also for those applied in commercial fertilizers and in other ways. It is no wonder that cation exchange, next to photosynthesis, is said to be "the most important chemical reaction in the whole domain of agriculture." [21]

4:12. CATION-EXCHANGE CAPACITY [22]

The capacity of soil colloids to adsorb nutrients can be determined rather easily. In methods commonly used, the original adsorbed nutrients are replaced by barium or ammonium ions and then the amount of ad-

---

[21] C. E. Marshall, *Colloids in Agriculture* (London: Edward Arnold, 1935), p. 79. It should be noted that anionic fixation may take place and in some cases assumes considerable importance. This is especially true in respect to the adsorption of phosphate ions. This phase is dealt with on page 440.

[22] The terms "cation-exchange capacity" and "cation-adsorption capacity" are used interchangeably in this text. Note that the cation-exchange capacity of a soil can be calculated in a rough way if its percentages of clay and humus are known. See note at bottom of page 94.

sorbed barium or ammonium is determined. The cation-exchange capacity is expressed in terms of *equivalents,* or more specifically, as *milliequivalents* per 100 grams. Before dealing with comparative exchange capacities of different colloidal materials, let us examine briefly this method of expression.

Method of expression. The unit employed in dealing with exchange capacities and reactions is the milliequivalent. This term is defined as *one milligram of hydrogen or the amount of any other ion that will combine with or displace it.*

Thus, if a clay has a cation-exchange capacity of 1 milliequivalent (1 m.e./100 gm),[23] it is capable of adsorbing and holding 1 milligram of hydrogen or its equivalent for every 100 grams of dry substance. This, of course, is 1 milligram to 100,000 milligrams of clay or 10 parts per million. Therefore, an acre-furrow-slice of such a clay weighing 2,000,000 pounds could adsorb 20 pounds of exchangeable hydrogen or its equivalent.

It is well to note this term—*equivalent*. It indicates that other ions also may be expressed in terms of milliequivalents. For example, let us consider calcium. This element has an atomic weight of 40 compared to 1 for hydrogen. Each Ca^{++} ion has two charges and thus is equivalent to 2 H^+ ions. Therefore, the amount of calcium required to displace 1 milligram of hydrogen is 40/2 or 20 milligrams. This, then, is the weight of 1 milliequivalent of calcium. If 100 grams of a certain clay are capable of adsorbing a total of 250 milligrams of calcium, the cation-adsorption capacity is 250/20 or 12.5 m.e./100 gms. The milliequivalent method of expression is so convenient and is so commonly used that a person dealing with the literature of soil science must be familiar with it.

Cation-exchange capacities of soil colloids.[24] As might be expected, the cation-exchange capacity of the colloidal fraction of soils exhibits a wide range, since humus and several minerals may be present in varying amounts. The cation-exchange capacities of humus, montmorillonite, hydrous mica, kaolinite, and hydrous oxides are more or less in the order of 200, 100, 30, 8, and 4 milliequivalents per 100 grams respectively. (See table 4:2.)

It is, thus, easy to see why the clay complex of Southern soils, when

[23] The abbreviation "m.e." will be used to express milliequivalent throughout this text. The number of milliequivalents are usually given for each 100 grams of material. Thus, the data may be given as, for example, 20 m.e./100 gms, etc.

[24] For exchange-capacity data on a large number of silicate-clay samples see P. F. Kerr, *et al., Analytical Data on Reference Clay Minerals,* Amer. Pet. Inst. Project No. 49, Preliminary Report No. 7, pp. 91–124, 1950.

dominated by kaolinite, should have a low-exchange capacity, ranging perhaps between 5 and 20 milliequivalents. On the other hand, the clay mixtures functioning in the soils of the Middle West, where illite and montmorillonite are likely to be prominent, have a much higher adsorptive capacity, ranging from 50 to possible 100 milliequivalents depending on conditions. Colloids of soils high in humus (such as mucks) will have cation exchanges in excess of 180 milliequivalents per 100 grams.

The practical significance of the figures quoted above is far-reaching. Colloids differ markedly in their cationic-exchange capacities. The soils carrying them also will differ widely in this all-important characteristic, not only because they possess different amounts of the different colloids but also because the colloids themselves are so variable. Undoubtedly, the heterogeneity of humus and soil clay is a fertility factor of tremendous importance.

4:13. THE CATION-EXCHANGE CAPACITY (C.E.C.) OF WHOLE SOILS [25]

Since the phenomenon of cation exchange is so important in soils, the question of the magnitude and variability of their total exchange capacity is sure to arise. This may be met by considering data regarding a wide variety of surface soils.

Variability of the C.E.C. of soils.   Comparative cation exchange capacities of a number of soils are shown in Table 4:5. In scanning the data one perhaps notices first of all, the great range in the figures presented, the highest approaching 60 milliequivalents per 100 grams. This is to be expected since soils vary so tremendously in humus content and in the amounts and kinds of clay present.[26] It is one thing to have kaolinite as the major clay and quite another if montmorillonite is dominant, so different are their individual capacities to adsorb cations. As already suggested, the adsorptive capability of montmorillonite commonly exceeds that of kaolin-

---

[25] One method for determining the amount of colloidal matter in soil involves a comparison of the relative water-adsorbing capacities of the whole soil and the colloidal separates contained in that soil. The relationship is as follows:

$$\frac{\text{Adsorption per gram of whole soil}}{\text{Adsorption per gram of extracted colloid}} \times \frac{100}{1} = \% \text{ of colloidal matter in soil sample}$$

[26] From the preceding section average figures for the cation-exchange capacity of representative silicate clay (0.5 m.e. for each per cent) and for well-humified organic matter (2.0 m.e. for each per cent) might be ascertained. Using these figures, it obviously is possible to calculate in a rough way the cation-exchange capacity of a humid-temperature region surface soil from the percentages of clay and organic matter present.

ite perhaps eight- to tenfold (see Table 4:2). Moreover, humic residues developed under different climates or from diverse plant tissues do not always possess the same adsorptive power. All of these factors contribute to the exceptional variability and wide range in the data presented.

TABLE 4:5

Cation Exchange Capacity of a Wide Variety of Surface Soils from Various Parts of the United States (in Milliequivalents per 100 Gms. of Dry Soil) [a]

Soil Type	Exch. Cap. m.e./100 gm	Soil Type	Exch. Cap. m.e./100 gm
Sands:		*Silt Loams:*	
Sassafras (N.J.)	2.0	Delta Miss.)	9.4
Plainfield (Wis.)	3.5	Fayette (Minn.)	12.6
		Spencer (Wis.)	14.0
Sandy loams:		Dawes (Nebr.)	18.4
Greenville (Ala.)	2.3	Carrington (Minn.)	18.4
Sassafras (N.J.)	2.7	Penn (N.J.)	19.8
Norfolk (Ala.)	3.0	Miami (Wis.)	23.2
Cecil (S.C.)	5.5	Grundy (Ill.)	26.3
Coltneck (N.J.)	9.9		
Colma (Calif.)	17.1	*Clays & Clay loams:*	
		Cecil clay loam (Ala.)	4.0
Loams:		Cecil clay (Ala.)	4.8
Sassafras (N.J.)	7.5	Coyuco sandy clay (Calif.)	20.2
Hoosic (N.J.)	11.4	Gleason clay loam (Calif.)	31.5
Dover (N.J.)	14.0	Susquehanna clay (Ala.)	34.2
Collington (N.J.)	15.9	Sweeney clay (Calif.)	57.5

[a] These data were compiled from a number of publications. See T. L. Lyon; H. O. Buckman; and N. C. Brady, *The Nature and Properties of Soils,* 5th ed. (New York: Macmillan, 1952), p. 111.

Relation of C.E.C. to texture and organic matter. A more careful examination of the table will reveal that a rough correlation exists between texture and exchange capacity, the latter, in general, increasing for soils with finer texture. Sands and sandy loams are low in colloidal clay and are very likely to be deficient in humus also. Heavier soils, in marked contrast, always carry more clay and generally more organic matter as well. Hence their cation-adsorption capacities are usually higher.

While variations in exchange capacity are expected to be rather pronounced between soils of different textures, it is perhaps a little surprising to find that the differences within textural groups are at times just as striking. In some instances organic-matter differences seem to account for the deviations. This may be the case with the silt loams of Minnesota, Wisconsin, and Nebraska and the clay soils of California cited in Table 4:5. But when the Cecil clay and clay loam of Alabama are compared with the Susquehanna clay of the same state, some other factor must be operative since all of these soils are rather low in organic matter. That the other factor might well be the type of clay present in each case is evidenced by the following tentative calculation.

Influence of type of colloid.   It is well known that the clay fraction of the Cecil soil is dominated by 1 to 1 type clays which have a cation-adsorption capacity of about 8 m.e./100 gms. Consequently, even if its total clay content should be 30 per cent, the Cecil soil probably would not possess a cation-exchange capacity due to the clay of much over 2 or 3 milliequivalents. The low figure of Table 4:5 is thus readily accounted for.

On the other hand, the inorganic-colloidal mixture of the Susquehanna clay is dominantly montmorillonitic in nature. Assuming in this case that the exchange capacity of its clay complex is approximately 90 m.e./100 gm and that the soil contained 30 per cent of this clay, its adsorptive power would be in the neighborhood of 27 m.e./100 gm. This is not taking into consideration the adsorptive capacity of humus that might be present. Thus the type of clay present probably accounts for the figure quoted for the Susquehanna soil.

These findings afford an opportunity again to voice a word of caution in respect to a previous generalization. It is suggested (p. 79) that the soils of our Southern states are to a considerable degree dominated by kaolinitic clays (1 to 1 lattice), while Northern soils often are characterized by clays of the 2 to 1 lattice type. That such a generalization should be applied with caution is evidenced by the case of the two Southern soils discussed in the preceding paragraph—one kaolinitic and the other montmorillonitic. Such situations are found not only in the same state but also in sites that are only a very few miles apart. Obviously then, the type of clay mixture that may characterize a soil is not necessarily determined entirely by climate. Parent material, time of weathering, drainage, and other factors participate in complicated interplay. It is not surprising, therefore, that montmorillonitic clay mixtures are found in Southern climes, and that both kaolinite and illite characterize certain Northern soils.

4:14. THE PERCENTAGE BASE SATURATION OF SOILS

Let us carry the consideration of the colloidal nature of soils one step farther and inquire briefly as to the relative amounts of exchangeable bases (that is, Ca, Mg, K, etc.) and exchangeable hydrogen ions that are carried by the colloidal complexes of various soils. This relationship ordinarily is shown by the *percentage base saturation*. It is the percentage extent to which the colloidal complex is occupied by exchangeable bases. Thus, if the percentage base saturation is 80, four fifths of the exchange capacity is satisfied by bases and only one fifth by hydrogen ions. The example in Figure 4:7 should be helpful in showing this relationship.

Figure 4:7. Diagrams explanatory of percentage base saturation. Three soils are pictured with percentage base saturations of 50, 80, and 80 respectively. The first is a clay loam; the second, the same soil satisfactorily limed; and the third, a sandy loam with a cation-exchange capacity of only 10 m.e.

Note especially that soil pH is correlated more or less closely with percentage base saturation. Also note that the sandy loam (right) has a higher pH than the acid clay loam (left) even though the latter contains more exchangeable bases.

Percentage base saturation and pH. The percentage base saturation data for different soils show wide variations. For example, the colloidal complexes in arid-region soils are practically saturated with bases. On the other hand, those of humid-region soils, due to ionic exchange and leaching, are likely to be comparatively low in metallic cations and correspondingly higher in adsorbed hydrogen. Such differences are extremely important not only from the fertility standpoint but also in respect to the H ion concentration of the soil solution.

A rather definite correlation exists between the percentage base saturation of a soil and its pH. As the base saturation is reduced, due to the loss in drainage of lime and other metallic constituents, the pH also is lowered in a more or less definite proportion.[27] This is in line with the common knowledge that leaching tends ordinarily to increase the acidity of humid-region soils. The mechanism by which colloids exert a control on soil pH will be considered later (see p. 358).

TABLE 4:6

Suggested Cation-Exchange Data for Representative Mineral Surface Soils in Humid-temperate and Semiarid-temperate Regions [a]

Characteristics	*Humid Region Soil*	*Semiarid Region Soil*
Exchangeable calcium—(Ca)[1]	6 to 9 m.e.	13 to 16 m.e.
Other exchangeable bases (B)	2 to 3 m.e.	6 to 8 m.e.
Exchangeable hydrogen (H)	4 to 6 m.e.	1 to 2 m.e.
Cation-exchange capacity	12 to 18 m.e.	20 to 26 m.e.
Percentage-base saturation	66.6	95 and 92
Probable pH	5.6 to 5.8	7±

[a] Note that the generalized formula—$\begin{matrix} x\text{Ca} \\ y\text{H} \\ z\text{B} \end{matrix}$ $\boxed{\text{Micelle}}$ —is being evaluated.

In order that the amounts of such exchangeable cations as Ca, Mg, K, etc., may be accurately compared with the amounts of adsorbed H, they must be expressed in milliequivalents. The conversion to pounds per acre-furrow-slice is easy but follow it through until you are familiar with every step. Its mastery is essential.

One milliequivalent of any cation per 100 grams of soil is equivalent on the basis of the acre-furrow-slice (2,000,000 lbs of dry soil) to 20 lbs. of hydrogen (p. 93) or to 1,000 lbs. of $CaCO_3$. This is a convenient conversion relation to remember. But be sure that you can prove it.

Applying this conversion to the maximum figures quoted for the humid-region soil, we find that the total exchange capacity of the soil in question is equivalent to 18,000 lbs. of $CaCO_3$ per acre-furrow-slice and that the actual amount of exchangeable calcium present is equal to $4\frac{1}{2}$ tons of $CaCO_3$. These figures provide a definite idea as to the magnitude of the exchange capacity of soils and as to the amount of replaceable calcium that might be present.

[27] Within the range of pH 5 to 6, the ratio for humid-temperate region mineral soils is roughly at 5 per cent base saturation change for every .10 change in pH. Thus, if the percentage-base saturation is 50 per cent at pH 5.5, it should be 25 and 75 per cent at pH 5.0 and 6.0 respectively. This relationship is worth remembering.

Humid-region soils. With the differences in cation-exchange capacity and base saturation of soils clearly in mind, the concept may be more or less completed by suggesting certain pertinent data of an average nature. A representative mineral surface soil from a humid-temperate region and at an intermediate fertility level, will be considered. The data (Table 4:6) are merely tentative but it is felt that they afford a more tangible idea of cationic adsorption and other related characteristics than has as yet been offered. The notes as well as the table itself merit diligent study.

Arid-region soils. The cationic-exchange situation in an arid-region surface soil is just as easily pictured. The adsorbed hydrogen is lower and the metallic cations are higher giving a percentage base saturation of 90 or even 100. The pH, of course, is around 7 or may exceed this figure if carbonates, especially those of sodium, are present. These changes definitely indicate the differences that in general can be expected when representative humid- and arid-temperate-region soils are compared in respect to their cation-exchange characteristics, percentage base saturation, and pH of their solutions. By way of illustration, tentative exchange data for a representative chernozem-surface soil, characteristic of certain semiarid, temperate regions, are offered in Table 4:6.

4:15. CATION EXCHANGE AND THE AVAILABILITY OF NUTRIENTS

It is generally assumed that adsorbed nutrients are rather readily available both to higher plants and to microorganisms. Experimental results unquestionably bear this out. But just how is the transfer from soil colloid to soil organisms effected? We have in cation exchange a mechanism that undoubtedly facilitates the availability of nutrients held in this way.

Nutrient absorption. Apparently, cation exchange functions in two ways as nutrients are released for the use of plants and microorganisms. In one case the nutrients freed by cation exchange find their way into the soil solution. There they may ultimately contact the adsorptive surfaces of roots and soil organisms or they may be removed by drainage water.

Second, if the contacts of the root hairs and microorganisms with the soil-colloidal surfaces are close enough, there may be a direct exchange of cations between the soil and the roots or microbes. (See Fig. 2:8.) Under such a condition, the H ions, generated at the surfaces of both the root hairs and the microorganisms, are thought to exchange with the adsorbed nutrient cations of the soil without any of these ions having first been released to the soil solution.

Cation saturation and nutrient absorption by plants.   The availability of adsorbed nutrients is not always so easy as the explanation above might lead one to surmise. This is because several factors operate to expedite or retard the release of nutrients to plants. First, there is the proportion of the cation-exchange capacity of the soil occupied by the nutrient cation in question. For instance, if the percentage calcium saturation of a soil is high, the displacement of this cation is comparatively easy and rapid. Thus, 6 milliequivalents of exchangeable calcium in a soil whose exchange capacity is 8 probably would mean ready availability. But 6 milliequivalents when the total exchange capacity of a soil is 30 present quite the opposite condition. This is one reason why when liming for a crop, such as alfalfa, that requires abundant calcium, the base saturation of at least part of the soil should approach or even exceed 90 per cent.

Influence of associated ions.   A second important factor influencing the plant uptake of a given cation is the effects of the ions held in association with it. For instance, assume that suitable amounts of exchangeable calcium are held by two soils and that the accompanying cation in one case is dominantly hydrogen and in a second case mostly sodium. Since the strength of adsorption is in general of the order: $H > Ca$ and $Mg > K$ and Na, it is obvious that in the first case postulated, Ca ions will be present in the soil solution in quantity because they are held less tenaciously than the associated H ions. In the second case, the concentration of the Ca ions in the soil solution will be relatively low since they are more tightly held by the soil colloids than are the Na ions.

The effect of type of colloid.   Third, the several types of colloidal micelles differ in the tenacity with which they hold specific cations. This, undoubtedly, will affect the ease of cation exchange. For instance, the tenacity with which Ca is held by montmorillonite is much greater than that of kaolinite. As a result it is suggested [28] that a montmorillonitic clay must be limed to at least 70 per cent base saturation before calcium will exhibit an ease and rapidity of exchange that will satisfy growing plants. A kaolinite clay, on the other hand, seems to liberate calcium much more readily, serving as a satisfactory source of this constituent at a much more lower percentage base saturation. Obviously, the liming programs of the two soils will be somewhat different, due in part to the factor under discussion.

[28] T. S. Chu and L. M. Turk, *Growth and Nutrition of Plants as Affected by Degree of Base Saturation of Different Types of Clay Minerals,* Mich. Agr. Exp. Sta., Tech. Bul. 214, June 1949.

4:16. OTHER PROPERTIES OF COLLOIDS—PLASTICITY AND COHESION, SHRINKAGE, SWELLING, AND FLOCCULATION

Without a doubt, the cation-exchange property of colloids is outstanding. Yet, from the practical as well as the technical standpoint, certain other characteristics also assume considerable importance. Those to receive attention here are six—*plasticity, cohesion, shrinkage, swelling, flocculation,* and *dispersion.* As might be expected, they all are surface phenomena and their intensity depends upon the amount and nature of the interfaces presented by the colloids.

Plasticity. Many soils, especially the siliceous clays of humid regions, exhibit *plasticity,* that is, pliability and the capacity of being molded. This property is probably due to the platelike nature of the clay particles and the lubricating yet binding influence of the adsorbed water. Thus, the particles easily slide over each other much like panes of glass with films of water between them. Usually those silicate clays with a high capacity for water of hydration exhibit the greatest plasticity. Thus, montmorillonite is more markedly plastic than kaolinite. Also the particular cation dominating the adsorptive interfaces is a factor, sodium encouraging a more viscous condition than calcium or hydrogen.

In a practical way, plasticity is extremely important since it encourages such a ready change in soil structure. This must be considered in tillage operations. As everyone knows, the cultivation of a fine-textured soil when it is too wet will result in a puddled condition which is detrimental to suitable aeration and drainage. With clayey soils, especially those of the montmorillonite type, plasticity presents a real problem. Suitable granulation there in is difficult to establish and often more difficult to maintain.

Cohesion. A second characteristic somewhat related to plasticity is *cohesion.* As the water of a clay gel is reduced, there is an increase in the attraction of the colloidal particles for each other. This tendency of the clay particles to stick together probably is due at least in part to the mutual attraction of the clay particles for water molecules held in between them. As one might expect, montmorillonite and illite exhibit cohesion to a much more noticeable degree than does kaolinite or hydrous oxides. Humus, by contrast, tends to reduce the attraction of individual clay particles for each other.

Swelling and shrinkage. The third and fourth characteristics of silicate clays to be considered are swelling and shrinkage. These properties are due to the relative inhibition of water, especially between the structural units of the micelles (see p. 77). If the clay in question has an expanding-crystal lattice, as is the case with montmorillonite, extreme swelling may occur upon wetting. Kaolinite and most hydrous oxides with a static lattice do not exhibit the phenomenon to any extent, while illite is intermediate in this respect. After a prolonged dry spell, montmorillonitic clay-soils often are criss-crossed by wide, deep cracks which at first allow rain to penetrate rapidly. (See Fig. 4:8.) But later, because of swelling, such a soil is likely to close up and become much more impervious than one dominated by kaolinite.

Figure 4:8. A field scene showing the cracks which result when a soil high in clay dries out. The type of clay in this case was likely montmorillonitic.

Apparently, swelling, shrinkage, cohesion, and plasticity are closely related. They are dependent, not only upon the clay mixture present in a soil and the adsorbed cation that is dominant, but also upon the nature and amount of humus that accompanies the inorganic colloids. These properties of soils are responsible to no small degree for the development of soil structure as has been previously stressed (see pp. 58 and ff.).

Flocculation and dispersion. In a clay suspension the colloidal particles are dispersed; that is, they are present as separate particles and not as groups.

Flocculation is a term applied to a coagulation of the dispersed particles. A very good example of flocculation is afforded by treating a colloidal clay suspension (wherein the particles are dispersed) with a small amount of calcium hydroxide. The tiny clay particles almost immediately coalesce into floccules. Because of their combined weight, these sink to the bottom of the containing vessel, leaving the supernatant liquid clear. The phenomenon is called *flocculation* because of the peculiar appearance of the aggregates. The same action apparently takes place in the soil itself, but, of course, much less rapidly.

Although the coagulating capacities of the several cations vary with the type of colloid under consideration, they may be ranked more or less in the order of Ca and $H > Mg > K > Na$. This is fortunate as the colloidal complexes of humid-region soils are usually dominated by calcium and hydrogen (p. 89). Such soils gradually tend to assume a coagulated condition in the field, which is of some consequence in respect to granulation. It is well to remark again (p. 60) that flocculation is not granulation, since the latter is most satisfactorily attained in the presence of organic matter. Flocculation really only sets the stage. The presence of organic matter and other cementing agents are necessary before stable granules are formed.

Reasons for flocculation. The reason for the greater tendency of a hydrogen- or calcium-saturated colloid to flocculate is associated with the so-called electrokinetic properties of the system. The number of negative charges which are responsible for the dispersion of colloidal particles is the same for a given particle regardless of the saturating cation. However, the *zeta potential* which determines the effectiveness of these charges in repelling a second particle is determined by the tightness with which the cations are held. Cations which, because of their size or hydration, are held very close to the colloidal surfaces tend to reduce the zeta potential [29] and to al-

---

[29] The zeta potential of a colloid-cation system can be determined by measuring the movement of colloidal particles in an electrical field. The rate of movement of the silicate clay particles toward the positive pole is directly proportional to the zeta potential. Thus, sodium-saturated colloidal particles will move more rapidly in an electrical field than will those saturated with calcium. See C. E. Marshall, *op. cit.,* Chap. 12.

low the particles to come together or to flocculate. Thus, divalent cations, which are more tightly held than monovalent cations of the same size, give colloid-cation systems with lower zeta potentials than do comparable monovalent cations. Also, highly hydrated ions such as sodium give colloid-cation systems with higher zeta potential than less hydrated ions such as potassium or rubidium. The water of hydration prevents the cation from being so closely adsorbed. These facts account for the tendency for sodium to encourage dispersion of soil colloids and for calcium to foster their flocculation.

It is plain that the six colloidal properties under discussion are of great importance in the practical management of arable soils. The field control of soil structure must definitely take them into account. With the colloidal viewpoint now provided, it might be worth while to review the discussion already offered (p. 62) relating to the structural management of cultivated lands.

4:17. CONCLUSION

No attempt will be made to summarize this chapter except to re-emphasize three things: (1) the unique and somewhat complicated physical and chemical organization of soil colloids; (2) their capacity to expedite certain phenomena vital to plant and animal life; and (3) the bearing of these phenomena on soil management and crop production.

Yet an understanding of these phases, even in detail, leaves the picture incomplete. The concept must be biocolloidal. Therefore, let us carry our knowledge of the colloidal state of matter with us as we consider soil organisms, soil organic matter, and the genesis of humus.

The Organisms of the Soil[1]

CHAPTER 5

In the preceding chapter, major emphasis was placed on the inorganic colloidal fractions—the clays. To complete our colloidal concept, we shall now turn our attention to the organic portion of this all-important state of matter, beginning with the life of the soil, the soil organisms. Once we obtain a general understanding of the activities of plant and animal life in the soil, our study of soil humus will be easier and more meaningful.

Humus, like clay, is a product of dissolution and synthesis. And the agency responsible is the organic population of the soil. Before a proper understanding of the various organic transformations and products can be acquired, some attention must be accorded the fauna and flora, the living colloidal fraction, of the soil. In this study it is well to note at the outset that the major stress will be placed, not on classification, but upon the biochemical changes induced by the various organisms. Consequently, the grouping employed (Table 5:1) is very broad and simple.

A vast number of organisms live in the soil. By far the greater proportion of these belong to plant life. Yet animals are not to be minimized, especially in regard to the early stages of organic decomposition. Most soil organisms, both plant and animal, are so minute as to be seen only by the aid of the microscope. The number ranging from this size to that of the larger rodents is comparatively small. For convenience the animals will be considered first. (See Table 5:1.)

[1] One of the better comprehensive treatises on the subject of soil organisms is S. A. Waksman, *Principles of Soil Microbiology* (Baltimore: Williams and Williams, 1932). See also, E. J. Russell and E. W. Russell, *Soil Conditions and Plant Growth* (New York: Longmans, Green, 1950); and H. J. Lutz and R. F. Chandler, Jr., *Forest Soils* (New York: Wiley, 1946).

TABLE 5:1

Chart Showing the More Important Groups of Organisms That Commonly Are Present in Soils. The Grouping Is Very Broad and General as the Emphasis Is To Be Placed, Not on Classification, but upon Biochemical Activity

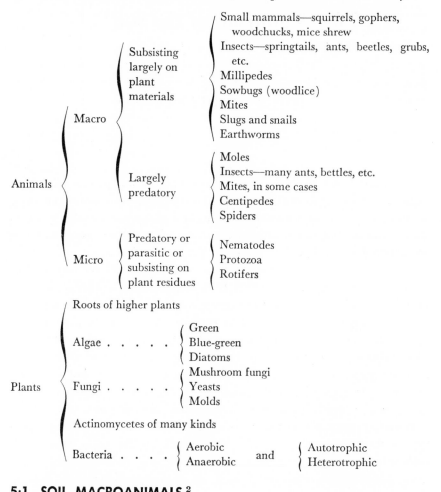

5:1. SOIL MACROANIMALS [2]

The larger animals of the soil are chiefly: (1) rodents and insectivora; (2) insects; (3) millipedes; (4) sowbugs (woodlice); (5) mites; (6) slugs and snails; (7) centipedes; (8) spiders; and (9) earthworms.

[2] For data concerning the animal life of the forest soils of northeastern United States, see T. H. Eaton, Jr., and R. F. Chandler, Jr., *The Fauna of Forest Humus Layers,* Memoir 247, Cornell Univ. Agr. Exp. Sta., 1942; and W. J. Hamilton, Jr., and D. V. Cook, "Small Mammals and the Forest," *Jour. of Forestry,* 38: 468–73, 1940.

The rodents are represented by the ground squirrel, pocket gopher, woodchuck, kangaroo rat, and prairie dog, depending upon the particular region under consideration. The activity of these animals results in the pulverization, granulation, and transfer of very considerable quantities of soil. Insect-eating animals, especially moles, are equally important in many cases. While the activities of these various animals are usually unfavorable to agricultural operations, the effect on the soil is often beneficial and analogous to that of tillage. Not only do these animals incorporate much organic matter into soils but also their burrows serve to aerate and drain the land. In some cases they so thoroughly disturb the various soil horizons as to make the original nature of soil profiles difficult to ascertain.

A great variety of insects is found in soils. Some of them have very little influence on the organic matter, while others, such as ants, beetles, spring-tails, etc., appreciably affect the humic constituents, either by translocation or by digestion. In some regions, the work of ants is often especially noticeable. In association with these insects are millipedes, sowbugs, mites, slugs, and snails, organisms that use more or less undecomposed plant tissue as food. They thus serve to initiate the decomposition processes that are continued by bacteria and fungi. (See Fig. 5:1.)

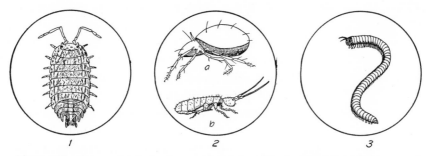

Figure 5:1. Four animals having much to do with the digestion of the organic matter especially of forest soils. 1, Sow-bug *(Trachelifus rathkei)*; 2a, mite *(Oribata Sp.)*; 2b, Spring-tail *(Tomocerus Sp.)*; 3, millipede *(Parajulus Sp.)*.

In peat soils, the millipedes often not only have much to do with the digestion of the organic matter but, by forming casts, they markedly influence the structure of the horizons in which they are active. Centipedes and spiders, being in large degree predatory, are of minor importance as far as the processes of humus synthesis are concerned.

Many of the animals just mentioned are rather unimportant in organic transfers as individual groups. In mass, however, they become highly significant even if they do nothing more than contribute at death to the accumulation of decomposable tissue. A number of these organisms are of more concern as plant or animal pests. Thus they are of greater interest to the pathologist and especially the entomologist than to the student of soil science. In any case, they are a part of perhaps the most intricate biological cycle in the world.

5:2. EARTHWORMS [3]

One of the most important of the macroanimals of the soil is the ordinary earthworm, of which there are a number of species. The *Lumbricus terrestris,* a reddish organism, and *Allolobophora caliginosa,* pale pinkish in color, are very common both in Europe and in eastern and central United States. (See Fig. 5:2.) In other parts of this country somewhat different species are dominant depending on the nature of the habitat. In the tropics and semitropics still other types are prevalent, some small and others surprisingly large. In respect to species, it is rather interesting to note that *Lumbricus terrestris* probably is not native to America. As the forests and prairies were put under cultivation, this European worm rapidly replaced the native types which could not withstand the changed conditions. Virgin lands, however, still retain at least part of their native populations.

Figure 5:2. Two earthworms common in arable soils. 1, *Lumbricus terrestris* and 2, *Allolobophora caliginosa.* While of about the same size, the former is darker and redder, the latter being pale and somewhat pinkish. Also there is a difference in the mouth parts. And as the diagram shows, the girdles of the organisms are located somewhat differently in respect to the segments.

Quantity of soil digested. Earthworms are important in many ways. The amount of soil that these creatures pass through their bodies annually may amount to as much as 15 tons of dry earth per acre, a startling figure.[4] At such a rate, a mass of soil equivalent to the acre-furrow-slice would be so processed in a period of only sixty or seventy years. During the passage through the worms, not only the organic matter, which serves the earthworm as food, but also the mineral constituents, are subjected to digestive enzymes and to a grinding

[3] G. E. Gates, "The Earthworm Fauna of the United States," *Science,* 70: 266–67, 1929; T. H. Eaton, Jr., "Earthworms of the Northeastern United States: A Key with Distribution Records," *Jour. Wash. Acad. Sci.,* 32: 242–49, 1942.

[4] Charles Darwin, *The Formation of Vegetable Mold* (New York: Appleton Century, 1885).

action within the animals. The rank growth of grass around earthworm casts suggests an increased availability of plant nutrients therein. Nitrogen perhaps is most markedly affected.

Earthworm casts on a cultivated field may weigh as much as 16,000 pounds an acre.[5] Compared to the soil itself, the casts are definitely higher in organic matter, total and nitrate nitrogen, exchangeable calcium and magnesium, available phosphorus, pH and percentage base saturation, and exchange capacity. These results support the observation in the preceding paragraph regarding the increased growth of grass observed on and around earthworm casts.

Influence on soil fertility and productivity. Over sixty years ago, Wollny [6] conducted experiments which indicated that earthworms have a favorable effect on soil productivity. Later studies [7] have confirmed these results, organic matter, cation-exchange capacity, and available phosphorus and potash all being increased through earthworm activity.

Other effects. Earthworms are important in other ways. The holes left in the soil serve to increase aeration and drainage, an important consideration in soil development. Moreover, the worms bring about a notable transportation of the lower soil to the surface. They also mix and granulate the soil by dragging into their burrows quantities of undecomposed organic matter, such as leaves and grass, which they use as food. In some cases, the accumulation is surprisingly large. In uncultivated soils, this is more important than in plowed land where organic matter is normally turned under in quantity. Without a doubt, earthworms have definitely increased both the size and stability of the soil aggregates,[8] especially in virgin soils.

Factors affecting earthworm numbers. Earthworms prefer a moist habitat. Therefore, they are found mostly in medium to heavy soils where moisture capacity is high, rather than in those of a sandy, droughty nature. They must have organic matter and thrive best in land where this con-

---

[5] H. A. Lunt and H. G. M. Jacobson, "The Chemical Composition of Earthworm Casts," *Soil Sci.,* 58: 367–75, 1944. The authors review the literature available on the subject.

[6] E. Wollny, "Untersuchung über die Beeinflussung der Fruchtbarkeit der Ackerkrume durch die Thätigkeit der Regenwürmer," *Forschungen a. d. Gebiete d. Agr.-Physik,* 13: 381–95, 1890.

[7] Y. C. Puh, "Beneficial Influence of Earthworms on Some Chemical Properties of the Soil," *Sci. Soc. China, Biol. Lab. Contrib.,* Zool. Ser., 15, No. 9: 147–55, 1941; H. Hopp and C. S. Slater, "Influence of Earthworms on Soil Productivity," *Soil Sci.,* 66: 421–28, 1948.

[8] R. C. Dawson, "Earthworm Microbiology and the Formation of Water-Stable Aggregates," *Proc. Soil Sci. Soc. Amer.,* 12: 512–16, 1947; and W. J. M. Guild, "Earthworms and Soil Structure," *Soil Zoology,* 1955, 83–98.

stituent is plentiful. It seems, also, that the nutrition of some earthworms depends on certain lime-secreting glands. Perhaps because of this, they are not usually found abundantly in soils that are low in replaceable calcium. There are some exceptions to this, however. Nevertheless, it is quite surprising to find how suddenly the earthworm population at times will change as to vigor, numbers, and even species within very short distances in response to pH and other soil conditions.

The numbers of earthworms are markedly affected by the application of farm manure. Considering their dependence upon organic matter and their response to fertility levels, this influence is to be expected. Russell[9] quotes them as ranging from 13,000 per acre in a soil receiving no farm manure to over 1,000,000 per acre on land to which farm manure in quantity was applied. These data are in line with figures cited by Lutz and Chandler[10] indicative of a range under normal conditions of from 250,000 to at least 1,000,000 individuals to the acre.

Using Russell's data as to numbers and assuming each worm to weigh on the average ½ gram, the live weight of these animals would range from approximately 15 pounds per acre in the one case to over 1,100 pounds in the other. These figures are merely suggestive, but they do indicate what may be expected in a general way as to the weight of the earthworm population in arable soils.

Earthworm ecology. In a study of earthworm ecology at College Park, Maryland, these organisms (mostly *Helodrilus caliginosus* and *H. chloroticus*) were found to follow a distinct reproductive cycle.[11] In sod, young earthworms were fewest in the spring and reach their peak in autumn. The numbers of mature worms were just reversed. In the fall before they became tolerant to cold, the new generation was easily killed by freezing. Hence, in bare, cultivated soils the population is often seriously reduced in late autumn by a sudden freeze unless the soil surface is covered by plant debris of some kind. Frost damage is not so likely to occur in sodded land.

Therefore, in regions where soil freezing is the rule, a surface protection of some type is necessary as winter sets in if the earthworm population is

[9] Russell and Russell, *op. cit.*, p. 414.

[10] Lutz and Chandler, *op. cit.*, p. 101.

[11] H. Hopp, "The Ecology of Earthworms in Cropland," *Proc. Soil Sci. Soc. Amer.*, 12: 503–507, 1947. See also C. S. Slater and H. Hopp, "Relation of Fall Protection to Earthworm Populations and Soil Physical Conditions," *Proc. Soil Sci. Soc. Amer.*, 12: 508–11, 1947.

to be carried over more or less intact. However, after the first severe weather, the earthworms not only acquire tolerance to the cold but also migrate to lower horizons where temperatures are more favorable. This penetration may range from 3 to 6 feet. For gardeners and others who wish to maintain a high earthworm population in their soils, surface protection is as essential as high organic matter, suitable moisture, good drainage and aeration, and low acidity.

5:3. SOIL MICROANIMALS

Of the abundant microscopic animal life in soils, two groups are particularly important—nematodes and protozoa. A third—the rotifers—at least deserves mention. The three groups will be considered in order. (See Table 5:1.)

Nematodes. Nematodes, threadworms, or eelworms as they are commonly called, are found in almost all soils, often in surprisingly large numbers. A maximum of 50 to the gram of dry soil would mean about 45 billions to the acre-furrow-slice. These organisms are round and spindle-shaped in form, the caudal end usually being acutely pointed. In size, they are almost wholly microscopic, seldom being large enough to be seen at all readily with the naked eye. (See Fig. 5:3.)

Three groups of nematodes [12] may be distinguished on the basis of their food demands: (1) those that live on decaying organic matter, (2) those that are predatory on other nematodes, small earthworms, and the like, and (3) those that are parasitic, attacking the roots of higher plants to pass at least a part of their life cycle imbedded in such tissue. The first and second groups are by far the most numerous in the average soil and most varied.

The last group, however, especially those of the genus Heterodera is the most important to the plant specialist. Due to their adaptable mouth-parts and pointed form they find it easy to penetrate plant tissue. The roots of practically all plants are more or less infested even in cool temperate regions,[13] and the damage done is often very great, especially to vegetable crops grown in southern United States. Even in greenhouses, nematodes

---

[12] For a discussion of soil nematodes see T. Goodey, *Soil and Fresh Water Nematodes* (New York: Wiley, 1951).

[13] The infection of the potato soils of Long Island, New York, with the golden nematode (Heterodera Rostochiensis) is a case in point, threatening the economic production of potatoes on soils that otherwise are satisfactory both as to yield and as to proximity to market.

may become a serious pest unless care is taken to avoid infestation. Due to the difficulties encountered in control, an appreciable nematode infection is a serious matter.[14]

Protozoa.   Protozoa [15] probably are the simplest form of animal life. Although one-celled organisms, they are considerably larger than bacteria and of a distinctly higher organization. Some are merely masses of naked protoplasm—amoeba—while others exhibit a much higher development and are even protected with siliceous or chitinous coverings. For convenience of discussion, soil protozoa are divided into three groups: (1) amoeba, (2) ciliates or infusoria, and (3) flagellates. The presence of numerous cilia or hairs and of flagella, long whiplike appendages of protoplasm, are the bases for the two latter subdivisions. (See Fig. 5:3.) The flagellates are usually most numerous in soil followed in order by the amoeba and the ciliates.

Figure 5:3.   Parasitic nematodes (left), a ciliated protozoan (center), and a common rotifier (right). *(First two after Waksman.)*

The protozoa are the most varied and numerous in the microanimal population of soils. More than 250 species have been isolated, sometimes as many as 40 or 50 of such groups occurring in a single sample of soil. The presence of protozoa has been reported in soils from most of the countries of Europe, the United States, and many other regions. Many of these organisms are highly adaptable and occur in habitats other than that of the soil. A considerable number of serious animal and human diseases are due to protozoan infections.

The numbers of protozoa in the soil are subject to extreme fluctuation, even when conditions apparently are continuously favorable. Aeration, as well as the available food supply, is probably a very important factor. Most of the organisms are therefore confined to the surface horizons. Usually, the numbers are highest in the spring and autumn. Perhaps 1,000,000

[14] R. R. Kincaid, "Soil Factors Affecting Incident of Root Knot," *Soil Sci.,* 61: 101–109, 1946.

[15] H. Sandon, *The Composition and Distribution of the Protozoan Fauna of the Soil* (Edinburgh: Oliver and Boyd, 1927).

protozoa of all kinds per gram of a representative dry soil might be considered a maximum. This might amount to a live weight of 100 or even 200 pounds to the acre.

The nutritional habits of protozoa are not well known. No doubt, most of those in the soil depend on nonliving organic matter as a source of food. There are some indications, however, that certain groups may ingest bacteria and thus, in an indirect way, may interfere with higher plants. The ingestion of bacteria having to do with the availability of plant nutrients, might appreciably interfere with the growth of higher plants.

Rotifers. That rotifers, the third group of microanimals to be considered, occur in the soil is well known and under moist conditions, especially in swampy land, their numbers may be great. As many as fifty different species have been found under such environs. These animals are mostly microscopic in size. Their anterior is modified into a retractile disk bearing circles of cilia which, in motion, give the appearance of moving wheels— hence, the name. These hairs sweep floating food materials into the animal. The posterior end of the rotifer tapers to a foot by which the rotifer can attach itself to convenient objects. (See Fig. 5:3.)

Just how important rotifers are in soils is unknown. No doubt they enter into the cycle of organic dissolution in a more or less important way, especially in peat bogs and in wet places occurring in mineral soils.

5:4. PLANT LIFE OF THE SOIL

The organisms of a plant nature are more numerous and, from some standpoints, are more important than are the animal forms. This is true especially in respect to the final stages of organic matter decomposition, the synthesis of humus and the production of compounds simple enough for the direct nutrition of higher plants. It must be remembered, however, that the initial digestion is very often due to animals such as millipedes and springtails greatly assisted by earthworms if the lime content and other conditions of the organic residues are favorable.

The plant life of the soil will be considered under five heads as follows: (1) roots of higher plants, (2) algae, (3) fungi, (4) actinomycetes, and (5) bacteria. (See Table 5:1.)

5:5. ROOTS OF HIGHER PLANTS

As a source of organic matter, the roots of higher plants are of supreme importance since they supply much more original tissue than all of the other organisms combined. In fact, the life of the soil might be divided into two distinct and, in some respects, opposing groups—(1) those that supply organic residues, and (2) those that are engaged primarily in tearing such residues down. Plant roots are, of course, the all-important representative of the first group, while millipedes, springtails, earthworms, bacteria, molds, and actinomycetes are principals in the second type of activity.

Amounts of organic tissue added.   A good crop of oats will produce perhaps 4,000 pounds of dry matter to the acre in its aboveground parts, while the figure for corn on the same basis would be about 6,000 pounds. If the roots left in the soil when such crops are harvested amount to even half these weights, the added organic residues are, by no means, inconsiderable. In fact, and this is a situation seldom appreciated even by farmers, the maintenance of a satisfactory supply of organic matter in arable soils is possible only because of root residues added in this automatic way. For a photo of elongating as well as dying rootlets see Figure 5:4.

Figure 5:4. Rootlets elongate rapidly and thereby are continually establishing new soil contacts. Were it not for this ready extension, crops growing on well drained arable soils would soon suffer from lack of moisture as well as nutrients. Since the life of these shoots is very short, they continually contribute to the supply of readily decomposable tissue and greatly stimulate microbial activity. Note the excellent granulation of this soil. *(N. Y. State College of Agriculture Photo.)*

The roots of higher plants also function in a more intimate manner than as a source of dead tissue for the nutrition of soil microbes. When alive, they not only influence the equilibrium of the soil solution by the withdrawal of soluble nutrients, but they also have something to do in a direct way with nutrient availability. Organic acids are formed at the root surfaces and hence become effective solvents. Again, the excretion of readily decomposable compounds such as amino acids as well as the sloughing of root tissue stimulate the microflora to an intensity of action not attained in other parts of the soil. The numbers of organism in the immediate root zone, the *rhizosphere*,[16] may be as many as 100 times

[16] Rhizosphere organisms are discussed by F. E. Clark, "Soil Microorganisms and Plant Roots," *Advances in Agronomy*, 1: 241–88, 1949. More recent research on this

as great as elsewhere in the soil, although a value of 10 times is probably more normal. This means that the adsorptive surfaces of the root hairs lie within the zone of unusual nutrient availability. This has already been explained (p. 37) and indicates in part why the roots of higher plants are classified as soil organisms. They not only force a transfer of nutrients but they also promote an availability that, under other conditions, might be very slow.

5:6. THE MICROPLANT ORGANISMS—DIFFICULT TO STUDY

Before considering the specific groups of the microplant organisms it may be well to mention the inadequacies of the methods which have been used in their study. For example, it should be pointed out that the estimation of the numbers of specific organisms in the soil is often quite inaccurate. This is due to the fact that all soil microorganisms do not grow equally as well on the various artificial media commonly employed in making counts. A given species might function very well in the soil and yet grow poorly, if at all, on any of the media commonly used.

The above example is a reminder of the extreme complexity of the microbiological population making it difficult to study the specific functions of the various groups. These situations should be kept in mind constantly in reading the following sections.

5:7. SOIL ALGAE [17]

Most algae are chlorophyll-bearing organisms and, as such, must live at or very near the surface of the soil, if they are to survive in a habitat of this nature. However, certain forms seem able to obtain their energy largely from organic matter and may readily exist within and below the surface horizon. The number of these, however, is not large. Thus, some algae live and function much like higher plants, while others in their nutritional habits are typical soil microorganisms. Over sixty species have been isolated from soils, those most prominent being the same the world over. Soil algae are divided into three general groups: (1) blue-green, (2) green, and (3) diatoms.

Naturally, soil algae in vegetative form are most numerous in the surface

---

subject was reported by A. D. Rovira, "Plant Root Excretions in Relation to the Rhizosphere Effect, I, II, and III," *Plant and Soil,* 7: 178–93 (I) 195–208 (II), and 206–16 (III), 1956.

[17] Most of this group can carry on photosynthesis just as do higher plants. The amounts of organic tissue thus produced, however, are small in comparison with those supplied by higher plant residues.

layers, especially in the upper inch of arable soils. In subsoils, most algae are present as resting spores, or cysts, or in vegetative forms that do not depend upon chlorophyll. Grassland seems especially favorable for the blue-green forms, while in old gardens, diatoms are often numerous. All of the ordinary types of algae are greatly stimulated by the application of farm manure.

Both the green and the blue-green algae outnumber the diatoms, 100,000 to a gram of dry surface soil being an estimated minimum under favorable conditions for each in Rothamsted soils.[18] In certain Utah soils, Martin [19] reports the total algal population as reaching a maximum of 800,000 to a gram of dry soil. Thus, algae undoubtedly contribute some to the organic content of the soil. Blue-green algae are especially numerous in rice soils and when such lands are waterlogged and exposed to the sun appreciable amounts of nitrogen are fixed by these organisms.[20] Moreover, algae fixation is enhanced when the rice crop occupies the paddies. Apparently, this stimulation is due to CO_2 which is at an especially high level when the rice plants are growing most vigorously.

5:8. SOIL FUNGI [21]

It is only within comparatively recent years that the importance of the role played by fungi in the soil has been recognized. While their influence is still by no means entirely understood, it is now known that they play a very important part in the transformations of the soil constituents. Over 200 species have been identified representing 42 genera. Like the bacteria and actinomycetes, fungi contain no chlorophyll and must depend for their energy and carbon on the organic matter of the soil.

The superficial characteristic that distinguishes fungi is the filamentous nature of their vegatative forms. Their mycelial threads may be simple and restricted or profusely branched and of such dimensions as to attract even casual attention. More than this, the special spore-forming or fruiting bodies often attain, with some groups, macroscopic sizes. Fungal organisms

---

[18] Russell, *op. cit.,* p. 420.

[19] T. L. Martin, "The Occurrence of Algae in Some Virgin Utah Soils," *Proc. Soil Sci. Soc. Amer.,* 4: 249, 1939.

[20] P. K. De and M. Sulaiman, "Fixation of Nitrogen in Rice Soils by Algae as Influenced by Crop, CO_2 and Organic Substances," *Soil Sci.,* 70: 137–51, 1950.

[21] J. C. Gilman, *A Manual of Soil Fungi* (Ames, Iowa: The Iowa State College Press, 1945).

S. A. Waksman, "Three Decades with Soil Fungi," *Soil Sci.,* 58: 89–115, 1944. This article carries a rather complete bibliography.

may thus vary from the simple microscopic yeasts to mushroom and bracket fungi of extraordinary dimensions.

For convenience of discussion, fungi may be divided into three groups as follows: (1) yeasts, (2) molds, and (3) mushroom fungi. Of these, only the last two are considered important in soils, as yeasts occur to a very limited extent in such a habitat. They, therefore, need not receive further consideration here.

Molds. The distinctly filamentous, microscopic, or semi-macroscopic fungi are commonly spoken of as molds. (See Fig. 5:5.) In soils, they play a role infinitely more important than the mushroom fungi, approaching or even excelling at times the influence of bacteria. They respond especially to soil aeration, their numbers and activities diminishing as air movement is retarded.

Molds will develop virogously in acid, neutral, or alkaline soils, some being favored, rather than otherwise, by a lowered pH. (See Fig. 14:5.) Consequently, they are noticeably abundant in acid soils, where bacteria and actinomycetes offer only mild competition. Were it not for fungi, there would be little decomposition and digestion of the organic residues in acid forest soils other than that effected by millipedes, springtails, mites, and other animals.

Molds are found in all horizons of the soil profile, the greatest numbers being, of course, in the surface layers where organic matter is ample and aeration adequate. Many genera are represented, four of the more evident being Penicillium, Mucor, Trichoderma, and Aspergillus. Species from at least eight other genera often are plentiful, however. All of the common species occur in most soils, conditions determining which shall dominate. Their numbers fluctuate greatly with soil conditions, perhaps 1,000,000 individuals to the gram of dry soil representing a more or less normal population.[22] This might well amount to 1,000 or 1,200 pounds of living organisms to the acre.

Perhaps the most important factor relating to the activity of fungi is food supply. The addition of almost any kind of decomposable organic matter to the soil, especially farm manure, has a surprising effect on mycelial development. Even commercial fertilizers increase the number of molds present. When conditions are unfavorable, the vegetative tissue diminishes, and spores are formed which have great powers of resistance.

[22] W. B. Brierley; S. T. Jewson; and M. Brierley, "The Quantitative Study of Soil Fungi," *Proc. and Papers, First Internat. Cong. Soil Sci.,* 3: 48–71, 1928.

Molds are an important part of the general-purpose, heterotrophic group of soil organisms that fluctuate so greatly in most soils.

In this connection it is interesting to note that fungal population is constantly changing not only in numbers but in respect to the species dominant. The complexity of the organic compounds being attacked seems to determine, at least in part, the particular mold or molds prevalent.[23]

Activities of fungi. In their ability to decompose organic residues, fungi are the most versatile and perhaps the most persistent of any group. Cellulose, starch, gums, lignin, as well as the more easily affected proteins and sugars, readily succumb to their attack. In respect to the processes of humus formation and aggregate stabilization [24] molds are perhaps more important than bacteria. This is certainly true in acid forest soils.

Moreover, fungi function more economically than bacteria in that they transform into their tissues a larger proportion of the carbon and nitrogen of the compounds attacked and give off as by-products less carbon dioxide and ammonium. As much as 50 per cent of the substances decomposed by molds may become fungal tissue. However, they apparently cannot oxidize ammonium compounds to nitrates as do certain bacteria, nor can they fix atmospheric nitrogen. Nevertheless, soil fertility depends in no small degree on molds, since they keep the decomposition processes going when bacteria and actinomycetes alone would not suffice.

Mycorrhiza. Numerous varieties of mushroom fungi, producing such fruiting bodies as mushrooms, toadstools, and puffballs, are found in forests and elsewhere, often in great profusion. The mycelia of certain members of this general group, especially the *Hymenomycetes*, often infest the roots of trees giving an association called *mycorrhiza*. The fungal threads in some cases merely form a mat around the absorbing root surfaces while in others they actually penetrate the root cells. The presence of the fungi is thought by many investigators to be of advantage both to the host and the parasite. The latter perhaps may digest and in some way pass on to the trees certain nutrient constituents that the host might not obtain so readily alone. Some workers suggest that the benefit, when it does occur, is due merely to an increase in the amount of effective absorptive surface presented by the association of the roots and the fungi.

[23] T. L. Martin; D. A. Anderson; and R. Goates, "Influence of the Chemical Composition of Organic Matter on the Development of Mold Flora," *Soil Sci.,* 54: 297–302, 1942.

[24] L. A. Pinck and F. E. Allison, "The Synthesis of Lignin-like Complexes by Fungi," *Soil Sci.,* 57: 155–61, 1944.

Although the nature of the benefit, which has so often been observed, is controversial, most investigators agree that trees growing on moderate to highly acid soils owe much to fungal associations. Under such conditions the mycorrhizal fungi perhaps may rival the ordinary free-living types in importance.[25]

5:9. SOIL ACTINOMYCETES

Actinomycetes resemble molds in that they are filamentous, often profusely branched, and produce fruiting bodies in much the same way. Their mycelial threads are smaller, however, than those of fungi. Actinomycetes are similar to bacteria in that they are unicellular and of about the same diameter. When they break up into spores, they resemble bacteria often rather closely. On the basis of organization, actinomycetes occupy a position between true molds and bacteria. Although they often are classified with the fungi, they are sometimes called thread bacteria. (See Fig. 5:5.)

Figure 5:5. The three most important plant microorganisms of the soil, from left to right, Fungal mycelium, various types of bacterial cells, and actinomycetes threads. The bacteria and actinomycetes are much more highly magnified than the fungi.

Actinomycetes develop best in moist, well-aerated soil. But in times of drought, they remain active to a degree not generally exhibited by either bacteria or molds. They are in general rather sensitive to acid soil conditions, their growth being practically prohibited in mineral soils at a pH of 5.0 or below. Their optimum development occurs at pH values between 6.0 and 7.5. (See Fig. 14:5.) This marked relationship to soil reaction is sometimes taken advantage of in practice, especially in respect to potato scab, an actinomycetes disease of wide distribution. It is often possible by the use of sulfur to effect a reduction in pH sufficient to keep the disease under control. (See p. 378.)

[25] For a brief statement regarding mycorrhizal associations and their benefits, see Lutz, Chandler, *op. cit.* For more detail, consult A. P. Kelley, *Mycotrophy of Plants* (Waltham, Mass.: Chron. Botanica Press, 1950).

Numbers and activities of actinomycetes.   Except for bacteria, no other microorganisms are so numerous in the soil as the actinomycetes, their numbers sometimes reaching 15 or perhaps 20 millions to a gram of dry soil. In actual live weight, they often excel bacteria but, by no means, equal in weight the amount of fungal tissue normally present. Under especially favorable conditions, perhaps 500 to 600 pounds of actinomycetes threads and spores might be present in an acre-furrow-slice. These organisms are especially numerous in soils high in humus such as old meadows or pastures when the acidity is not too great. There they sometimes exceed in numbers all other microscopic forms of life. The addition of farm manure markedly stimulates their activities. The aroma of freshly plowed land, that is so noticeable at certain times of the year, is probably due to actinomycetes, as well as to certain molds.

Actinomycetes undoubtedly are of great importance in respect to the dissolution of soil organic matter and the liberation of nutrients therefrom. Apparently, they reduce to simpler forms even the more resistant compounds such as lignin. The presence of actinomycetes in such abundance in soils long under sod is some indication of this latter capacity.

The capacity of actinomycetes to simplify humus is important, especially in respect to nitrogen. Considerable amounts of this element seem to be tied up in complex humic forms and might long remain unavailable to higher plants. The actinomycetes apparently have the unusual ability of putting it in circulation again. This one service alone ranks the actinomycetes with molds and bacteria as fertility agents in the average arable soil.

5:10. SOIL BACTERIA

A better knowledge has been gained of bacteria than of any of the other microorganisms common in soils. And as a result, they have been considered, until recent years, the most important class. But as more becomes known of the other forms of life, scientists are beginning to question whether the fungi and perhaps certain of the animals, may not, at times, equal or even outrank the bacteria.

Characteristics.   Bacteria are single-cell organisms, one of the simplest and smallest forms of life known. They multiply by elongating and dividing into two parts. They are, therefore, often called *fission* fungi. The process is, under favorable conditions, surprisingly rapid. A new organism may develop in twenty or thirty minutes with ease. This almost unlimited capacity to increase in numbers is extremely important in soils. It allows certain groups quickly to assume their normal functions under favorable conditions, even though their numbers were originally small.[26]

Bacteria may thus be considered as a force of tremendous magnitude in the soil, held more or less in check by food supply, competition, and other conditions, but ever ready to exert an influence of profound importance. They, with the fungi and actinomycetes, largely make up that general-purpose group of microorganisms, already mentioned, that fluctuates so markedly in response to soil conditions.

Bacteria are very small, the larger individuals seldom exceeding 4 or 5 microns (0.004 to 0.005 mm.) in length while the smaller ones approach the size of an average clay particle. Many soil bacteria are equipped with extremely delicate vibrating hairs called *flagella* which enable the organisms, on occasion, to swim through the soil water. This movement probably occurs sparingly, however, as the cells are held by the viscous surfaces of the soil colloidal mass or are imbedded in its gelatinous depths.

The shape of bacteria is varied in that they may be nearly round, rod-like, or spiral. In the soil, the rod-shaped organisms seem to predominate. (See Fig. 5:5.) Because of their minute size and their chemical make-up, bacteria, as well as other soil microorganisms, are highly colloidal in respect to both their cell wall and cell contents. This has much to do with their remarkable biochemical activity.[27]

Bacterial population in soils. The numbers of bacteria present in soil are variable, as many conditions markedly affect their growth. In general, the greatest population is in the surface horizons, since conditions of temperature, moisture, aeration, and food are here more favorable. It is fairly certain that the numbers of bacteria in soil are very large, possibly ranging as high as three or four billions to a gram of soil. Four or five hundred pounds of live weight bacterial tissue to the acre-furrow-slice is probably a modest estimate. Good soils seem, in general, to carry the greatest numbers. The bacterial flora, as well as the other soil organisms, fluctuates

---

[26] If a single bacterium and every subsequent organism produced subdivided every hour, the offspring from the original cell would be about 17,000,000 in twenty-four hours. In six days, the organisms theoretically would greatly surpass the earth in volume.

[27] The surface exposed by soil bacteria is remarkable. Assuming that a single bacterium is, on the average, 1μ long by 0.5μ thick and that one billion are present to 1 gm. of soil, the external surface exposed would amount to about 10 sq. ft. to the pound of dry soil, or about 460 acres to the acre-furrow-slice.

markedly with season, the numbers in humid-temperate regions usually being the greatest in early summer and in the autumn.

In the soil, bacteria exists as mats, clumps, and filaments, called *colonies,* on and around the soil particles wherever food and other conditions are favorable. The jelly-like mixture of mineral and organic colloidal matter makes an almost ideal medium for their development. While natural and artificial forces tend to distribute the organisms through the soil, most colonies enlarge, function, and die out in more or less their original position. Their existence depends on soil conditions, particularly food supply. Thus, there is a constant and rapid fluctuation—multiplication and death, often by starvation.

Many of the soil bacteria are able to produce spores or similar resistant bodies, thus presenting both a vegetative and a resting stage. This latter capacity is important as it allows the organisms more readily to survive unfavorable conditions.

Source of energy.   Soil bacteria are commonly classified under two heads, *autotrophic* and *heterotrophic.* The former obtain their energy from the oxidation of mineral constituents, such as ammonium, sulfur, and iron, and most of their carbon from carbon dioxide. In numbers, they are comparatively insignificant, but since they include the organisms that support nitrification and sulfur oxidation, they are tremendously important in the sustenance of higher plants.

Most soil bacteria, however, are heterotrophic, that is, their energy and carbon both come directly from the soil organic matter. The general-purpose decay and ammonifying bacteria, as well as the fungi and actinomycetes, are all heterotrophic in character.

Importance of bacteria.   The attention paid by man to the various conditions influencing the growth of bacteria is far beyond that usually allotted to other forms of soil life. One need not look far for the reasons. In the first place bacteria, as a group, almost without exception participate vigorously in all of the organic transactions so vital if a soil is to successfully support higher plants. They not only rival but they often excel both fungi and actinomycetes in this regard. Second, they hold, for all practical purposes, monopolies on three basic enzymic transformations, (1) *nitrification,* (2) *sulfur oxidation,* and (3) *nitrogen fixation.* If these were to fail, life for higher plants and for animals would soon fade out. Looked at from this angle, bacteria, the simplest and most numerous of all life-forms, are perhaps basically the most consequential.

5:11. CONDITIONS AFFECTING THE GROWTH OF SOIL BACTERIA

Many conditions of the soil affect the growth of bacteria. Among the most important of these are the supplies of oxygen and moisture, the temperature, the amount and nature of the soil organic matter, and the H ion concentration of the soil solution as well as the amount of exchangeable calcium present. These effects are briefly outlined below:

1. Oxygen requirements
    a. Some bacteria use mostly oxygen gas (Aerobic).
    b. Some use mostly combined oxygen (Anaerobic).
    c. Some use either of the above forms (Facultative).
    d. All three of the above types usually function in a soil at one time.
2. Moisture relationships
    a. Optimum moisture level for higher plants usually best for most bacteria.
    b. The moisture content affects oxygen supply (see 1 above).
3. Suitable Temperature range
    a. From 70° to 100° F., bacterial activity generally the greatest.
    b. Ordinary soil temperature extremes seldom kill bacteria.
4. Organic Matter requirements
    a. Used as energy source for majority of bacteria (heterotrophic).
    b. Organic matter not required as energy source for others (autotrophic).
5. Exchangeable Calcium and pH relationships
    a. High Ca, pH from 6 to 8 generally best for most bacteria.
    b. Calcium and pH values determine the specific bacteria present.
    c. Certain bacteria function at very low pH (3.0±) and others at high pH values.
    d. Exchangeable Ca seems to be more important than pH.

5:12. INJURIOUS EFFECTS OF SOIL ORGANISMS ON HIGHER PLANTS

Soil fauna. It has already been suggested that certain of the soil fauna are injurious to higher plants. For instance, rodents and moles may, in certain cases, greatly damage crops. Snails and slugs in some climates are exceedingly important pests, while the activity of ants, especially as to their transfer and care of aphids on certain plants, must be diligently combated by gardeners. Also, most plant roots are infested with nematodes, sometimes so seriously as to make the successful growth of certain crops both difficult and expensive. Protozoa, even though their effect may be indirect, also can promote a serious adverse influence.

Microflora and plant diseases.   However, it is the plant forms of soil life that, in general, exert the most devastating effects on higher plants. All three groups—bacteria, fungi, and actinomycetes—contribute their quota of plant diseases. Some of the more common diseases produced by soil flora are: wilts, damping off, root rots, clubroot of cabbage and similar crops, and the actinomycetes scab of potatoes. In short, disease infestations occur in great variety, induced by many different organisms.

Injurious organisms live for variable periods in the soil. Some of them will disappear within a few years if their host plants are not grown, but others are able to maintain existence on almost any organic substance. Once a soil is infested, it is likely to remain so for a long time. Infection usually occurs easily. Organisms from infested fields may be carried on implements, plants, or rubbish of any kind. Even stable manure containing infected plants or the feces resulting from the feeding of such plants to animals act as disease carriers. Erosion, if soil is washed from one field to another, may be a means of transfer.

Disease control by soil management.   Prevention is one of the best defenses against diseases produced by such soil organisms, hence the strict quarantines often attempted. Once a disease has procured a foothold, it is often very difficult to eradicate it. Rotation of crops is adequate for some diseases, but the entire absence of the host plant is often necessary.

The regulation of the pH is effective to a certain extent with potato scab and the clubroot of cabbage. If the pH is held somewhat below 5.3 or even 5.5, the former disease, which is due to an actinomycete, is much retarded. With clubroot, a fungus disease, the addition of hydroxide of lime until the pH of the soil is definitely above 7.0 seems fairly effective but is objectionable with certain types of rotation.

Steam sterilization is a practical method of treating greenhouse soils for a number of diseases. The breeding of plants immune to particular diseases has been successful in the case of the cowpea, cotton, and a number of other crops.

Competition for nutrients.   Another way in which soil organisms may detrimentally affect higher plants, at least temporarily, is by competition for available nutrients. Nitrogen is the element usually most vigorously contested for, although organisms may utilize appreciable quantities of phosphorus, potash, and lime to the exclusion of the crops growing on the land. Competition for trace elements may even be serious. Soil organisms usually exact their nutrient quota first and higher plants must subsist, if they can, on what remains available.[28] This subject will be considered in greater detail in the next chapter.

Other detrimental effects. Under conditions of somewhat restricted drainage, active soil microflora may deplete the already limited oxygen supply of the sod. This may affect plants adversely in at least two ways. First, the plant roots require a certain minimum amount of O_2 for normal growth and nutrient uptake. Second, oxidized forms of several elements including nitrogen, sulfur, iron, and manganese will be chemically reduced by further microbial action. In the cases of nitrogen and sulfur, some of the reduced forms are gaseous and these elements may be lost to the atmosphere. Iron and mangenese reduction may result in soluble forms of these elements being present in toxic quantities, especially if the soil is quite acid. Thus nutrient deficiencies and toxicities, both microbiologically induced, can result for the same basic set of conditions.

5:13. COMPETITION BETWEEN SOIL MICROORGANISMS [29]

In addition to competition between microorganisms and higher plants, there exists in soils an intense intermicrobial rivalry for food. When fresh organic matter is added the vigorous heterotrophic soil organisms (bacteria, fungi, and actinomycetes) entirely supersede the less numerous autotrophic bacteria. Only after the rapid decay processes have spent their forces and humification is well advanced may the autotrophic bacteria function with any degree of vigor.

Undoubtedly, such food competition is the rule and not the exception in soils. In fact, microbial activity therein may be characterized as a series of contests for food in which certain organisms enjoy a temporary domination and certain others suffer temporary suppression. Life in the soil is far from harmonious. (See Fig. 5:6.)

Antibiotics produced in soils. Besides the food competition just stressed, there is another type of microbial rivalry just as intense and even

---

[28] Assuming that microbial tissue contains on the dry basis an average of 2.50 per cent P_2O_5, 10 per cent N, 0.60 per cent K_2O, and 0.60 per cent CaO, the synthesis of 500 lb. of such material dry (equal to approximately 1 ton of live-weight organisms) would require the equivalent of about 80 lb. of 16 per cent superphosphate, 312 lb. of commercial nitrate of soda, and 6 lb. each of commercial muriate of potash and ground limestone. Obviously, the feeding of the soil microorganisms is a problem in itself.

[29] R. Weindling, "Microbial Antagonism and Disease Control," *Soil Sci.,* 61: 23–30, 1946. See also L. G. Nickell, and P. R. Burkholder, "Inhibition of Azotobacter by Soil Actinomycetes," *Jour. Amer. Soc. Agron.,* 39: 771–779, 1947; and S. A. Waksman, *Microbial Antagonisms and Antibiotic Substances* (New York: The Commonwealth Fund, 1947).

more deadly. Certain bacteria, fungi, and actinomycetes have the capacity of producing substances that will inhibit, or even actually kill, other microbes. Not only are organisms alien to the soil thus affected but also many

Figure 5:6. Organisms compete with each other in the soil. The growth of a fungus (fusarium) was rapid when this organism was grown alone in a soil (left), but when a certain bacteria (agrobacterium) was also introduced, the fungal growth did not appear. *(Photo courtesy M. A. Alexander, Cornell University.)*

of those that normally flourish vigorously therein. The capacity of certain organisms to lay down chemical barrages, which insure their own dominance within a restricted area, is an unique situation. It adds immeasurably to the difficulty of forecasting the trend of microorganic influences.

The discovery that many soil organisms can produce *antibiotics,* as they are called, has in some respects revolutionized the treatment of certain human and animal diseases, greatly minimizing their seriousness. Many preparations carrying specific bactericidal ingredients are now on the market such as penicillin, streptomycin and aureomycin. Undoubtedly, many new and valuable substances of this type are yet to be discovered. Although the soil harbors numerous types of disease organisms, it at the same time supports others that are the source of life-saving drugs, the discovery of which marks an epochal advance in medical science.

In addition to the competition among the microorganisms mentioned above it should be pointed out that they are often mutually helpful. Certain groups yield metabolic products which are used by others as a source of food. Perhaps the most evident example of this is the release by general-purpose decay organisms of ammonium ions which are used as a source of food and energy by the other organisms, especially the nitrifiers.

5:14. ACTIVITIES OF SOIL ORGANISMS BENEFICIAL TO HIGHER PLANTS [30]

In their influence on crop production, the soil fauna and flora are, of course, indispensable. Of their many beneficial effects on higher plants only the most important can be emphasized here.

Organic matter decomposition. Perhaps the most significant contribution of the soil fauna and flora to higher plants is that of organic matter decomposition. By this process, plant residues are broken down, thereby preventing an unwanted accumulation. Furthermore, nutrients held in organic combinations within these residues are released for use by plants; nitrogen is a prime example. At the same time, the stability of soil aggregates is enhanced not only by the slimy, intermediate products of decay, but by the more resistant portion, humus. Plants naturally profit from these beneficial chemical and physical effects.

One group of compounds, products of the above decomposition process, are of special soil fertility significance. These are acids, both organic and inorganic which are known to have a solvent effect especially on certain minerals. The unique solvent action of H_2CO_3 on limestone ($CaCO_3$) is a case in point. Similar reactivity of inorganic acids such as very dilute HNO_3 and H_2SO_4, both of which result from microbial processes, have an effect on the availability of nutrients such as phosphorus, iron, and manganese.

Inorganic transformations. The appearance in the soil of ammonium compounds and nitrates is the result of a long series of biochemical transfers beginning with proteins and related compounds. (See p. 138.) These successive changes are of vital importance to higher plants, since the latter adsorb most of their nitrogen in ammoniacal and nitrate forms. Reduce or cut them off and higher plants must suffer.

The production of sulfates is roughly analogous to the biological simplification of the nitrogen. (See p. 139.) Here again a complicated chain of enzymic activities culminates in a simple soluble product—in this case the sulfate. This is the only important form in which sulfur may enter higher plants in appreciable amounts. Fortunately the microbial competition for sulfur usually is not as keen as that for nitrogen, hence sulfates

---

[30] The following article dealing with many of the phases already discussed is well worth reading if a person is interested in pursuing further the microorganisms-higher plant relationships: A. G. Norman, "Recent Advances in Soil Microbiology," *Proc. Soil Sci. Soc. Amer.,* 11: 9–15, 1946.

are not likely to be as critical in cropped soils as are the simple compounds of nitrogen.

Other biologically instigated inorganic changes that may be helpful to plants are those relating to mineral elements such as iron and manganese. In well-drained soils these elements are oxidized by autotrophic organisms to their higher valent states in which forms their solubilities are very low at intermediate pH values. This keeps the greater portion of iron and manganese even under fairly acid conditions, in insoluble and nontoxic forms. If such oxidation did not occur, plant growth would be jeopardized because of toxic quantities of these elements in solution.

Nitrogen fixation.   An outstanding relationship of tremendous practical import is the fixation of elemental nitrogen. Such nitrogen, so plentiful in the atmospheric air, cannot be used directly by higher plants. It must be in combined form before it can satisfy their nutritional needs. Two groups of bacteria participate in the capture of gaseous nitrogen: the *nodule organisms,* especially those of legumes, and the so-called *free-fixing* bacteria of several kinds.

The legume bacteria, as they are often called, use the carbohydrates of their hosts as an energy source, fix the nitrogen, and pass part of it on to the infected host. However, some is left in the root tissue and in the sloughed nodules (see Fig. 16:3). This is likely to appear later in ammoniacal and nitrate forms due to the enzymic influence of other microbial organisms.

The free-fixing soil bacteria acquire their energy from the soil organic matter, fix the free nitrogen, and make it a part of their own tissue. When they die, decay, ammonification and nitrification render at least a part of this air nitrogen available to higher plants. Although nitrogen-fixing organisms are special purpose as to the transfer of nitrogen, they are, unlike the nitrifiers and sulfur oxidizers, heterotrophic since their energy and carbon apparently come exclusively from organic matter of various kinds.

It is obvious that the organisms of the soil must have energy and nutrients if they are to function efficiently. In obtaining them they break down organic matter, aid in the production of humus, and leave behind compounds that are useful to higher plants. These biotic features and their practical significance are considered in the next chapter which deals with soil organic matter.

The Organic Matter
of Mineral Soils[1]

CHAPTER **6**

Organic matter influences physical and chemical properties of soils far out of proportion to the small quantities present. It commonly accounts for at least half the cation-exchange capacity of soils and is responsible perhaps more than any other single factor for the stability of soil aggregates. Furthermore, it supplies energy- and body-building constituents for the microorganisms whose general activities have just been considered.

6:1. THE SOURCES OF SOIL ORGANIC MATTER

The original source of the soil organic matter is plant tissue. Under natural conditions, the tops and roots of trees, shrubs, grasses, and other native plants annually supply large quantities of organic residues. A good portion of the plants are commonly removed from cropped soils, but some of the tops and all of the roots are left in the soil. As these materials are decomposed and digested by soil organisms of many kinds, they become a part of the underlying horizons by infiltration or by actual physical incorporation.

Animals are usually considered as secondary sources of organic matter. As they attack the original plant tissues, they contribute waste products and leave their own bodies as their life cycles are consummated. Certain forms of animal life, especially the earthworms, centipedes, and ants, also play an important role in the translocation of plant residues.

6:2. THE COMPOSITION OF HIGHER-PLANT TISSUE

About 75 per cent, or even more, of green tissue of higher plants is water. The dry matter is made up of carbon, oxygen, hydrogen, nitrogen

---

[1] For general articles dealing with soil organic matter, see J. M. Bremner, "A Review of Recent Work on Soil Organic Matter," Part I, *Jour. Soil Sci.*, 2: 67–82, 1951. Part II, *Jour. Soil Sci.*, 5: 214–32, 1954. See also two articles by F. E. Broadbent, "The Soil Organic Fraction," *Advances in Agronomy*, 5: 153–83, 1953, and "Basic Problems in Organic Matter Transformations," *Soil Sci.*, 79: 107–14, 1955.

and mineral elements. (See Fig. 6:1.) Although over 90 per cent of the dry matter is carbon, oxygen, and hydrogen, the other elements play a vital role in plant nutrition. Nitrogen, sulfur, phosphorus, potassium, and calcium from organic sources are particularly important. A very large proportion of the soil nitrogen originally became a part of the solum as a constituent of the tissue of plants and animals.

The actual compounds in plant tissue are many and varied. (See Table 6:1.) The general composition of representative mature and dry plant tissue has been estimated to be about as follows: [2]

Carbohydrates	Sugars and starches	1– 5%
	Hemicelluloses	10–28%
	Cellulose	20–50%
Fats, waxes, tannins, etc		1– 8%
Lignins		10–30%
Proteins	Simple water soluble & crude proteins	1–15%

It should be emphasized that these figures are very general and serve only to give an idea of the range of those constituents commonly encountered in plant material.

The carbohydrates which are made up of carbon, hydrogen, and oxygen range in complexity from simple sugars to the celluloses. The fats and oils are glycerides of fatty acids such as butyric, stearic, oleic, etc. These are associated with resins of many kinds and are somewhat more complex than most of the carbohydrates. They too, are made up mostly of carbon, hydrogen, and oxygen.

Lignins occur in older plant tissue such as stems and other woody tissues. They are complex compounds, some of which may have so called "ring" structures. The major components of lignins are carbon, hydrogen, and oxygen. They are very resistant to decomposition.

Of the various groups, the crude proteins are probably the most complicated. They carry not only carbon, hydrogen,

Figure 6:1. Diagram showing the generalized composition of green plant tissue. The nitrogen is included in the ash. Plant tissue is made up largely of carbon, hydrogen, and oxygen. *(After Stoddard.)*

[2] These figures are essentially the same as those given by S. A. Waksman, *Humus* (Baltimore: Williams and Wilkins, 1938), p. 95.

TABLE 6:1

An Outline Showing, in a General Way, the Changes That the Organic Compounds of Plant Tissue Undergo in the Soil

I. Compounds Characteristic of Fresh Plant Tissue

Decomposed with difficulty	*Decomposed easily*
Lignin	Cellulose
Oils	Starches
Fats	Sugars
Resins, etc.	Proteins, etc.

II. Complex Intermediate Products of Decay

Resistant compounds	*Decomposition compounds*
Resins	Amino acids
Waxes	Amides
Oils and fats	Alcohols
Lignin, etc.	Aldehydes, etc.

III. Products of Soil-decomposition Processes

Resistant complex	*Simple end products*
Humus—a colloidal complex in which the lignoproteinate is considered especially important	Carbon dioxide and water
	Nitrates
	Sulfates
	Phosphates
	Ca compounds, etc.

and oxygen, but also nitrogen and such elements as sulfur, iron, phosphorus, and others in lesser amounts. They are compounds of high molecular weight and many are of unknown constitution. As found in fresh plant tissue, they are present in the colloidal state which complicates their study.

6:3. THE DECOMPOSITION OF ORGANIC TISSUE AND THE PRODUCTS OF DECAY

It is evident from the above statements that the chemical nature of plant tissue is very complicated. Its addition to the soil must set up complex reactions which give rise to residues which are equally complex. Consequently, identification of individual substances is in general very uncertain. It is only when the processes are more or less consummated that simple compounds other than carbon dioxide and water are produced in abundance. (See Table 6:1.)

Rate of decomposition. Regardless of the complexity of the original tissues, there are research data to indicate the relative resistance of their various organic groups to decomposition—a phase of great practical significance. The compounds found in plant tissue may be listed in terms of their ease of decomposition as follows:

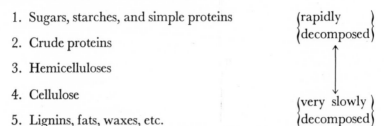

1. Sugars, starches, and simple proteins   (rapidly decomposed)

2. Crude proteins

3. Hemicelluloses

4. Cellulose   (very slowly decomposed)

5. Lignins, fats, waxes, etc.

It should be remembered that all these compounds are usually decomposing simultaneously when fresh plant tissue is added to a soil. The rate at which decomposition occurs, however, decreases as one moves from the top to the bottom of the list. Thus, sugars and water-soluble proteins are examples of readily available energy sources for soil organisms. Lignins are a very resistant source of food, although they eventually supply much total energy.

Decomposition a burning process. In spite of these differences in the rates of decomposition of the various organic compounds, the similarity of the ultimate end products of decay is quite striking, especially if aerobic organisms are involved. Under such conditions the major portion of all these compounds undergoes essentially a "burning" or oxidation process. The oxidizable fractions of organic materials are composed largely of carbon and hydrogen, which make up more than half of the dry weight. (See Fig. 6:1.) Consequently, we may express the complete oxidation of most of the organic compounds in the soil as follows:

$$-[C, 4H] + O_2 \xrightarrow[\text{Oxidation}]{\text{Enzymic}} CO_2 + 2H_2O + \text{Energy}$$

Carbon & hydro-
gen containing
compounds

It is recognized, of course, that many intermediate steps are involved in this over-all reaction. Also important side reactions are occurring simultaneously which involve elements other than carbon and hydrogen. Neither of these facts, however, detract from the importance of this basic reaction in accounting for most of the organic matter decomposition in the soil.

The breakdown of proteins. The plant proteins and related compounds yield other very important products upon decomposition in addition to the carbon dioxide and water mentioned above. For example, they break down into amides and amino acids [3] of various kinds, the rate of breakdown depending on conditions. Bacteria, fungi, actinomycetes, and other soil organisms engage in the transformations, incorporating some of the nitrogen into their own body tissues as the digestion proceeds.

Some of the protein may combine with lignin and other resistant compounds and become a part of the soil humus. The protein is thus protected, at least for a time, from enzymic decomposition. Once amino acids are formed, they may be hydrolyzed readily to carbon dioxide, ammonium compounds, and other products. By the process of nitrification, ammonium compounds may be changed to nitrates, the form in which higher plants take up a large proportion of their nitrogen.

An example of organic decay. Now let us view the process of organic decay in cyclic sequence. (See Fig. 6:2.) First assume a situation where no readily decomposable materials are present in a soil. The microbial activity is at a minimum and living soil organisms are much reduced in numbers. Now, under favorable conditions, let us introduce an abundance of fresh, decomposable tissue. A tremendous change immediately occurs. In the presence of compounds which furnish readily available energy and nutrients, the multiplication of soil microorganisms suddenly increases many fold. Microbial activity is soon at its peak, as is shown by the rapid liberation of energy and the tremendous evolution of carbon dioxide. That great group of general-purpose decay organisms, bacteria, fungi and actinomycetes, is soon fully active, and are decomposing, as well as synthesizing at the same time. (See Fig. 6:2.)

The soil organic matter at this stage contains a great variety of substances—intermediate products of all kinds, ranging from the more stable bodies such as lignins, to microbial cells, both living and dead. Indeed, the microbial tissue may even at times account for as much as one half of the

---

[3] Amino acids are produced by replacing one of the alkyl hydrogens in an organic acid with NH_2. Acetic acid (CH_3COOH) thereby becomes aminoacetic acid or glycocoll (CH_2NH_2COOH). Amides are formed from organic acids by replacing the hydroxyl of the carboxyl group with NH_2. Acetic acid (CH_3COOH) thus becomes acetamide (CH_3CONH_2).

Protein simplification probably progresses as follows:

$$\text{Proteins} \rightarrow \text{Proteoses} \rightarrow \text{Peptones} \begin{array}{c} \nearrow \text{Amino acids} \searrow \\ \searrow \text{Acid amides} \nearrow \end{array} \text{ammonium compounds}$$

organic fraction of a soil.[4] These dead organisms are soon subject to decay, the compounds present being attacked by the living microbes. The process is accompanied, of course, by the copious evolution of carbon dioxide.

Figure 6:2. Outline showing the biochemical trend as organic residues undergo microbial digestion in the soil. Note the intense microbial competition that occurs, especially during the early stages of decomposition. This is accompanied by a copious loss of carbon as CO_2, and a great liberation of energy. Only when humification nears completion can the nitrifiers function vigorously and nitrate nitrogen appear in the soil.

Finally, as the readily available energy is used up and food supplies diminish, microbial activity gradually lessens, and the general-purpose soil organisms sink back again into comparative quiescence. This is associated with a more or less abundance of simple products, such as nitrates and sulfates. The organic matter that now remains is a dark incoherent and heterogeneous colloidal mass and is usually referred to as *humus*. In short, we are back again to the condition first postulated after a complex cycle of decay.

It is well to emphasize that the decomposition of both plant residues and soil organic matter is nothing more than a process of enzymic digestion. It is just as truly a digestion as though the plant materials entered the stomach of a domestic animal. The products of these enzymic activities, although numerous and tremendously varied, may be listed for convenience of discussion under three headings: (1) energy appropriated by the

[4] See A. G. Norman, "I. Problems in the Chemistry of Soil Organic Matter," *Proc. Soil Sci. Soc. Amer.,* 7: 7–15, 1942.

microorganisms or liberated as heat; (2) simple end products; and (3) humus. They will be considered in order.

6:4. THE ENERGY OF THE SOIL ORGANIC MATTER AND ITS TRANSFER [5]

The microorganisms of the soil, must not only have substance for their tissue synthesis but energy as well. For most of the microorganisms,[6] both of these are obtained from the soil organic matter. All manner of compounds are utilized as energy sources, some freely, others slowly and indifferently.

Potential energy in organic matter. As might be expected, organic matter contains considerable potential energy, a large proportion of which is readily transferable to other latent forms or is liberated as heat. Plant tissue, such as that entering the soil, has a heat value in the neighborhood of 4 or 5 kilocalories per gram of air-dry substance. The application of 10 tons of farm manure, for example, containing 5,000 pounds of dry matter, would mean an addition in round numbers of 9,000,000 to 11,000,000 kilocalories of latent energy. A soil containing 4 per cent of organic matter carries from 150,000,000 to 180,000,000 kilocalories of potential energy per acre-furrow-slice. This is equivalent in heat value perhaps to 20 to 25 tons of anthracite coal.

Of this large amount of energy carried by the soil organic matter, only a part is used by soil organisms. The remainder is left in the residues or is dissipated as heat. This heat loss represents a large and continual removal of energy from the soil.

Rate of energy loss from soils. A rather interesting phase of the subject is the rate at which energy is dissipated from soils. Certain estimates made at the Rothamsted Experiment Station,[7] England, on two plots of the Broadbalk field, give some idea concerning this rate. It was calculated that 1 million kilocalories an acre were lost annually from the untreated, low-producing soil, while about 15 million kilocalories were dissipated from the more productive soil receiving liberal supplies of farm manure. The magnitude of such loss is surprising even for the poorer plot.

[5] For a discussion of these phases, see Waksman, *op. cit.*

[6] Autotrophic bacteria such as the nitrifiers and sulfur oxidizers are good examples of exceptions to this as their carbon comes mostly from carbon dioxide and their energy largely from the oxidation of inorganic substances.

[7] E. J. Russell, and E. W. Russell, *Soil Conditions and Plant Growth* (London: Longmans, Green, 1950), p. 194.

6:5. THE SIMPLE PRODUCTS OF ORGANIC MATTER DECOMPOSITION

As the enzymic changes of the soil organic matter proceed, simple products begin to manifest themselves. Some of these, especially carbon dioxide and water, appear immediately. Others, such as nitrate nitrogen, accumulate only after the peak of the vigorous decomposition is over and the general-purpose decay organisms have diminished in numbers. Since these simple end products, if not used by higher plants or microorganisms, are readily lost, they soon sink to a minimum, unless fresh tissue is added at frequent intervals.

The more common simple products that result from the activity of the soil microorganisms may be listed as follows:

Carbon	CO_2, $CO_3^=$, HCO_3^-, CH_4, elemental carbon
Nitrogen	NH_4^+, NO_2^-, NO_3^-, gaseous nitrogen
Sulfur	S, H_2S, $SO_3^=$, $SO_4^=$, CS_2
Phosphorus	$H_2PO_4^-$, $HPO_4^=$
Others	H_2O, O_2, H_2, H^+, OH^-, K^+, Ca^{++}, Mg^{++}, etc.

Some of the significant relationships of each of the five groups are presented in the following sections. They are considered in the order listed above.

6:6. SIMPLE PRODUCTS CARRYING CARBON—THE CARBON CYCLE

Carbon is the common constituent of all organic matter. As a consequence, its movements during the microbial digestion of plant tissue are extremely significant. Much of the energy acquired by the fauna and flora within the soil comes from the oxidation of carbon. As a result, its oxide is evolved continuously and in large amounts. The various changes that this element undergoes within and without the soil are collectively designated as the *carbon cycle* and are shown graphically in Fig. 6:3.

Release of CO_2.   As the compounds in plant residues are digested, carbon dioxide is given off. This is the main soil source of this gas, although small amounts are excreted by plant roots and are brought down in rain water. The carbon dioxide of the soil,[8] evolved both in summer

---

[8] Under optimum conditions as much as 100 pounds of CO_2 per acre per day may be evolved. Twenty to 30 pounds are probably more common. See A. G. Norman, *Mineral Nutrition of Plants*, E. Truog (ed.), (Wisconsin: University of Wisconsin Press, 1951), pp. 167–86.

and winter, ultimately escapes in large degree to the atmosphere, where it may again be used by plants. Thus the cycle is completed.

Figure 6:3. Diagramatic representation of the transformations of carbon, commonly spoken of as the *carbon cycle*. Note the stress placed on carbon dioxide both within and without the soil.

A lesser amount of carbon dioxide reacts in the soil, producing carbonic acid (H_2CO_3), and the carbonates and bicarbonates of calcium, potassium, magnesium, and other bases. These salts are readily soluble and may be lost in drainage or be used by higher plants. Thus, not only are Ca, Mg, and K ions presented to the absorbing surfaces of microorganisms and higher plants, but $CO_3^=$ and HCO_3^- ions are made available as well. Small amounts of carbon may enter plants in this way (see note on p. 37). Most of the carbon present in higher plants, however, is acquired from the atmosphere by photosynthesis.

Other carbon products of decay.   Besides carbon dioxide, carbonates, and bicarbonates, the simplification of organic matter results in other carbon products. Elemental carbon is found in soils to a certain extent, and while not especially important, its presence is significant. Under certain conditions, methane (CH_4) and carbon bisulfide (CS_2) may be produced in small amounts. But of all the simple carbon products, carbon dioxide is by far the most abundant.

It is now obvious that the carbon cycle is all inclusive since it involves not only the soil and its teeming fauna and flora, and higher plants of every description, but also all animal life including man himself. Its failure to function properly would mean disaster to all. It is an energy cycle of such vital import that, with its many ramifications, it might properly be designated as the "Cycle of Life."

6:7. SIMPLE PRODUCTS CARRYING NITROGEN—AMMONIUM, NITRITE AND NITRATE IONS, AND ELEMENTAL NITROGEN

While carbon dioxide may result from the decomposition of any organic substance, ammonium salts are formed only when nitrogenous compounds are involved. They are the first inorganic nitrogen compounds produced by microbial digestion. Proteins split up into amino acids and similar nitrogenous materials which readily yield ammonium compounds by enzymic hydrolysis. These complex transformations are brought about by a large number of heterotrophic organisms—bacteria, fungi, and actinomycetes. The ammonium ion is readily available to microorganisms and most higher plants.

Nitrification.   If conditions are now favorable, ammonium ions are subject to ready oxidation, principally by two special-purpose organisms, the *nitrite* and the *nitrate* bacteria. These enzymic processes are affected by moisture conditions, temperature, aeration, and especially by available calcium. The transformations take place most readily when adequate calcium is present. Also the activity of the general-purpose decay organisms must be at a minimum. Otherwise, due to competition, there would be no ammonium for the nitrifiers. In other words, humification must be fairly complete (see Fig. 6:2).

Nitrification may be shown simply and diagrammatically as follows:

$$2\,NH_4^+ + 3\,O_2 \xrightarrow[\text{Oxidation}]{\text{Enzymic}} 2\,NO_2^- + 2\,H_2O + 4\,H^+ + \text{Energy}$$

$$2\,NO_2^- + O_2 \xrightarrow[\text{Oxidation}]{\text{Enzymic}} 2\,NO_3^- + \text{Energy}$$

The autotrophic bacteria obtain energy by these transfers and leave as a by-product nitrogen in the nitrate form. The second reaction usually follows so closely on the first as to prevent any appreciable accumulation of nitrites. Nitrates are a form of nitrogen that some plants seem to need for their best growth. And it is in this combination that most of the loss of nitrogen in drainage occurs. Such removal is often so large as to seriously deplete soils of their nitrogen supply. (See p. 216.)

The hydrogen ions formed in the first of the above reactions are of considerable practical importance. They show that nitrification tends to result in an increase in soil acidity. This effect is of even greater importance when dealing with commercial fertilizers containing ammonium salts such as $(NH_4)_2SO_4$. Extra increments of lime are often added to counteract this acidifying effect.

Release of gaseous nitrogen. One more group of end products awaits consideration—gaseous nitrogen compounds. Under certain conditions, the reduction of nitrates and nitrites takes place in soils, and free nitrogen or oxides of nitrogen may be evolved. This transfer is considered most likely to occur in poorly drained soils or in acid soils containing nitrites. The processes are very complicated and as yet are not fully understood. They apparently may be chemical as well as biochemical. In any case, the reduction is serious since these nitrogen gases ordinarily are relatively inert and are not recombined into compounds useful to higher plants. Some authorities believe that soils lose considerable nitrogen in this way. (See p. 417 and ff.)

6:8. SIMPLE PRODUCTS CARRYING SULFUR—SULFITES, SULFATES, AND OTHER PRODUCTS

Many organic compounds, especially those of a nitrogenous nature, carry sulfur, which appears in simple forms as decay progresses. General-purpose heterotrophic types of organisms apparently simplify the complex organic compounds. The sulfur of these simplified by-products is then subjected to oxidation by special autotrophic bacteria, available calcium being of some aid in facilitating the transaction. Calcium is not as vital, however, as in the case of the nitrifiers since sulfur oxidation can occur even when bases are deficient. The final transformation, which is carried to completion by the sulfur oxidizing organisms, may be shown diagrammatically as follows:

$$-[HS] + 2\ O_2 \xrightarrow[\text{Oxidation}]{\text{Enzymic}} SO_4^{=} + H^+ + E$$
$$\text{Organic}$$
$$\text{combinations}$$

The organisms involved obtain energy by the transfer and leave the sulfur in the sulfate form. Unlike nitrification, which occurs in two distinct steps and requires two groups of organisms, sulfur oxidation apparently occurs, as indicated above, as one continuous reaction. Thus, the sulfur originally present in complicated combinations, emerges finally as the SO_4 ion, the form in which higher plants absorb practically all of their sulfur. Considerable amounts of sulfate sulfur are lost in drainage, a phase that deserves some attention from the standpoint of fertility maintenance. (See p. 216.)

6:9. ORGANIC PHOSPHORUS AND ITS MINERALIZATION

A large proportion of the soil phosphorus is carried in organic combinations (see p. 435) upon attack by microorganisms the organic phosphorus compounds are *mineralized,* that is they are changed to inorganic combinations. The particular forms, as we already know (p. 36), depend to a considerable degree upon soil pH. As the pH goes up, say from 5.5 to 7.5, the available phosphorus changes from H_2PO_4 to HPO_4. Both of these forms are available to higher plants. Since the small amount of phosphorus held in complex mineral combinations in soils usually is very slowly available, the organic sources mentioned above become especially important.

It must not be assumed, however, that the maintenance of soil organic matter at normal or even high levels will solve the phosphorus problem. Far from it. Most field soils need liberal applications of superphosphate or other phosphatic fertilizers. Yet strangely enough, the economic use of such phosphorus depends to a considerable degree upon the organic transformation already cited. Since microorganisms utilize phosphorus freely, some of that added commercially quickly becomes a part of the soil organic matter. Thus, this phosphorus is held in an organic condition and is later mineralized by microbial activity.

6:10. OTHER SIMPLE PRODUCTS OF ORGANIC DISSOLUTION

A number of simple products resulting from the humification of organic residues need hardly more than mere enumeration. Water, elemental oxygen, and free hydrogen fall into this group. The developmnt of H ions, however, is quite a different matter as the following paragraph will affirm.

One feature of the carbon cycle that has been emphasized is the copious production of carbon dioxide and the development, when in contact with water, of carbonic acid. Although very weak, carbonic acid develops enough active hydrogen to influence the trend of many soil reactions. Its solvent action on limestone ($CaCO_3$) is important in removing this mineral from soils of humid regions.

Because of its high adsorptive capacity, it is not surprising that soil organic matter usually carries considerable amounts of exchangeable potassium, calcium, magnesium, and other bases. Also, some of these same bases are present as integral constituents of the organic material itself. Hence, the addition of organic residues to soils and their subsequent decomposition therein cannot help but enhance the store of nutrient elements.

6:11. HUMUS—GENESIS AND DEFINITION [9]

The formation of humus, although an exceedingly complicated biochemical process, may be described in general terms rather simply. As organic tissue is incorporated into a moist warm soil it is immediately attacked by a host of different soil organisms. The easily decomposed compounds quickly succumb, first yielding intermediate substances and finally the simple, soluble products already enumerated.

Modified lignin.[10]   The oils, fats, resins, and especially the lignins are more resistant and tend to persist, in a modified condition. The lignin is apparently partially oxidized and those ionizable groups responsible for cation exchange are increased in number. These modifications are of especial concern, since they are thought to enable the lignin and other resistant materials to unite with and protect nitrogen containing compounds.

Just how the lignins and similar substances are associated with the nitrogen is largely conjectural. Whether the union results from the synthetic activity of the microorganisms or is a direct chemical reaction or both, cannot as yet be asserted. The net result, however, is clean-cut. The product which results is persistent enough to influence soil character. At the same time nitrogen is protected from immediate microbial dissolution.

Resistant microbial tissue.   In addition to the altered lignin residues, a second group of compounds known as *polysaccharides* or *polyuronides* may be of considerable significance as constituents of humus. These compounds are thought to be synthesized by microorganisms, becoming a part of the microbial tissue. They are quite resistant to rapid decomposition when the organisms die. As a result, they may account for much of the residual organic matter present in soils. In some cases the quantity of the compounds containing uronic groups is quite high, uronic carbon making

[9] See F. E. Broadbent, *op. cit.*

[10] Lignin is a waxy or resinous material that impregnates the cell walls of plants as they increase in age. It is exceedingly complex, and varies with different plants and with different tissues of the same plant. The chemical formulae of the various lignins are in doubt.

up as much as one-third of the total carbon. Thus, it is possible that dead microbial tissue may account for an appreciable fraction of the resistant organic matter (humus) present in soils.

The polysaccharides react in some cases with nitrogen just as does lignin. The compounds formed are called *amino polysaccharides*. They too are probably of microbial origin, having been found as constituents of many soil organisms.

Protein-clay combinations. In considering the stabilization of nitrogenous compounds in the soil, the possibility of a reaction between certain clays and proteinaceous substances should not be overlooked. Clays with expanding lattices, such as montmorillonite, seem to have such a faculty, the proteins perhaps functioning as bases in satisfying the adsorption capacity of the inorganic colloids.[11] How important this is in the average soil it is difficult to say. Nevertheless, it suggests that intermixed with the nitrogen-containing modified lignin and the polysaccharides, there may be clay-protein combinations in greater or lesser amounts. Such a postulate serves as a further reminder of the complexity and heterogeneity of this group of substances that we speak of collectively as humus. It is not at all surprising, therefore, to find widely different types of humus in different soils and even considerable variations from horizon to horizon in the same soil.

Humus defined. From the above discussion two facts are obvious: (1) humus is a mixture of complex compounds and is not a single material; and (2) these compounds are either (a) resistant materials which have been only modified from the original plant tissue, or (b) compounds synthesized within microbial tissue which remain as the organisms die. These two facts lead to the following definition: *humus is a complex and rather resistant mixture of brown or dark brown amorphous and colloidal substances that have been modified from the original tissues or have been synthesized by the various soil organisms.* It is a natural body and, though exceedingly variable and heterogeneous, it possesses properties that distinguish it sharply from the original parent tissues and from the simple products that develop during its synthesis. Its nature is considered in the next section.

[11] L. E. Ensminger and J. E. Gieseking, "Resistance of Clay-adsorbed Proteins to Proteolytic Hydrolysis," *Soil Sci.,* 53: 205–09, 1942. See also F. E. Allison; M. S. Sherman; and L. A. Pinck, "Maintenance of Soil Organic Matter: I. Inorganic soil colloid as a factor in retention of carbon during formation of humus," *Soil Sci.,* 68: 463–78, 1949.

6:12. HUMUS—NATURE AND CHARACTERISTICS AS COMPARED WITH SILICATE CLAY

Humus is highly colloidal, but unlike its mineral counterpart in the soil, it is amorphous and not crystalline. Moreover, its surface area and adsorptive capacity are far in excess of those exhibited by any of the clays. The cation exchange capacity of silicate clays commonly ranges from 8 to 100 milliequivalents per 100 grams. Comparable exchange capacities for well-developed humus from mineral soils, in sharp contrast, would range from 150 to 300. In general, the presence of 1 per cent of humus in a mineral soil under humid-temperate conditions infers an exchange capacity of perhaps 2 milliequivalents per 100 grams of soil. The comparable figure for clays would range from about 0.1 to 1.0, perhaps 0.5 being an average value.

In respect to adsorbed water, the contrast is of the same order. The fully synthesized humus of a mineral soil will adsorb from a saturated atmosphere perhaps 80 or 90 per cent of water. Clay, on the other hand, may be able to thus acquire possibly only 15 or 20 per cent. The significance of these figures in respect to soil properties is obvious.

Physical properties. The low plasticity and cohesion of humus is a significant practical feature. The maintenance of this constituent in fine-textured soils helps alleviate unfavorable structural characteristics induced by large quantities of clay. This is due to a considerable extent to granulation which it so markedly encourages.

Another physical character that is of outstanding interest is the color imparted to soils by humus. It is well to note definitely that the development of a black pigment in humus varies with climate. In chernozem soils, occurring in northern semiarid regions with an annual rainfall around 20 inches, the pigment is very dark and abundant. In humid-temperate zones, the pigmentation is less intense, while the least coloration is found in the humus of the tropics and semitropics. Color thus in a very general way is an expression of climate. This is a point well worth remembering as it indicates that organic pigmentation cannot always be used satisfactorily as a comparative measure of the amount of organic matter present in soils.

Colloidal constitution. Soil humus, as a colloidal complex, is organized in much the same way as clay. (See p. 88.) The modified lignin, the polyuronides, the clay-proteins, and no doubt other constituents as well, function as complex micelles. Under ordinary conditions, these carry innumerable negative charges. But instead of being made up principally of Si, O, Al, and Fe, as are the silicate crystals, the humic micelles are composed of C, H, O, N, S, P, and other elements. The negative charges arise from exposed —COOH and —OH groups from which the hydrogen may be replaced by cation exchange.

The humic micelles, like the particles of clay, carry a swarm of adsorbed cations (Ca^{++}, H^+, Mg^{++}, H^+, Na^+, etc.). Thus, humus colloidally may be represented by the same structural formula used for clay namely—

Ca
H | Micelle | and the same reactions will serve to illustrate cation ex-
B

change in both. (See p. 88.) *B* represents all bases other than Ca.

Effect of humus on nutrient availability. There is one particular characteristic of humus that merits attention—the capacity of this colloid when saturated with H^+ ions to increase the availability of certain nutrient bases, such as calcium, potassium, and magnesium. It seems that an H-humus, as is the case with an H-clay, acts much like an ordinary acid and can react with soil minerals in such a way as to extract their bases.[12] Acid humus has an unusual capacity to effect such a transfer, since the organic acid is comparatively strong. Once the exchange is made, the bases so affected are held in a loosely adsorbed condition and are easily available to higher plants. The following is a generalized reaction to illustrate this point, microcline being used as an example of the various soil minerals so affected:

$$KAlSi_3O_8 + H \boxed{\text{Humus}} \longrightarrow HAlSi_3O_8 + K \boxed{\text{Humus}}$$

microcline acid silicate adsorbed K

The potassium is changed from a molecular to an adsorbed status in which condition it is rated as rather readily available to higher plants.

Humus-clay complex in soils. In considering all the colloidal matter of a mineral soil, it must always be remembered that one is dealing with a mixture of many very different kinds of colloids. The crystalline clayey nucleus is markedly stable under ordinary conditions and is active mainly in respect to cation exchange. The amorphous organic micelle, on the other hand, is susceptible to microorganic attack and hence has a twofold

---

[12] The capacity of clayey acids to effect the dissolution of soil minerals, liberate nutrient bases, and hasten the development of more clay is considered on page 269.

activity—cation exchange and a marked energy liberation. These contrasting details are just as important practically as the colloidal similarities already noted.

6:13. DIRECT INFLUENCE OF ORGANIC COMPOUNDS ON HIGHER PLANTS

One of the early beliefs in regard to plant nutrition was that organic matter, as such, is directly absorbed by higher plants. Although this opinion was later discarded, there is some evidence that certain organic nitrogen compounds can be absorbed by higher plants, often rather readily.[13] Such substances ordinarily do not satisfy plant needs for nitrogen as is indicated by the ready response that most plants make to an application of nitrates.

The beneficial effects of an exceedingly small absorption of organic compounds might be accounted for by the presence of growth-promoting substances. In fact, it is quite possible that vitamin-like compounds are developed as organic decay progresses in soils.[14] If this be the case, the direct effect of humic substances upon higher plants might be much more important than hitherto has been suspected. Undoubtedly, hormones and vitamins are carried by the soil humus and may at times stimulate both higher plants and microorganisms.

On the other hand, some soil organic compounds no doubt may be harmful.[15] As an example, dihydroxystearic acid may be mentioned, as this was one of the first to be so studied. This compound which is toxic to higher plants, was isolated from twenty soils, out of a group of sixty taken in eleven states. It may be, however, that such compounds are merely products of unfavorable soil conditions. And when such conditions are righted, the so-called toxic matter disappears. Apparently, good drainage and tillage, lime, and fertilizers reduce the probability of organic toxicity.[16]

---

[13] H. B. Hutchinson and N. H. J. Miller, "The Direct Assimilation of Inorganic and Organic Forms of Nitrogen by Higher Plants," *Jour. Agr. Sci.,* 4, Part 3: 282–302, 1912. Also, O. Schreiner and J. J. Skinner, *Nitrogenous Soil Constituents and Their Bearing upon Soil Fertility,* Bul. 87, Bureau of Soils, U. S. Dept. of Agriculture, 1912.

[14] Evidence that some B-vitamins and other growth factors may be produced by soil organisms is given by A. G. Lochhead, "Qualitative Studies of Soil Microorganisms; XV. Capability of the Predominant Bacterial Flora for Synthesis of Various Growth Factors," *Soil Sci.,* 84: 395–404, 1957.

[15] O. Schreiner and E. C. Shorey, *The Isolation of Harmful Organic Substances from Soils,* Bul. 53, Bureau of Soils, U.S. Dept. of Agriculture, 1909. See also O. Schreiner, and J. J. Skinner, *op. cit.*

[16] J. D. Davidson, "A Comparative Study of the Effects of Cumarin and Vanillin on Wheat Grown in Soil, Sand, and Water Culture," *Jour. Amer. Soc. Agron.,* 7: 145–58, 1915.

6:14. CARBON-NITROGEN RATIO [17]

Attention has been called several times to the close relationship that exists between the organic matter and nitrogen contents of soils. Since carbon makes up a large and rather definite proportion of this organic matter, it is not surprising that the *carbon to nitrogen* ratio of soils is fairly constant. The importance of this fact in controlling the available nitrogen, total organic matter, and the rate of organic decay, should unfold as we consider the subject further.

Ratio in soils.   The ratio of carbon to nitrogen in the organic matter of the furrow-slice of arable soils commonly ranges from 8:1 to 15:1, the median being between 10 and 12 to 1. In a given climatic region, little variation is found in this ratio, at least in similarly managed soils. The variations which do occur seem to be correlated in a general way with climatic conditions, especially temperature and the amount and distribution of rainfall. For instance, it is rather well established that the carbon-nitrogen ratio tends to be lower in soils of arid regions than in those of humid regions when annual temperatures are about the same. It is also lower in warmer regions than in cooler ones, providing the rainfalls are of about the same magnitude. Also the ratio is narrower for subsoils, in general, than for the corresponding surface layers.

Ratio in plants, microbes.   Before discussing reasons for this relative constancy of the C:N ratio in soils, let us consider briefly the ratio of these two elements in plant residues and microbial tissue. As one would expect, the ratio of carbon to nitrogen of plant material is variable, ranging from 20 or 30 to 1 for legumes and farm manure to as high as 90 to 1, or even more, in certain strawy residues (see Fig. 6:5). All gradations between these extremes are found. The carbon-nitrogen ratio of the bodies of microorganisms, on the other hand, is not only more constant but much narrower, ordinarily falling between 4:1 and 9:1. Bacterial tissue, in general, is somewhat richer in protein than that of fungi and consequently has a narrower ratio.

It can be seen, therefore, that most organic residues entering the soil

[17] The following articles deal with the carbon-nitrogen ratio: L. A. Pinck; F. E. Allison; and V. L. Gaddy, "The Effect of Green Manure Crops of Varying Carbon-Nitrogen Ratios upon Nitrogen Availability and Soil Organic Matter Content," *Jour. Amer. Soc. Agron.*, 40: 237–47, 1948; M. S. Anderson and H. G. Byers, "The Carbon-nitrogen Ratio in Relation to Soil Classification," *Soil Sci.*, 38: 121–38, 1934; H. Jenny, *A Study on the Influence of Climate upon the Nitrogen and Organic Matter Content of the Soil*, Research Bulletin 152, Missouri Agr. Exp. Sta., 1930.

carry large amounts of carbon and comparatively small amounts of total nitrogen—that is, their carbon-nitrogen ratio is wide, and the C:N ratio values for soils are in between those of higher plants and the microbes.

6:15. THE SIGNIFICANCE OF THE CARBON-NITROGEN RATIO

The carbon-nitrogen ratio in soil organic matter is an important factor in a number of ways, the two most significant of which are as follows: (1) competition for available nitrogen results when residues having a high C:N ratio are added to soils; (2) due to the constancy of this ratio in soils, the maintenance of carbon, and hence soil organic matter, is dependent to no small degree on the soil nitrogen level. Let us consider these two factors in order starting with a practical example of the influence of highly carbonaceous material on the availability of nitrogen.

A practical example. Suppose that we are dealing with a representative cultivated soil in a condition favoring vigorous nitrification. Nitrates are present in relatively large amounts and, of course, the C:N ratio is narrow. The general-purpose decay organisms are at a low level of activity and CO_2 production is at a minimum. (See Fig. 6:4.)

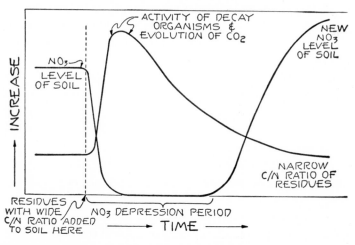

Figure 6:4. Diagram showing the cyclical relationship between the stage of decay of organic residues and the presence of nitrate nitrogen in soil. So long as the C/N ratio is wide, the general-purpose, decay organisms are dominant and the nitrifiers are more or less inactive. During the period of nitrate depression that results, higher plants can obtain but little nitrogen from the soil. The length of this period will depend upon a number of factors of which the C/N ratio is of prime importance. This figure is another version of Figure 6:2.

Now suppose large quantities of organic residues with a wide C:N ratio (say 50:1) are incorporated in this soil under conditions supporting vigorous digestion. A change quickly occurs. The heterotrophic flora—bacteria, fungi, and actinomycetes—becomes active and multiplies rapidly, yielding CO_2 in large quantities. Under these conditions, nitrate nitrogen practically disappears from the soil due to the insistent microbial demand for this element to build their tissues. And for the time being little or no nitrogen, even ammoniacal, is in a form available to higher plants. As decay occurs the C:N ratio of the plant material decreases since carbon is being lost and nitrogen conserved.

This condition persists until humification nears completion, at which time the activities of the decay organisms gradually subside due to a lack of easily oxidizable carbon. Their numbers decrease, CO_2 formation drops off, nitrogen ceases to be at a premium and nitrification can proceed. Nitrates again appear in quantity and the original conditions again prevail except, for the time being, the soil is somewhat richer both in nitrogen and humus. The sequence of events, an important phase of the carbon cycle, is diagramatically represented in Figure 6:4. Study it carefully.

Reason for C:N constancy. As the decomposition processes above continue, both carbon and nitrogen are now subject to loss—the carbon as carbon dioxide and the nitrogen as nitrates which are leached or absorbed by plants. It is only a question of time until their percentage rate of disappearance from the soil becomes approximately the same, that is, the percentage of the total nitrogen being removed equals the percentage of the total carbon being lost. At this point the carbon-nitrogen ratio, whatever it happens to be, becomes more or less constant, always being somewhat greater than the ratios that characterize microbial tissue. As already stated, the carbon-nitrogen ratio in humid temperate region soils, especially if under cultivation, usually stabilizes in the neighborhood of 10 or 12 to 1.

Period of nitrate depression. The time interval of nitrate depression (Fig. 6:4), may be long or short depending on conditions. The rate of decay will lengthen or shorten the period as the case may be. And, of course, the greater the amount of residues applied the longer will nitrification be blocked. Also, the narrower the C:N ratio of the residues applied, the more rapidly the cycle will run its course. Hence alfalfa and clover residues should interfere least with nitrification and yield their nitrogen more quickly than though oats or wheat straw was plowed under. Also mature residues, whether legume or nonlegume, have much higher C:N ratio than do younger succulent materials. (See Fig. 6:5.) These facts are of much practical significance and should be considered when organic residues are added to a soil.

Moreover, cultivation by hastening oxidation, should encourage nitrification while a vigorous sod crop, such as bluegrass, always maintains the soil in an almost nitrateless condition. This is because the root and top residues maintain a wide C:N ratio, and the small quantities of nitrate and ammoniacal nitrogen which appear are immediately appropriated by the sod crop itself. All of this is illustrative of the influence that the C:N ratio exerts upon the transfer of nitrogen in the soil and its availability to crop plants.

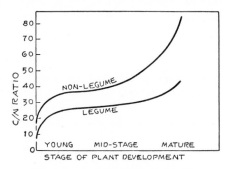

Figure 6:5. The C/N ratio of organic residues added to soil will depend upon the maturity of the plants turned under. The older the plants, the wider will be the C/N ratio and the longer will be the period of nitrate suppression. Obviously leguminous tissue will have a distinct advantage over nonlegumes since the former will promote a more rapid organic turnover in soils.

C:N ratio and organic matter level. Since carbon and nitrogen are reduced to a more or less definite ratio (say 11 to 1), the amount of soil nitrogen largely determines the amount of organic carbon present when stabilization occurs. Thus, the greater the amount of nitrogen present in the original residue, the greater will be the possibility of an accumulation of organically combined carbon. And since a rather definite ratio (about 1:1.7) exists between the organic carbon and the soil humus, the amount of organic matter that can be maintained in any soil is largely contingent upon the amount of organic nitrogen present.[18]

Practical deductions respecting the carbon-nitrogen ratio are thus clearcut. Apparently the ratio is related not only to the availability of soil nitrogen but also to the maintenance of soil organic matter. In practical handling of cultivated soils both of these phases must receive due consideration.

---

[18] The ratio between nitrogen and organic matter is thus rather constant. A value for the O.M./N ratio of 20/1 is commonly used for average soils. See page 151.

6:16. AMOUNTS OF ORGANIC MATTER [19] AND NITROGEN IN SOILS

The amounts of organic matter in mineral soils vary so widely that it is difficult to present representative figures. Mineral surface soil, corresponding roughly to the furrow-slice, may contain from a trace to 15 or 20 per cent of organic matter. The average organic matter and nitrogen contents of large numbers of soils from different areas of the United States are shown in Table 6:2. One is immediately impressed by the relatively wide

TABLE 6:2

The Average Nitrogen and Organic Matter Contents of Mineral Surface Soils In Several Areas of the U.S. The Ranges Found for These Two Constituents Are Also Given.[a]

	% Organic Matter		% Nitrogen	
Soils	*Range*	*Ave.*	*Range*	*Ave.*
240 West Va. soils	0.74–15.1	2.88	.044–.54	.147
15 Penn. soils	1.70– 9.9	3.60	—	—
117 Kansas soils	0.11–3.62	3.38	.017–.27	.170
30 Nebraska soils	2.43–5.29	3.83	.125–.25	.185
9 Minn. Prairie soils	3.45–7.41	5.15	.170–.35	.266
21 Southern Great Plains soils	1.16–2.16	1.55	.071–.14	.096
21 Utah soils	1.54–4.93	2.69	.088–.26	.146

[a] These data were obtained from a number of sources. See T. L. Lyon; H. O. Buckman; and N. C. Brady, *The Nature and Properties of Soils* (New York: Macmillan, 1952), p. 171.

ranges in organic matter encountered in these soils, even in comparatively localized areas. Thus, the West Virginia soils have a range from 0.74 per cent to more than 15 per cent of organic matter. The several factors which may account for this wide variability as well as for the differences between averages in Table 6:2 will be considered in the next section.

It will be noted that the data in the table are for surface soils only. As might be expected, the organic matter contents of the subsoils are generally much lower. (See Fig. 6:6.) This is readily explained when we consider that most of the organic residues in both cultivated and virgin soils are

[19] It is to be noted that no figures are offered as to the amount of humus present in mineral soils. This is partly due to the fact that no very satisfactory method is available for its determination.

Unfortunately there is no very satisfactory method of determining directly the exact quantity of total organic matter present in soil. The usual procedure is to find first the amount of organic carbon which can be done quite accurately. This figure multiplied by the factor 1.7 will give the approximate amount of organic matter present.

incorporated in or deposited on the surface. This increases the possibility for organic matter accumulation in the upper layers.

Figure 6:6.   Diagrams showing the distribution of organic matter in four soil profiles.* Note that the prairie soils have a higher organic matter content in the profile as a whole compared to the corresponding soils developed under forest vegetation. Poor drainage results in a higher organic matter content, particularly in the surface horizon.

* The forest soils are reported by R. A. Weaver, T. M. Bushnell, and G. D. Scarseth, "Correlative Studies of Indiana Soils: I. Some Physical and Chemical Characteristics of Seven Major Soil Types," *Proc. Soil Sci. Soc. Amer.*, 13: 484–93, 1948.

The prairie soils are averages obtained from C. O. Rast, and F. J. Alway, "Minnesota Glacial Soil Studies: I. A. Comparison of Soils on the Late Wisconsin and Iowan Drifts," *Soil Sci.*, 11: 206, 1921.

The organic matter to nitrogen ratio.   Before turning to the specific factors affecting the organic matter and nitrogen contents of soils, let us consider one more significant feature of the data in Table 6:2. In comparing the average organic matter and nitrogen contents of the soils listed one finds that there is about 20 times as much organic matter as nitrogen. This figure is fairly consistent as long as average data on a large number of soils are compared.

The explanation for the above constancy is obvious if we consider the information already presented concerning nitrogen, carbon and organic matter. It will be remembered that the C:N ratio of mineral soils is rather constant, and that the organic matter content is about 1.7 times as great as the carbon content. Thus, if a C:N ratio of 11.7 to 1 is assumed, the organic matter to nitrogen ratio is 11.7 × 1.7 or about 20:1. This figure is of considerable value in making rough calculations respecting these two constituents.[20]

[20] It goes without saying that the percentage of organic matter in a single sample of soil, when calculated from the percentage of total nitrogen by the factor (N × 20), is an extremely untrustworthy figure. But when the factor is applied to the average percentage of nitrogen in a large number of soils, it gives a comparatively accurate group figure, especially for arable soils.

6:17. VARIATIONS AND CORRELATIONS OF SOIL ORGANIC MATTER AND NITROGEN

In scanning the data presented in the preceding section, one is impressed by the variability in organic matter and nitrogen contents of representative mineral soils. Wide differences are evident, not only between soils of different physiographic provinces but also between closely contiguous areas in any particular locality. Heterogeneity seems to be the rule. This is expected by all pedologists. Let us consider the broader aspects first.

The influence of climate. Climatic conditions,[21] especially *temperature* and *rainfall,* exert a dominant influence on the amounts of nitrogen and organic matter found in soils. As one moves from a warmer to a cooler climate, the organic matter and nitrogen of comparable soils tend to increase. At the same time, the C:N ratio widens somewhat. In general, the decomposition of organic matter is accelerated in warm climates while a lower loss is the rule in cool regions. Within belts of uniform moisture conditions and comparable vegetation, the average total organic matter and nitrogen increase from two to three times for each 10° C. fall in mean annual temperature.

The situation is well illustrated by conditions in the Mississippi Valley region. (See Fig. 6:7.) Here, the northern prairie soils and chernozems contain in general considerably greater amounts of total organic matter and nitrogen than those that lie to the south. When the amount of original tissue yearly added to the soil is taken into consideration, the tropics, where plants grow so luxuriantly, afford an even better example of the influence of temperature on the rapidity of decay and disappearance of organic materials. In spite of this, however, many tropical surface soils are surprisingly high in organic matter.

Effective soil moisture also exerts a very positive control upon the accumulation of organic matter and nitrogen in soils. In general, under comparable conditions, the nitrogen and organic matter increase as the effective moisture becomes greater. (See Fig. 6:7.) At the same time, the C:N ratio becomes wider. This is especially true for the grasslands. The explanation lies not only in the rapidity of microbial action and hence a more complete humification in areas of moderate to low rainfall but also in the scantier vegetation of these regions. In arriving at the rainfall correlation such as advanced above, it must not be forgotten that the organic situation

[21] See H. Jenny, *op. cit.;* and *Factors of Soil Formation* (New York: McGraw-Hill, 1941).

in any one soil is in large degree an expression of both temperature and precipitation plus other factors as well. Climatic influences never work singly.

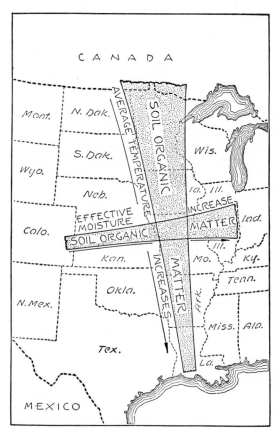

Figure 6:7. Map showing the influence of the average annual temperature and the effective moisture on the organic matter contents of grassland soils of the Midwest. Of course, the soils must be more or less comparable in all respects except for climatic differences.

Note that the higher temperatures yield soils lower in organic matter. The effect of increasing moisture is exactly opposite, favoring a higher level of this constituent. These climatic influences affect forest soils in much the same way.

The effect of texture, drainage, and other factors. Besides the two broader aspects discussed above, there are numerous local relationships that should be mentioned. In the first place, the *texture* of the soil, other factors being constant, seems to influence the percentage of humus and nitrogen present. A sandy soil, for example, usually carries less organic matter and nitrogen than one of a finer texture. (See Table 6:3.) This is probably due to the lower moisture content and to the more ready oxidation that occurs in the lighter soils. Also the natural addition of residues normally is less with the lighter soil.

TABLE 6:3

The Relationship Between Soil Texture and Approximate Organic Matter Contents of a Number of North Carolina Soils [a]

| Soil Type | No. of Soils | % Organic Matter | |
		Topsoil	Subsoil
Cecil sands	15	0.80	0.50
Cecil clay loams	10	1.32	0.56
Cecil clays	27	1.46	0.64

[a] These figures were calculated by multiplying the % N by 20. The original data came from C. B. Williams, *et al.*, *Report on the Piedmont Soils particularly with reference to their nature, plant-food requirements and adaptability for different crops*, Bul. North Car. Dept. Agr., 36, No. 2, 1915.

Again, *poorly drained* soils because of their high moisture relations and their relatively poor aeration are generally much higher in organic matter and nitrogen than their better drained equivalents. (See Fig. 6:6.) For example, soils lying along streams are often quite high in organic matter. This is due in part to their poor drainage, as well as to the wash they receive from the uplands.

The *lime content* of a soil, its *erosion* status, and its *vegetative cover,* are other factors that may exert an influence upon the accumulation and the activity of the soil organic matter and its nitrogen.

The various factors enumerated, due to their interlocking and interdependent influences, are difficult to evaluate individually. Collectively, however, they determine rather definitely the level at which the nitrogen and organic matter will become more or less stabilized in any particular case. As one would expect, this level will be different in different soils and will change in any one soil according to the modification made in its vegetative cover and other details of management.

Normally, a very marked change occurs when a virgin soil, either forest or prairie, is placed under cultivation. New and usually lower levels of organic matter and nitrogen are gradually established. (See Fig. 6:8.) It is not surprising, therefore, to find cultivated land much lower in organic matter and nitrogen, by perhaps 30 to 60 per cent, than its virgin equivalent. Such a drop is perfectly normal and is difficult to forestall. Hence in practice it is hardly worth while to attempt a maintenance much above certain percentages, providing good crops can be grown under these conditions. But more about that later.

6:18. INFLUENCE OF SOIL ORGANIC MATTER ON SOIL PROPERTIES

Before discussing the practical maintenance of soil organic matter, it might be well to review very briefly what is expected from this all-important constituent.

The most obvious influences may be outlined as follows:

1. Effect on soil color—brown to black
2. Influence on physical properties
   a. Granulation encouraged
   b. Plasticity, cohesion, etc. reduced
   c. H_2O holding capacity increased
3. High cation-adsorption capacity
   a. Two to thirty times as great as mineral colloids
   b. Accounts for 30 to 90 per cent of the adsorbing power of mineral soils
4. Supply and availability of nutrients
   a. Easily replaceable cations present
   b. N, P, and S held in organic forms
   c. Extraction of elements from minerals by acid humus

6:19. THE ORGANIC MATTER PROBLEM

The fact that crop yields in areas long under cultivation have been maintained or even at times raised somewhat does not mean that organic matter and nitrogen are being held at satisfactory levels. In fact, comparisons in Ohio and Missouri [22] of soils cropped for long periods with their virgin equivalents indicate a reduction on the average of about 35 per cent in respect to their nitrogen. This would mean a more or less proportionate lowering in total organic matter.

That it is impossible in most cases to maintain the organic matter and nitrogen of our soils, whether forest or prairie, at their virgin levels is obvious. Nor is this necessary or even desirable. Yet a decline in organic matter content of 30 to 40 per cent is serious and should go no further.

[22] R. M. Salter, R. D. Lewis, and J. A. Slipher, *Our Heritage—The Soil*, Extension Bul. 175, Ohio Agr. Exp. Sta., 1941; and A. W. Klemme and O. T. Coleman, *Evaluating Annual Changes in Soil Productivity*, Bul. 405, Missouri Agr. Exp. Sta., 1939.

(See Fig. 6:8.) Such exploitation, if continued, may ultimately result in a definite decrease in crop yield. In practice it is not enough simply to bring to a halt this slow decline in the inherent capacity of soils to produce crops. It should be raised, not sharply or to any great degree, for this would be too expensive, but enough to insure a continuance of our present crop yields. Hence, the importance of the maintenance of soil organic matter above a certain level and with it a satisfactory nitrogen supply.

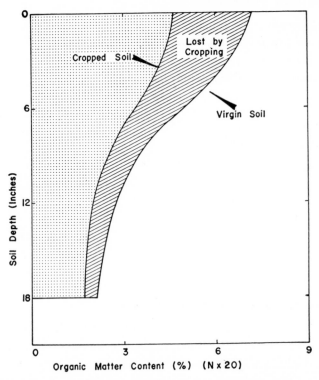

Figure 6:8. The average organic matter content of three North Dakota soils before and after an average of 43 years of cropping. About 25 per cent of the organic matter was lost from the 0 to 6-inch layer as a result of cropping. (*From H. J. Haas, et al.,* Nitrogen and Carbon Changes in Great Plains Soils as Influenced by Cropping and Soil Treatments, *Tech. Bul. No. 1167, U.S. Dept. of Agric., 1957.*)

6:20. THE REGULATION OF SOIL ORGANIC MATTER

The preceding discussion has established two definite conclusions regarding the organic matter and nitrogen of soils, especially of those under cultivation. *First,* the inherent capacity of soils to produce crops is closely and directly related to their organic matter and nitrogen contents. *Second,* a satisfactory level of these two constituents is difficult to maintain in the majority of farm soils. Because of this situation, methods of organic matter additions and upkeep should receive early consideration in all soil management programs.

For convenience, let us deal with the problem under four headings: (1) the sources of organic supplies; (2) soil conditions favoring the satisfactory decay and utilization of the added residues; (3) crop rotation in its relation to humus maintenance; and (4) the economy of organic matter upkeep. These phases will be considered in order.

Source of supply.   Organic matter may be added to cultivated soils in a number of different ways. One is the plowing under of crops when in an immature, succulent stage. This is called *green-manuring* and is a very satisfactory practice when it can be accommodated to the rotation. Such crops as rye, buckwheat, oats, peas, soybeans, and vetch, as well as others, lend themselves to this method of soil improvement. Not only do these crops help maintain the actual organic content of a soil, but in the case of legumes, at least a part of the nitrogen may be drawn from the air. This is a great advantage as such residues have a comparatively narrow C:N ratio, decay rapidly, and yield more humus than do tissues with a smaller amount of nitrogen.

A second source of organic matter supply on many farms, especially in dairy sections, is *farm manure*. When applied at the usual rates, say 10 or 15 tons per acre during a five-year rotation, perhaps from 1,000 to 1,500 pounds of dry matter go into the soil as a yearly acre average. Such additions cannot but greatly aid in organic matter maintenance.

Moreover, farm manure is valuable because of the nitrogen that it carries which influences soil organic matter in two ways. As a nutrient it tends to increase crop yields and organic residues that remain in the soil. Also, nitrogen exerts some control on the amount of organic carbon in a soil. Hence, farm manure which supplies much nitrogen for growing plants is by no means unimportant in the struggle to maintain soil organic matter. In the same category with farm manure, but of much less concern, are *artificial farm manures* and *composts* (p. 513). The latter are employed mostly in the management of nursery, garden and greenhouse soils.

The third and, in general, the most important sources of organic residues, especially with arable soils, are the *current crops* themselves. Stubble, aftermath, and especially root residues of various kinds left in the soil to decay, make up the bulk of such contributions. Few farmers realize how much residual root systems aid in the conditioning of their soils. Without them, the practical maintenance of the humus in most cases would be impossible.

In this connection it should also be remembered that the maintaining of high crop yields through proper *liming* and *fertilizer practices* may be just as effective as adding manure or other organic residues. (See Fig. 6:9.) Apparently in some cases organic matter can be maintained by simply raising bumper crops. Optimum yields usually mean more residues to return to the soil and certainly increase the amount of roots remaining after harvest.

Figure 6:9. Diagram showing the influence of soil treatment upon the organic matter of an Illinois black soil (Bloomington series) over a period of 29 years. The rotation was corn—oats—wheat—clover. The organic matter was calculated (N X 20).

The curves show two things: (1) the disastrous effect of farming this soil with no treatment, and (2) the possibility of maintaining, or even increasing, the organic matter and nitrogen contents. After 29 years, the treated soil apparently was at a high level of fertility. *(Data from H. J. Snider, "Soil Building with Legumes," Ill. Agr. Exp. Sta. Bul. 539, 553, 1950.)*

Proper soil condition.   In order that organic materials added to any soil may perform their normal functions, soil conditions, in general, should be of the best. This means careful and opportune tillage and cultivation. Proper drainage systems should be installed, if necessary, in order to promote satisfactory aeration and granulation. Lime should be added if basic materials are lacking, for it promotes bacterial activity as well as plant growth. The addition of commercial fertilizers will often be physically advantageous. In any case increased crop growth should make possible a larger addition of organic matter, especially through crop residues and farm manures.

Crops and crop sequence. It has already been suggested that certain sod crops, such as meadow and pasture grasses and legumes, tend to facilitate humus accumulation. This is partly due to their liberal contributions of organic residues, the slow decay of these materials and their wide C:N ratios. Under these conditions little nitrogen can appear in the soil in the nitrate form (p. 147), and hence rather slight losses of this constituent will occur. In the case of legumes this may be offset, at least in part, by nitrogen fixation. Since the amount of humus depends to a considerable extent upon the amount of organic nitrogen (p. 149) sod crops by their nitrogen economy promote the highest possible yields of humus. Everyone knows that sod begets humus.

Cultivated crops, on the other hand, remove as much or even more nitrogen at harvest than do sod crops. Besides, tillage and other features of their management encourage an extremely rapid rate of decay and dissipation of organic matter. As a result the C:N ratio quickly becomes narrow thereby encouraging vigorous nitrification and a probable loss of nitrates in drainage. Thus, intertilled crops are associated with nitrogen depreciation instead of with economic stabilization, and with humus reduction instead of with humus accumulation. Small grains, such as oats and wheat, are in the same category—that is, they are humus wasters but to a lesser degree.

In practice, advantage is taken of the tendencies outlined above and crop sequences are so arranged as to offset humus depreciation with humus conservation and even appreciation. That much can be accomplished by the utilization of a suitable rotation, unaided by farm manure and commercial fertilizers is evidenced by the data shown in Table 6:4 from Wooster, Ohio, where unfertilized plots were cropped in various ways for a long period of time.

Note again that the land, although limed sufficiently to grow clover, was treated with neither farm manure nor commercial fertilizers. Hence, the differences apparently are largely due to the crops grown and their sequence. Furthermore, it is safe to infer that if commercial fertilizers and farm manure in normal amounts had been used the stabilization levels for the organic matter and nitrogen of the rotation plots would have been even closer to those of the land originally.

Economy in humus maintenance. Since the rate at which carbon is lost from the soil increases very rapidly as the organic content is raised, the

TABLE 6:4

Organic Matter and Nitrogen Contents of Unfertilized Soil Plots at Wooster, Ohio, After Being Cropped in Various Ways for 32 Years [a]

Cropping	*Organic Matter Tons per Acre*	*Nitrogen Pounds per Acre*
Original crop land	17.5	2,176
Continuous corn	6.4	840
Continuous oats	11.4	1,425
Continuous wheat	11.0	1,315
Corn, oats, wheat, clover, timothy	13.4	1,546
Corn, wheat, clover [b]	14.8	1,780

[a] R. M. Salter; R. D. Lewis; and J. A. Slipher, *Our Heritage—The Soil,* Extension Bul. 175, Ohio Agr. Exp. Sta., 1941, p. 9.
[b] Continued for 29 years instead of 32.

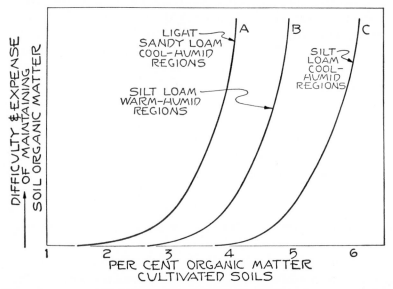

Figure 6:10. A generalized diagram showing how the difficulty and expense of maintaining the organic matter of cultivated soils increase as the support level is raised. While the curves are quite similar, their position in relation to the percentage of organic matter possible varies with *texture* (A vs C) and *climate* (B vs C). Other factors also are involved, especially the type of crop rotation employed.

In practice the average amount of organic matter maintained in a cultivated soil should be held at the maximum level economically feasible.

maintenance of the humus at a high level is not only difficult but also expensive. (See Fig. 6:10.) It is, therefore, unwise to hold the organic matter above a level consistent with crop yields that pay best. Just what this level should be will depend on climatic environments, soil conditions, and the particular crops grown and their sequence. Obviously, it should be higher in the chernozem region of North Dakota than in central Kansas where the temperature is higher or in northern Montana where the effective rainfall is lower. In any event, the soil organic matter, as well as the nitrogen, should always be maintained at an economic maximum consistent with a suitable physical condition of the soil, satisfactory biochemical activity, an adequate availability of nutrients, and paying crop yields.

Good soil management, therefore, seeks to adjust the addition of organic residues, the physical and chemical conditions of the soil, the sequence of crops, and the losses through biological activity in such a way that paying crops may be harvested without reducing the humus supply of the soil below a definite level. Any system of agriculture that does not do this is impractical and unscientific.

Forms of Soil Water, Their Movement, and Their Plant Relationships

We are interested in soil-water [1] relationships for several reasons. In the first place, large quantities of water must be supplied to satisfy the evapo-transpiration requirements of growing plants. Furthermore, this water must be available when the plants need it and most of it must come from the soil. Second, water acts as the solvent which together with the dissolved nutrients make up the soil solution. The significance of this soil component has already been adequately stressed.

As we shall see in a succeeding chapter, soil moisture also helps control two other important components so essential to normal plant growth—soil air and soil temperature. And last but not least, the control of the disposition of water as it strikes the soil determines to a large extent the incidence of soil erosion, that devastating menace which constantly threatens the impairment or even destruction of our soils.

7:1. RETENTION OF SOIL MOISTURE—A SIMPLE CASE

From a practical standpoint we are most concerned with soil properties as they affect the following factors: (1) The movement of water into and within the soil. (2) the moisture-storing capacity of soils and (3) the availability of soil moisture to higher plants. Each of these factors is related directly or indirectly to the size and distribution of soil pores and to the

[1] For interesting and non-technical articles on water in relation to soils see *The Yearbook of Agriculture* (Water), U.S. Dept. of Agriculture, 1955 and *The Yearbook of Agriculture* (Soil), U.S. Dept. of Agriculture, 1957.

attraction of the soil solids for moisture. The evidence of these relationships can be seen if we follow some of the changes which take place during and following a rainstorm or the application of irrigation water.

Maximum retentive capacity. Assume that water is applied to the surface of a well-granulated silt loam soil which is relatively uniform in texture and structure.[2] The water might come from a heavy steady rain or from irrigation. As the water enters the soil, air is displaced and the surface soil "wets up"—that is, the soil pores, large and small, are filled with water. Continued application will result in further downward movement and air replacement. At this point, all the pores in the upper part of the soil will be filled with water. The soil is said to be saturated with respect to water and is at its *maximum retentive capacity*.[3] (Figure 7:1.)

Field capacity. If we now cut off the supply of water to the soil surface—that is, it stops raining or we shut off the irrigation water—there will be a continued relatively rapid downward movement of some of the water. After a day or so, this rapid downward movement will essentially cease. The soil is then said to be at its *field capacity*. At this point an examination of the soil will show that water has moved out of the larger or *macropores* and that its place has been taken by air. The *micropores* are still filled with water and it is from this source that the plants will adsorb moisture for their use. Moisture movement will continue to take place but the rate of movement is quite slow since it is due primarily to capillary forces which are effective in only the micropores. (Fig. 7:1.)

Wilting coefficient. Plants growing in our soil will absorb water and will reduce the quantity of moisture remaining in the soil. Some of the water will be translocated from the roots to the leaves where most of it will be lost by evapo-transpiration at the leaf surfaces. A second important avenue of loss is evaporation directly from the soil surface which will aid materially in the removal of soil moisture. Both of these losses are taking place simultaneously and are responsible for a markedly rapid rate of water dissipation from soils.

As the soil dries out plants will begin to show the effects of reduced soil moisture. During the daytime they will tend to wilt, especially if temperatures are high and if there is some wind movement. At first this daytime wilting will be associated with renewed nighttime turgor or plant vigor

[2] For soils containing texturally different layers the situation is much more complicated than that presented here. (See p. 188.)

[3] An approximation of these conditions may be obtained if a very thin layer of soil (5 to 10 millimeters deep) is allowed to absorb water from a free water table. See E. W. Hilgard, *Soils* (New York: Macmillan, 1911) p. 209.

Ultimately the rate of the supply of water to the plants will be so slow that the plant will remain wilted night and day. Although not dead, the plants are now existing in a permanently wilted condition and will die if water is not added.

Figure 7:1. Diagrams showing the volumes of solids, water, and air in a well-granulated, silt loam soil at different moisture levels. The top bar shows the situation when a representative soil is completely saturated with moisture. This situation will usually occur for short periods of time during a rain or when the soil is being irrigated. Water will soon drain out of the larger or *macropores*. The soil is then said to be at the *field capacity*. Plants will remove moisture from the soil quite rapidly until the *wilting coefficient* is approached. Permanent wilting of the plants occurs at this point even though there is still considerable moisture in the soil (wilting coefficient). A further reduction in moisture content to the *hygroscopic coefficient* is illustrated in the bottom bar. At this point, the water is held very tightly, mostly by the soil colloids. (Upper drawings modified from "Irrigation on Western Farms" published by the U.S. Depts. of Agriculture and Interior.)

An examination of the soil at this point will show a considerable amount of moisture remaining. The soil moisture content at this stage is called the *wilting coefficient*[4] or the *critical moisture*. The water remaining in the soil is found in the smallest of the micropores and around individual soil particles. (See Fig. 7:1.) Obviously then, a considerable amount of water present in soils is not available to higher plants. The soil moisture must be maintained considerably above the wilting coefficient if plants are to grow and function normally.

Hygroscopic coefficient.[5]   To obtain a more complete picture of the soil-moisture relations let us take a sample into the laboratory and allow the soil to dry out further. If it is kept in an atmosphere which is essentially completely saturated with water vapor, it will lose the liquid water held in even the smallest of the micropores. The remaining water will be associated with the surfaces of the soil particles, particularly the colloids, as adsorbed moisture. It is held so tightly that much of it is considered nonliquid and can move only in the vapor phase. The moisture content of the soil at this point is termed the *hygroscopic coefficient*. As might be expected, soils high in colloidal materials will hold more water under these conditions than will sandy soils and those low in clay and humus. (See Fig. 7:1.)

As we have followed the depletion of moisture from a saturated soil, two facts have become obvious: (1) moisture is held in the soil with a suction or tension and work must be done to remove this water; and (2) the tension with which water is held depends upon the amount present, the smaller the amount the greater the tension. Let us now see how this water is held and then turn our attention to the actual energy-moisture relationships.

7:2. FORCES OF RETENTION

Two forces largely account for the retention of moisture by soil solids. (See Figure 7:2.) One is the attraction of the solid surfaces for water

[4] The wilting coefficient is usually determined in a greenhouse using seedlings such as sunflower or some grain such as wheat or rye. This determination gives essentially the same value regardless of which of the common crops are used. See L. J. Briggs and H. L. Schantz, *The Wilting Coefficient for Different Plants and Its Indirect Determination*, Bulletin 230, Bureau of Plant Industry, U.S. Dept. of Agriculture, 26–33, 1912; and F. J. Veihmeyer and A. H. Hendrickson, "Methods of Measuring Field Capacity and Permanent Wilting Percentage of Soils," *Soil Sci.,* 68: 75–94, 1949.

[5] The method of determining the hygroscopicity of a soil at any given vapor pressure is simple in outline. Air-dry soil in thin layer is exposed to an atmosphere of definite humidity under conditions of constant temperature. When equilibrium is reached, the moisture content of the sample is determined.

Many investigators favor the use of a 3.3 per cent solution of sulfuric acid which gives a relative humidity at laboratory temperature of 98.2 per cent and a tension of about 31 atmospheres. See L. D. Baver, *Soil Physics* (New York: Wiley, 1956), pp. 34–43.

molecules (adhesion). The other is the attraction of water molecules for each other (cohesion). By adhesion, solids hold water molecules rigidly at their soil-water interfaces. These molecules in turn hold by cohesion other water molecules further removed from the solid surfaces. Together, these forces make it possible for the soil solids to retain water and to control to a considerable degree its movement and utilization. Furthermore, they emphasize that energy is involved in soil-water relations and suggest that the tension with which water is held will vary with the distance of the molecules from the soil solids.

Figure 7:2. Diagramatic representation of the progressive thickening of a water film in a macropore and the corresponding decline in the tension at which the surface molecules are held. While an increment of water can be extracted easily from the surface of a thick film, a similar removal from a thin film is much more difficult. Soil water is held in two ways—*adhesion* and *cohesion*.

Water held by these two forces not only can keep the smaller capillary pores entirely full of water but also can maintain relatively thick films in the macropores. As these films thicken, they become progressively heavier and the moisture at the outer surface of the film less tenaciously held. (See Fig. 7:2.) This outer moisture is subject to ready movement in response to the pull of gravity and especially the pull of adjoining moisture films that are not so thick. Thus, when the soil is near saturation, it should be easy to remove a small increment of water. But as the moisture becomes less and less in a soil, the greater and greater will be the force necessary to remove a unit amount.

Methods of expressing energy. Before investigating actual energy values, let us consider briefly the units in which they are expressed. One means of expressing the suction or tension is in terms of the height in centimeters of a unit water-column whose weight just equals the tension under consideration. The greater the centimeter height, the greater is the tension measured. We may thus express the tenacity with which water is held by soils in centimeters or we may convert such readings into other forms. In any case, the method of expressing the tension with which moisture films are held should be as simple as possible.

Perhaps a more generally accepted method is that of *bars* or *atmospheres*—the standard atmosphere (the average air pressure at sea level) being 14.7 pounds per square inch. The negative pressure exerted by a column of water 10 centimeters high under standard conditions is about 1/100 of an atmosphere (10 millibars); that by a column 100 centimeters high, 1/10 of an atmosphere (100 millibars); that by a 1,000 centimeter column of water, approximately 1 atmosphere of tension and so on. The table which appears below [6] presents further conversions.

7:3. THE ENERGY CONCEPT OF MOISTURE RETENTION [7]

The previous two sections have suggested that moisture is held in soils by attractive forces. Let us now examine changes in soil moisture in relation to the energy with which this important constituent is held.

Tension vs. film thickness. In Figure 7:3, the relationship between

[6]

A TABLE OF PRESSURE EQUIVALENTS

Height of a Unit Column of Water in Centimeters	Approximate Atmospheres (Bars) of Pressure	Equivalent pF Values
1	1/1000	0
10	1/100	1
100	1/10	2
346	1/3	2.54
1,000	1	3
10,000	10	4
15,849	15	4.2
31,623	31	5.4
100,000	100	5
1,000,000	1,000	6
10,000,000	10,000	7

pF is the logarithm of the centimeter height of the water column in any given case. Since this method of expression is used in the earlier literature dealing with soil-moisture tension, it is included with the other two.

[7] For further information consult L. D. Baver, *op. cit.*, pp. 224–47; and L. A. Richards, "Methods of Measuring Soil Moisture Tensions," *Soil Sci.*, 68: 95–112, 1949.

film thickness and the energy of retention (tension) at the outer edge of the moisture film is shown. This diagram should help us explain some of the observations made in the last two sections. For example, during and immediately following a heavy rain even the macropores are essentially filled with water—that is, the moisture films around and between solid particles are very thick. The tension with which the water is held at the edge of the film is very small. Consequently, some of the water held in these larger pores is pulled downward into drier soil layers where the moisture films are thin and the tension high. Gravitational forces as well as those associated with the moisture films insure reasonably rapid movement, unless, of course, the pores are extremely small.

Figure 7:3. Diagrams showing relationship between thickness of water films and the tension with which the water is held at the liquid-air interface. The tension is shown in atmospheres. (Upper) Sketch of water film thickness at several moisture levels. (Lower) Logarithmic change in tension with increase in thickness of moisture film.

Field capacity and wilting coefficient.   As the average film thickness decreases, the tension at the air-water interface increases and is finally great enough to drastically reduce the downward movement. Water has been removed from the macropores but is still present in the micropores. At this point (field capacity),[8] the tension at the outer surface of the film is between 0.1 and 0.5 atmospheres depending on the soil. (An average value of ⅓ will be used; see Fig. 7:3.)

Utilization of water by plants will decrease further the average film thickness in a soil. Water will be removed from the larger of the micropores where it is least tightly held (because of the relative thickness of the films), and will remain in the smallest pores and around the solid particles (where the moisture films are very thin). This will continue so long as the plant can effectively remove water from the films. When the rate of this removal is too slow to maintain plant turgidity, permanent wilting occurs and the soil is said to be at its critical moisture level or at the wilting coefficient.[9] The average-moisture tension at the outer surface of the moisture films is now about 15 atmospheres. (See Fig. 7:3.)

Hygroscopic coefficient. Continued moisture removal will result in a decrease in film thickness and a marked increase in the tenacity with which the water is held (tension). At the hydroscopic coefficient, the tension is 31 atmospheres and much of the water is held so tightly that it is essentially nonliquid. As the film is progressively decreased in thickness, the tension increases to values as high as 10,000 atmospheres. (See Fig. 7:3.) These high energies of retention emphasize the significance of soil-water attraction in determining the water relations in soils.

Energy-moisture content correlation. By determining tension values at various moisture contents for particular soils, graphs may be constructed showing moisture-energy relationships. One such graph showing moisture-tension relationships for different soils—a sand, a sandy loam, and a silt loam is shown in Figure 7:4. Note that atmospheres of tension are plotted against percentages of moisture based on dry soil.[10]

---

[8] Because of the difficulty of measuring accurately the field capacity, a laboratory method is often used to obtain an arbitrary moisture figure, the *moisture equivalent.* This figure closely approximates the field capacity of medium textured soils. It is determined by subjecting the soil to a centrifugal force equivalent to about ⅓ atmosphere tension.

See L. T. Briggs and J. W. McLane, *The Moisture Equivalent of Soils,* Bulletin 45, Bureau of Soils, U.S. Dept. of Agriculture, 1907. See also R. M. Smith and D. R. Browning, "Soil Moisture Tension and Pore Space Relations for Several Soils in the Range of the Field Capacity," *Proc. Soil Sci. Soc. Amer.,* 12: 17–21, 1947.

[9] This term applies especially to humid-region plants. Desert plants, able to reduce their transpiration to a very low magnitude or even capable of storing water in special tissue soils, do not have a critical moisture in the sense used here.

[10] The usual method of expressing the amount of water present in a soil is in terms of percentage based on dry soil. Thus, if 100 gms. of moist soil (soil + water) when dried loses 20 gms. of water, the 80 gms. of dry matter are used as a basis for the percentage calculation. Therefore, (20 ÷ 80) × 100 = 25 per cent. The weight of the wet soil is undesirable as a basis for calculation since it changes with every moisture fluctuation.

It is clearly apparent from the graphs that some of the water present in soils is held under tremendous negative pressures. On the other hand, when soils are well supplied with water, a very slight suction is sufficient to withdraw a minute amount. The tension curves show all gradations between these extremes, indicating a *gradual* change in energy of retention. Thus, unless zones of demarcation are arbitrarily established, a clear-cut classification of soil water on the basis of energy units is not possible.

Figure 7:4. Tension curves for three representative mineral soils. The atmospheres of tension are plotted against percentage of soil moisture present. Note the rapid drop in tension as the amounts of soil moisture increase and the films thicken. The silt-loam has, of course, the greatest water capacity.

It must always be borne in mind that tension values express only the tension of water at the liquid-air interfaces—that is, moisture at the outer surface of the film. Thus, a thin film might be subject to a negative pressure of 100 atmospheres but, if thickened by additions, the water occupying the position of the original film will be subject to considerably less tension and will move much more freely than before. This must not be forgotten in the use of tension values, if a serious misconception is to be prevented.

Further examination of the illustrative curves (Fig. 7:4) will show that they vary characteristically with soil texture. The finer-textured soils retain a greater percentage of moisture through the entire energy range. This is to be expected since they have a greater percentage of total colloidal matter, greater total pore space, and a much greater adsorptive surface.

7:4. THE PHYSICAL CLASSIFICATION OF SOIL MOISTURE

The moisture-tension curves in Figures 7:3 and 7:4 remind us that as soil moisture is raised or lowered there is a *gradual* change in the tension with which the water is held. There are no sharp lines of demarcation, therefore, on which to base a classification of soil water. Just as was the case in dealing with the classification of particles according to size, however, a somewhat arbitrary classification system may be used in order to supply convenient terms for discussion. These terms should be used with caution, recognizing that there are no clear-cut lines of distinction between the different forms of soil water.

On the basis of relative degree of retention, soil water has been classified

Figure 7:5. Diagramatic representation of the moisture distribution in a soil column of uniform texture saturated at the bottom but well drained at the surface. Three forms of soil water are shown—*hygroscopic, capillary,* and *drainage* or *free.* The latter when present occupies the volume designated in the diagram as airspace. The tension ranges are shown in atmospheres of pressure. The exact quantity of moisture present at any particular tension will, of course, vary with the soil under consideration and its physical condition.

simply under three heads—*free, capillary,* and *hygroscopic.* (See Figs. 7:5 and 7:6.) Two other forms, both already mentioned—*water of crystallization* held as part of the crystal makeup of the silicate clays, and the *water vapor* of the soil air—need not be considered here.

For our purposes the following brief outline will describe the general characteristics of the three forms of water under discussion.

1. Free (drainage) water
    a. Water in the soil above that held at field capacity.
    b. Loosely held, less than 0.1 to 0.5 atmosphere tension.
    c. Undesirable, removed in drainage.
    d. Moves in response to film tension and gravitational forces.
    e. Nutrients leached with the water.

2. Capillary water
    a. Held between field capacity and hygroscopic coefficient in micropores.
    b. Tension of films varies from about 0.1 to 31 atmospheres.
    c. Not all available to plants.
    d. Moves by film adjustment from thick to thin films.
    e. Functions as the soil solution.

3. Hygroscopic water
    a. Held at the hygroscopic coefficient.
    b. Tension varies from 31 to 10,000 atmospheres.
    c. Held mostly by the soil colloids.
    d. Largely nonliquid.
    e. Moves mostly in the vapor form.

Data reported in Table 7:1 illustrate the variations in the amounts of hygroscopic and capillary water retained by soils of different texture and organic matter. Moisture equivalent figures (see fn., p. 169) are considered as approximating field capacities. Several relationships are clearly evident even from a casual examination of the data. The amounts of hygroscopic and capillary water, as well as the maximum retentive capacity, are correlated definitely with both the texture and the organic matter contents of these soils. From what we know about colloidal characteristics this is no surprise but it is to be noted that the relationships are by no means uniform.

7:5. THE BIOLOGICAL CLASSIFICATION OF SOIL WATER

From the discussions already presented, it is evident that not all moisture present is available or suitable for the rapid vegetative growth of a plant.

TABLE 7:1

Hygroscopic and Capillary Water Capacities of Various Soils

Soils	*1* Organic Matter	*2* Hygro- scopic Coeff.	*3* Field Capacity (Moisture Equiv.)	*4* Capillary Water (Column 3–2)	*5* Maximum Retentive Capacity (Tension near 0)
	Per Cent	Per Cent	Per Cent	Per Cent	Per Cent
Western Soils [a]					
Sandy soil (Nebr.)	1.22	3.3	7.9	4.6	34.2
Red loam (N. Mex.)	1.07	10.0	19.2	9.2	49.0
Silt loam (Nebr.)	4.93	10.2	27.8	17.8	60.9
Black adobe (Ariz.)	2.22	12.9	25.8	12.9	60.3
Iowa Soils [b]					
Dickinson fine sand	2.13	3.4	7.6	4.2	44.5
Clarion sandy loam	3.01	6.9	15.5	8.6	58.0
Marshall silt loam	3.58	10.4	24.0	13.6	76.5
Wabash silty clay	5.91	16.1	30.4	14.3	87.0

[a] F. J. Alway and G. R. McDole, "The Relation of Movement of Water in a Soil to Its Hygroscopicity and Initial Moisture," *Jour. Agr. Res.*, 10: 391–428, 1917.

[b] M. B. Russell, "Soil Moisture Sorption Curves for Four Iowa Soils," *Proc. Soil Sci. Soc. Amer.*, 4: 51–4, 1939.

Three tentative divisions of the soil water may be made on this basis: *superfluous, desirably available,* and *unavailable.* (See Fig. 7:6.)

Superfluous water. In general, moisture in excess of that held at the field capacity is of no benefit to higher plants. When too much of this free water is present, conditions detrimental to growth are encouraged, the situation becoming more adverse as the saturation point is approached. From the standpoint of plants, the free water is, therefore, designated as *superfluous.* (See Fig. 7:6.)

The unfavorable effects of such moisture on the plant arise largely from poor aeration. Not only are the roots deprived of their oxygen, but favorable bacterial activities, such as nitrification, nitrogen fixation, and ammonification, are much retarded. Moreover, adverse biochemical changes may be encouraged.

Another detrimental effect of superfluous water is that its removal entails nutrient loss as well. In fine-textured soils, this may mean only a downward displacement to a lower horizon where the nutrients can be utilized later by penetrating roots. In coarse-textured soils the nutrients are often completely lost to the plant roots by removal through the drainage water.

Figure 7:6. Diagram showing the relationship of the various forms of soil moisture to higher plants. By inserting the wilting coefficient, the physical classification of soil water can be converted into a biological classification and the plant significance of moisture tensions and adjustments graphically pictured.

Available water.   The available moisture is generally considered as that held between the field capacity and the wilting coefficient. The latter measurement is essentially the same for all common crop plants grown on a given soil.[11] Apparently, any small differences in the ability of plants to absorb the soil moisture is masked by the rapid increase in tension as the moisture-film thickness decreases. The wilting coefficient can thus be considered to be a characteristic of the soil and not of the plant used to determine it. This fact must be kept in mind.

The question as to whether moisture is equally available to plants throughout the entire range between the field capacity and the wilting coefficient has been debated for many years. Apparently the answer depends to a considerable extent on the crop to be grown, and the proportion of the soil profile being exploited by the crop roots. However, for most of our common annual crop plants, the optimum moisture zone appears to be between the field capacity and some level considerably above the wilting coefficient.[12] (See Fig. 7:6.)

[11] It must not be inferred from this conclusion that all plants have the same drought resistance. With humid-region plants, root spread is by far the most important factor in this regard. Plants with the more extended root systems are, of course, able to draw on a greater amount of water and better withstand a drought period. Moreover, some plants can reduce their transpiration to a surprising degree, thus satisfactorily meeting the lessened intake of water. Desert species are good examples.

[12] Stanhill reviewed 80 studies of the comparative availability of moisture in the range of the field capacity to the wilting point. In general, yields were somewhat reduced as the wilting point was approached, especially where annual crops were used.

See H. Stanhill, "The Effect of Differences in Soil-Moisture Status on Plant Growth," *Soil Sci.* 84: 205–14, 1957.

Irrigation research indicates that for optimum crop growth, water should be applied when from 50 to 85 per cent of the available moisture has been used.[13] This means that when the moisture content approaches that of the wilting point, the rate of water uptake by plants is not rapid enough to maintain optimum growth. The desirability of keeping the moisture well above the wilting point has been clearly demonstrated.

Unavailable water. Brief mention should be made of the so-called *unavailable* water—that held in the soil at the permanent wilting point. Such moisture includes the hygroscopic water and that portion of the capillary water which is removed too slowly by plants to prevent wilting. Except for certain plants adapted to arid regions, this *inner capillary* moisture is of little concern to higher-plant life. Its use by bacteria and fungi growing on the organic colloids may be advantageous but even here the rate of microbial activity is very low compared to that under more ideal moisture conditions.

7:6. FACTORS AFFECTING THE AMOUNT AND USE OF AVAILABLE SOIL MOISTURE [14]

Before evaluating the soil factors affecting water-use by plants, we should recognize that other factors influence the absorption of soil water. A number of plant and climatic factors have a marked effect on the amount of water which plants can absorb efficiently from a given soil. Rooting habits, resistance to drought, and stage and rate of growth, are all plant factors which are significant. Air temperature and humidity are climatic variables which influence the efficiency of utilization of soil water and the amount which can be lost through nonplant channels such as by evaporation from the soil surface.

Among the important soil characteristics influencing available soil moisture are: (1) moisture tension relations; (2) salt content; (3) soil depth; and (4) soil stratification or layering. These will each be discussed briefly.

Moisture tension relations. The effect of moisture tension relations on the amount of available moisture in a soil should be obvious. Those factors which affect the amount of water in a soil at the field capacity, and in turn at the wilting coefficient, will influence the available water. The

[13] See L. A. Richards and S. T. Richards, "Soil Moisture," *The Yearbook of Agriculture (Soils),* U.S. Dept. of Agric. 1957, pp. 49–60.

[14] For a review on this phase see V. C. Jamison, "Pertinent Factors Governing the Availability of Soil Moisture to Plants," *Soil Sci.,* 81: 459–71, 1956. See also O. J. Kelley, "Requirement and Availability of Soil Water," *Advances in Agronomy,* 6: 67–94, 1954.

texture, structure, and organic matter content, all influence the quantity of water a given soil can supply to growing plants. The general influence of texture is shown in Figure 7:7. Note that as fineness of texture increases, there is a general increase in available moisture storage, although clays frequently have a smaller capacity than do well-granulated silt loams. The comparative available-water-holding capacities in terms of inches of water per foot of soil are also shown by this graph.[15]

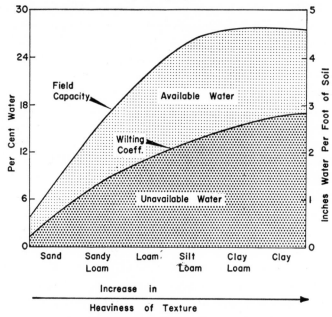

Figure 7:7. The general relationship between soil moisture characteristics and soil texture. Note that the wilting coefficient increases as the texture becomes heavier. The field capacity increases until we reach the silt loams, then levels off. Remember, these are representative curves. Individual soils would probably have values different from these shown.

The influence of organic matter deserves special attention. A well-drained mineral soil containing 5 per cent organic matter will probably have a higher available moisture capacity than a comparable soil with 3 per cent organic matter. One might make the mistake of assuming that this favorable effect was all due directly to the moisture-holding capacity of the organic matter. Such is not the case. Most of the benefit of organic

[15] These available water figures approximate those given by V. C. Jamison and O. W. Beale, *Irrigation of Corn in the Eastern United States*, U.S. Dept. of Agric. Handbook 140, 1958.

matter in this case is due to its favorable influence on soil structure and in turn on soil porosity. Although humus does have a high field capacity, its wilting coefficient is proportionately high. Thus, the net contribution toward available moisture is less than one would suppose.

Salt concentration. The presence of salts in soils, either from applied fertilizers or as natural-occurring compounds can influence soil-water uptake. Osmotic pressure effects in the soil solution will tend to reduce the range of available moisture in such soils by increasing the wilting coefficient. The total moisture stress in such soils at this point is the soil moisture tension plus the osmotic pressure of the soil solution. Although in most humid-region soils this osmotic pressure effect is insignificant, it becomes of practical importance in some saline soils of arid and semiarid regions.

Soil depth and layering. All other factors being equal, deep soils will have greater available moisture-holding capacities than will shallow ones. For deep-rooted plants, this is of practical significance, especially in those subhumid and semiarid regions where supplemental irrigation is not possible. Soil moisture measurements to depths as great as 5 to 6 feet are sometimes used as bases for predicting wheat yields in the Great Plains area of the United States. Shallow soils are obviously not well suited to these climatic conditions.

Soil stratification or layering will influence markedly the available water and its movement in the soil. Hardpans or impervious layers, for example, slow down drastically the rate of movement of water and also influence unfavorably the penetration of plant roots. They sometimes restrict root growth and effectively reduce the soil depth from which moisture is drawn. Sandy layers also act as barriers to soil moisture movement from the finer-textured layers above. Movement through a sandy layer is very slow at intermediate and high tensions. The moisture tension in the overlying layers must be less than about 0.5 atmosphere before movement into the sand will take place. The explanation for this unusual situation should be apparent as we consider Sections 7:12 and 7:15 dealing with moisture movement in soils. (See Figure 7:15.)

The available moisture-storage capacity of soils determines to a great extent their usefulness in practical agriculture. This capacity is often the buffer between an adverse climate and crop production. It becomes more significant as the utilization of water for all purposes—industrial, domestic, as well as agricultural—begins to tax the supply of this all-important natural resource.

7:7. HOW PLANTS ARE SUPPLIED WITH WATER—CAPILLARITY AND ROOT EXTENSION

At any one time, only a small proportion of the soil water lies in the immediate neighborhood of the adsorptive surfaces of plant root systems. Consequently, a question arises as to how the immense amount of water (see p. 198) necessary to offset transpiration is so readily and steadily acquired by vigorously growing crops. Two phenomena seem to account for this acquisition: (1) the capillary movement of the soil water to plant roots; and (2) the growth of the roots into moist soil.

Rate of capillary movement.   When plant rootlets begin to absorb water at any particular point or locality in a moist soil, the thick water films in the soil pores are thinned and their energy of retention is increased. The pull of moisture in this direction is intensified and water tends to move toward the points of plant absorption. The rate of movement depends on the magnitude of the tension gradients developed and the conductivity of the soil pores. A more complete explanation of this mechanism is offered on pages 186–188.

With some soils, the above adjustment may be comparatively rapid and the flow appreciable; in others, especially heavy and poorly granulated clays, the movement will be sluggish and the amount of water delivered meager. Thus, a root hair, by absorbing some of the moisture with which it is in contact, automatically creates a tension gradient and a flow of water is initiated toward its active surface.

How effective the above flow may be under field conditions is questionable. Many of the early investigators greatly overestimated the distance through which capillarity may be effective in satisfactorily supplying plants with moisture. They did not realize that the rate of water supply is the essential factor and that capillary delivery over appreciable distances is very slow. Plants must have large amounts of water delivered rapidly and regularly. The influence of capillarity is exerted through only a few centimeters as far as the hour-by-hour needs of plants are concerned.

The above statement must not be taken to mean that capillary adjustments in the aggregate are not important. It is not always necessary for capillary water to move great distances in the soil to be of significance to plants. As roots absorb moisture, capillary movement of no more than an inch (if occurring throughout the soil volume) may be of practical importance. Capillary adjustment along with vapor movement is undoubtedly a factor in supplying water for plants growing at very low moisture contents. Since there is little root extension at moisture tensions approaching the wilting coefficient, it is likely that some water must move to the plants.

Rate of root extension. The limited water-supplying capacity of capillarity directs our attention even more forcibly to the rate of root extension and here early workers made an underestimate. They failed to recognize the rapidity with which root systems expand and the extent to which new contacts are constantly established. (See Fig. 5:4 page 114.) During favorable growing periods, roots often elongate so rapidly that satisfactory moisture contacts are maintained even with a lessening water supply and without any great aid from capillarity. The mat of roots, rootlets, and root hairs in a meadow, between corn or potato rows, or under oats or wheat is ample evidence of the enormous root system of plants.[16]

The rate of root extension is surprising even to those engaged in plant production. On the basis of the data available, the elongation may be rapid enough [17] to take care of practically all of the water needs of a plant growing in a soil at optimum moisture. If this be the case, the plant is more or less independent of capillary adjustment for its immediate water supply from soils which are relatively high in moisture.

As was pointed out earlier, the above generalizations may need some modification under conditions of high moisture-tension. In spite of the phenomenal number of roots and the surface area which they possess, calculations will show that these roots are probably in contact with no more than about 1 to 2% of the soil solids. Under conditions wherein roots are not growing, it is obvious that moisture must move to the roots if the plants are to survive.

7:8. DETERMINATION OF SOIL MOISTURE [18]

Before considering the movement of moisture in soils, a brief comment should be made concerning the methods of determining the quantity of

---

[16] H. J. Dittmer, "A Comparative Study of the Subterranean Members of Three Field Grasses," *Science,* N.S., 88: 482, 1938.

Dittmer reports as follows regarding the roots and root hairs in 1 cu. in. of soil.

Plant	Number of Roots	Number of Root Hairs	Combined Length, Feet	Combined Surface, Square Inches
Oats	110	150,000	630	15
Rye	150	300,000	1,300	30
Ky. Bluegrass	2,000	1,000,000	4,000	65

See also H. J. Dittmer, "A Quantitative Study of the Roots and Root Hairs of a Winter Rye Plant," *Amer. Jour. Bot.* 24: 417–20, 1927.

[17] P. J. Kramer and T. S. Colie, "An Estimation of the Volume of Water Made Available by Root Extension," *Plant Physiol.,* 15: 743–47, 1940.

[18] For a non-technical discussion of this subject see H. R. Haise, "How to Measure the Moisture in the Soil," *The Yearbook of Agriculture (Water),* pp. 362–71, 1955.

this important soil constituent. The major methods that are in use may be classified as follows: (1) gravimetric; (2) tensiometers; (3) resistance; (4) neutron scattering.

The *gravimetric* method is the one most commonly used. By this procedure a sample of moist soil of known weight is placed in an oven for a specified time at 100 to 110° C., and again weighed. The moisture lost by heating represents the soil moisture present in the moist sample.

Tensiometers such as the one shown in Figure 7:8 measure the tension with which the water is held and not the absolute quantity of water present. They are most useful in determining the need for irrigation water when the moisture is being kept near the field capacity.

Figure 7:8. The tensiometer method of determining moisture stress. (Left) Tensiometers in place in the field and (right) cross section showing essential components of a tensiometer. Water will move through the porous end of the instrument in response to the pull of the soil. This creates a tension which is measured by the gauge. *(Photo courtesy T. W. Prosser Co., Arlington, California.)*

When *resistance* blocks which are commonly made of gypsum are placed in contact with soil, the blocks absorb moisture from the soil. The resistance of a given block to an electric current is related to the water it absorbs. By calibrating the resistance readings with soil moisture content, one can obtain an approximation of the amount of moisture in the soil. The gypsum blocks are used to measure either moisture tension or percentage, and are probably most sensitive at tensions from 1 to 15 atmospheres.

The most recently developed procedure of determining soil moisture is the so-called neutron-scattering method.[19] (See Fig. 7:9.) Advantage is

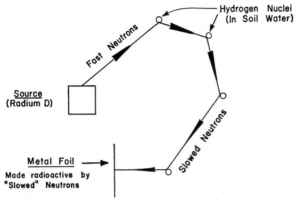

Figure 7:9. An allustration of the "neutron moderation" method of estimating soil moisture. Neutrons are emitted by the source (radium D) at a very high speed. When these neutrons collide with a small atom such as hydrogen contained in soil water their direction of movement is changed, they lose part of their energy and are slowed down. These "slowed" neutrons can be measured by using a metal foil composed of rhodium or silver which is rendered radioactive when struck by the neutrons. The more water (and thus hydrogen) present in the soil the larger will be the number of "slowed" neutrons which strike the metal foil and the greater will be the resulting radioactivity which can be measured easily.

taken of the fact that hydrogen atoms contained in soil water are effective in reducing the speed of fast moving neutrons, and in scattering them. Because of the scattering and change in direction of these neutrons some of them return to a point near the original source as slow moving particles. The number of these slowed neutrons is related to the quantity of hydrogen atoms (and in turn H_2O molecules) present in the soil. This method has the advantage of being one that can be used without disturbing the soil and can be used on soils containing salts.

Sections 7:9 through 7:16 cover the mechanisms of moisture movement in soils. Although these sections will strengthen the technical concept of the reader they are not absolutely essential from a practical standpoint.

7:9. THE MOVEMENT OF SOIL WATER—TYPES OF

In discussing the characteristics of the different forms of moisture commonly recognized in soils, movement has been stressed again and again. And rightly so, as water is a notably dynamic soil constituent. Three types of movement within the soil are recognized—*unsaturated flow, saturated flow,* and *vapor equalizations.* So important, both theoretically and practically, are these three changes in position, that

[19] See G. L. Stewart and S. A. Taylor, "Field Experience With the Neutron-scattering Method of Measuring Soil Moisture," *Soil Sci.,* 83: 151–58, 1957.

they merit individually more than passing reference. Since the first type of water movement—unsaturated flow—involves capillary adjustment, certain fundamentals with respect to capillarity should be kept clearly in mind. They will be briefly reviewed herewith.

7:10. CAPILLARY FUNDAMENTALS AS THEY RELATE TO SOIL WATER

First, consider an ideal case of capillarity. If the lower end of a glass tube of capillary dimensions is placed vertically in water, the liquid will rise in the tube above the level of the water surface outside. (See Fig. 7:10.) The phenomenon, called *capillarity,* is initiated by the attraction of the glass for the water (adhesion) which causes the liquid to rise around the sides of the tube. At the same time, because of the attraction of the molecules of water for each other (cohesion), that portion of the liquid unaffected directly by adhesion is progressively pulled upward, thus keeping the column intact.

In other words, surface-tension forces at the liquid-air interface are powerful enough to support that portion of the column not directly attracted by the walls of the tube. Hence, a continuous column of water rises until its weight just equals the adhesive attraction pulling the liquid upward. Thus, the mechanics of *capillary adjustment* as it operates in this particular case can be very simply stated.

It is a common observation that the smaller the capillary channel, the higher will be the rise of the water column. (See Fig. 7:10.) This is because for a unit section of the capillary tube, the amount of adhesive surface per unit weight of water is greater in a small tube than in a larger one. Thus, a longer column of water can be supported by the adhesive attraction exerted by the walls of the smaller tube.[20]

Figure 7:10. The upward capillary movement from a water table, (a) in a large glass capillary tube, (b) in a small capillary tube, and (c) in a soil column. Note the higher rise in the small capillary tube and the greater curvature of film. While the mechanism is the same in both the tubes and in the soil, the adjustment is extremely irregular in the latter due to the tortuous nature of the channels, their variability in size, and the presence of entrapped air.

[20] This truism can be established mathematically as follows: The height (h) to which water rises in a capillary tube is expressed by the formula:

$$h = \frac{2T}{rdg}$$

where T is surface tension in dynes per centimeter, r, the radius of the tube in centimeters, d, the density of the liquid, and g, gravity in dynes per centimeter. It is obvious from the formula that the smaller the radius of the tube, the higher will be the rise of the liquid in it.

Note that there is a concave curvature at the top of the water columns in Figure 7:10, and that the degree of curvature is related to the height of capillary movement—the greater the height, the greater the curvature. The curvature is due to the weight of water column which is being supported by the surface film. And the longer the column, the greater will be the weight per unit of supporting surface at the top of the column, and the more pronounced will be the concavity or sag. As might be expected, water will move toward points in a system where the greatest curvature of the concave films occurs. This simple concept will be applied later in explaining the capillary adjustments of the film water of field soils.

7:11. UNSATURATED FLOW FROM A SOIL WATER TABLE

When water moves upward from a water table through the micropores of a soil, the phenomenon of capillarity, sometimes called *unsaturated flow,* is identical in principle to the capillary rise already described for a glass tube. Adhesion and cohesion are active in exactly the same way. The water columns as they elongate are subject to the same mechanisms, and concave films are established at their summits. The curvatures of these films will depend upon the sizes of the pores at these points and upon the lengths of the individual columns.

In contrast with the capillary adjustment in a glass tube, the unsaturated flow in soils ordinarily proceeds very irregularly. Also, the rising front of water is greatly distorted and deformed. The swelling of the soil colloids and the presence of entrapped air impede the rate of movement while many of the large soil pores cannot be bridged at all. In spite of these factors which tend to complicate unsaturated flow in soils, the same basic principles that govern capillary movement in a glass tube are at work here.

Height of capillary rise. Usually the height of rise resulting from capillarity is greater with the fine-textured soils, if sufficient time is allowed, and the pores are not too small. This is readily explained on the basis of the capillary size and the continuity of the pores. With sandy soils, the adjustment is rapid, but so many of the pores are either noncapillary or only weakly exhibit this capacity, that the height of rise cannot be great. (See Fig. 7:11.)

The situation in any particular case is sure to be greatly modified by the particular structural condition involved. Compacting a sandy soil and thereby reducing the size of the micropores, and increasing their number may increase the height of water rise. But with a heavy soil, compaction as well as the infiltrated clay are likely to impede greatly the rate of unsaturated flow. Hence, granulation, especially with a soil of fine texture usually tends to enhance the rate of adjustment if not the height of rise.

Contrary to popular opinion, the type of capillary adjustment just described is important in only those field soils where a water table exists. This water table may be temporary or more or less permanent. In most arable mineral soils that are well drained, either naturally or artificially, there is no internal accumulation of free water for any length of time. Or if a water table actually does appear within the solum, it is temporary and usually is present at a time of year when it is of no practical consequence.

However, in some cases, the type of capillary setup under discussion is of practical importance. For instance, in poorly drained, sandy soils and in peat lands, where the water table can be lowered or raised at will, the water level can be maintained near enough the surface at certain critical times to provide subirrigation by capil-

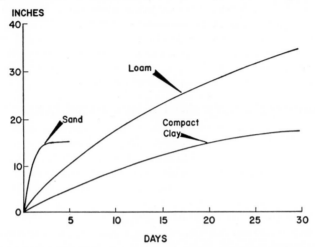

Figure 7:11. Upward movement of moisture from a water table through soils of different textures and structures. Note the very rapid rise in the sand, but the moderate height attained. Apparently, the pores of the loam are more favorable for movement than are those in the compact clay. The rate of movement is thus seen to be of greater significance than the total height.

larity. Also, in certain poorly drained areas of the arid West where irrigation is practiced, a water table may be found within a few feet of the surface especially in the spring of year. Although this water is a source of supply for growing plants, its movement upward in the profile is sometimes accompanied by undesirable salts which tend to accumulate in the surface areas.

7:12. UNSATURATED FLOW AS IT MOST COMMONLY OCCURS IN SOILS

When a large amount of water is received at the soil surface, tension adjustment, aided by gravity flow through the larger pores, will ultimately moisten the whole profile unless an impervious layer is encountered. But if the addition is limited, as is usually the case under natural conditions, the downward adjustment will soon become wholly capillary. The rate of such movement will be drastically curtailed as the moisture content is reduced below that of the field capacity. Eventually, of course, this downward movement will essentially cease.

Evaporation will now take place at the soil surface, and plants will absorb water from localized zones around their roots. These processes will result in greater moisture depletion from some soil areas than from others, and differences in the tension with which the moisture is held will be found. Unsaturated flow will occur in response to these differences in tension, the water moving from regions of low tension (high moisture) to depleted moisture zones when the water films are thin and the tensions high.

This moisture movement back and forth according to film tension represents the setup commonly operating in soils. Unlike the movement upward from a water table previously described, the unsaturated flow under discussion may be downward, upward, or lateral. The direction of movement depends on the tension of the water films surrounding and between soil particles. And what is especially important, the removal of water from any given pore initiates a movement in this direction by decreasing the film thickness and hence, increasing the pull at this point.

The type of movement just described is continually operating in soils. Yet, due to the dynamic nature of soils, capillary equilibrium is seldom attained. Of all the forms of water movement within the soil, this type of film adjustment is perhaps of greatest significance in respect to soil conditions and plant growth.

7:13. SATURATED FLOW THROUGH SOILS—PERCOLATION

As water either from rain or irrigation is added to a soil, it penetrates the surface, replacing the air in first the macro- and then the micropores. Additional water will result in downward movement by a process called saturated flow which will be encouraged by *both* gravitational and capillary forces. Such movement will continue so long as there is adequate moisture being supplied, and no barriers to downward movement are encountered. (See Fig. 7:12.)

Figure 7:12. Comparative rates of irrigation water movement into a sandy loam (left) and a clay loam (right). Note the much more rapid rate of movement in the sand, especially in a downward direction. (Redrawn from J. J. Coony and J. E. Pehrson, *Avocado Irrigation,* Calif. Agric. Ext. Leaflet 50, 1955.)

Amount of percolation water. The quantity of water which moves through the profile will be determined by a number of factors, including the following: (1) the amount of water applied; (2) infiltration capacity of the surface soil; (3) total moisture conductivity of the lower horizons; and (4) the amount of water which the profile will retain at its field capacity. From a practical standpoint, the texture and structure of the various soil horizons determine to a large degree the influence of these factors. Thus, sandy soils have high infiltration capacities and total conductivities. Their ability to hold moisture is low, and water percolation through them takes place easily and rapidly.

Colloidal swelling and entrapped air.   In contrast to sandy soils, those finer in texture have lower percolation rates which may be more variable because of differences in soil structure. Certain factors undoubtedly further complicate the percolation of water through these soils. First, clayey-colloidal matter may clog the small connecting channels, or even the larger micropores. Such colloidal matter may offer little obstruction at first but as it swells it may nearly close the smaller pores. This is likely to be the case, especially with montmorillonitic clays. Thus, fine-textured soils that crack during dry weather, at first allow rapid percolation of water. Later, these cracks swell shut, thus reducing percolation to a minimum. Unless granulation is encouraged by organic matter and other means, drainage in such cases will be slow and often rather ineffective. In fact, unless a clayey field soil possesses considerable granulation, it may not drain rapidly enough to permit agricultural operations sufficiently early in the spring or soon enough after a heavy rain later in the season.

Percolation water will receive more attention in connection with the loss of nutrients and with practical means of its control. (See pp. 215.)

7:14. THE RATE OF MOVEMENT THROUGH SOILS [21]

In discussing the mechanics of water movement, frequent reference has been made to the rate at which the movement takes place. This rate is determined by two factors: (1) the water moving force; and (2) the hydraulic conductivity. An equation showing the relationship between these factors and the volume of water moving through the soil may be given as follows:

$$v = kf$$

where v = total volume moved, f is the water moving force, and k the hydraulic conductivity.

The water moving force, sometimes called the driving force, is determined by two factors: (1) *gravity* and (2) differences in film tension or *tension gradient*. Gravity, of course, is effective only in influencing downward movement. The tension gradient, on the other hand, may act in any direction.

If it is high, that is, if the difference in moisture tension between two points a unit distance apart is great, water will adjust toward the higher tension with comparative rapidity. Under comparable conditions, on the other hand, a low gradient means a slower adjustment, and consequently a lower delivery. This influence of tension gradient is well illustrated by moisture curves drawn from Gardner and Widtsoe.[22] (See Fig. 7:13.) Here the rate of water movement from a moist soil into a drier one is shown. The higher the percentage of water in the moist soil, the greater is the tension gradient, and the more rapid is the delivery. In this case the rate of movement obviously is a function of the tension gradient.

Hydraulic conductivity is determined by a number of factors, including pore size and the tension with which the water is held. For saturated flow, the moisture ten-

[21] See L. A. Richards and S. J. Richards, *op. cit.*
[22] W. Gardner and J. A. Widtsoe, "The Movement of Soil Moisture," *Soil Sci.,* 11: 230, 1921.

sion is low and consequently the conductivity is closely related to pore size, clay soils having low conductivities compared to sands. As the moisture content is lowered to the field capacity and below, the hydraulic conductivity, now more prop-

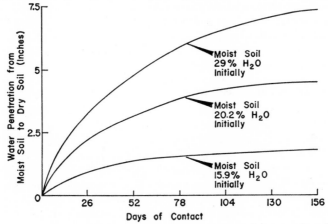

Figure 7:13. Curves showing the rate of water movement from a moist soil at three moisture levels to a drier one. The higher the water content of the moist soil, the greater will be the tension gradient and the more rapid will be the delivery. Water adjustment between two slightly moist soils at about the same water content will be exceedingly slow. *(After Gardner.)*

erly termed *capillary conductivity*, decreases rapidly. At 0.2 atmospheres tension, for example, the conductivity is 10,000 times that at 10 atmospheres tension. (See Fig. 7:14.) Furthermore, this decrease in conductivity is more pronounced with sandy

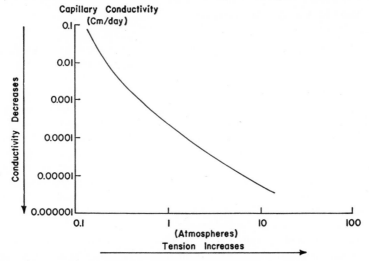

Figure 7:14. Relationship between capillary conductivity and soil moisture tension in a sandy loam soil. Note that conductivity is drastically reduced as the tension increases. *(From L. A. Richards and S. J. Richards, "Soil Moisture," Yearbook of Agriculture (Soil), 1957, pp. 49–60.)*

soils than with finer-textured soils. Apparently, at high tensions the water in sands is held only at points of contact between the relatively large sand particles. Under these conditions, there is no continuous water film and thus no opportunity for liquid movement. Water transfer, if it occurs must take place in the vapor state. This accounts for the fact previously referred to (p. 177), that layers of sand in a profile often act as moisture barriers just as do compact clay or silt pans. Apparently, the moisture tension must be 0.5 atmospheres or less before water movement will take place readily into sandy layers.

7:15. WATER MOVEMENTS IN STRATIFIED SOILS

The discussion up to now has dealt almost entirely with soils which are assumed to be quite uniform in texture and structure. In the field, of course, layers differing in physical makeup from the overlying horizons are common. Since these layers have such a profound influence on water movement, they deserve specific attention.

Various kinds of stratification are found in many soils. Impervious silt or clay pans are common as are sand and gravel lenses or other subsurface layers. In all these cases, the effect on water movement is similar—that is—the downward movement is impeded. The influence of layering can be seen by referring to Figure 7:15. Apparently, the change in texture from that of the overlying material results in conductivity differences which prevent rapid downward movement.

The significance of this effect of stratification is obvious. For example, it definitely influences the amount of water the upper part of the soil holds at the field capacity. The layer acts as a moisture barrier until a relatively high moisture level is built up. This gives a much higher field capacity than that normally encountered in freely drained soils. It also illustrates a well known weakness of the field-capacity concept, especially if it is to be related to some definite moisture tension value.

7:16. WATER VAPOR MOVEMENT

Water vaporization as it relates to soils may be distinguished for convenience of discussion as *internal* and *external*. In the one case, the change from the liquid to the vapor state takes place within the soil, that is, in the soil pores. In the second case, the phenomenon occurs at the land surface, and the resulting vapor is lost to the atmosphere by diffusion and convection. The latter commonly is spoken of as *surface evaporation* and will be considered later (p. 193). For the present, only vaporization and vapor adjustment tendencies *within* the soil are pertinent.

Relative humidity of the soil air. The soil air is maintained essentially saturated with water vapor so long as the moisture content is not below that of the hygroscopic coefficient. At this tension (31 atmospheres) and less, water seems to be free enough to maintain the air at approximately 100 per cent relative humidity. But when the moisture drops below the hygroscopic coefficient, and consequently is held with a greater tenacity, water vaporizes with greater and greater difficulty and its vapor pressure becomes lower and lower.

This maintenance of the soil air at or very near a relative humidity of 100 per cent is of tremendous importance, especially in respect to biological activities. This is perhaps the most important single feature in respect to the vapor-liquid interrelations within soils. Nevertheless, the actual amount of water present in the vapor form in a

Figure 7:15. Photographs illustrating the downward water movement in soils having a stratified layer of coarse material. (Top) Water applied to the surface of a medium-textured top soil. Note that at the end of 40 minutes, downward movement is no greater than movement to the sides, indicating that in this case the gravitational force is insignificant compared to the tension gradient between dry and wet soil. (Lower left) The *downward* movement stops when a *coarse* textured layer is encountered. After 110 minutes, no movement into the sandy layer has occurred. After 400 minutes (lower right), the moisture content of the overlying layer becomes sufficiently high to give a moisture tension of 0.5 atmosphere or less, and downward movement into the coarse material takes place. Thus, sandy layers, as well as compact silt and clay, influence downward moisture movement in soils. *(Photographs courtesy W. H. Gardner, Washington State College.)*

189

soil at optimum moisture is surprisingly small, being, at any one time, perhaps not over 10 pounds to the acre-furrow-slice.

Mechanics of water vapor movement.   The diffusion of water vapor from one area to another in soils does occur. The motive force is due to differences in vapor pressure, the adjustment tendencies being from points of high vapor pressure to those that are lower. That is, a *vapor-pressure gradient* [23] per unit distance is operative. Thus, if a moist soil where the vapor pressure is high, is in contact with an air-dry layer where the vapor pressure is lower, a diffusion into the drier area will tend to occur. Likewise, if the temperature of one part of a uniform moist soil mass is lowered, the vapor pressure of the air would be decreased and water vapor will tend to move in this direction. Heating will have the opposite effect.

The two soil conditions mentioned above—differences in relative humidity and in temperature—seem to set the stage for the movement of water vapor under ordinary field conditions. However, they may work at cross purposes and reduce vapor transfer tendencies to a minimum, or they may be so co-ordinated as to raise them to a maximum. The possible situation is set forth in Fig. 7:16.

Figure 7:16. Diagram indicating the vapor movement tendencies that may be expected between soil horizons differing as to temperature and moisture. In (a) the tendencies more or less negate each other; but in (b) they are coordinated and considerable vapor transfer might be possible if the liquid water in the soil capillaries does not interfere.

Undoubtedly, some vapor transfer does occur within soils. The extent of the movement by this means, however, even from one continuous macropore to another, probably is not great if the soil water is within the range optimum for higher plants. In dry soils, however, some moisture movement may take place in the vapor form. Such movement may be of some significance in supplying moisture to drought-resistant desert plants, many of which can exist at moisture levels below the commonly determined wilting coefficient.

[23] A *vapor-pressure gradient* is simply the difference in vapor pressure of two points a unit distance apart. The greater this difference, the more rapid diffusion tends to become and the greater is the transfer of vapor water during a unit period.

Vapor Losses of
Soil Moisture and
Their Regulation

CHAPTER 8

The ultimate objective in the field control of soil water is the maintenance of an optimum moisture condition for plants. In order to obtain a clear insight as to how this is done, let us first consider what happens when precipitation and irrigation water are received and utilized and the extent to which losses occur.

8:1. TYPES OF WATER LOSS FROM SOILS

The various ways by which moisture is lost from soils both before and after infiltration may be grouped for convenience of discussion under two very general heads: (1) *vapor* losses, and (2) losses in *liquid* form. The situation is presented in diagramatic form in Figure 8:1, in which the individual losses are shown in their proper positions. Since this sketch will be used as a basis for further discussion, its visualization, at least in a general way, will be found worth while.

On the basis of both logic and convenience, the vapor losses will be disposed of first, leaving the liquid removals for the next chapter. But before beginning such a consideration, a generalization that should be kept in mind constantly will be emphasized. Vapor losses from soils are subject to no appreciable practical control except in special cases. In fact, one vapor loss, that of transpiration by crops, is deliberately enhanced by promoting increased crop yields, an objective that most farmers strive to attain.

8:2. INTERCEPTION OF RAIN WATER BY PLANTS

Rainfall data are often dealt with as though precipitation ordinarily reaches the soil in its entirety. Such is far from the case as a person must realize when he considers the intercepting capacity of the vegetative cover, especially that presented by a dense forest. The degree to which rain is thus caught and returned to the air by evaporation is surprisingly large.

Figure 8:1. Diagram showing the various ways by which water may be lost from soils. In practice more control can be exerted over liquid losses than over those of vaporization. Note that the latter entails only a loss of water, while in the case of drainage and runoff, losses of nutrients are also involved. Runoff often results in serious erosion in addition.

In general, the lower the rainfall the greater is the percentage diversion by the vegetative cover. And as might be expected, the proportionate loss is markedly higher when the rain is received in light showers. Such precipitation is often entirely lost as far as the soil is concerned. Forests in humid-temperate regions divert on the average perhaps 25 per cent of the yearly precipitation, allowing less than 5 per cent to run down the limbs and trunks into the soil.[1]

Surprisingly enough, the influence of field crops, during the season that they occupy the soil, may approach that of forests in many cases. The yearly interception is, of course, much less. The figures in Table 8:1 are most significant.

Although these data cover such short periods and are subject to very high experimental errors, they indicate something as to the magnitude of

[1] See R. E. Horton, "Rain Interception," *Monthly Weather Review*, 47: 603–23, 1919; and C. L. Wicht, "An Approach to the Study of Rainfall Interception by Forest Canopies," *Jour. S. African Forestry Assoc.*, 6: 54–70, 1941.

TABLE 8:1

Seasonal Interception of Rainfall by Crops at Bethany, Missouri, and Sussex, New Jersey. Average of Three Years' Records for Alfalfa and Corn and One Year for Soybeans [a]

Fate of Rainfall	Percentages in Terms of Total Seasonal Rainfall for Each Crop		
	Alfalfa	*Corn*	*Soybean*
	%	%	%
Direct to soil	64.7	70.3	65.0
Ran down stem	13.7	22.8	20.4
Total to soil	78.4	93.1	85.4
Remainder to atmosphere	21.6	6.9	14.6

[a] J. L. Haynes, "Ground Rainfall under Vegetative Canopy of Crops," *Jour. Amer. Soc. Agron.,* 32: 176–84, 1940.

rainfall interception by field crops. In general, it may be safe to conclude that from 5 to perhaps 20 per cent of the seasonal rainfall of humid-temperate regions will be caught and returned to the atmosphere by ordinary field crops, the magnitude in any particular case depending in part on the kind, vigor, and stage of maturity of the crop occupying the land. Of a seasonal rainfall of 15 inches, for instance, only 12 to 14 inches might finally reach the soil, to say nothing of the inequality of the distribution in the soil due to the passage down the stems. While interception losses undoubtedly reduce the economic use of rain water, little can be done to control such waste.

8:3. EVAPO-TRANSPIRATION

Vapor losses from soils occur in two ways: (1) by the *evaporation* of water at the soil surface; and (2) by *transpiration* from the leaf surfaces of water which has been adsorbed by the plants and translocated to the leaves. The combined loss resulting from these two processes, termed *evapo-transpiration,* is responsible for most of the water removal from soils under normal field conditions. On irrigated soils located in arid regions, for example, it commonly accounts for the loss of 30 to 40 inches of water during the growing season of a crop such as alfalfa. Obviously, the phenomenon is of special significance to growing plants.

Before considering the magnitude of moisture losses through evapo-transpiration as it occurs in the field, let us enumerate and discuss briefly the various factors influencing this important process.

8:4. FACTORS AFFECTING EVAPO-TRANSPIRATION [2]

The rate of water loss by evaporation either from the soil or by transpiration is determined basically by the *vapor-pressure gradient*—that is by the difference in the vapor pressure at the leaf or soil surface, and that of the atmosphere. The vapor-pressure gradient, in turn, is related to a number of other common climatic and soil factors.

Radiant energy.   Much thermal energy is required to evaporate water, whether from the soil directly or from leaf surfaces. The primary source of this energy is the sun. The radiant energy absorbed by soils and plants varies greatly from area to area and from day to day within a given area. Thus, the solar heat is high in regions such as the southwestern part of the United States, where there is little cloudiness to reduce the full sunshine. In the humid Northeast, by contrast, there is less direct sunshine and the annual solar energy is low. In any given area, there are notable day-by-day variations in solar heat because of the presence or absence of clouds.

So long as moisture is available for evaporation, one would expect a close relationship between evaporation and the absorption of radiant energy. Such is the case. The potential evapo-transpiration is dependent upon the energy being adsorbed from the sun as well as the other factors discussed below.

Atmospheric vapor pressure.[3]   The vapor pressure of the atmosphere helps control evaporation from soils and plants. If it is low compared to the vapor pressure at the plant and soil surfaces, evaporation takes place rapidly. If it is high, such as is the case on "humid" days, evaporation is slow. That atmospheric vapor pressure markedly influences evapo-transpiration is shown by the relatively high vapor losses from irrigated soils in arid climates. In humid regions with comparable temperatures, evapo-transpiration losses are considerably less.

Temperature.   The evaporation of water is greatly influenced by temperature. Consequently, during warm or hot days, the vapor pressure at the leaf surfaces or the surface of a moist soil is quite high. Temperature does not have a similar direct effect on the vapor pressure of the atmos-

[2] For a general discussion of this topic see C. E. Evans and E. R. Lemon, "Conserving Soil Moisture," *The Yearbook of Agriculture (Soil)*, 1957, pp. 343–48.

[3] There is in general a correlation between relative humidity and evaporation so long as there is no drastic change in temperature.

phere. As a result, on hot days there is a large difference in vapor pressure between leaf or soil surfaces and the atmosphere—a greater vapor-pressure gradient—and evaporation proceeds rapidly. The fact that on bright, clear days plants and especially soils may be warmer than the atmosphere further emphasizes the importance of temperature in controlling evapo-transpiration.

Wind. A dry wind will continually sweep away moisture vapor from a wet surface. The moist air thus moved is replaced by air with a lower content of moisture. This tends to maintain the vapor-pressure gradient and evaporation is greatly encouraged. The drying effect of even a gentle wind is noticeable even though the air in motion may not be at a particularly low humidity level. Hence, the capacity of a high wind operating under a steep vapor-pressure gradient to enhance evaporation both from soils and plants is tremendous. Farmers of the Great Plains dread the *hot winds* characteristic of that region.

Soil moisture supply. In discussing the influence of the other factors on evapo-transpiration, the assumption has been made that the soil and plant surfaces are plentifully supplied with moisture. Under these conditions, the climatic factors already considered will largely control vapor losses. At lower moisture contents, however, soil moisture tension will limit the rate of supply of water to the soil and plant surfaces and evapo-transpiration losses will decrease accordingly. (See Table 8:2.)

TABLE 8:2

The Effect of Soil Moisture Level on Evapo-transpiration Losses. Where the Surface Moisture Content Was Kept High, Total Evapo-transpiration Losses Were Greater than when Medium Level of Moisture Was Maintained [a]

Moisture Condition of Soil	Evapo-transpiration (inches)	
	Corn	*Alfalfa*
High	17.7	24.4
Medium	12.7	20.5

[a] Data quoted by O. J. Kelly, "Requirement and Availability of Soil Water," *Advances in Agronomy,* 6: 67–94, 1957.

High moisture—irrigated when upper soil layers were 50 per cent depleted of available water.

Medium moisture—irrigated when upper layers were 85 per cent depleted of available water.

As moisture is depleted from the soil surface and the root zone, evaporation losses decrease. The plant responds to this moisture deficiency by the closing of leaf stomata and ultimately by wilting. In the soil, capillarity will at first partially replenish moisture lost by evaporation at the surface. With time, however, the rate of loss by evaporation and plant uptake will deplete the surface soil. Capillarity to the upper layers will then be too slow to be of much practical importance. Under these conditions, some movement of moisture in the vapor phase from lower horizons will then take place.

In respect to the depth to which soils may be depleted by evapo-capillary pumping, soil physicists are agreed that the distance is far short of the 4, 5, or even more feet sometimes postulated. The conditions that impede and interrupt the flow are such as to allow it to deliver important amounts of water to the surface only through comparatively short distances. Some investigators think that a 20- or 24-inch depth is probably a maximum range. In most cases, however, perhaps only the water of the furrow-slice suffers appreciable diminution by surface evaporation, especially if vigorously absorbing roots are present to intercept the upward moving water.

8:5. MAGNITUDE OF EVAPORATION LOSSES [4]

Let us first consider the combined losses by evaporation from the soil surface and by transpiration. Together, they account for the so-called *consumptive use* which is a measure of the total water lost by evapo-transpiration in producing crops. This is an important practical figure, especially in areas where irrigation must be employed to meet crop needs.

Consumptive use.   As might be expected there is a marked variation in the consumptive use of water to produce different crops in different areas. All of the factors previously considered as influencing evapo-transpiration are operative. In addition, plant characteristics such as depth of rooting and length of growing season become important.

Consumptive use may vary from as little as 12 inches to as much as 85 inches or more. The low extreme might be encountered in cool mountain valleys where the growing seasons are short while the higher figure has been found in irrigated desert areas.[5] The ranges commonly encountered are 15 to perhaps 30 inches in unirrigated, humid to semiarid areas and 20 to 50 inches in hot, dry regions where irrigation is used.

---

[4] Practical information on evapo-transpiration losses in corn production is given by J. S. Robins and H. F. Rhoades, *"Irrigation of Field Corn in the West,"* leaflet No. 440, U.S. Dept. of Agric., 1958; and by V. C. Jamison and O. W. Beale, *Irrigation of Corn in the Eastern United States,* Handbook No. 140, U.S. Dept. of Agric., 1958.

[5] See C. O. Stanberry, "Irrigation Practices for the Production of Alfalfa," *The Yearbook of Agriculture (Water)*, 1957, 435–43.

From a practical standpoint, daily consumptive use figures are in some cases more significant than those for the growing season. During the hot dry periods in the summer, daily consumptive use rates for corn, for example, may be as high as 0.4 to 0.5 inches. Even with deep soils having reasonably high capacities for storing available water, this rapid rate of moisture removal soon depletes the plant root zone of easily adsorbed moisture. Sandy soils, of course, may lose most of their available moisture in a matter of a few days under these conditions. The importance of these vaporization losses is obvious.

Surface evaporation vs. transpiration. It is a matter of interest to consider the comparative water losses from the soil surface and from transpiration. As one might expect, a number of factors determine these relative losses. Among them are the following: (1) plant cover in relation to soil surface; (2) efficiency of use of water by different plants; (3) proportion of time crop is on the land, especially during the summer months; and (4) climatic conditions.

In humid regions, there is some evidence that vapor losses might, in some cases, be divided about equally between evaporation from the soil and transpiration. As might be expected, this generalization would not hold in all cases since there are so many factors influencing vapor losses from both crops and soils.

Loss by evaporation from the soil is thought to be proportionately higher in semiarid regions than in humid areas. Such vapor loss has been estimated at 70 to 75 per cent of the total rainfall for the Great Plains Area of the United States.[6] Losses by transpiration account for 20 to 25 per cent, leaving about 5 per cent for runoff.

8:6. EFFICIENCY OF WATER USE

The crop production which can be obtained from the use of a given amount of water is an important figure, especially in areas where moisture is scarce. This efficiency may be expressed in terms of (1) consumptive use (in pounds) per pound of plant tissue produced, or (2) transpiration (in pounds) per pound of plant tissue produced. The latter figure, called *transpiration ratio,* emphasizes the fact that large quantities of water are required to produce one pound of dry matter.

Transpiration ratio. This figure ranges from 200 to 500 for crops in humid regions, and almost twice as much for those of arid climates. The

[6] See J. C. Hide, "Observations on Factors Influencing the Evaporation of Soil Moisture," *Soil Sci. Soc. Amer. Proc.,* 18: 234–39, 1956.

data in Table 8:3 drawn from various investigators give some idea of the
water transpired by different crops.

TABLE 8:3

Transpiration Ratios of Plants as Determined by Different Investigators [a]

Crop	Harpenden, England	Munich, Germany	Dahme, Germany	Madison, Wisconsin	Pusa, India	Akron, Colorado
Barley	258	774	310	464	468	534
Beans	209	...	282	...	...	736
Buckwheat	...	646	363	...	...	578
Clover	269	...	310	576	...	797
Maize	...	233	...	271	337	368
Millet	...	447	...	...	...	310
Oats	...	665	376	503	469	597
Peas	259	416	273	477	563	788
Potatoes	...	...	...	385	...	636
Rape	...	912	...	...	...	441
Rye	...	...	353	...	...	685
Wheat	247	...	338	...	544	513

[a] These data were assembled from different publications. See T. L. Lyon; H. O.
Buckman; and N. C. Brady, *The Nature and Properties of Soils* (New York, Macmillan, 1952), p. 221.

Much of the variation observed in the ratios quoted arises from differences in climatic conditions. As a rule, the less the rainfall, the lower is
the humidity, and the greater is the relative transpiration. This accounts
for the high figures obtained in arid and semiarid regions. In general, temperature, sunshine, and wind vary together in their effect on transpiration.
That is, in areas of more intense sunshine, the temperature is higher, the
humidity is lower, and the wind velocity is frequently greater. All this
tends to raise the transpiration ratio.

It is obvious from the transpiration ratios quoted that the amount of
water necessary to mature the average crop is very large. Let us assume,
for example, that a representative crop of oats produces 4,000 pounds of
dry matter an acre and has a transpiration ratio of 500. The amount of
water withdrawn from the soil during the growing season would be equivalent to almost 9 inches of rain. The corresponding figure for corn, assuming the dry matter as 6,000 pounds and the transpiration ratio as 350,
would be over 9 inches. It should be emphasized that these amounts of
water, in addition to that evaporated from the surface, must be supplied

during the growing season. The possibility of moisture being a critical, if not the most critical, factor in crop production, is thus obvious.

Factors influencing efficiency. The efficiency of water use in crop production is influenced by climatic, soil, and nutrient factors. The climatic factors have already received adequate attention (pp. 194–195). Within a given climatic zone, the other effects can be seen.

In general, highest efficiency is found where optimum crop yields are being obtained. Conversely, where yields are limited by some factor or combination of factors, efficiency is low, that is, more water is required to produce a pound of plant tissue. A few examples can be cited.

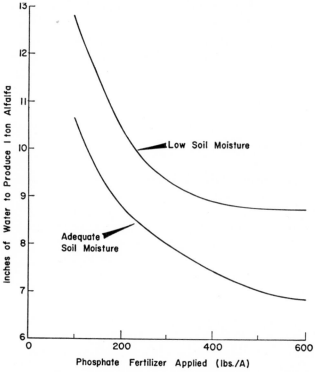

Figure 8:2. The effect of phosphate applications and soil moisture level on the amount of water required to produce one ton of alfalfa hay. Most efficient moisture was obtained when the fertility level was high and the moisture supply adequate. *(From O. J. Kelly, "Requirement and Availability of Soil Water," Adv. in Agron., VI: 67–94, 1954.)*

In general, maintaining the moisture content of a soil too low or too high for optimum growth will increase the water required to produce one pound of dry matter. Similarly, the amount of available nutrients and their balanced condition are also concerned in the economic utilization of water. In general, the more productive the soil, the lower is the transpiration ratio, provided the water supply is held at optimum (see Fig. 8:2). Therefore, a farmer in raising the productivity of his soil by drainage, lime, good tillage, farm manure, and fertilizers provides at the same time for a greater amount of plant production for every unit of water utilized. The total quantity of water taken from the soil, however, will probably be larger. (See Table 8:2.)

8:7. EVAPORATION CONTROL—MULCHES

Any material used at the surface of a soil primarily to prevent the loss of water by evaporation, or to keep down weeds may be designated as a mulch. In some cases, foreign materials, that is substances not already on the land, are merely spread over the soil surface. Sawdust, manure, straw, leaves, and other litter may be used successfully. Such mulches, while highly effective in checking evaporation and in preventing weed growth, are not generally applicable to most field crops, especially those that require intertillage. Their use is, therefore, limited to strawberries, blackberries, fruit trees, and such other crops as require infrequent cultivation, if any.

Paper and plastic mulches.   Specially prepared paper and plastics have been used as mulches. This cover is spread and fastened down either between the rows or over the rows, the plants in the latter case growing through suitable openings. This mulch can be used, however, only with crops planted in rows or in hills. As long as the ground is covered, evaporation and weeds are checked and, in some cases, remarkable crop increases have been reported. Unless the rainfall is torrential, the paper or plastic does not seriously interfere with the infiltration of the rain water.

The paper mulch has been employed with considerable success in the culture of pineapples in Hawaii, where the idea originated and with other crops elsewhere. Whether this type of mulch will ever be used to any extent in trucking and vegetable gardening in the United States is doubtful. The cost of the paper and the difficulty of keeping it in place may be such as to offset entirely any increase in crop that may result.

Stubble mulch.   A mulch somewhat different from those already described, especially as to mode of establishment, is the *stubble* or *trash mulch* used mostly in subhumid and semiarid regions. In this case the mulching materials have been grown in place and consist of the refuse of the previous crop. Oats, stubble, and straw, corn stalks, and like residues are good examples. By the use of suitable implements, a seedbed can be prepared and the crop planted, leaving the organic trash on the surface to act as a mulch. (See Fig. 8:3.) In the case of row crops, modified tillage implements make cultivation possible without greatly disturbing the surface layer. Although the use of such a mulch has been found to conserve moisture in some cases, its main effectiveness seems to be that of controlling wind erosion.[7]

Figure 8:3. The preparation of a trash mulch by incomplete incorporation of surface residues. Now that satisfactory machinery is available, this type of mulch is gaining popularity in subhumid and semiarid regions. It seems to have little effect on moisture control, but it protects the soil from wind erosion during fallow periods. *(U.S. Soil Conservation Service photo.)*

Soil mulch. One of the early misconceptions with respect to the control of evaporation was that the formation of a *natural* or *soil mulch* was a desirable moisture-conserving practice. Years of experimentation and practice have shown that stirring the surface soil to form a natural mulch does not necessarily conserve moisture. In fact, in some cases it may en-

[7] For an excellent summary of results of research on stubble mulches, see A. W. Zing and C. J. Whitfield, *Stubble-mulch Farming in the Western States,* Tech. Bul. 1166, U.S. Dept. of Agric., 1957.

courage moisture loss. Since natural mulch formation involves cultivation, the effect of this tillage operation on soil moisture control will now receive our attention.

8:8. CULTIVATION AND MOISTURE CONTROL

For many years, cultivation has been advocated in humid regions for three reasons: (1) the maintenance of a more satisfactory physical condition of the surface soil; (2) the killing of weeds; and (3) the conservation of moisture. The validity of the first two is unquestioned, if the tillage is applied with judgment, but there is much evidence to disprove the third, especially when a crop is on the land. Experimental results show that no more moisture is available to a crop which is cultivated, and thereby mulched, than is available to a comparable crop unmulched. Of course, weeds must be under control and the physical condition of the soil satisfactory in both cases. The ineffectiveness of the natural mulch seems to hold even during severe dry spells.

Moisture conservation vs. weed control.   Such a conclusion is borne out by data from Illinois (Table 8:4) which indicate that, when weeds

TABLE 8:4

Effects of Various Methods of Tillage on the Yield of Corn and the Average Percentage of Moisture in the Soil to a Depth of 40 Inches. Average of Eight Years' Test at the University of Illinois. Mean Rainfall, 33.7 Inches [a]

Treatment	Yield of Corn, Bushels per Acre	Average Percentage of Moisture in Soil
Plowed and seedbed well prepared:		
1. Kept bare of weeds only	45.9	22.3
2. Weeds allowed to grow	7.3	21.8
3. Three shallow cultivations	39.2	21.9
Seedbed poorly prepared:		
4. Kept bare of weeds only	31.4	23.1

[a] J. G. Mosier, and A. F. Gustafson, *Soil Moisture and Tillage for Corn*, Bulletin 181, Ill. Agr. Exp. Sta., 1915.

and physical conditions are controlled, the mulching effect of cultivation is of little benefit to the crop. In fact, the data hint that cultivation may at times be rather detrimental, possibly through damage to roots as well as waste of water. The main service of cultivation seemed to be the killing of weeds and the encouragement of a desirable tilth. These results are corroborated by a number of other investigations.

The failure of cultivation to be of benefit is by no means limited to field crops. Thompson,[8] after six years of experimentation with vegetables on a New York sandy soil, reported that cultivation and mulch formation gave no increase in the yield of carrots, cabbage, and tomatoes over uncultivated plots also kept free of weeds. The influence of mulching on beets and onions was very slight, probably within the experimental error. Beet yields were increased only 4 per cent by the maintenance of a soil mulch and 550 per cent by an adequate reduction of weed competition. The yield of only one vegetable crop, celery, was definitely increased by cultivation. The benefit here was likely due to the influence on the physical condition of the soil and not to the conservation of water.

Why soil mulches do not conserve moisture Three reasons are commonly advanced for the ineffectiveness of cultivation in moisture control. In the *first* place, a large amount of moisture always escapes by evaporation long before the soil is dry enough for cultivation. *Second,* in many cases, this precultivation loss has already established a thin protective surface layer of air dry soil, which may successfully reduce evaporation. *Third,* the crop itself, if its root spread is wide and comparatively dense, intercepts upward moving moisture that might otherwise reach the soil surface.

The mere fact that a soil mulch fails to conserve water, even if the drought period is long, does not mean that cultivation is unnecessary or undesirable. The Illinois experiments show it to be vitally necessary for the control of weeds and in some soils, for the maintenance of a well-aerated condition. But once these phases are taken care of, there is no need for further cultivation. In fact, the waste of water and damage to roots may render overcultivation decidedly objectionable and extremely expensive. (See Fig. 8:4.)

8:9. VAPORIZATION CONTROL IN HUMID REGIONS

From what has been said, it seems that little in general can be done in humid regions in respect to the control of the vaporization removal of water from farm lands. Losses due to crop transpiration and interception are conceded as beyond control. The more vigorous the growth of the

[8] H. C. Thompson, *Experimental Studies of Cultivation of Certain Vegetable Crops,* Memoir 107, Cornell Univ. Agric. Exp. Sta., 1927.

crops, the larger will be these two removals, especially transpiration. The ineffectiveness of a soil mulch and the waste of water incidental to its establishment have been cited. Although stubble and trash mulches are effective as well as feasible, they have not met with any great favor in humid regions. Artificial mulches, although satisfactory in gardens, nurseries, and orchards, are more or less out of the question with field crops.

Figure 8:4. The deep cultivation of intertilled crops such as corn (right) may result in serious root pruning. Hence cultivation for the killing of weeds should be shallow (left) even early in the season. If weeds are under control and the structure of the soil is satisfactory, further intertillage usually is unnecessary. *(From L. Donald, "Don't Blame the Weather,"* Comm. Fert., *pp. 19–24, February 1946.)*

This leaves the control of weeds as about the only effective and practicable means in humid regions of influencing vaporization. Their elimination, however, usually does not result in a reduction of soil moisture loss *in toto* but merely insures a greater amount of water available for crop transpiration. This, of course, is very desirable and usually is the ultimate objective in the moisture management of field soils. The attention now being given to improved methods of weed control is well placed.

8:10. VAPORIZATION CONTROL IN SEMIARID AND SUBHUMID REGIONS

When the average annual rainfall of a region is very much below 25 inches, it would seem that crop production would be impossible without irrigation. Yet between the limits of 15 to 20 inches, certain crop plants may be grown successfully, especially when much of the rainfall comes in the spring and early summer. The system adopted is often called *dry-land farming.* It consists essentially of: (1) using special varieties of such crops as wheat, corn, sorghums, and rye; (2) reducing the rate of seeding to correspond to the limited amounts of moisture that probably will be available; and (3) employing tillage practices that conserve and economize water. It is only the latter phase that need concern us here.

Tillage operations. The tillage operations practiced in dry-land agriculture should keep weeds under control and at the same time reduce wind erosion to a minimum. This means rough furrows at right angles to the prevailing high winds, listing, strip-cropping, and the use of a stubble mulch when practicable. At times of rain, the land should be highly permeable and retentive, and protected from water erosion if the rainfall is torrential. As to vapor losses of water from the soil, the situation in general is much the same as that already described for humid regions except for lower humidity and higher wind velocities.

Summer fallow. Dry-land farming often includes a *summer fallow,* the idea being to catch and hold as much of one season's rain as possible and carry it over for use during the next. The soil profile is used as a large reservoir.

A common procedure for summer fallowing is to allow the previous year's stubble to stand on the land until the spring of the year. The soil is then tilled before appreciable weed growth has taken place and the land is kept from weeds during the summer by occasional cultivation or by the use of chemical weed killers. In this way, evaporation loss is limited to that taking place at the surface of the soil.

The effectiveness of summer fallow in carrying over moisture from one year to another is somewhat variable. A conservation of perhaps one fourth of the fallow season rainfall would be expected under most conditions.[9] Even though this efficiency of moisture-storage is lower than would be desirable, yields of succeeding crops have been augmented significantly by summer fallow. (See data in Table 8:5.)

Here, then, is a situation where an appreciable amount of moisture may be conserved by the proper handling of the land. But it is a case specific for dry-land areas and should not be confused with the situation in humid regions. In the latter, summer fallowing is detrimental and unnecessary. Moreover, the creation of a soil mulch by cultivation occurs when intertilled crops occupy the lands. This is quite a different setup, climatically as well as otherwise, from the simple summer fallowing practiced in dry-land agriculture, where there is no crop on the land and the mulch remains dry over a considerable period of time.

[9] See Evans and Lemon, *op. cit.,* p. 349.

TABLE 8:5

The Influence of Summer Fallow in Alternate Years on the Available Moisture
at Wheat Seeding Time and the Yield of Wheat Fallowing [a]

Treatment	Available Water at Seeding Time	Wheat Yields
MANDAN, N. D. (AVE. 20 YEARS)		
Wheat after fallow	7.08 inches	4120 lbs.[b]
Wheat after wheat	2.48 "	2300 lbs.
HAYS, KAN. (AVE. 23 YEARS)		
Wheat after fallow	7.96 inches	27.3 Bu.
Wheat after wheat	2.90 "	17.4 Bu.
GARDEN CITY, KAN. (AVE. 13 YEARS)		
Wheat after fallow	4.67 inches	15.5 Bu.
Wheat after wheat	1.08 "	8.2 Bu.

[a] North Dakota data from J. C. Thysell, *Conservation and Use of Soil Moisture at Mandan, North Dakota,* U.S. Dept. of Agriculture, Tech. Bul. 617, 1938. Kansas Data from R. I. Throckmorton and H. E. Meyers, *Summer Fallow in Kansas,* Kans. Agr. Exp. Sta., Bul. 293, 1941.
[b] Total plant yields.

8:11. EVAPORATION CONTROL ON IRRIGATED LANDS

In areas of low rainfall, or when precipitation is so distributed as to be insufficient for crops at critical times, *irrigation,* the artificial application of water to land, is common. (See Fig. 8:5.) In the United States, most of the irrigated land lies west of the one hundredth meridian and embraces perhaps twenty-one million acres. Moreover, irrigation in the more humid areas to the eastward is decidedly on the increase.

Control principles.   It is hardly necessary to emphasize that the principles already discussed relating to the movement and distribution of moisture through the soil, its losses, and its plant relationships, apply just as rigidly for irrigation water as for that reaching the soil in natural ways. Although the problems inherent to liquid water such as runoff and erosion, infiltration, percolation, and drainage are subject to better control under irrigation, they are met and solved in much the same way as for humid-region soils.

The situation regarding vapor losses is much more critical, indeed more so at times than even with contiguous soils under dry-land cropping. In irrigated areas, conditions are ideal for evaporation and transpiration loss.

The climate is dry, the sunshine intense and wind velocities are often high. Furthermore, the soils are kept as moist as they are in well-drained humid-region soils. These conditions are ideal for evaporation loss.

Figure 8:5. A typical irrigation scene. The use of easily installed siphons (foreground) reduces the labor of irrigation and not only speeds up the rate of application of the water but also makes it easier to control. Note the upward capillary movement of water along the sides of the rows. *(Photo from Bureau of Reclamation, U.S. Dept. of Interior.)*

The only practical control over evaporation under these conditions is through irrigation practices. The surface of the soil should be kept only as moist as is needed for good crop production. (See Table 8:2.) The irrigation schedule should be such as to keep more than just the surface soil wet. Deep penetration of roots should be encouraged.

Salt accumulation. A phenomenon closely correlated with evaporation and often met with on arid-region lands under irrigation is that of the concentration of soluble salts at or near the soil surface. So-called *saline* or even *alkali* soils may contain soluble salts in the upper horizons in sufficient quantities to inhibit the growth of many cultivated plants. Irrigation practices on these soils can improve or impair their usefulness as crop soils. By flood irrigation, some of the soluble salts can be temporarily washed down from the immediate surface. Subsequent upward movement of the water and evaporation at the soil surface may result in salt accumulation and concentration which are harmful to young seedlings. (See Fig. 8:6.) Al-

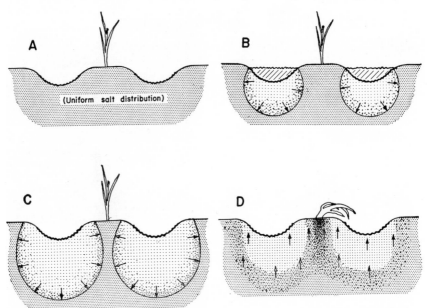

Figure 8:6. Diagrams showing the effect of irrigation on salt movement in a saline soil. (A) Soil before irrigation. Notice the relatively uniform salt distribution. (B) Water running in the furrow. Some has moved downward in the soil carrying soluble salts with it. (C) Soon after irrigation. Water continues to move downward and toward center of row. (D) A week or so after irrigation. Upward movement of water by capillarity carries salts toward the surface. Salts tend to concentrate in the center of the row, and in some cases causes injury to plants. *(Concept obtained from Bernstein, et al., "The Interaction of Salinity and Planting Practice on the Germination of Irrigated Row Crops," Proc. Soil Sci. Soc. of Amer., 19: 240–43, 1955.)*

though little can be done to prevent evaporation and upward capillary movement of the salt-containing water, timing and method of irrigation may prevent the salts from being concentrated in localized areas.

Liquid Losses
of Soil Water
and Their Control

CHAPTER 9

Two types of liquid losses of water from soils are recognized: (1) the downward movement of free water (percolation) which frees the surface soil and upper subsoil of superfluous moisture; and (2) the runoff of excess water over the soil surface. (See Figure 8:1.) Percolation usually results in the loss of soluble salts (leaching) and thereby may seriously deplete soils of certain nutrients. Runoff losses often include not only water, but also may carry away appreciable amounts of soil (erosion). These two liquid losses of soil water with their concomitant effects will be considered in the order of their introduction above.

9:1. PERCOLATION AND LEACHING—METHODS OF STUDY

Two general methods of procedure are available for the study of percolation and leaching losses—the use of an effective system of *tile drains* specially installed for the purpose, and the employment of *lysimeters*.[1] For the first method, an area should be chosen where the tile drain receives only the water from the land under study and where the drainage is efficient. The advantage of the tile method is that water and nutrient losses can be determined from relatively large areas of soil under normal field conditions.

The lysimeter method has been used most frequently to determine leaching losses. This method involves the measurement of percolation and

[1] From *lysi* meaning loosening and *meter,* to measure. Lysimeters are used to measure both percolation (downward movement of water through soils) and leaching (removal of soluble elements by percolation).

209

nutrient losses under somewhat more controlled conditions. The advantages over a tile drain system are that the variations in a large field are avoided, the work of conducting the study is not as great and the experiment is more easily controlled.

Types of lysimeters.[2]   Three major types of lysimeters have been used to study percolation: (1) the *block* or *monolith* type; (2) the *tank* type; and (3) the *Russian* type. In the *block* or *monolith* type of lysimeter, a small column of natural field soil is entirely isolated by appropriate means from the land surrounding it and its drainage water measured and analyzed. (See Fig. 9:1.) Sets of these lysimeters have been used in Europe as well as in this country.

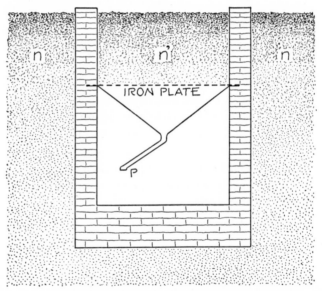

Figure 9:1. Cross section of monolith type of lysimeter at the Rothamsted Experiment Station, England. (N′) soil block under study; (N) surrounding soil not under study; (P) outlet for drainage water.

The advantage of such a method of construction lies in the fact that the structural condition of the soil is undisturbed. However, the possibility of the water passing down between the soil column and the walls of the drain gauge may be listed as a disadvantage. Also, the blocks of soil being

[2] For a discussion of results obtained by different methods see H. Kohnke, *et al., A Survey and Discussion of Lysimeters and a Bibliography of their Construction and Performance,* Misc.Publication 372, U.S. Dept. of Agric., 1940; and L. L. Harrold and F. R. Dreibelbis, *Evaluation of Agricultural Hydrology by Monolith Lysimeters,* Tech. Bul. 1179, U.S. Dept. of Agric., 1958.

compared may have had initially somewhat different physical properties. Because of the extreme variability that characterizes some soils, this might be marked and would make comparisons invalid.

A second type of lysimeter, the *tank* type was used for much of the early work in the United States. The soil to be studied by this method is removed from the field and packed into tanks or some other suitable containers. Free drainage is allowed through the tanks and arrangements are made to collect the leachate. An example of the tank lysimeters is shown diagramatically in Figure 9:2.

The advantage of this type of lysimeter is that several different soils and cropping systems can be compared at one location. Also, the variability of results obtained are somewhat less than under field conditions.

Figure 9:2. Cross section of the lysimeter tanks at Cornell University, Ithaca, New York. Each tank is one of a series, one tunnel serving two rows. Soils under investigation (a), outlet (b), and can for catching drainage water (c). Surface runoff was not allowed.

There are two main disadvantages to the tank lysimeters, both of which are very serious. First, the soil has been very much disturbed and it presumably never assumes its original physical condition. Second, runoff usually has not been allowed in this method. Consequently, a greater proportion of the precipitation received passes into the soil than would otherwise have been the case. Percolation and nutrient loss data by this method thus often are higher than those obtained by other methods.[3]

A lysimeter of an entirely different type has been perfected in Europe, called in this country the *Russian lysimeter*.[4] A trench is dug beside the block of soil to be studied, and the small tunnels at various levels are excavated horizontally under the soil profile. In each tunnel is placed a shallow funnel-shaped pan perforated at the center. This is wedged tightly against the soil horizon above. Drainage tubes are then installed, one for each pan, and the tunnels filled with soil. Each funnel drains separately into the trench, where the water of percolation is caught in suitable receptacles and later measured and analyzed.

Such a lysimeter deals with undisturbed soil, and thus avoids the objectionable feature of the tank type. Data obtained by this method, however, show a considerable amount of variation and are at times contradictory. Apparently these discrepancies are due to variations in the profile and to possible lateral movement of the water or percolation through wormholes, root passages, and cracks. This type of lysimeter can be expected to operate satisfactorily only in soils with fairly vertical drainage channels.

9:2. PERCOLATION LOSSES OF WATER

When at any time the amount of rainfall entering a soil becomes greater than its water-holding capacity, losses by percolation will occur if opportunity is offered. Percolation losses are influenced by the amount of rainfall and its distribution, by evaporation, by the character of the soil, and by the presence of a crop. As the rainfall increases, percolation also tends to increase, being much greater in Pennsylvania, for example, than in Kansas. Evaporation has a marked influence, reducing drainage losses to a considerable degree. The percolation through sandy soils is generally greater than through clayey soils. Yet when evaporation is especially high, sandy soils have been known to percolate less annually than those of a finer texture. Field crops, in that they not only intercept rain water but also absorb large amounts of moisture, have always been found to reduce percolation losses, often very drastically.

Loss from bare soils. The results from the Rothamsted (England) lysimeters from 1871–1912 on a bare clay loam 5 feet deep are interesting

---

[3] For a criticism of the tank type of lysimeters, see J. S. Joffe, "Lysimeter Studies: Moisture Percolation through the Soil Profile," *Soil Sci.*, 34: 123–42, 1932.

[4] J. S. Joffe, "A New Type of Lysimeter at the New Jersey Agricultural Experiment Station," *Science*, 70: 147–48, 1929.

in a comparative way (Table 9:1). The actual percolation is probably somewhat higher than under field conditions because of reduced runoff from the lysimeters. They are comparable, however, to those obtained by Wollny [5] for eighteen European soils through which 41 per cent of the precipitation was lost by percolation.

TABLE 9:1

Percolation Through a 60-inch Column of Bare Clay Loam. Rothamsted Experiment Station, Annual Average of Forty-two Years [a]

Periods	Rainfall, Inches	Drainage, Inches	Percentage of Rainfall as Drainage
Dec.–Feb.	6.77	5.58	82.4
Mar.–May	5.96	2.11	35.4
June–Aug.	7.83	1.82	23.2
Sept.–Nov.	8.29	4.50	54.2
Mean Total	28.85	14.01	48.5

[a] A. D. Hall, *The Book of the Rothamsted Experiments* (New York: Dutton, 1917), p. 22.

Under the above conditions, about 50 per cent of the rainfall was lost by percolation through this bare soil. The drainage loss was much lower in summer than in winter, the ratio being about 1 to 3. This was, no doubt, due to the high evaporation during the warmer season, as the rainfall was as great for the June-August period as for the December-February interval. Such a discrepancy serves again to emphasize the great loss of water from bare soil by vaporization.

That the figures cited above are much too high for soils of low rainfall is, of course, to be expected. Percolation under arid and semiarid conditions may be nil in some cases. Nor can the figures above be applied specifically to other humid-region soils. This latter statement is clearly substantiated by data from Illinois obtained with an erosion type of monolith lysimeter by Stauffer.[6] (See Fig. 9:3.) The slope was 1.4 per cent, the average annual precipitation 37.5 inches, and the duration of the study about 6.5 years. Of the six bare silt loam blocks used, one (Muscatine)

[5] E. Wollny, "Untersuchunger uber die Sickerwassermengen in verschiedenerarten," Forsch, a. d. Gebiete d. Agri.-Physik., 2: 1–68, 1888.

[6] R. S. Stauffer, "Runoff, Percolate, and Leaching Losses from Some Illinois Soils," *Jour. Amer. Soc. Agron.*, 34: 830–35, 1942.

allowed ready drainage while another (Cowden) permitted only slow percolation. As a result, 22.7 per cent of the annual precipitation drained through the first soil but only 3.6 per cent was lost from the latter in this manner. Obviously, soils vary tremendously as to percolation losses.

Figure 9:3. View of a set of monolith lysimeters at the University of Illinois. The pit between the two rows of lysimeters contains the vessels which catch the drainage water from the respective soil columns. Surface runoff is allowed and the amounts of soil and water lost in this manner are determined. *(Courtesy of University of Illinois.)*

Percolation through cropped soils. It is interesting to consider now a situation where plants were growing on the soil. In New York, a study was made of two soils, bare and cropped, held in tank-type lysimeters. The crops, grown in rotation, were corn, oats, wheat, and hay. The data (Table 9:2) for the Dunkirk and Volusia soils are for ten and fifteen years respectively.

As might be expected, the presence of ordinary field crops definitely reduced the amount of drainage. If runoff had been allowed and less water had entered the soil, the influence of crops upon drainage loss would probably have been more marked. In fact, some cropped soils with annual rainfalls in excess of 30 inches show practically no percolation.[7] This occurs

[7] V. J. Kilmer, *et al.,* "Plant Nutrients and Water Losses from Fayette Silt Loam as Measured by Monolith Lysimeters," *Jour. Amer. Soc. Agron.,* 36: 249–63, 1944. See also Harrold and Dreibelbis, *op. cit.*

TABLE 9:2

Average Annual Loss of Water by Percolation from Bare and Cropped Soils. Cornell Lysimeter Tanks (No Runoff Allowed) [a]

Conditions	Rainfall, Inches	Percolation, Inches
Dunkirk silty clay loam:		
Bare	32.41	24.92
Cropped	32.41	18.70
Volusia silt loam:		
Bare	33.22	20.90
Cropped	33.22	19.10

[a] T. L. Lyon; J. A. Bizzell; B. D. Wilson; and E. W. Leland, *Lysimeter Experiments, III,* Memoir 134, Cornell Univ. Agr. Exp. Sta., 1930 and T. L. Lyon and J. A. Bizzell, *Lysimeter Experiments, IV,* Memoir 194, Cornell Univ. Agr. Exp. Sta., 1936.

because of crops and evaporation draught and because runoff is high, accounting in some cases for perhaps 30 or 40 per cent of the annual precipitation. The type of rainfall, whether gentle or torrential, will be an important factor in respect to the amount of water entering the soil and hence upon the magnitude of percolation loss.

9:3. LEACHING LOSSES OF NUTRIENTS

Due to variable weather conditions, to differences in soils, and to diversity in their management, it is practically impossible to forecast what the magnitude of the leaching losses of nutrients from any one soil is likely to be. Reference to almost any lysimeter data substantiates this conclusion. Data thus obtained, therefore, must be used with caution and by no means subjected to unwarranted interpretation and application.

Lysimeter data from various experiments are in fair agreement with respect to nitrogen and phosphoric acid losses. (See Tables 9:3 and 9:4.) The leaching of calcium, potassium, magnesium, and sulfur, however, was much higher from the Cornell lysimeters. Undoubtedly, this was due largely to the fact that no runoff was allowed from these tanks since the rainfall was about the same at the other locations under consideration. That the soils used in the Cornell investigation had been greatly disturbed in filling the tanks also may have been a factor.

In spite of the great variability of the data from the different sources, certain features of practical importance can be cited. In the *first* place, the

TABLE 9:3

Average Annual Loss of Nutrients by Percolation through Bare and Cropped Soils. Cornell Lysimeters Average of Ten and Fifteen Years Respectively (No Runoff Allowed) [a]

Soil Condition	Pounds per Acre per Year					
	N	P_2O_5	K_2O	CaO	MgO	SO_3
Dunkirk silty clay loam:						
Bare	69.0	Trace	86.8	557.2	104.4	132.5
Rotation	7.8	Trace	69.1	322.0	73.2	108.5
Grass	2.5	Trace	74.5	364.0	83.1	111.1
Volusia silt loam:						
Bare	43.0	Trace	77.3	452.6	68.3	88.5
Rotation	6.6	Trace	68.9	350.5	45.7	82.0

[a] J. A. Bizzell and T. L. Lyon, "Composition of Drainage Waters from Lysimeters at Cornell University," *Proc. and Papers, First Internat. Cong. Soil Sci.*, II: 342–57, 1927. And T. L. Lyon and J. A. Bizzell, *Lysimeter Experiment, IV*, Memoir 194, Cornell Univ. Agr. Exp. Sta., 1936.

TABLE 9:4

Average Annual Loss of Nutrients by Percolation through Soils from Three Different Areas Using the Monolith Type of Lysimeters (Runoff Allowed from Illinois and Wisconsin Lysimeters)

Condition	Pounds per Acre per Year					
	N	P_2O_5	K_2O	CaO	MgO	SO_3
ROTATION ON A SCOTTISH SOIL [a] (AVE. 6 YEARS)						
No treatment	6.7	Trace	10.6	69.6	25.5	—
Manure and fertilizers	6.3	Trace	9.9	78.5	26.5	—
Manure, fertilizers & lime	7.9	Trace	9.2	111.4	31.2	—
UNCROPPED ILLINOIS SOILS [b] (AVE. 3½ YEARS)						
Muscatine (well drained)	76.6	—	1.5	125.8	77.1	26.2
Cowden (poorly drained)	6.1	—	0.7	15.2	5.6	3.5
FAYETTE SILT LOAM, WISCONSIN [c] (AVE. 3 YEARS)						
Fallow	—	—	1.4	53.0	30.8	7.2
Cropped to Corn	—	—	0.5	20.6	9.6	2.0

[a] J. Hendrick and H. D. Welch, "The Substances Removed by the Drainage from a Scottish Soil," *Proc. and Papers, First Internat. Cong. Soil Sci.*, II: 358–66, 1927.
[b] R. S. Stauffer, "Runoff, Percolate and Leaching Losses from Some Illinois Soils," *Jour. Amer. Soc. Agron.*, 34: 830–35, 1942.
[c] V. J. Kilmer, *et al.*, "Plant Nutrient and Water Losses from Fayette Silt Loam as Measured by Monolith Lysimeters," *Jour. Amer. Soc. Agron.*, 36: 249–63, 1944.

amount of lime carried away by drainage usually is large for humid-region soils no matter what the soil condition or treatment may be. This, together with the loss of magnesia, accounts for the tendency of such soils to become acid. *Second,* there apparently is an extremely low loss of phosphorus by leaching. This is probably due to the small amount present in the soil and the tenacity with which it is held.[8] *Third,* the losses of potassium and sulfur, while appreciable, probably are not important except in certain cases. And *fourth,* crops markedly reduce the removal of all nutrients in drainage. This is especially important in respect to the nitrogen, the loss of which usually is very low from cropped soil. It is obviously poor management to allow a soil to remain bare during the summer season in a humid region. Plants differ markedly, in their influence, grass especially reducing the drainage loss of nitrogen. This may be due in part to the high carbon to nitrogen ratio of the grass residues which helps prevent nitrate accumulation. (See p. 000.) Practically all of the nitrogen lost in soil drainage, be it remembered, is removed in nitrate form.

The generalizations outlined above logically lead to the question of the control of leaching of essential nutrients. Can the losses be in any way reduced remembering that the removal of excess water must be facilitated? Only one suggestion of any moment can be made for field soils and this is clearly apparent from the data quoted. Keep a crop on the land as much as possible since less water passes through cropped soils than through soils that are bare. Beyond this, little more can be suggested. Obviously, it is impossible to adequately drain humid-region soils and yet hold the leaching losses, especially of lime and magnesia, at negligible levels.

Leaching vs. crop removal. One more feature of particular interest in respect to leaching losses remains—their magnitude relative to the corresponding removals by crops occupying the land. Such a comparison can be made only in a very tentative way by postulating the drainage losses from a representative humid-region silt loam and the nutrient removals on the average due to crops grown in rotation on such a soil. (See Table 9:5.)

It is quite obvious under the conditions postulated that, ignoring possible erosion removals, most of the nitrogen, phosphoric acid, and potash is lost to the crops occupying the land. Quite the reverse is true for calcium, while magnesium and sulfur losses in the two directions are about equal.

[8] It is probable that present-day analytical methods would have shown more than a trace of phosphorus in the drainage waters of some of the earlier experiments, especially if the leachates had come from fertilized sandy soils.

TABLE 9:5

A Comparison of the Average Annual Loss of Nutrients by Drainage from a Representative Humid-region Silt Loam, Cropped to a Standard Rotation, with the Nutrients Removed by an Average Rotation Crop

Losses	Pounds per Acre, Annually					
	N	P_2O_5	K_2O	CaO	MgO	SO_3
Leached from a representative silt loam	5	Trace	20	125	30	25
Removed by average rotation crop	75	30	60	35	25	25

If such generalizations are accepted, it would seem that the seriousness of leaching centers in a practical way on the high combined loss of calcium and magnesium, the increase of acidity in humid-region soils due to such losses, and the biochemical modifications that result. Were it not for leaching, our lime problem would be less serious. The idea that crops alone are responsible for fertility decline is fallacious. Leaching, as well as erosion, plays its part in reducing the fertility of humid-region soils.

9:4. LAND DRAINAGE [9]

It is generally wise to facilitate percolation, at the same time checking the loss of available nutrients as much as possible by means of crops. The encouragement of percolation is spoken of as *land drainage*. It is the process of removing the superfluous water from the soil profile, especially from its surface layer and upper subsoil, as rapidly as possible. While the drainage of swamps and the reclamation of overflow areas are urgent, the drainage of lands already under tillage is often much more important. Practical farm drainage is paramount in almost every community, even in arid regions, especially where irrigation is practiced.

9:5. TYPES OF DRAINAGE—TILE DRAINS

Two general types of drains are in use, *open* and *closed*. Ditch drainage represents the first group. The ditches may be deep and narrow such as those used in draining peat soils or they may be relatively shallow and

[9] For an excellent general discussion of the subject see T. W. Edminister and R. C. Reeve, "Drainage Problems and Methods," *The Yearbook of Agriculture* (Soils), 1957, pp. 378–85. A more comprehensive review of this subject is given in *Drainage of Agricultural Lands* (Agronomy, Vol. 7), American Society of Agronomy, Madison, Wis., 1957.

broad. The latter are designed to permit *surface drainage* or the controlled removal of water from heavy soils before it infiltrates into the soil. Ditches have the advantage of large capacity and are able to carry water at a low grade. On the other hand, they waste land, are somewhat inconvenient, and demand some upkeep expenditure. While ditches have a place in land drainage, closed or underdrains should be used where economically feasible.

Tile drains are the most reliable means of underdrainage in the majority of cases. While stone drains [10] are of value under certain conditions they must always be short and are likely to clog. Besides, their drainage is slow and rather inefficient. On silty soil, they do not remain in service for any length of time. Mole drains,[11] brush drains, box drains, and the like, are recommended only for special situations.

The nature and operation of tile drain. Land tile are generally 12 or more inches long with a diameter varying with the amount of water to be carried. They are laid end to end in strings on the bottom of a trench of sufficient slope. A carefully protected outlet should be provided. The tile are then covered with earth, straw or surface soil often being placed directly around the tile to facilitate the entrance of the water. The superfluous water enters the tile through the joints, mostly from the sides and bottom. (See Fig. 9:4.) As a consequence, the tops of the joints may be covered with paper, cloth, or even be cemented in order to prevent the entrance of silt or quicksand. The function of a tile-drain system is two-fold: (1) to facilitate the collection of the superfluous water; and (2) to discharge it quickly from the land.

Tile drains are simply a means of encouraging percolation. They are most effective when the macropores are large and numerous enough and so connected as to permit the rapid downward movement of gravity water.

---

[10] Stone drains are of historical interest only. They were built by arranging stone in a graded trench in such a manner as to provide a continuous channel or throat from the upper end of the drain to the lower. The spaces between the stones provided for the movement of the drainage water.

[11] A mole drain is simply an unwalled, cylindrical channel, 3 or 4 inches in diameter, located at a satisfactory distance below the soil surface. This channel is established by means of a special plow equipped with a sharp blade to which is attached the *mole,* a pointed cylindrical metal plug that looks much like the shell of a field gun. As this plug is pulled through the soil, it leaves a compressed-wall channel with the proper depth and fall.

Although this type of drain is best used on heavy mineral soils, it is employed at times in peat. Needless to say, the life of such a drain is usually short compared with that of a properly installed system of tile.

Good drainage is thereby established on land that might otherwise maintain a temporary water table too close to the surface at certain times of the year or that might be handicapped by a permanent water table at too high a level.

Figure 9:4. Demonstration of the saturated flow patterns of water toward a drainage tile. The water, containing a colored dye, was added to the surface of the saturated soil and drainage was allowed through the simulated drainage tile shown by the arrow on the extreme right. *(Photo courtesy G. S. Taylor, Ohio State University.)*

Systems of tile installation.   Where the land possesses considerable natural drainage, the strings of tile are laid only along the depressions. This is spoken of as the *natural* system of drainage in that the tile facilitate the quick removal of the water from the places of natural accumulation. But where the land is level or gently rolling, it often needs more uniform drainage. A *regular* system must then be installed. This may be either of the *fishbone* or *gridiron* style, or a modification or combination of the two, natural drainage being taken advantage of when possible. Where springs or seepage occur, *cutoff* system must be devised. (See Fig. 9:5.)

Every regular system consists of two parts, the laterals and the main drain. The laterals are usually constructed of 4-, or preferably 5-inch tile. These laterals should always enter the main at an angle of about 45 degrees. This causes a joining of the water currents with little loss of impetus and allows the more rapidly moving lateral streams to speed up the flow in the main drain. The size of the main depends on the amount and intensity of the rainfall, the acreage drained, and the slope. The main, of course, must be larger near the outlet than at any other point. Any good text on land drainage will present tables from which the proper size of the main drain may be determined.

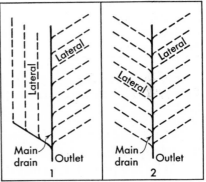

Figure 9:5. *(Left)* Natural (1) and interception (2) systems for laying tile drains. The object in both cases is to give efficient drainage at low cost.

(Right) Gridiron (1) and fishbone (2) systems for laying tile drains. Drainage on heavy level land can be effected only by a uniform layout system.

The grade, or fall, necessary for the satisfactory operation of a tile-drain system varies with the system itself and portion under consideration. The grade of the main drain may be very low, especially if the laterals deliver their water with a high velocity. In general, the grade will vary from 2 to 20 inches to the 100 feet, 3 to 6 inches being more or less ideal. When the grade is reduced abruptly, the installation of a silt-well may be advisable.

The depth of the tile beneath the surface of the land and the distance between laterals will vary with the nature of the soil. In most cases, however, a depth of about 3 feet is recommended. For sandy soils or poorly drained saline soils of arid regions, a depth of 4 feet or even more is commonly employed. On slow permeable soils where the laterals are close together a depth of 2½ feet has been used. This is about the shallowest depth that can be used with safety on mineral soils because of the danger of tile breakage by heavy machinery.

The interval between tile lines is also reduced as the soil becomes more compact or finer in texture. On a clayey soil, the distance between the strings is sometimes as low as 30 feet, although 50 to 75 feet is commoner. (See Table 9:6.)

TABLE 9:6

**Suggested Spacing between Tile Laterals for Different Soil
and Permeability Conditions** [a]

Soil	Permeability	Spacing in Feet
Clay and clay loam	very slow	30–70
Silt and silty clay loam	slow to moderately slow	60–100
Sandy loam	moderately slow to rapid	100–300
Muck and peat	slow to rapid	50–200

[a] This table modified from K. H. Beaucamp, "Tile Drainage—Its Installation and Upkeep," *The Yearbook of Agriculture* (Water), 1955, p. 513.

The maintenance cost of a properly installed tile-drain system is low, the only special attention usually needed being at the outlet. All outlets should be well protected, so that the end tile may not be loosened and the whole system endangered by clogging with sediment. It is well to imbed the end tile in a masonry or a concrete wall or block. The last 8 or 10 feet of tile may even be replaced by a galvanized iron pipe or with sewer tile, thus insuring against damage by frost. The end tile of the system may be covered by a gate or by wire in such a way as to allow the water to flow out freely but preventing rodents from entering in dry weather.

9:6. BENEFITS OF LAND DRAINAGE

Granulation, heaving, and root zone.   Draining the land promotes many conditions favorable to higher plants and soil organisms. By giving a freer rein to the forces of aggregation, granulation is definitely encouraged. At the same time, heaving is reduced, as it is only when the soil approaches saturation with water that alternate freezing and thawing have their most disastrous effects on plant roots. It is the heaving of small grain crops and the disruption of such taprooted plants as alfalfa and sweet clover that are especially feared. (See Fig. 10:5.) Also drainage, by quickly lowering the water table at critical times, maintains a sufficiently deep and effective root zone. (See Fig. 9:6.) By this means, the quantity of nutrients available to plants is maintained at a higher level.

Soil temperature.   The removal of excess water also lowers the specific heat of soil, thus reducing the energy necessary to raise the temperature of the layers thus drained. (See p. 000.) At the same time, surface evaporation, which has a cooling effect, may be reduced. The two effects together tend to make the warming of the soil easier. The converse of the old saying that in the spring "a wet soil is a cold soil" applies here. Good drainage is necessary if the land is to be satisfactorily cultivated and

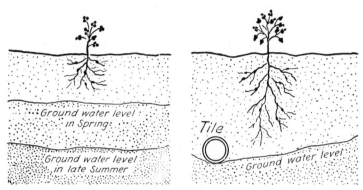

Figure 9:6. *Left,* root zone restriction that occurs when natural drainage is too slow. *Right,* lower water table and enlarged root zone that are developed by a properly installed tile drain.

is imperative in the spring if the soil is to warm up rapidly and properly. At this season of the year, an inadequately drained surface soil may be from 5° to 15° F. cooler than a contiguous area relieved of its excess water.

Aeration effects. It is perhaps in respect to aeration that the greatest benefits, both directly and indirectly, are derived from drainage. Although soil aeration problems will be dealt with in greater detail later, their over-all significance should be recognized here.

In a well-drained soil, perhaps one half or even more of the pore space in general may be occupied by air. Under such a condition, the furrow-slice and the upper subsoil are usually adequately supplied with oxygen, the air of the macropores almost equaling the atmospheric air in respect to this gas.

In the case of fine-textured soils, however, the air space may remain well below 50 per cent of the total porosity. Most of the pores are of microsize, and they tenaciously retain their water. Moreover, the atmosphere that is present is likely to be too low in oxygen to supply the plant roots with amounts of this gas sufficient for their metabolic processes. Nutrient intake is slowed down even in the presence of abundant amounts of the necessary constituents and the growth of aerobic soil organisms is adversely affected.

9:7. RUNOFF AND SOIL EROSION

In most all soils where the land is sloping or the soil is somewhat impermeable to water, a considerable amount of the moisture received is likely to be lost by runoff. Under such conditions, two considerations are important: (1) the loss of water that might otherwise enter the soil and perhaps be of use to plants; and (2) the removal of soil that usually occurs when water escapes too rapidly in this manner. This detachment and transfer of soil is spoken of as *erosion*.[12]

Effects of runoff. In some humid regions, loss by runoff may rise as high as 50 or 60 per cent of the annual precipitation. In arid sections, it is usually lower, unless the rainfall is of the torrential type as it often is in southwestern United States. While the loss of the water itself is deplorable, the erosion that accompanies it is usually even more serious. The surface soil is gradually taken away. This means not only a loss of the natural fertility but also of the nutrients that have been artificially added. Also it is the finer portion of this soil that is always removed first and this fraction, as already emphasized (p. 45), is highest in fertility. For example, the eroded material from a Collington sandy loam (New Jersey) in comparison with the original soil contained, in total, 4.7 times as much organic matter, 5.0 times as much nitrogen, 3.1 times as much phosphorus, and 1.4 times as much potassium.[13] Moreover, the erodate carried almost 4 times more fine material and its available potassium was 3.7 times greater than that of the original soil.

Thus, the objectives of any scheme of soil management are seriously interfered with. The furrow-slice becomes comprised of subsoil, which usually is less fertile, and the maintenance of a satisfactory physical condition is made difficult. Many farmers, especially in southern United States, are cultivating subsoils today unaware that the surface soils have been stolen from under foot.

The destructive action of erosion in upland regions and the deplorable deposition in the lowlands have been more or less disregarded until rather recently. This is partly due to the fact that erosion has been considered as more or less uncontrollable, an ill that could not be avoided. The major factor, has been a lack of observation—a failure to appreciate or measure

[12] The literature on soil erosion is exceedingly voluminous. See H. H. Bennett, *Soil Conservation* (New York: McGraw-Hill, 1939). Also see the various publications of the U.S. Soil Conservation Service.

[13] O. R. Neal, "Removal of Nutrients from the Soil by Crops and Erosion," *Jour. Amer. Soc. Agron.,* 36: 601–07, 1944.

the magnitude of the insidious removal. An effect much more easy to appreciate is the silting up of reservoirs which in many places is seriously reducing storage capacity and adding greatly to the expense of upkeep.[14]

The early colonists of the Americas were from western Europe where erosion is not especially serious. Undoubtedly this was a contributing factor in the apathy so long existent in this part of the world in respect to erosion damage of all kinds.

Extent of erosion. The publicity that erosion losses have received makes the quotation of extensive loss figures unnecessary. Davis[15] has estimated that 870 million tons of suspended material are carried yearly into the ocean by the streams of the United States—enough in ten years to cover Ohio or Kentucky with approximately 2.5 inches of sediment. And this is only a part of the soil brought down from the uplands. Much more is deposited on the way, to the detriment of the lower lands.

Bennett[16] estimated that 63 million tons of plant nutrients are annually swept from the cultivated fields and pastures of the farms of the United States. This is perhaps twenty times the loss due to crop removal. The money value of such an erosion loss is probably well over two billion dollars yearly and represents crop reduction values running into millions of dollars.

Later estimates by Bennett[17] indicate that perhaps upward to 50 million acres of cropland have been more or less ruined in continental United States, another 50 million reduced to a marginal state of productivity, while erosion is making rapid progress on 200 million acres more. Excluding the 100 million acres practically ruined, erosion is a serious threat to perhaps one third or even one half of the currently arable land in this country. (See Fig. 9:7.)

The figures for individual states are equally striking. For instance, it is estimated that perhaps 83 per cent of Alabama shows some erosion, with approximately 29 per cent rather seriously affected. The corresponding figures for Iowa are 58 per cent and 18 per cent. Although 34 per cent of

[14] H. M. Eakin, *Silting of Reservoirs,* Technical Bulletin 524, U.S. Dept. of Agric., 1936. This author states that few reservoirs in the United States have a life of two hundred years, while most will completely silt up, unless periodically cleaned, in from fifty to one hundred years.

[15] R. O. E. Davis, "Economic Waste from Soil Erosion," *The Yearbook of Agriculture,* 1913, p. 213.

[16] H. H. Bennett, "The Problem of Soil Erosion in the United States," *Proc. and Papers, First Internat. Cong. Soil Sci.,* IV: 748–57, 1939. See also *Soil Erosion a National Menace,* Circular 33, U.S. Dept. of Agric., 1928.

[17] Bennett, *op. cit.,* pp. 57–9.

New York is said to exhibit some erosion, only about 2 per cent is greatly influenced.[18]

Figure 9:7. Erosion map of the United States: 1, severe sheets and gully erosion; 2, moderate to severe erosion of mesas and mountains; 3, moderate to severe wind erosion with some gullying; 4, moderate sheet and gully erosion with some wind action; 5, moderate sheet and gully erosion serious locally; 6, erosion rather unimportant. *(After U.S. Soil Conservation Service.)*

These estimates were made in the early years of the United States Soil Conservation Service before the erosion situation in this country had been fully investigated and undoubtedly are too high. Nor was it realized that eroded lands, if not appreciably gullied, can in many cases be readily reclaimed.[19] Nevertheless, soil erosion ravages should not be minimized on this account. It is very serious in many sections of the United States and special precaution must be taken to insure its control. These precautions, however, are now considered as an integral part of the over-all scheme for maintaining the fertility and productivity of the land. Whether they receive major or minor attention will depend upon circumstances.

The effects of erosion are no less serious in countries other than the United States—China, India, Syria, Palestine, to name but a few. Moreover, erosion in ancient times evidently was a menace—in Greece, Italy, Syria, North Africa, and Persia. Perhaps the fall of empires, such as that

---

[18] *Reconnaissance Erosion Survey Data,* Soil Conservation Service, U.S. Dept. of Agric., 1935

[19] For a case, see O. E. Hays, *et al.,* "Increased Production on an Eroded Loess-derived Soil," *Jour. Amer. Soc. Agron.* 40: 1061–69, 1948.

of Rome, was hastened by the exhausting influence on agriculture of the washing away of fertile surface soils.

9:8. ACCELERATED EROSION—MECHANICS [20]

Water erosion is one of the commonest of geologic phenomena. It accounts in large part for the leveling of our mountains and the development of plains, plateaus, valleys, river flats, and deltas. The vast deposits that now appear as sedimentary rocks originated in this way. This is *normal* erosion. It operates slowly, yet inexorably. When erosion exceeds this normal rate and becomes unusually destructive, it is spoken of as *accelerated*. This is the water action that especially concerns agriculture.

Two steps are recognized in accelerated erosion—the *detachment* or loosening influence, which is a preparatory action, and *transportation* by floating, rolling, dragging, and splashing. Freezing and thawing, flowing water, and rain impact are the major detaching agencies. Raindrop splash and especially running water facilitate the carrying away of the loosened soil. In gullies most of the loosening and cutting is due to water flow, but on comparatively smooth soil surfaces, the beating of the raindrops effects most of the detachment.

Influence of raindrops. Raindrop impact exerts three important influences—(1) it detaches soil; (2) its beating tends to destroy granulation; and (3) its splash, under certain conditions, effects an appreciable transportation of soil. (See Fig. 9:8.) So great is the force exerted by dash-

Figure 9:8. A raindrop (left) and the splash (right) that it creates when the drop strikes a wet bare soil. Such rainfall impact not only tends to destroy soil granulation and encourage sheet and rill erosion but it also effects considerable transportation by splashing. A ground cover, such as sod, will largely prevent this type of erosion. *(Photo from J. H. Stallings, taken at U.S. Naval Research Laboratory.)*

[20] For a discussion of the detachment and transportation phases of soil erosion, see B. Osborn, "How Rainfall and Runoff Erode Soil," *The Yearbook of Agriculture (Water)*, 1955, pp. 126–35.

ing rain that soil granules not only are loosened and detached but in addition they may be beaten to pieces. Under such hammering, the aggregation of a soil so exposed practically disappears. If the dispersed material is not removed by runoff it may develop into a hard crust upon drying. Such a layer is unfavorable in many ways. For example, certain seedlings, such as beans have difficulty in pushing through a soil crust.

The protective importance of a vegetative shield, such as forest or bluegrass, or an artificial covering, say straw or a stubble mulch, is very great indeed. Such a protection, by absorbing the energy of rain impact, prevents the loss of both water and soil and reduces degranulation to a minimum.

Transportation of soil—splash effects.   In soil translocation, runoff water plays the major role. So familiar are most people with the power of water to cut and carry that little more need be said regarding these capacities. In fact, so much publicity has been given to runoff that the public, in general, ascribes to it all of the damage done by torrential rainfall.

However, splash transportation [21] is, under certain conditions, of considerable importance. (See Fig. 9:8.) On a soil subject to easy detachment, a very heavy torrential rain may splash as much as 100 tons of soil an acre, some of the drops rising as high as 2 feet and moving horizontally perhaps 4 or 5 feet. On a slope or if the wind is blowing, splashing greatly aids and enhances runoff translocations of soil, the two together accounting for the total wash that finally occurs. Before considering methods of control let us examine the factors that influence the magnitude of accelerated erosion.

9:9. ACCELERATED EROSION—CAUSES AND RATE FACTORS

Two main factors are responsible for accelerated erosion: (1) the removal of the natural vegetative cover; and (2) the undue exposure of arable soils through the use of soil-exposing crops. Dense natural vegetation intercepts the rainfall and thus nullifies the impact of raindrops. In addition, both forest and natural grassland-cover contribute organic matter residues. These are incorporated into the surface soil thus giving greater aggregate stability and absorptive capacity. Again the plant roots hold the soil in place and thus prevent erosion even when the runoff is great.

A cause of serious erosion on arable land is the use of too many crops

---

[21] P. C. Ekern and R. J. Muchenhirn, "Water Drop Impact as a Force in Transporting Sand," *Proc. Soil Sci. Soc. Amer.*, 12: 441–44, 1947.

that either do not check erosion themselves or whose management and tillage greatly encourage washing. For instance, buckwheat, although it completely covers the land, is notorious in its incapacity to prevent erosion. And intertilled crops, such as corn and potatoes, especially if the rows run with the slope, tremendously augment the removal of top soil. Moreover, the loss of water that might otherwise enter the root zone is of much significance to crop production.

Rate of erosion.   The rate of erosion in specific cases depends on a number of factors. Those of importance are: (1) the amount, intensity, and seasonal distribution of rainfall; (2) the steepness of the slope and its length as well as the general topography of the land; (3) the size and shape of the watershed; (4) the absence or presence of channels of concentration; (5) the type of vegetative covering; and finally, (6) the nature of the soil and subsoil. Acting together, these factors determine how much water enters the soil, how much runs off, and the manner and rate of its removal.

Rainfall effects.   Of the two phases, amount of *total rainfall* and its *intensity,* the latter is usually the more important. A heavy annual precipitation, received gently, may cause little erosion, while a lower yearly rainfall descending torrentially may result in tremendous damage. This accounts for the marked erosion often recorded in semiarid regions.

The *seasonal distribution* of the rainfall is also critical in determining soil erosion losses. For example, in the northern part of the United States, precipitation which runs off the land in the early spring when the soils are still frozen is ineffective in bringing about erosion. The same amount of runoff a few months later, however, often carries considerable amounts of soil with it. In any climate, heavy precipitation which occurs at a time of year when the soil is bare is likely to cause soil loss. Examples of such conditions are seedbed preparation-time and after the harvesting of crops such as beans, sugar beets, early potatoes, etc.

Slope, topography, and channels.   The greater the *degree of slope,* other conditions remaining constant, the greater the erosion due to increased velocity of water flow. Also, more water is likely to run off. Theoretically, a doubling of the velocity enables water to move particles 64 times larger, allows it to carry 32 times more material in suspension, and makes the erosive power in total 4 times greater.

The *length* of the slope is of prime importance since the greater the extension of the inclined area, the greater is the concentration of the flooding water. For example, research in southwestern Iowa, showed doubling the length of a 9 per cent slope increased the loss of soil by 2.6 times and the runoff water by 1.8 times.[22] This influence of slope is, of course, greatly modified by the size and general *topography* of the drainage area. Another modifying factor is the presence of *channels*, not only in the eroded area itself but in the watershed. The development of such channels controls the intensity of water concentration.

Effect of vegetation. Forests and grass are the best natural soil protective agencies known and are about equal in their effectiveness. But their influence varies. For instance, a forest with a heavy ground cover of organic matter and with a dense undergrowth is markedly superior to open woods with little organic accumulation. Again, the kind of grass, the thickness of its stand, and the vigor of its growth greatly affect erosiveness and are of great importance in control measures.

Field crops also vary in their influence. Some, such as wheat and oats, offer considerable obstruction to surface wash, while others, especially intertilled crops, tend to encourage erosion. (See Table 9:7.) A trash or

TABLE 9:7

Losses from Erosion on a Shelley Silt Loam Soil at the Missouri Agricultural Experiment Station. The Slope was 3.7 per cent, the Plots 90 Feet Long and the Average Rainfall 40 Inches. (Average of Fourteen Years)[a]

Treatment	Runoff, Per Cent of Rainfall	Tons of Soil Lost per Acre per Year	Relative Erosion, Bluegrass as 1	No. Yrs. to Erode 7 In. of Soil
No crop, plowed 4 inches deep and cultivated regularly	30.7	41.64	122	24
Corn grown continuously	29.4	19.72	58	50
Wheat grown continuously	23.3	10.10	30	100
Rotation; corn, wheat & clover	13.8	2.78	8	368
Bluegrass sod continuously	12.0	0.34	1	3043

[a] M. F. Miller and H. H. Krusekopf, *The Influence of Systems of Cropping and Methods of Culture on Surface Runoff and Soil Erosion*, Research Bulletin 177, Mo. Agr. Exp. Sta., 1932.

stubble mulch, where it can be utilized satisfactorily with field crops, would not only check erosion but also increase infiltration, reduce evaporation, and preserve granulation.

[22] G. M. Browning, *et al.*, *Investigations in Erosion Control and the Reclamation of Eroded Land at the Missouri Valley Loess Conservation Experiment Station, Clarinda, Iowa*, Tech. Bul. 959, U.S. Dept. of Agric., Soil Conservation Service, 1948.

Nature of the soil. The two most significant soil characteristics influencing erosion are: (1) the infiltration capacity, and (2) structural stability. They are closely related. The infiltration capacity is influenced greatly by structural stability, especially in the upper soil horizons. In addition, soil texture, the kind and amount of swelling clays, soil depth, and the presence of impervious soil layers all influence the infiltration capacity.

The stability of soil aggregates affects the extent of erosion damage in another way. Resistance of surface granules to the beating action of rain saves soil even though runoff does occur. The marked granule stability of certain tropical clay soils high in hydrous oxides of iron and aluminum accounts for the resistance of these soils to the action of torrential rains. Downpours of a similar magnitude on temperate-region clays would be disastrous.

9:10. TYPES OF WATER EROSION [23]

Three more or less distinct types of water erosion are generally recognized: *sheet, rill,* and *gully.* (See Figs. 9:9 and 9:10.) In the first, soil is

Figure 9:9. The perched stones and pebbles shown in the picture are mute evidence of sheet erosion—the higher the pedestals, the greater the erosion. The soil under each rock has been protected from the beating action of the rain. The pedestal in the center is about 3 inches in height. (*U.S. Soil Conservation Service photo.*)

[23] A voluminous literature in regard to water erosion has developed in the last few years, of which a rather complete list may be obtained by writing to the Soil Conservation Service, U.S. Dept. of Agric., Washington, D.C.

removed more os less uniformly from every part of the slope. However, this type is often accompanied, especially on bare land newly planted or in fallow, by tiny gullies irregularly dispersed. This is *rill* erosion. But where the volume of water is concentrated, the formation of large or small ravines by undermining and downward cutting occurs. This is called *gully* erosion. While all types may be serious, the losses due to sheet and rill erosion, although less noticeable, are undoubtedly the most important from the standpoint of field soil deterioration.

9:11. SHEET AND RILL EROSION—LOSSES UNDER REGULAR CROPPING

A number of different methods for the reduction and control of sheet and rill erosion may be currently utilized. Anything that will increase the absorptive capacity of the soil, such as deep plowing, surface tillage, and more organic matter, will lessen the runoff over the surface. Trash and stubble mulches are of great aid. The nature of the crops grown is an especially important factor.

Figure 9:10. Sheet and rill erosion on an unprotected slope with serious gullying imminent if protective measures are not instituted soon. Strip cropping or even terracing should be employed if cultivated crops are to be grown. Perhaps, better, the field could be seeded and used as pasture or meadow. In any case a diversion ditch well up the slope would be advisable. (*U.S. Soil Conservation Service photo.*)

Influence of crops. Intertilled crops such as corn or potatoes may actually encourage erosion, especially if the rows possess much slope. Small grains, on the other hand, tend to impede such loss. Of all field crops, however, grasses are perhaps the most effective in checking erosion. This is so well recognized that a sod is almost always recommended in places where serious erosion is likely to take place.

Data from Missouri (Table 9:7) indicate that sod is extremely effective on moderate slopes. In scanning these data, it is well first to note the large amount of soil lost especially from the bare plot and that cropped to corn. In the first case, the surface soil would disappear in only one generation; while in the other, two generations would suffice to bring the furrow-slice entirely into the subsoil.

The contrasts in respect to the different crops are just as significant. Corn allows the greatest soil loss, with wheat next. And while a good rotation exerts an appreciable erosion control, grass is by far more effective. The erosion loss here is negligible. A well-managed forest is of the same order of efficiency as grass. Since a vigorous sod is more effective than one in a less healthy condition, the fertilization and management of pastures and meadows have become an important feature of practical erosion control.

Nutrient losses. Considering the Missouri experiments (Table 9:7) still further, it is interesting to note the amount of some of the important nutrients that were swept away by erosion. These losses are likely to be greater than one might expect since the finer particles of soil, much higher in fertility than the whole soil, are sorted out and carried away. This means an accelerated loss of all of the fertility elements. For comparison, tentative figures as to the nutrients withdrawn from the soil by the average crop of a standard rotation are quoted. The data, in round numbers, are shown in Table 9:8.

TABLE 9:8

Nutrients Removed Annually in Pounds to the Acre in the Missouri Erosion Experiment Compared to the Yearly Draft of an Average Field Crop [a]

Condition	N	P_2O_5	K_2O	CaO	MgO	SO_3
Erosion Removal						
Corn grown continuously	66	41	729	309	145	42
Rotation: corn, wheat, and clover	26	18	258	120	48	15
Crop Removal						
Average for standard rotation	75	30	60	35	25	25

[a] These data are for two years only.

While such data are not of universal application, certain conclusions may be drawn. Erosion losses, even on a 4 per cent slope, may easily exceed the removal of nutrients by crops occupying the land. This seems to be true especially for calcium, magnesium, and potassium. The data indicate that large savings are automatically made by the practices that most successful farmers employ.

9:12. SHEET AND RILL EROSION—METHODS OF CONTROL

One of the most important and at the same time the most underrated means of erosion control is the maintenance of high soil fertility and productivity. The growing of bumper crops not only gives a maximum of ground cover but at the same time supplies sufficient organic matter to aid in the maintenance of this all-important soil constituent. The increased permeability of soils to water under such conditions is certainly a factor of major importance. Although not usually recognized as erosion control features, the wise use of fertilizers, lime, and manure may do more to prevent soil erosion, especially sheet and rill, than some of the more obvious mechanical means of control.

Mechanical measures. In the growing of corn and similar crops, it is important that the cultivation be across the slope rather than with it. This is called *contour tillage*. On long slopes subject to sheet and rill erosion, the fields may be laid out in narrow strips across the incline, alternating the tilled crops such as corn and potatoes with hay and grain. Water cannot attain an undue velocity on the narrow strips of cultivated land, while the hay and grain tend to markedly check the runoff flow. Such a layout is called *strip cropping* and is the basis of much of the erosion control now advocated. (See Fig. 9:11.)

When the cross strips are laid out rather definitely on the contours, the system is called *contour strip cropping*. The width of the strips will depend primarily upon the degree of slope and upon the premeability of the land and its erodibility. Table 9:9 from Gustafson [24] gives some idea as to the practicable widths. Contour strip cropping often is guarded by diversion ditches and waterways between fields. When their grade is high, they should be grass covered. This precaution is a number one rule in most erosion control.

However, when slopes are subject to very serious erosion, they should either be reforested or kept in permanent pasture, guarding always against

[24] A. F. Gustafson, *Soils and Soil Management* (New York: McGraw-Hill, 1941), p. 207.

incipient gullying. Even in permanent pastures and in young plantations *contour furrowing* at suitable intervals often is practical as it not only aids in stabilizing the soil but also provides more water for the crop. This is especially important on droughty slopes.

Figure 9:11. Aerial photograph over a soil conservation district in Minnesota. In spite of contour strip cropping some erosion has occurred (near lower right-hand corner), perhaps as a result of torrential showers. (*U.S. Soil Conservation Service photo.*)

TABLE 9:9

Suggested Strip Widths in Feet for Contour Strip Cropping

Slope Per Cent	Soil Conditions		
	Well-drained, Erodibility Low	*Medium Drainage, Erodibility Moderate*	*Poor Drainage, Erodibility High*
5	125	100	75
10	100	75	50
15	75	50	—

When the simpler methods of checking sheet erosion on cultivated lands are inadequate, it is often advisable to resort to *terraces* constructed across the slope. These catch the water and conduct it away at a gentle grade. Opportunity is thus given for more water to soak in. The *Mangum* terrace and its modifications are now largely in vogue. Such a terrace is generally a broad bank of earth with gently sloping sides, contouring the field at a grade from 6 to 8 inches to 100 feet. It is usually formed by back-furrowing and scraping. The interval between the successive embankments depends on the slope and erodibility of the land.

Since the terrace is low and broad, it may be cropped without difficulty and offers no obstacle to cultivating and harvesting machinery. It wastes little or no land, and is quite effective if properly maintained. Where necessary, waterways are sodded. Such terracing is really a more or less elaborate type of contour strip cropping.

9:13. GULLY EROSION AND ITS CONTROL

Small gullies, while at first insignificant, soon enlarge into unsightly ditches or ravines. They quickly eat into the land above, exposing its subsoil and increasing the sheet and rill erosion, already undesirably active. (See Fig. 9:10.) If small enough, such gullies may be plowed in and seeded down, using a nurse crop such as oats, barley, or wheat, which will check runoff until the grass obtains a start. Once the sod is established it may almost entirely stop the erosion.

When the gully erosion is too active to be thus checked and the ditch is still small, dams of rotted manure or straw at intervals of 15 or 20 feet are very effective. Such dams may be made more secure by strips or wire netting staked below them. After a time, the ditch may be plowed in and the site of the gully seeded and kept in sod permanently. It thus becomes a *grassed waterway,* an important feature of almost all successful erosion projects.

With moderately sized gullies, larger dams of various kinds may be utilized. These are built at intervals along the channels. If brush is used, it is piled in the gully at the desired location with the butt ends upstream. If the stakes are wired together before being driven down, the brush will be compressed and held firmly in place. Straw thrown above such dams will make them more effective in catching the eroded soil. Dams just as effective may be constructed from woven wire properly staked and secured. These are just a few of the details relating to this phase of water control.[25]

[25] For the control of gullies of all kinds, see Q. C. Ayres, *Recommendations for the Control and Reclamation of Gullies,* Bulletin 121, Ia. Eng. Exp. Sta., Iowa State College, 1935; and H. G. Jepson, *Prevention and Control of Gullies,* Farmers' Bulletin 1813, U.S. Dept. of Agric., 1939.

With very large gullies, dams of earth, concrete, or stone are often successfully used. Most of the sediment is deposited above the dam and the gully is slowly filled. The use of semipermanent check dams, flumes, paved channels, and diversion ditches are also recommended on occasion. The only difficulty with engineering features at all extensive is that the cost may exceed the benefits derived or even the value of the land to be served. They thus may prove uneconomical.

9:14. WIND EROSION—ITS IMPORTANCE AND CONTROL [26]

The consideration of water erosion leads naturally to the question of the movement of soil by winds. This type of soil destruction, while most common in arid and semiarid regions, occurs to some extent in humid climates as well. It is essentially a dry-weather phenomenon and hence, in a sense, is a moisture problem. All kinds of soils and soil materials are affected and at times their more finely divided portions are carried to great heights and for hundreds of miles.

In the great dust storm of May 1934, which originated in western Kansas, Texas, Oklahoma, and contiguous portions of Colorado and New Mexico, clouds of powdery debris were carried eastward to the Atlantic seaboard and even hundreds of miles out over the ocean. Such aeolian activity is not a new phenomenon but has been common in all geologic ages. The wind energy that gave rise to the loessial deposits now so important agriculturally in the United States and other countries, belongs in this category. (See Fig. 11:11.)

The destructive effects of wind erosion are often very serious. Not only is the land robbed of its richest soils but crops are either blown away or left to die with roots exposed or they may be covered up by the drifting debris. Even though the blowing may not be great, the cutting and abrasive effects, especially of sand, upon tender crops often is disastrous. The area in the United States subject to greatest wind action is that broad expanse called the Great Plains. Here the mismanagement of plowed lands and the lowered holding power of the range grasses due to overgrazing, have greatly encouraged wind work. In dry years, as experience has shown, the results have been most deplorable.

Areas of excessive wind erosion. Two great *dust bowls* (see Fig. 9:7) exist in the United States. One, the larger, occupies much of western

---

[26] For a discussion of wind erosion see W. S. Chepel, *Soil Conditions that Influence Wind Erosion,* Tech. Bul. 1185, U.S. Dept. of Agric., 1958. A popular discussion is given by the same author in "Erosion of Soil by Wind," *The Yearbook of Agriculture (Soil),* 1955, pp. 308–14.

Kansas, Oklahoma, and Texas, extending into southeastern Colorado and eastern New Mexico. The other, irregular and somewhat scattered, lies across the centers of three states—Nebraska, and the two Dakotas. Eastern Montana is also affected. Curiously enough, areas of severe water erosion lie contiguous to these so-called dust bowls, while gully and sheet erosion, due to torrential rainfall, are not at all uncommon within their borders.

Possibly 12 per cent of continental United States is somewhat affected by wind erosion, 8 per cent moderately so, and perhaps 2 or 3 per cent badly. While most of the damage is confined to regions of low rainfall, some serious wind erosion occurs in humid sections. Sand dune movement is a good example. More important agriculturally, sandy soils used for vegetables are often affected by the wind. This type of erosion is especially destructive on cultivated peats, particularly those that have been long and intensively cropped. The drying out of the cultivated and finely divided surface layers of sandy loams and peats leaves them both extremely susceptible to wind drift.

Mechanics of wind erosion. As was the case for water erosion, the loss of soil by wind movement involves two processes: (1) detachment, and (2) transportation. The abrasive action of the wind results in some detachment of tiny soil grains from the granules or clods of which they are a part. When the wind is laden with soil particles, however, its abrasive action is greatly increased. The impact of these rapidly moving grains dislodges other particles from soil clods and aggregates. These particles are now ready for movement.

The transportation of the particles once they are dislodged takes place in several ways. The first and most important is that of *saltation* or movement of soil by a short series of bounces along the surface of the ground. The particles remain fairly close to the ground as they bounce, seldom rising more than a foot or so. Depending on the conditions, this process may account for 50 to 75 per cent of the total movement.

Saltation also encourages *soil creep* or the rolling and sliding along the surface of the larger particles. The bouncing particles carried by saltation strike the larger aggregates and speed up their movement along the surface. Soil creep may account for 5 to 25 per cent of the total movement.

The most spectacular method of transporting soil particles is by movement in *suspension*. Here, dust particles of a fine-sand size and smaller are moved parallel to the ground surface and upward. Although some of them are carried at a height no greater than a few yards, the turbulent action of the wind results in others being carried miles upward into the atmosphere and hundreds of miles horizontally. They return to the earth only when the wind subsides and when precipitation washes them down. Although it is the most obvious manner of transportation, suspension movement generally accounts for no more than perhaps 3 to 40 per cent of the total movement.

Factors affecting wind erosion.   Susceptibility to wind erosion is related rather definitely to the moisture content of soils. Wet soils do not blow. The moisture content is generally lowered by hot dry winds to the wilting point and lower before wind erosion takes place.

Other factors which are known to influence wind erosion are: (1) wind velocity, (2) soil surface condition, and (3) soil characteristics. Obviously, the rate of wind movement, especially gusts having greater than average velocity, will influence erosion. Wind turbulence will also influence the transporting capacity of the atmosphere. Although the wind itself has some direct influence in picking up fine soil, the impact of wind-carried particles on those not yet disengaged is probably more important.

Wind erosion is less severe where the soil surface is rough. This roughness can be obtained by proper tillage methods which leave large clods or ridges on the soil surface. Leaving stubble mulch is perhaps an even more effective way of reducing wind-borne soil losses.

In addition to moisture content, several other soil characteristics influencing wind erosion are: (1) mechanical stability of dry soil clods and aggregates; (2) the presence of a stable soil crust; and (3) bulk density and size of erodible soil fractions. The clods must be resistant to the abrasive action of wind-carried particles. If a soil crust resulting from a previous rain is present it too must be able to withstand impact without deteriorating. The importance of cementing agents here is quite apparent.

Soil particles of a given size and bulk density are apparently more susceptible to erosion than are others. Apparently those particles about 0.1 mm. in diameter are most erodible, those larger or smaller in size being less susceptible to movement. Particles about 0.1 mm. in size apparently are responsible to a degree for that movement of larger or smaller particles which does occur. By saltation, the most erodible particles bounce against larger particles causing surface creep and against the smaller dust particles resulting in movement in suspension.

Control of wind erosion.   Factors just discussed give clues as to methods of reducing wind erosion. Obviously, if the soil can be kept moist there is little danger of wind erosion. A vegetative cover also discourages soil blowing, especially if the plant roots are well established. In dry-farming areas, however, sound moisture-conserving practices require summer fallow on some of the land and hot, dry winds reduce the moisture in the soil surface. Consequently, other means must be turned to on cultivated lands of these areas.

By roughening the soil surface, the wind velocity can be decreased and some of the moving particles trapped. Stubble mulch has proven to be effective in this manner. Tillage to provide for a cloddy surface condition should be at right angles to the prevailing winds. Likewise strip cropping and alternate strips of cropped and fallowed land should be perpendicular to the wind. Barriers such as tree shelterbelts (see Fig. 9:12) are effective in reducing wind velocities for short distances and for trapping drifting soil.

Figure 9:12. Shrubs and trees make good wind breaks and add beauty to a North Dakota farm homestead. *(Photo courtesy North Dakota State Soil Conservation Committee.)*

In the case of the blowing of sands, sandy loams, and cultivated peat soils in humid regions, various control devices are used. Windbreaks and tenacious grasses and shrubs are especially effective. Picket fences and burlap screens, while less efficient as windbreaks than such trees as willows, are often preferred because they can be moved from place to place as crops and cropping practices are varied. Rye, planted in narrow strips across the field, is sometimes used on peat lands. All of these devices for wind-erosion control, whether applied in arid or humid regions and whether vegetative or purely mechanical, are, after all, but phases of the broader problem of soil moisture control.

9:15. SUMMARY OF SOIL MOISTURE REGULATION

In the effective control of soil water, four more or less closely related phases must be considered. They are : (1) weed transpiration, (2) surface evaporation, (3) percolation and leaching, and (4) runoff and erosion.

Weed transpiration and surface evaporation, by drawing on the available soil water, compete directly and seriously with the crop. Cultivation is the remedy commonly recommended for weeds, although herbidices are being utilized more and more in connection with a suitable rotation. Surface evaporation is subject to little control except through the use of organic mulches.

Percolation losses are serious because of the nutrients carried away, rather than because of the waste of the water. In fact, the removal of such water is necessary in order to promote soil aeration and encourage other desirable conditions. Keeping crops on the land as much as possible is the only practicable means of reducing leaching losses of nutrients.

The detrimental influence of runoff over the surface is due to the bodily removal of soil, as well as the loss of the water itself. Control measures involve organic matter maintenance to encourage infiltration, an effective vegetative cover, and mechanical practices such as contour strip cropping to allow an orderly removal of excess surface water.

Soil Air and Soil Temperature

CHAPTER 10

As was pointed out in Chapter 1, approximately one half the total volume of a representative mineral surface soil is occupied by solid materials. The remaining nonsolid or pore space is occupied by water and gases. The previous three chapters (7, 8, and 9) have placed major emphasis on the soil moisture phase. They have, nevertheless, constantly reminded the reader of the interrelationship of soil air and soil water. We cannot affect one without also changing the other.

In spite of the fact that this reciprocal relationship already has been duly stressed, there are certain aspects of soil aeration which deserve separate and special consideration. This is true particularly in respect to certain plant processes.

It is logical also to include in this chapter another important physical property—the temperature of the soils. Although subject to little direct control under field conditions, soil temperature is closely related to soil moisture and soil air and, of course, exerts a tremendous influence upon microorganisms and higher plants. Let us begin with the major problems of soil aeration.

10:1. SOIL AERATION DEFINED

Before considering the more detailed phases of soil aeration, it may be well to define, at least in a general way, what is meant by this particular soil property. In keeping with our edaphological viewpoint, soil aeration will be considered in relation to *plant growth*. Thus, we may look upon a well-aerated soil as *one in which gases are available to growing organisms (particularly higher plants) in sufficient quantities and in the proper proportions to encourage optimum rates of the essential metabolic processes of these organisms.*

242

A soil in which aeration is considered satisfactory must have at least two characteristics. *First,* sufficient space devoid of solids and water should be present. *Second,* there must be an ample opportunity for the ready movement of essential gases into and out of these spaces. Water relations largely control the *amount of air* space available, but the problem of adequate *air exchange* is probably a much more complicated feature. The supply of oxygen, a gas that is constantly being used in biological reactions,[1] must be continually renewed. At the same time the concentration of CO_2, the major product of these or similar reactions, must not be allowed to build up excessively in the air spaces.

10:2. SOIL AERATION PROBLEMS IN THE FIELD

Under actual field conditions there are in general two situations which may result in poor aeration in soils: (1) when the moisture content is excessively high, leaving little or no room for gases; and (2) when the exchange of gases with the atmosphere is not sufficiently rapid to keep the concentration of soil gases at desirable levels. The latter may often occur even when sufficient *total air space* is available.

Excess moisture. In the first case referred to above, essentially a waterlogged condition is established. This may be quite temporary, but, nevertheless, often seriously affects plant growth. Such a situation is frequently found on poorly drained, fine-textured soils which have a minimum of macropores through which water can move rapidly. It also occurs in soils that normally are fairly well drained if the rate of water supply at the soil surface is sufficiently rapid. A low spot in a field or even a flat area in which water tends to stand for a short while are good examples of this condition. Such complete saturation of the soil with water can be disastrous for certain plants in a short time, a matter of a few hours being critical in some cases. Plants which have previously been growing under conditions of good soil aeration are actually more susceptible to damage

---

[1] Two biological reactions largely account for the O_2 and CO_2 changes referred to above. They are (1) the respiration of higher-plant roots; and (2) the aerobic decomposition of incorporated organic residues by microorganisms. Although differing in many respects, these processes are surprisingly similar with regard to the gases involved. This similarity makes it possible to express both reactions in terms of the following very general equation:

$$[C] + O_2 \longrightarrow CO_2$$

Both processes result in the oxidation of carbonaceous compounds, oxygen being used up and CO_2 being evolved. Either a deficiency of O_2 or an excess of CO_2 would thus tend to cut down the rate of these reactions. In fact, both inhibitions commonly operate concurrently.

from flooding than are plants growing on soils where poor aeration has prevailed from the very start.[2]

The prevention of this type of poor aeration requires the rapid removal of excess water either by land drainage or by controlled runoff. Because of the large volume of small capillary pores in some soils, even these precautions leave only a small portion of the soil volume filled with air soon after a rain. This often makes the artificial drainage of heavy soils surprisingly ineffective.

Gaseous interchange.   The seriousness of inadequate *interchanges* of gases between the soil and the free atmosphere above it is dependent primarily on two factors: (1) the rate of biochemical reactions influencing the soil gases; and (2) the actual rate at which each gas is moving into or out of the soil. Obviously, the more rapid the usage of O_2 and the corresponding release of CO_2, the greater will be the necessity for the exchange of gases. Factors markedly affecting these biological reactions such as temperature, organic residues, etc., undoubtedly are of considerable importance in determining the air status of any particular soil. (See p. 247.)

The exchange of gases between the soil and the atmosphere above it is facilitated by two mechanisms: (1) *mass flow* and (2) *diffusion*. Mass flow of air is apparently due to pressure differences between the atmosphere and the soil air and is relatively unimportant in determining the total exchange that occurs. Its extent is determined by factors such as soil and air temperatures, barometric pressure, and wind movements.

Apparently most of the gaseous interchange in soils occurs by diffusion.[3] Through this process each gas tends to move in a direction determined by its own partial pressure. (See Fig. 10:1.) The partial pressure of a gas in a mixture is simply the pressure which this gas would exert if it alone were present in the volume occupied by the mixture. Thus, if the pressure of air is 1 atmosphere, the partial pressure of oxygen, which makes up about 21 per cent of the air by volume, is approximately 0.21 of an atmosphere.

Diffusion allows extensive movement from one area to another even though there is no over-all pressure gradient. Thus, even though the total soil-air pressure and that of the atmosphere may be the same, a higher concentration of O_2 in the atmosphere will result in a net movement of this particular gas into the soil. An opposite movement of CO_2 and water

[2] B. S. Meyer and D. B. Anderson, *Plant Physiology* (New York: Van Nostrand, 282–283).

[3] The literature on soil aeration as it relates to plant growth has been summarized by M. B. Russell, a chapter in "Soil Physical Conditions and Plant Growth," *Amer. Soc. Agron.*, Monograph I, 1952.

vapor is simultaneously taking place, since the partial pressures of these two gases are generally higher in the soil air than in the atmosphere. A representation of the principles involved in diffusion is given in Figure 10:1.

In addition to being affected by partial pressure differences, diffusion seems to be directly related to the volume of pore spaces filled with air. On heavy-textured topsoils, especially if the structure is poor, and in compact subsoils the rate of gaseous movement is seriously slow. Moreover, such soils allow very slow penetration of water into the surface layer. This prevents the rapid replacement of air high in CO_2 and the subsequent inward movement of atmospheric air after a heavy rain or after irrigation.

Figure 10:1. Diagram showing how the process of diffusion takes place. The total gas pressure is the same on both sides of boundary (A-A). The partial pressure of oxygen is greater, however, in the top portion of the container. Therefore, this gas tends to diffuse into the lower portion where fewer oxygen molecules are found. The CO_2 molecules, on the other hand, move in the opposite direction due to the higher partial pressure of this gas in the lower half. Eventually equilibrium will be established when the partial pressures of O_2 and CO_2 respectively are the same in both sides of the boundary.

10:3. COMPOSITION OF SOIL AIR

In Table 10:1, data are given showing the composition of soil air at various locations as compared to that of the atmosphere itself. These data are for topsoils only and consequently do not afford complete information as to the variabilities encountered, especially in the subsoil.[4] They do illustrate, however, the higher CO_2 concentration and lower O_2 content of soil air as compared to that of the atmosphere. Also, there is a general inverse relationship between oxygen and carbon dioxide contents, that of O_2 decreasing as the CO_2 increases.

Although the actual differences in CO_2 contents are not impressive, comparatively speaking they are significant. Thus, when the soil air contains only 0.25 per cent CO_2 this gas is *more than 8 times* as concentrated as it is in the atmosphere. In cases where the CO_2 content becomes as high as 10 per cent, there is more than 300 times as much present as is found in the air above.

[4] For example, under conditions of extremely poor aeration O_2 contents of soil air as low as 1 per cent have been found. See D. Boynton, *Soils in Relation to Fruit Growing in New York, Part XV. Seasonal and Soil Influences on Oxygen and Carbon Dioxide Levels of New York Orchard Soils*, Cornell Univ. Agr. Exp. Sta. Bul., 763, 1941.

TABLE 10:1

The Composition of Soil Air at Various Locations Compared
to That of the Atmosphere [a]

	Percentage by Volume		
Location	O_2	CO_2	N_2
Soil air:			
England	20.65	0.25	79.20
Iowa	20.40	0.20	79.40
New York	15.10	4.50	81.40
Atmospheric air:			
England	20.97	0.03	79.0

[a] These data were obtained from several sources. See T. L. Lyon; H. O. Buckman; and N. C. Brady, *The Nature and Properties of Soils* (New York: Macmillan, 1952), p. 278.

Compared to the atmosphere, soil air usually is much higher in water vapor, being essentially saturated except at or very near the surface of the soil. This fact has already been stressed in connection with the movement of water. Also the concentration of gases such as methane, hydrogen sulfide, etc., which are formed by organic-matter decomposition is somewhat higher in soil air.

In addition to the free soil air already discussed, the small quantities of certain gases dissolved in the soil moisture must be considered. Also, the soil colloids are thought to hold at their surfaces small quantities of the various gases by physical adsorption. Undoubtedly, gases held in these two ways are of some importance and should not be disregarded in the study of soil aeration. Thus, oxygen so held may be utilized in oxidation reactions while dissolved carbon dioxide is of universal importance, especially in respect to soil pH and the solubility of soil minerals.

10:4. FACTORS AFFECTING THE COMPOSITION OF SOIL AIR

The composition of soil air is largely dependent upon the amount of *air space available* together with the rates of *biochemical reactions* and *gaseous interchange*. In poorly drained soils, a high proportion of the pore space is filled with water. Consequently, these soils offer only small amounts of oxygen to growing organisms. When the air space becomes as low as 10 to 12 per cent of the total soil volume, soil-oxygen renewal is extremely slow and most plants are likely to suffer.[5]

The concentrations of both O_2 and CO_2 are definitely related to the biological activity in the soil. Microbial composition of organic residues, apparently accounts for the major portion of the CO_2 evolved. Incorporation of large quantities of manure, especially if moisture and temperature are optimum, will alter the soil-air composition appreciably. Respiration by higher plants as well as the continuous contribution of their roots to the organic mass by sloughage should not be disregarded. These influences are well illustrated by data from Russell and Appleyard [6] in Figure 10:2. The

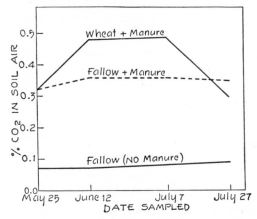

Figure 10:2. The carbon dioxide content of soil air at four different sampling dates, showing the effects of manure and cropping. Air samples were taken from the topsoil only. An unaccountable variation occurred in the data of June 10, hence this sampling date was omitted. *(From Russell and Appleyard.)*

effects of a growing crop and especially that of organic manures are clearly shown.

Subsoil vs. topsoil. As might be expected, subsoils are usually more deficient in oxygen than are topsoils. The total pore space as well as the average size of the pores is generally much less in the deeper horizons. Boynton,[7] working on orchard sites, determined the aeration status of several soils with depth. The average oxygen contents for the months of May and June in two of the soils studied are shown in Figure 10:3.

[5] See G. R. Blake and J. B. Page, "Direct Measurements of Gaseous Diffusion in Soils," *Proc. Soil Sci. Soc. Amer.*, 13: 37–42, 1948.

[6] E. J. Russell and A. Appleyard, "The Atmosphere of the Soil: Its Composition and the Causes of Variation," *Jour. Agr. Sci.*, 7: 25–6, 1915.

[7] D. Boynton, *op. cit.*, pp. 26–43.

In both cases the oxygen percentage in the soil air decreased with depth, the rate of decrease being much more rapid with the heavier soil. Throughout the depth sampled, the lighter-textured sandy loam contained a much higher oxygen percentage. In both cases the decrease in O_2 content could be largely, but not entirely, accounted for by a corresponding increase in CO_2 content. For example, CO_2 percentages as high as 14.6 were recorded for the lower horizons of the heavier-textured soil.

Figure 10:3. The average oxygen contents of two orchard soils during the months of May and June 1938. Normal root growth and functions would occur at much deeper levels on the sandy soil. *(From D. Boynton.)*

Seasonal differences. As would be expected, there is a marked seasonal variation in the composition of soil air. The oxygen content is generally higher during the summer and lower during the winter. The CO_2 content, as might be surmised, is just the reverse. Most of this variation can be accounted for by taking soil-moisture and soil-temperature differences into consideration. Everything else being equal, during those periods of the year when soil moisture is well above average a relatively high CO_2 content and low O_2 content is to be expected. High temperatures encourage this same relationship due to the more rapid microbiological activity. The dependence of soil-air composition on soil moisture and temperature cannot be overemphasized.

10:5. EFFECTS OF SOIL AERATION ON BIOLOGICAL ACTIVITIES

On microorganisms. Perhaps the most apparent effect of poor soil aeration on microbiological processes is a decrease in the rate of organic-matter oxidation. This decrease seems to be associated more with a lack of O_2 than with an excess of CO_2. The slow rate of decay of plant residues in swampy areas is a somewhat exaggerated example of how a lack of oxygen prevents rapid organic-matter decomposition.

All aerobic organisms are unable to function properly in the absence of gaseous oxygen. For example, special purpose bacteria such as those responsible for the oxidation of the elements nitrogen and sulfur are relatively ineffective in poorly aerated soils. This is also true for the symbiotic nitrogen fixers and for some of the nonsymbiotic *(azotobacter)* groups. (See p. 426.)

The microorganism population, therefore, is drastically affected by soil aeration. Only the anaerobic and facultative organisms function properly under poor aeration conditions. They are able to do so because of their ability to utilize combined oxygen. Their activities consequently yield reduced forms of certain elements such as iron and manganese which are often toxic to higher plants. Organic toxins may also develop. Further attention will be given these effects in a subsequent section.

On activities of higher plants.   Higher plants are adversely affected in at least four ways by conditions of poor aeration: (1) the growth of the plant, particularly the roots, is curtailed; (2) the absorption of nutrients and (3) also of water is generally lessened; and (4) the formation of certain inorganic compounds toxic to plant growth are favored by poor aeration. Since the last of these is considered in Section 10:6, only the first three phases will be discussed here.

The abnormal effect of insufficient aeration on root development has often been observed. With root crops such as carrots and sugar beets the influence is most noticeable. Abnormally shaped roots of these plants are common on compact, poorly aerated soils. Even with sod crops the presence of an impervious soil layer generally results in restricted growth particularly of the smaller roots. An example of this is shown in Figure 10:4, in which is pictured the root system of Western wheat grass growing on a clay-pan soil. It is interesting to note the lack of extensive root penetration within the impervious layer. Such restricted root systems can hardly be expected to effectively absorb sufficient moisture and nutrients for normal plant growth.

Apparently, different levels of soil oxygen are required for the various functions of roots. For example, Boynton and co-workers [8] found that apple tree roots required at least 3 per cent of oxygen in the soil air to subsist, while 5 to 10 per cent was sufficient for the growth of existing roots. At least 12 per cent of O_2 was required for new root growth. Their results clearly emphasize the complexity of soil aeration problems.

A deficiency of oxygen has been found to curtail nutrient and water absorption by plants. The exact reasons for the effects of aeration on these two processes are not well understood. However, these processes are known to be influenced quite markedly by the rate of root respiration. Apparently, the *energy* of respiration is utilized in bringing about at least part of the nutrient and water absorption. Since a supply of oxygen must be available

[8] D. Boynton; J. E. DeVilliers; and W. Reuther, "Are there Different Critical Oxygen Concentrations for the Different Phases of Root Activity?" *Science*, 88: 569–70, 1938.

Figure 10:4. Effect of soil structure and aeration upon the root development of Nebraska range grass. *Left*—normal distribution. *Right*—influence of a compact, poorly aerated zone (indicated by arrow). *(Photos by J. E. Weaver.)*

if roots are to respire normally, a deficiency of this gas naturally results in sluggish nutrient and water uptake. It is surprising as well as ironical that an oversupply of water in the soil tends to reduce the amount of water which plants will absorb.

The effect of aeration on nutrient absorption is of considerable practical significance. Under poor aeration conditions, for example, plants exhibit nutrient-deficiency symptoms on soils fairly well supplied with available nutrient elements. Also, on certain soils, improper tillage may destroy the granulation leaving conditions that lead to inefficient nutrient utilization.[9] The desirability of the frequent cultivation of heavy, poorly granulated soils when planted to row crops is undoubtedly related to this problem of nutrient uptake.

10:6. OTHER EFFECTS OF SOIL AERATION

As previously noted, anaerobic decomposition of organic materials is much slower than that occurring when ample gaseous oxygen is available. Moreover, the products of decomposition are entirely different. For example, the complete anaerobic decomposition of sugar occurs as follows:

$$C_6H_{12}O_6 \longrightarrow 3CO_2 + 3CH_4$$

$$\text{Sugar} \qquad\qquad \text{Methane}$$

Less complete decomposition yields other products such as organic acids, which under extreme conditions may accumulate in toxic quantities. Examples of acids occurring by anaerobic decay are lactic, butyric, and citric.

When decomposed anaerobically, organic nitrogen compounds usually yield amines and gaseous nitrogen compounds in addition to ammonia. Of course, these nitrogen compounds remain in reduced forms, not being subject to nitrification under anaerobic conditions. The absence of oxygen thus completely changes the nature of the decay processes as well as the rates at which they occur.

The chemical forms of certain elements found in soils in the oxidized and reduced states are shown in Table 10:2. In general, it can be stated that the oxidized forms are much more desirable for most of our common crops. The advantages of the oxidized states of the nitrogen and sulfur compounds have already been discussed. (See p. 36.) The desirability of the higher-valent forms of iron and manganese is associated with the solubility of these elements, at least in humid-region soils. The reduced

[9] See J. B. Page; C. J. Willard; and G. W. McCuen, "Progress Report on Tillage Methods in Preparing Land for Corn," *Proc. Soil Sci. Soc. Amer.*, 11: 77–80, 1946.

TABLE 10:2

Oxidized and Reduced Forms of Several Important Elements [a]

Element	Normal Form in Well-oxidized Soils	Reduced Form Found in Waterlogged Soils
Carbon	CO_2	CH_4
Nitrogen	NO_3^-	N_2 and NH_4^+
Sulfur	$SO_4^=$	H_2S and $S^=$
Iron	Fe +++ (Ferric oxides)	Fe ++ (Ferrous oxides)
Manganese	Mn ++++ (Manganic oxides)	Mn ++ (Manganous oxides)

[a] Modified from R. Bradfield; L. P. Batjer; and J. Oskamp, *Soils in Relation to Fruit Growing in New York, IV: Significance of the Oxidation-reduction Potential in Evaluating Soils for Orchard Purposes,* Cornell Univ. Agr. Exp. Sta. Bul. 592, 1934.

states, being more soluble than the oxidized forms, are often present in such quantities as to be toxic. This is true especially if the poor aeration occurs in an acid soil. Lack of lime thus intensifies the adverse effects of poor aeration on iron and manganese toxicity. The insolubility of the oxidized forms of iron and manganese under alkaline conditions may result in a deficiency of these elements. Consequently, the interrelation of soil pH and aeration is very important in determining whether an excess or a deficiency of iron and manganese is apt to occur.

In addition to the chemical aspect of these differences, *soil color* is markedly influenced by the oxidation status of iron and manganese. Colors such as red, yellow, reddish brown, etc., are encouraged by well-oxidized conditions. More subdued shades such as grays and blues predominate if insufficient O_2 is present. These facts are made use of in field methods of determining the need for drainage. Imperfectly drained soils usually show a condition wherein alternate streaks of oxidized and reduced materials occur. This *mottled* condition indicates a zone of alternate good and poor aeration—a condition not conducive to proper plant growth.

10:7. AERATION IN RELATION TO SOIL AND CROP MANAGEMENT

In view of the overwhelming importance of soil oxygen to the growth of most of the common crop plants, the question naturally arises as to the practical means of facilitating its supply. Interestingly enough, almost all methods employed for aeration control are concerned directly or indirectly with the management of soil water.

Measures that will encourage soil aeration logically fall into two categories: (1) those designed to remove excess soil moisture; and (2) those concerned with the aggregation and cultivation of the soil. Each of these will be considered briefly.

Both surface and under drainage is essential if one expects an aerobic soil environment. Since the nonsolid spaces in the soil are shared by air and water, the removal of excess quantities of the latter must take place if sufficient oxygen is to be supplied. The importance of surface runoff and tile drainage in this respect have already received attention and only need re-emphasis in connection with soil aeration. (For influence of drainage see p. 222.)

The maintenance of a stable soil structure should not be overlooked as a means of augmenting good aeration. Pores of macrosize, usually greatly encouraged by large stable aggregates, are soon freed of water following a rain, thus allowing gases to move into the soil from the atmosphere above. Organic-matter maintenance by the addition of farm manure and the growth of legumes is perhaps the most practical means of encouraging aggregate stability, which in turn will encourage good drainage and better aeration. These features have received adequate attention elsewhere. (See p. 61.)

In heavy soils, however, it is often impossible to maintain optimum aeration without resorting to the mechanical stirring of the soil by some type of cultivation. Thus, in addition to controlling weeds, cultivation in many cases has a second very important function—that of aiding soil aeration. Yields of row crops, especially those with large tap roots such as sugar beets and rutabagas, are often increased by frequent light cultivations that do not injure the fibrous roots. Part of this increase, undoubtedly, is due to aeration.

Crop-soil adaptation.   In addition to the direct methods of controlling soil aeration, one more phase of soil and crop management should be mentioned—that of crop-soil adaptation. The seriousness of oxygen deficiency depends to a large degree on the crop to be grown. Alfalfa, fruit trees, and other deep-rooted plants, for example, require deep, well-aerated soils and are quite sensitive to a deficiency of oxygen, even in the lower soil horizons. Shallow-rooted plants such as alsike and ladino clovers, on the other hand, do very well on soils which tend to be poorly aerated, especially in the subsoil. These facts should not be overlooked in deciding what crops should be grown and how they are to be managed in areas where aeration problems are acute.

The dominating influence of moisture on the aeration of soils is everywhere apparent. And the control of the former means at least a partial control of the latter. This leads to a second important physical property that is at times influenced by soil water—that of soil temperature. Let us direct our attention first to some of the fundamentals concerned with this important physical characteristic.

10:8. SOIL TEMPERATURE [10]

It is universally recognized that chemical and biological activities are an energy expression. It is also known that such changes, especially the latter, will not continue with adequate intensity unless certain temperatures are maintained. The temperature of the soil is thus a factor of vital concern. For instance, nitrification does not begin until the soil reaches a temperature of about 40° F., the most favorable limits being 80° to 90° F. Temperatures optimum for seed germination and plant growth, as might be expected, vary widely, being low for such crops as bluegrass and high for corn.

In addition to the direct influence of temperature on plant and animal life the effects of freezing and thawing must be considered. Frost action along with later thawing is responsible for some of the physical weathering which takes place in soils. As ice forms in rock crevices it forces the rocks apart causing them to disintegrate. Similarly, alternate freezing and thawing subjects the soil aggregates and clumps to pressures and thus alters the physical set up in the soil. Freezing and thawing of the upper layers of soil can also result in so-called *heaving* of perennial forage crops such as alfalfa. (See Fig. 10:5.) This action which is most severe on bare, imperfectly drained soils can drastically reduce the stand of alfalfa, some clovers, and trefoil.

The temperature of soils in the field is dependent directly or indirectly upon at least three factors: (1) the net amount of heat the soil absorbs; (2) the heat energy required to bring about a given change in the temperature of a soil; and (3) the energy required for changes such as evaporation which are constantly occurring at or near the surface of soils. These phases will be considered in order.

10:9. ABSORPTION AND LOSS OF HEAT

The amount of heat absorbed by soils is determined primarily by the quantity of effective solar radiation reaching the earth. (See Fig. 10:7.)

---

[10] For a rather full edaphological discussion of soil heat, see T. L. Lyon and H. O. Buckman, *Nature and Properties of Soils* (New York: Macmillan, 1922), Chap. 9. See also L. D. Baver, *Soil Physics* (New York: Wiley, 1940), Chap. 8.

The latter in any particular locality depends fundamentally upon climate. But the amount of energy entering the soil is, in addition, affected by other factors such as: (1) the color; (2) the slope; and (3) the vegetative cover

Figure 10:5. Alternate freezing and thawing of soils result in the "heaving" of perennial plants out of the ground. The above alfalfa crowns were exposed as a result of this type of action during the winter and spring months.

of the site under consideration. It is well known that dark soils will absorb more energy than light-colored ones [11] and that red and yellow soils will show a more rapid temperature rise than will those that are white. Observation has also shown that the nearer the angle of incident of the sun's rays approaches the perpendicular, the greater will be the absorption. (See Fig. 10:6.) As an example, a southerly slope of 20 degrees, a level soil, and a northerly slope of 20 degrees receive energy on June 21 at the 42nd parallel, north, in the proportion of 106, 100, and 81, respectively.

The temperature of southward slopes varies with the time of year. For example, in the northern hemisphere the southeasterly inclination is generally warmest in the early season, the southerly slope during midseason, and the southwesterly slope in the fall. Southern or southeasterly slopes are often preferred by gardeners. Orchardists and foresters consider exposure

[11] This does not imply that dark-colored soils are always warmer. Actually the opposite may be true since dark-colored soils usually are high in organic matter and consequently hold large amounts of water which must also be warmed.

an important factor not only in regard to the species or variety of tree to be grown but also in respect to sunscald and certain plant diseases.

Whether the soil is bare or covered with vegetation is another factor that markedly influences the amount of insulation received. The effect of a forest is universally recognized. Even an ordinary field crop, such as bluegrass, has a very noticeable influence, especially upon temperature fluctuations. Bare soils warm up more quickly and cool off more rapidly than those covered with vegetation, or with artificial mulches. Frost penetration during the winter is considerably greater in bare noninsulated land.

Figure 10:6. Diagram showing the area of soil warmed as affected by the angle at which the sun's rays strike the soil. If a given amount of radiation from the sun strikes the soil at right angles (left above), the radiation is concentrated in a relatively small area and the soil warms up quite rapidly. If that same amount of radiation strikes the soil at a 45° angle (right above), the area affected is larger, the radiation is not as concentrated and the soil warms up more slowly. This is one of the reasons why north slopes tend to have cooler soils than south slopes. It also accounts for the colder soils in winter as compared to summers.

Loss of heat to atmosphere. It should be pointed out that part of the solar radiation is not permanently retained by the soil but rather is lost directly to the atmosphere. The processes which are responsible for these losses are: (1) *conduction* [12] to the atmosphere, and (2) *radiation* [13] into outer space. (See Fig. 10:7.) While conduction no doubt is of considerable importance, especially if the air above the soil is in rapid movement, radiation probably accounts for a great loss of energy. Terrestrial bodies are continually giving off energy waves into the atmosphere. Since these rays are mostly of the infrared type and make no impression on the eye, they are often spoken of as *dark rays*. Suffice it to say, their energy capacity is high and, as their emission is continuous, much heat is lost in this way. This accounts in part, especially during clear weather, for rapid changes in surface-soil temperatures.

10:10. SPECIFIC HEAT OF SOILS

Another major factor affecting the temperature relations of a soil is its specific heat or its thermal capacity compared with that of water. Specific

[12] A molecular transfer of energy from one body to another when they are in contact or from one part of a particular body to another. The energy is conceived as communicated progressively from molecule to molecule.

[13] A transfer of energy through space by means of waves or pulsations which are transformed into heat values when they encounter an obstructing body.

heat may be expressed as a ratio of the quantity of heat required to raise the temperature of a given substance from 15° to 16° C. compared to that required for the same temperature rise of an equal weight of water. The

Figure 10:7. A diagram showing the acquisition, loss, and movement of heat in soils.

importance of this property in soil-temperature control undoubtedly is great. The mere absorption of a given amount of heat by a soil does not necessarily assure a rapid rise in temperature. Everything else being equal, a soil with a high specific heat exhibits much less rapid temperature changes than does one having a low specific heat.

Under actual field conditions the soil moisture content determines, more than any other factor, the energy required to raise the temperature of soils. For instance, the dry-weight specific heat of mineral soils, in spite of variations in texture and organic matter, is about 0.20. But if the moisture is advanced to 20 per cent, the specific heat of the wet mass becomes 0.33, while an increase of 30 per cent of moisture raises the wet-weight specific heat to 0.38.[14] Obviously, therefore, since moisture is one of the major factors in respect to the heat capacity of a soil, it has much to do with the rate both of the warming up and the cooling off of soils.

---

[14] These figures can be easily verified. For example, consider the above soil at 20 per cent moisture content. Remembering that soil moisture is expressed as grams of water per 100 grams of soil solids, we have in this case 20 gms. of H_2O with each 100 gms. of soil. The number of calories required to raise the temperature of 20 gms. of water by 1° C. is:

$$20 \text{ (gms.)} \times 1 \text{ (cal. per gm.)} = 20 \text{ calories}$$

The corresponding figure for the 100 gms. of soil solids is:

$$100 \text{ (gms.)} \times 0.2 \text{ (cal. per gm.)} = 20 \text{ calories}$$

Thus, a total of 40 calories are required to raise the temperature of 120 gms. of the moist soil by 1° C. Since the *specific heat* is the number of calories required to raise the temperature of one gram of wet soil by 1° C., in this case it is:

$$40/120 = 0.33 \text{ calories per gram}$$

Now verify the 0.38 figure for the soil with a 30 per cent moisture content.

10:11. HEAT OF VAPORIZATION

Soil moisture is also of major importance in determining the amount of heat used in the process of the evaporation of soil water. Vaporization is caused by an increased activity of the soil water molecules. This requires the expenditure of a certain amount of energy which results in a cooling effect especially at the surface where most of the evaporation occurs. It requires about 585 gram calories to evaporate 1 gram of water at 68° F. Similarly, 265 kilogram calories are required to evaporate 1 pound of water at the same temperature. This latter figure is sufficient to lower the temperature of a cubic foot of a representative mineral soil at optimum moisture about 28° F., providing that all of the energy of evaporation comes from the soil and its water. Such a figure is, of course, empirical as only a part of the heat of vaporization comes from the soil itself. Nevertheless, it indicates the tremendous cooling influence of evaporation.

The low temperature of a wet soil is due partially to evaporation and partially to high specific heat. King [15] found during April that an undrained soil in Wisconsin ranged from 2.5° F. to 12.5° F. lower than one of the same type well drained. Drained and undrained soils at Urbana, Illinois,[16] showed maximum differences of 13.7° F., 9.0° F., and 6.2° F. at depths of 1, 2, and 4 inches respectively. The influence upon the surface layers is especially marked.

Soil color and temperature. At this point it is appropriate again to call attention to the interrelationship of soil color and soil temperature. Although dark-colored soils absorb heat readily, such soils, due to their usually high organic-matter status often have high moisture contents. Under such soil conditions, the evaporation and specific heat relationships become especially important. Consequently, a dark-colored soil, particularly if it happens to be somewhat poorly drained, may not warm up as quickly in the spring as will a well-drained light-colored soil nearby.

10:12. MOVEMENT OF HEAT IN SOILS

Before dealing with actual temperature data, let us consider briefly the movement of thermal energy in the soil. As already mentioned, much of the solar insulation is dissipated into the atmosphere. Some, however, slowly penetrates the profile largely by *conduction*. (See Fig. 10:7.) While this type of movement is influenced by a number of factors, the most im-

[15] F. H. King, *Physics of Agriculture,* pub. by author, Madison, Wis., 1910, p. 20.

[16] J. G. Mosier and A. F. Gustafson, *Soil Physics and Management* (Philadelphia: Lippincott, 1917), p. 302.

portant is probably the moisture content of the soil layers. Heat passes from soil to water about 150 times easier than from soil to air. As the water increases in a soil, the air decreases and the transfer resistance is lowered decidedly. When sufficient water is present to join most of the soil particles, further additions will have little effect on heat conduction. Here again the major role of soil moisture comes to the fore.

The significance of conduction in respect to field temperatures is not difficult to grasp. It provides a means of temperature adjustment but, because it is slow, the subsoil-changes tend to lag behind those to which the surface layers are subjected. More than this, the changes that do occur are always less in the subsoil. In temperate regions, we expect surface soils in general to be warmer in summer and cooler in winter than the subsoil, especially the lower horizons of the latter.

10:13. SOIL TEMPERATURE DATA

The temperature of the soil at any time depends on the ratio of the energy absorbed and that being lost. The constant change in this relationship is reflected in the *seasonal, monthly,* and *daily* temperatures. The accompanying data from College Station, Texas (Fig. 10.8) are representative of average seasonal temperatures in relation to soil depth.

Figure 10:8. Average monthly soil temperatures for 6 of the 12 months of the year at different soil depths at College Station, Texas (1951–55). Note the lag in changes in soil temperature at the lower depths. (Reprinted from Fluker, B. J. "Soil Temperature" *Soil Sci.,* 86: 35–46, 1958.)

It is apparent from these figures that the seasonal variations of soil temperature are considerable even at the lower depths. The surface layers vary more or less in accord with the air temperature and, therefore, exhibit a greater fluctuation than the subsoil. On the average, the surface 6-inch layer of soil is warmer than the air at every season of the year, while the subsoil is warmer in autumn and winter but cooler in spring and summer due to its protected position and the lag in conduction.

This lag in temperature change in the subsoil is especially noticeable when the monthly march of soil temperature at Lincoln, Nebraska is considered. The monthly average temperatures, plotted in Figure 10:9, show a greater annual range in temperature for the surface soil than for the air. Daily data would, of course, show the greatest range for the soil air. It must be kept in mind that changes in soil temperature, except at the very surface, are gradual while the air may vary many degrees in a very short time.

Figure 10:9. Average monthly air and soil temperatures at Lincoln, Nebraska (12 years). Note that the 3-inch soil layer is consistently warmer than the air above and that the 36-inch soil horizon is cooler in spring and summer, but warmer in the fall and winter than surface soil.

The daily and hourly temperatures of the atmospheric air and the soil in temperate zones may show considerable agreement or marked divergence according to conditions. Fluctuations are, of course, more rapid in the case of air temperatures, and in temperate regions usually are greater. It is well to remember, however, that the maximum temperature of a dry surface soil may definitely exceed that of the air, possibly approaching in some cases 125° or 130° F. But in winter even surface soils do not fall greatly below freezing.

With a solar control and a clear sky, the air temperature in temperate regions rises from morning to a maximum at about two o'clock. The surface soil, however, does not reach its maximum until later in the afternoon due to the usual lag. (Fig. 10:10.) This retardation is greater and the temperature change is less as the depth increases. The lower subsoil shows little daily or weekly fluctuation, the variation, as already emphasized, being a slow monthly or seasonal change.

10:14. SOIL TEMPERATURE CONTROL

The temperature of field soils is subject to no radical human regulation. The use of organic mulches will give lower and more uniform surface-soil temperatures. (Fig. 10:10.) Such a practice has limited application, however, over large acreages and is used mostly for gardens and flower beds.

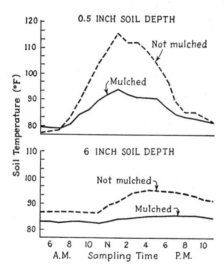

Figure 10:10. The effect of a sawdust mulch on the temperature at two depths of a Georgia soil on August 11. Note that the mulched area is cooler and is less subject to fluctuations than the area where no mulch was applied. (From A. W. White, Jr.; J. E. Giddens; and H. D. Morris, "The Effect of Sawdust on Crop Growth and Physical and Biological Properties of Cecil Soil," *Proc. Soil Sci. Soc. Amer.*, 23: 365–368, 1959.)

Soil-management methods, especially those that influence soil moisture, do provide for small but biologically vital modifications. Let us compare briefly the temperature relations of a well-drained and a poorly drained soil in a humid temperate region. The latter soil has a high specific heat. Therefore, large amounts of radiant energy must be absorbed to raise the soil temperature by those few extra degrees so badly needed in early spring. And since the excess water will not percolate through this soil, much of it must be removed by evaporation, another costly process in terms of heat dissipation. The low temperatures of poorly drained soils, especially in the spring, are well known. Experienced men expect a range from 6 to 12° F. lower in the surface layer than in comparable well-drained areas. Drainage is, of course, the only practicable expedient.

Besides the control relations already mentioned, there is the influence of downward moving water on soil temperature. In general, it has a cooling effect except possibly in the early spring. Precipitation is usually cooler than the soil in temperate regions, especially in the summer. But even if rain water should be 10° F. warmer than the soil, an improbable assumption, an average rain would raise the temperature of the surface 6 inches only slightly, and this would be quickly offset by the cooling effects of surface evaporation.

As was the case with soil air, the controlling influence of soil water on soil temperature is everywhere apparent. Whether it is a question of acquisition of insolation, loss of energy to the atmosphere, or the movement of heat to and fro within the soil, the percentage of water present is always important. Water regulation seems to be the key to what little practical temperature control it is possible to exert on field soils.

The Origin, Nature, and Classification of Parent Materials

CHAPTER 11

The influence of weathering is evident on all sides. Nothing escapes it. It breaks up the country rocks, it modifies or destroys their physical and chemical characteristics, and carries away the soluble products and even some of the solids as well. The unconsolidated residues, *the regolith*, are left behind. But weathering goes further. It synthesizes a soil from the upper layers of this heterogeneous mass. Hence, the regolith, or at least its upper portions, may be designated as *parent material* of soils.[1]

Nor are these parent materials always allowed to remain undisturbed on the site of their development. Climatic agencies often shift them from place to place, with further grinding and leaching, until at last they are allowed to rest long enough for soil profile development to take place. A study of weathering and of the parent materials that result is not only interesting in itself, but it is also a necessary introduction to soil formation and classification.

We shall begin the study of parent materials with a brief review of kinds of rocks from which the regolith and in turn the soils have formed.

11:1. CLASSIFICATION AND PROPERTIES OF ROCKS

The rocks found in the earth's crust are commonly classified as (1) igneous, (2) sedimentary, or (3) metamorphic. Those of igneous origin

---

[1] *Parent material* may be defined as "the unconsolidated and more or less chemically weathered mineral material from which soils may be synthesized." It is the C horizon of the pedologist. (See note on p. 294 for a more complete statement.) For a detailed discussion of weathering, see: M. L. Jackson and G. D. Sherman, "Chemical Weathering of Minerals in Soils," *Advances in Agronomy,* 5: 219–318, 1953.

are formed from molten lava and include such common rocks as *granite* and *diorite* (Fig. 11:1). They are composed of primary minerals such as (1) quartz, (2) the feldspars, and (3) the dark-colored minerals in-

Figure 11:1. Diagram showing the classification of some igneous rocks in relation to mineralogical composition and the size of mineral grains in the rock (rock texture). Light-colored minerals and quartz are generally more prominent than are the dark-colored minerals.

cluding biotite, augite, and hornblende. In general, gabbro and basalt (Fig. 11:2) which are high in the dark-colored, iron- and magnesium-containing minerals are more easily weathered than are the granites and other lighter colored rocks.

Sedimentary rocks have resulted from the deposition and recementation of weathering products of other rocks. For example, quartz sand weathered from a granite and deposited in the bottom of a prehistoric sea, may, through geological changes, have become cemented into a solid mass. This would be called a *sandstone*. Similarly, recemented clays are termed *shale*. Other important sedimentary rocks are shown in Table 11:1, along with a list of their dominant minerals. As might be expected, the resistance of a

TABLE 11:1

Some of the More Important Sedimentary and Metamorphic Rocks and the Minerals Commonly Dominant in Them

Sedimentary Rocks	Dominant Mineral	Metamorphic Rocks	Dominant Mineral
Limestone	Calcite ($CaCO_3$)	Gneiss	(Varies) [a]
Dolomite	Dolomite $CaMg(CO_3)_2$	Schist	(Varies) [a]
Sandstone	Quartz (SiO_2)	Quartzite	Quartz (SiO_2)
Shale	Clays	Slate	Clays
Conglomerate	(Varies) [b]	Marble	Calcite ($CaCO_3$)

[a] The minerals present are determined by the original rock which has been changed by metamorphism. Primary minerals present in the igneous rocks commonly dominate these rocks, although some secondary minerals are also present.

[b] Small stones of various mineralogical makeup will be cemented into conglomerate.

given sedimentary rock to weathering is determined by the particular minerals which are dominant and by the cementing agent.

Metamorphic rocks are those which have formed by the metamorphism or change in form of other rocks. Igneous and sedimentary masses which have been subjected to tremendous pressures and high temperature have succumbed to metamorphism. Igneous rocks are commonly modified to form *gneisses* and *schists* while those of sedimentary origin such as sandstone and shale may be changed to *quartzite* and *slate*, respectively. Some of the common metamorphic rocks are shown in Table 11:1. As was the case with those of igneous and sedimentary origin, the particular mineral or minerals which dominate a given metamorphic rock will influence its resistance to weathering. (See Table 11:2 for a listing of the more common minerals.)

11:2. WEATHERING—A GENERAL CASE

Before we consider the various kinds of parent materials which develop from rocks, let us first examine the general trends of weathering which are responsible for the formation of the regolith and in turn, the soils. In a very general way some of the changes which take place during weathering are illustrated by the diagram in Figure 11:2. Study it carefully, keeping in mind that it deals primarily with weathering as it occurs in temperate regions.

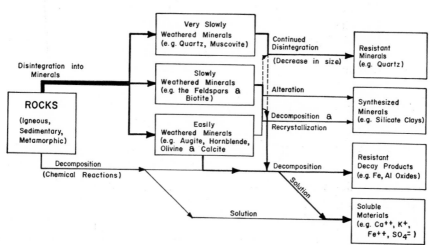

Figure 11:2. A generalized diagram showing trends in weathering which take place under acid conditions common in humid-temperate regions. One would expect climate to modify the exact relationships. In arid regions, physical breakdown (disintegration) would dominate and soluble ions would not be lost in large quantities. In humid regions decomposition becomes more important.

TABLE 11:2

**The More Important Original and Secondary Minerals Found in Soils.
(The original minerals are also found abundantly in igneous and
metamorphic rocks. Secondary minerals are commonly found in
sedimentary rocks.)**

Original Minerals	
Name	*Formula*
Quartz	SiO_2
Microcline)	
Orthoclase)	$KAlSi_3O_8$
Na-plagioclase	$NaAlSi_3O_8$
Ca-plagioclase	$CaAl_2Si_2O_8$
Muscovite	$KAl_3Si_3O_{10}(OH)_2$
Biotite	$KAl(Mg \cdot Fe)_3Si_3O_{10}(OH)_2$
Hornblende [a]	$Ca_2Al_2Mg_2Fe_3, Si_6O_{22}(OH)_2$
Augite [a]	$Ca_2(Al \cdot Fe)_4(Mg \cdot Fe)_4Si_6O_{24}$

Secondary Minerals	
Name	*Formula*
Calcite	$CaCO_3$
Dolomite	$CaMg(CO_3)_2$
Gypsum	$CaSO_4 \cdot 2H_2O$
Apatite	$Ca_5(PO_4)_3 \cdot (Cl, F)$
Limonite	$Fe_2O_3 \cdot 3H_2O$
Hematite	Fe_2O_3
Gibbsite	$Al_2O_3 \cdot 3H_2O$
Clay minerals	Al-silicates

[a] These are approximate formulas only since these minerals are so variable in their composition.

Weathering is basically a combination of destruction and synthesis. Rocks, which are the original starting point in the weathering process, are first broken down into smaller rocks and eventually into the individual minerals of which they are composed. Simultaneously, rock fragments and the minerals therein are attacked by weathering forces and are changed to new minerals either by minor modifications (alterations) or by complete chemical changes. These changes are accompanied by a continued decrease in particle size and by the release of soluble constituents, most of which are subject to loss in drainage waters.

The minerals which are synthesized are shown (Fig. 11:2) in two groups: (1) the silicate clays, and (2) the very resistant end products including iron and aluminum oxides. Along with the very resistant primary minerals such as quartz these two groups dominate temperate-region soils.

The processes. Two basic processes are concerned in the changes indicated in Figure 11:2. These are mechanical and chemical. The former is often desigated as *disintegration,* the latter as *decomposition.* Both are operative as you move from left to right in the weathering diagram. Forces responsible for disintegration bring about a decrease in size of rocks and minerals without appreciably affecting their composition. By decomposition, however, definite chemical changes take place, soluble materials are released, and new minerals are synthesized or are left as resistant end products. Mechanical and chemical processes may be outlined as follows:

1. Mechanical (disintegration)
   a. Temperature—differential expansion of minerals, frost action, and exfoliation.
   b. Erosion and deposition—by water, ice, and wind.
   c. Plant and animal influences.
2. Chemical (decomposition)
   a. Hydrolysis.
   b. Hydration.
   c. Carbonation and related acidity processes.
   d. Oxidation.
   e. Solution.

The reader who is interested in only a general coverage of this subject may not be concerned with sections 11:3–11:5 inclusive. They are of significance, however, in obtaining an understanding of how weathering forces work.

11:3. MECHANICAL FORCES OF WEATHERING

Temperature effects. Variations of temperature, especially if sudden or wide, greatly influence the disintegration of rocks. During the day, rocks become heated and at night often cool much below the temperature of the air. This warming and cooling is particularly effective as a disintegrating agent. Rocks are aggregates of minerals which differ in their coefficients of expansion upon being heated. With every temperature change, therefore, differential stresses are set up which eventually must produce cracks and rifts, thus encouraging mechanical breakdown.

Due to slow heat conduction, the outer surface of a rock is often at a markedly different temperature than the inner and more protected portions. This differential heating and cooling tend to set up lateral stresses which, in time, may cause the surface layers to peel away from the parent mass. This phenomenon is spoken of as *exfoliation* and at times is markedly accelerated by the freezing of included water.

The presence of water, if freezing occurs, greatly increases the mechanical effects just mentioned. The force developed by the freezing of water is equivalent to about 150 tons to the square foot, an almost irresistible pressure.[2] It widens cracks in huge boulders and dislodges mineral grains from smaller fragments. Nor is this influence of temperature ended when rocks are reduced to fragments. It carries onward in the parent material and finally in the resultant soil. Freezing and thawing are of great practical importance in altering the physical condition of medium- and fine-textured soils.

Influence of water, ice, and wind.   Rainwater beats down upon the land and then travels oceanward, continually shifting, sorting, and reworking unconsolidated materials of all kinds. When loaded with such sediments, water has a tremendous cutting power as is amply demonstrated by the gorges, ravines, and valleys the country over. The rounding of sand grains on an ocean beach is further evidence of the abrasion which accompanies water movement.

Ice is an erosive and transporting agency of tremendous capacity, and next to water is perhaps the most important and spectacular physical agent of weathering. One must visit Greenland or Alaska to realize its power. The abrasive action of glaciers as they move under their own weight disintegrates rocks and minerals alike. Not only do glaciers affect the underlying solid rock, but also they grind and mix unconsolidated materials which have been picked up as they move over the countryside. Even though they are not so extensive at the present time, glaciers in ages past have been responsible for the transportation and deposition of parent materials over millions of acres. The importance of ice as a mechanical agent is not to be minimized. (See p. 311 and ff.)

Wind has always been an important carrying agent and, when armed with fine debris, exerts an abrasive action also. Dust storms of almost continental extent have occurred in the past, with the result that tons of material have been filched from one section and transferred to another. As dust is transferred and deposited, abrasion of one particle against another occurs. The rounded rock remnants in some arid areas of the West are caused largely by wind action.

Plants.   Simple plants, such as mosses and lichens, grow upon exposed rock, there to catch dust until a thin film of highly organic material accumulates. Higher plants sometimes exert a prying effect on rock which results in some disintegration. This is most noticeable in the case of tree roots in rocky sections. Such influences, as well as those exerted by animals, are, however, of little import in producing parent material when compared to the drastic physical effects of water, ice, wind, and temperature changes.

11:4. CHEMICAL PROCESSES OF WEATHERING

Scarcely has the disintegration of rock material begun when its decomposition usually is also apparent. This is especially noticeable in humid regions where chemical and physical processes are particularly active and markedly accelerate each other.

Hydrolysis.   The reaction of minerals with water is perhaps the most im-

---

[2] This is equivalent to a pressure of about 142 atmospheres or over 4 times the negative tension exerted upon the water molecules at the liquid-air interface of a soil when its moisture content is at the hygroscopic coefficient.

portant way by which chemical breakdown occurs. Hydrolysis, which is a decomposition reaction, is important in the weathering of a wide range of minerals including the feldspars and micas. The change may be indicated as follows, using microcline ($KAlSi_3O_8$) as the mineral undergoing hydrolysis:

$$KAlSi_3O_8 + HOH \longrightarrow HAlSi_3O_8 + KOH$$
$$2HAlSi_3O_8 + 8HOH \longrightarrow Al_2O_3 \cdot 3H_2O + 6H_2SiO_3$$

The potassium released by this reaction is soluble and can be adsorbed by the soil colloids, used by plants or removed in the drainage water. The aluminum and silicon compounds may recrystallize into a clay mineral such as kaolinite. If conditions are suitable, one or both may remain in the soil as their respective oxides, or they may be removed in the drainage.

Hydration. Hydration involves the rigid attachment of H and OH ions to the compound being attacked. In most cases, these ions become an integral part of the mineral crystal lattice. As micas become hydrated, some H and OH move in between the platelike layers. In so doing, they tend to expand the crystal and make it more porous, thus hastening other decomposition processes.

A good example of hydration is the development of limonite from hematite. It may be shown as follows:

$$2Fe_2O_3 + 3H_2O \longrightarrow 2Fe_2O_3 \cdot 3H_2O$$
$$\text{Hematite (red)} \qquad\qquad \text{Limonite (yellow)}$$

When the products of hydration dry out due to varying weather conditions, dehydration may occur. Thus, limonite may readily be changed to hematite, with a noticeable change in color. Variations in the color of subsoils in the Southeastern states are due to a considerable extent to the reaction cited above.

Carbonation and other acidic processes. The disintegration and decomposition of mineral matter are greatly hastened by the presence of the hydrogen ion in percolating waters. Even that contained in carbonic acid is effective in this respect. For example, this acid is known to result in the chemical solution of calcite in limestone, the following reaction being illustrative of what takes place:

$$CaCO_3 + H_2CO_3 \longrightarrow Ca(HCO_3)_2$$
$$\text{Calcite} \qquad\qquad \text{Soluble Bicarbonate}$$

Other acids much stronger than carbonic are also present in most humid region soils. They include very dilute inorganic acids such as HNO_3 and H_2SO_4 as well as some organic acids. Also present are the H ions associated with soil clays which are available for reaction with other soil minerals.

An example of the reaction of H ions with soil minerals is that of an acid clay with a feldspar such as anorthite.

$$CaAlSi_2O_8 + \begin{matrix} H \\ H \end{matrix} \boxed{\text{Micelle}} \longrightarrow H_2AlSi_2O_8 + Ca \boxed{\text{Micelle}}$$
$$\text{Anorthite} \qquad\qquad\qquad\qquad \text{Acid Silicate}$$

The mechanism is simple, the H ions of the acid clays replacing the bases of the fresh minerals which they may closely contact. An acid silicate results which is subject to recrystallization, thus producing clay. Thus, "clay begets clay" by a mechanism that depends upon the removal of bases from the weathering mass of minerals by insoluble inorganic acids.[3]

Oxidation.   Of the various chemical changes due to weathering, oxidation is usually one of the first to be noticed. It is particularly manifest in rocks carrying iron, an element which is easily oxidized. In some minerals the iron is present in the reduced or ferrous (Fe^{++}) form. If the oxidation to the ferric ion takes place while the iron is still part of the crystal lattice, other ionic adjustments must be made since a 3-valent ion is replacing a 2-valent one. These adjustments result in a less stable crystal which is then subject to both disintegration and decomposition.

In other cases, the ferrous iron may be released from the crystal and almost simultaneously oxidized to the ferric form. An example of this is the hydration of olivine and the release of ferrous oxide which may be immediately oxidized to ferric oxide (hematite).

$$3MgFeSiO_4 + 2H_2O \longrightarrow H_4Mg_3Si_2O_9 + SiO_2 + 3FeO$$

Olivine   Serpentine   Ferrous Oxide

$$4FeO + O_2 \longrightarrow 2Fe_2O_3$$

Ferrous Oxide   Hematite

Solution.   The solvent action of water and the ions it carries as it moves through and around rocks and minerals furthers the weathering process. The solution effects of dissolved CO_2 and the H ions in water have already been mentioned. Also, the release of soluble potassium by hydrolysis of orthoclase has been cited. In each case, ions of the alkali metals (Na, K, etc.) or the alkaline earths (Ca, Mg, etc.) were represented as being solubilized rather readily. (See Table 11:3.) Less spectacular is the slower dissolution of some iron, silicon, and aluminum. These elements are subject to solution, the specific climatic conditions determining the extent to which it occurs.

11:5. FACTORS AFFECTING WEATHERING OF MINERALS

Many factors influence the rate of weathering of minerals. Because of this, few generalizations can be made concerning the rate at which their breakdown will occur. It has been established, however, that certain general factors have a marked effect on the weathering process. For example, the following are known to be significant: (1) climatic conditions; (2) physical properties; and (3) chemical characteristics of the rocks and minerals. These will each be discussed briefly.

Climatic conditions.   If sufficient time is allowed, the climatic conditions, more than any other factor, will tend to control the kind and rate of weathering which take place. Only a few examples of the many effects of varied climatic factors will be cited.

Under conditions of low rainfall, there is a dominance of mechanical processes of weathering, which decrease particle size with little change in composition. The presence of more moisture encourages chemical as well as mechanical changes, new

[3] For a more detailed consideration of acid clays as weathering agents see: E. R. Graham and H. C. Turley, "Soil Development and Plant Nutrition: III. The Transfer of Potassium from the Nonavailable Form as Reflected by the Growth and Composition of Soybeans," *Proc. Soil Sci. Soc. Amer.*, 12: 332–35, 1947.

minerals and soluble products resulting. In humid-temperate regions, silicate clays are among the minerals synthesized. They account for much of the strong agricultural character of soils in these areas.

TABLE 11:3

Comparative Loss of Mineral Constituents as Weathering Takes Place in a Granite and in a Limestone. (The losses are compared to that of aluminum which was considered in these cases to have remained constant during the weathering process.) [a]

Granite to Clay		Limestone to Clay	
Constituent	*Comparative Loss (%)*	*Constituent*	*Comparative Loss (%)*
CaO	100.0	CaO	99.8
Na_2O	95.0	MgO	99.4
K_2O	83.5	Na_2O	76.0
MgO	74.7	K_2O	57.5
SiO_2	52.5	SiO_2	27.3
Fe_2O_3	14.4	Fe_2O_3	24.9
Al_2O_3	0.0	Al_2O_3	0.0

[a] The losses are given in per cent of that presumed to be present originally for each constituent. The granite data were taken from G. P. Merrill, *Weathering of Micaceous Gneiss*, Bul. 8, Geol. Soc. Amer., 1879, p. 160. Those for limestone are from J. S. Diller, *Educational Series of Rock Specimens*, Bul. 150, U.S. Geol. Survey, 1898, p. 385.

Weathering rates are generally more rapid in regions of high annual temperatures, especially if sufficient moisture is present to encourage chemical decomposition. Furthermore, the more resistant products of chemical weathering, such as the hydrous oxides of iron and aluminum, tend to be most prominent in the humid-tropical areas. This is due to the fact that less resistant minerals have succumbed to the intense weathering common to these areas. Even quartz, which is perhaps the most resistant of the common macro-grained primary minerals, disappears in time under these conditions.

Climate also largely controls the dominant types of vegetation present over wide areas. In this way it indirectly influences the biochemical reactions in soils and in turn their effect upon mineral weathering. For example, conifer trees, whose presence is often determined by climate, markedly influence the kind and rate of weathering occurring in the soil or parent material. Needles of these plants are low in metallic cations and when decomposed they encourage very acid conditions. Other trees or grasses are generally less apt to effect weathering in this manner.

Physical characteristics. Particle size, hardness, and degree of cementation are three physical characteristics which influence weathering. In rocks, large crystals of different minerals encourage disintegration. This is due to the fact that there is some variation in the amount of expansion and contraction which take place with each mineral as temperatures change. The resulting stress helps to develop cracks and to break these rocks into their mineral components. Finer grained materials are apparently more resistant to mechanical breakdown.

Particle size also influences the chemical breakdown of minerals. In general, a given mineral is more susceptible to decomposition when present in fine particles than when in larger grains. The much larger surface area of finely divided material presents greater opportunity for chemical attack. Apparently, this greater ease of weathering of small particles is more pronounced with some minerals than with others. For example, quartz particles of sand-size are extremely resistant to chemical weathering. In contrast, clay-size quartz, although not subject to ready decomposition, is not as resistant as many of the other minerals of that size.

Hardness and cementation apparently influence weathering primarily by their effect on the rate of disintegration into particles small enough for decomposition. Thus, a dense quartzite or a sandstone cemented firmly by a slowly weathered mineral will resist mechanical breakdown and will present a small amount of total surface area for chemical activity. Porous rocks such as volcanic ash or coarse limestones, on the other hand, are readily broken down into smaller particles. These have in total a larger surface area for chemical attack and are obviously more easily decomposed.

Chemical and structural characteristics.   For minerals of a given particle size, chemical and crystalline characteristics determine the ease of decomposition. Minerals such as gypsum ($CaSO_4 \cdot 2H_2O$) which are sparingly soluble in water are quickly removed if there is adequate rainfall. Water charged with carbonic acid likewise dissolves less soluble minerals such as calcite and dolomite. (See p. 269.) Consequently, these minerals are seldom found in the surface of the regolith in areas with even moderate rainfall.

The dark-colored primary minerals, sometimes called ferromagnesian because of their iron and magnesium contents, are more susceptible to chemical weathering than are the feldspars and quartz. The presence of iron (and perhaps less tightness of crystal packing) helps account for the more rapid breakdown of the ferromagnesian minerals. The ease with which iron-containing minerals become "stained" with oxides of this element is well known. Iron is quite subject to oxidation and hydration. As it is pulled from the crystal lattice of the primary minerals, a breakdown, both chemical and physical occurs. Obviously, the presence of this element denotes a notable weakness in the stability of a mineral.

Tightness of packing of the ions in the crystal units of minerals is thought to influence their weathering rates.[4] For example, olivine and biotite which are relatively easily weathered have crystal units that are less tightly packed than zircon and muscovite, comparable minerals which are quite resistant to weathering.

Climatic and biotic conditions will likely determine the relative stability of the various soil forming minerals. Consequently, one cannot present a listing of minerals based on their resistance to weathering under all climatic conditions. However, studies of minerals remaining in the soil and the regolith under various environmental conditions have led to the following general order of weathering resistance

[4] See a chapter on "Soil Development" by I. Barshad, in F. E. Bear, *Chemistry of the Soil* (New York: Reinhold, 1955), pp. 1–52.

of the sand- and silt-size particles of some common minerals; quartz (most resist-ant) > muscovite, K-feldspars > Na- and Ca-feldspars > biotite, hornblende and augite > olivine > dolomite and calcite > gypsum.[5] It is expected that this order would be changed slightly depending on the climatic and other environmental conditions. This listing accounts for the absence of gypsum, calcite, and dolomite in soils of humid regions and for the predominance of quartz in the coarser fraction of most soils.

11:6. WEATHERING IN ACTION—GENESIS OF PARENT MATERIALS

A general understanding of the influences of the separate forces of weathering makes it possible to picture in a simple way the development of parent material from bedrock. A physical weakening, due usually to temperature changes, initiates the process, but it is accompanied and supplemented by certain chemical transformations. Such minerals as the feldspars, mica, hornblende, and the like, suffer hydrolysis and hydration, while part of the combined iron is oxidized and hydrated. The minerals soften, lose their luster, and become more porous. If hematite or limonite is formed, the decomposing mass becomes definitely red or yellow. Otherwise, the colors are subdued.

Coincident with these changes, such active cations as calcium, magnesium, sodium, and potassium suffer carbonation and solution. Then, as the water present drains away, these constituents are removed, leaving a residue more or less bereft of its easily soluble bases. As the process goes on, all but the most resistant of the original minerals disappear, and their places are occupied by: (1) secondary hydrated silicates that tend to recrystallize into highly colloidal clay; and (2) more resistant products such as Fe and Al oxides. (See Fig. 11:2.)

Such a brief statement of rock weathering demands certain supplementary explanations. In the first place, it must be recognized that the intensity of the various agencies will fluctuate with climate. Under arid conditions, the physical forces will tend to dominate, and the resultant soil material will contain the less weathered minerals. Temperature changes, wind action, and water erosion will be accompanied by a minimum of chemical action.

In a humid region, however, the forces are more varied, and practically the full quota will be energetically at work. Vigorous chemical changes

---

[5] Clay-size particles include a large number of secondary minerals in addition to some of those listed here. Their relative resistance to weathering is given by Jackson and Sherman, *op. cit.,* p. 235.

will accompany disintegration, and the result will be shown in the greater fineness of the product. Clayey materials will be more evident, and a higher colloidality can be expected. Moreover, the process is more likely to be hastened and intensified by decaying organic matter.

It must be remembered that the forces of weathering lose their intensity as one goes downward from the surface. Both the physical and chemical transformations are in general somewhat different. The lack of organic matter is a factor as well as the decrease in the porosity and aeration of the under layers. This differentiation with depth is the forerunner of a profile development if and when soil genesis takes place.

11:7. GEOLOGIC CLASSIFICATION OF PARENT MATERIALS

In discussing weathering, it was tacitly assumed that parent material could originate in a number of different ways. In addition, it was suggested that this unconsolidated debris might lie in its original position above bedrock for centuries or it might sooner or later be moved to new positions by the mechanical forces of nature.

On this basis, two groups of inorganic parent materials, designated as *sedentary* and *transported,* are usually recognized. The latter may be subdivided according to the agencies of transportation and deposition as follows: (See also Fig. 11:3.)

1. Sedentary.	Still at original site . . . . Residual	
	Gravity . . . . Colluvial	
2. Transported.	Water	⎧Alluvial ⎨Marine ⎩Lacustrine
	Ice . . . . Glacial	
	Wind . . . . Aeolian	

While these terms relate only to the placement of the parent materials, it has become customary to use them loosely in referring to the soils that have been developed by the weathering of these deposits. Hence, much is heard of *glacial* soils, *alluvial* soils, *residual* soils, and the like. Such a grouping is very general, however, as a wide diversity is sure to occur within each soil group so recognized. This renders the terms of little specific significance.

11:8. RESIDUAL PARENT MATERIAL

This type of regolith develops in place from the country rock below and has suffered little transportation. If typically developed, it has usually suffered long and often intense weathering. In a warm, humid climate, it is likely to be thoroughly oxidized and well leached. Even though it may come from rocks such as limestone, it is often comparatively low in calcium due to the ready loss of this constituent. Red and yellow colors are characteristic when weathering has been intense, as may be demonstrated by a trip through the Piedmont Plateau of the eastern United States. In cooler, and especially in drier climates, residual weathering is much less drastic, and the oxidation and hydration of the iron may be hardly noticeable. Also, the lime content is higher and the colors of the debris subdued. Tremendous areas of this type of debris are found on the Great Plains and in other regions of western United States.

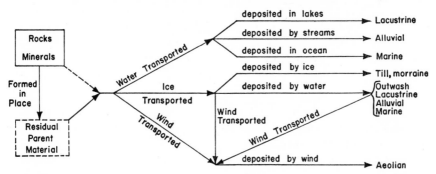

Figure 11:3. Diagram showing how various kinds of parent material are formed, transported, and deposited.

Residual materials are of wide distribution on all of the continents. In the United States, a glance at the physiographic map (Fig. 11:4) shows six great eastern and central provinces—the Piedmont Plateau, Appalachian Mountains and plateaus, the limestone valleys and ridges, the limestone and sandstone uplands, and the Great Plains region. The first three groups alone encompass about 10 per cent of the area of the United States. In addition, great expanses of these sedentary accumulations are found west of the Rocky Mountains.

As might be expected, a great variety of soils occupy these regions covered by residual debris, since climate and vegetation, two of the determining factors in soil characterization, vary so radically over this great area. It has already been emphasized that the profile of a mature soil is largely a reflection of climate and its accompanying vegetation.

11:9. COLLUVIAL DEBRIS

Colluvial debris is made up of the fragments of rock detached from the heights above and carried down the slopes mostly by gravity. Frost action has much to do with the development of such deposits. Talus slopes, cliff detritus, and similar heterogeneous materials are good examples. Avalanches are made up largely of such accumulations.

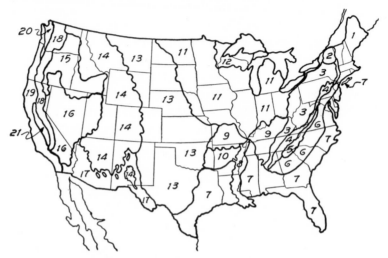

Figure 11:4. Generalized physiographic and regolith map of the United States. The regions located are as follows:

1. New England, mostly glaciated crystalline rocks.
2. Adirondacks, glaciated crystalline and sedimentary rocks.
3. Appalachian Mountains and Plateaus, shales and sandstones.
4. Limestone Valleys and Ridges, mostly limestone.
5. Blue Ridge Mountains, sandstones and shales.
6. Piedmont Plateau, crystalline rocks.
7. Atlantic Gulf and Coastal Plain, sands, clays, and limestones.
8. Mississippi Flood Plain and Delta, alluvium.
9. Limestone Uplands, mostly limestone and shale.
10. Sandstone Uplands, mostly sandstone and shale.
11. Central Lowlands, mostly glaciated sedimentary rocks of many kinds. Great areas are overlaid with loess, a wind deposit of great agricultural importance (see Fig. 11:11).

12. Superior Uplands, glaciated crystalline and sedimentary.
13. Great Plains Region, sedimentary rocks of many kinds.
14. Rocky Mountain Region, mountains, uplands, and valleys.
15. Northwest Intermountain, mostly igneous crystalline rock. Great areas in Columbia and Snake Rivers basins are covered by loess (see Fig. 11:8).
16. Great Basin, gravels, sands, alluvial fans from various rocks.
17. Southwest Arid Region, gravel, sand and other debris of desert and mountain.
18. Sierra Nevada and Cascade Mountains, mountains, uplands, and valleys.
19. Pacific Coast Province, mountains and valleys, mostly sedimentary rocks.
20. Puget Sound Lowlands, glaciated sedimentary.
21. California central valley, alluvium and outwash.

Parent material developed from colluvial accumulation is usually coarse and stony, as physical rather than chemical weathering has been dominant. Such deposits are not of great importance in the production of agricultural soils because of their small area, their inaccessibility, and their unfavorable physical and chemical characteristics.

11:10. ALLUVIAL STREAM DEPOSITS

There are three general classes of alluvial deposits: (1) flood plains, (2) alluvial fans, and (3) deltas. They will be considered in order.

Flood plains. A stream on a gently inclined bed usually begins to swing from side to side in variable curves, depositing alluvial material on the inside of the curves and cutting on the opposite banks. This results in so-called *oxbows* and *lagoons,* which are ideal for the further deposition

of alluvial matter and development of swamps. This state of meander naturally increases the probability of overflow at high water, a time when the stream is carrying much suspended matter. Part of this sediment is deposited over the flooded areas; the coarser near the channel, building up natural levees; the finer farther away in the lagoons and slack water. Thus, there are two distinct types of first-bottom deposits —*meander* and *flood.* As might be expected, flood-plain deposits are variable, ranging texturally from gravel and sands to silt and clay.

Due to a change in grade, a stream may cut down through its already well-formed alluvial deposits, leaving *terraces* on one or both sides. Often two, or even three, terraces of different heights may be detected along some valleys, marking a time when the stream was at these elevations.

Figure 11:5. The flood plain and delta of the lower Mississippi River. This is the largest continuous area of alluvial soil in the United States.

Flood-plain deposits are found to a certain extent beside every stream, the greatest development in the United States occurring along the Mississippi. (See Fig. 11:5.) This area varies from 20 to 75 miles in width and from Cairo, Illinois, to the Gulf is over 500 miles long. The soils derived from such sediments usually are very rich, but if they are first bottoms, they may require drainage and protection from overflow.

Alluvial fans.   Where streams descend from uplands, a sudden change in gradient sometimes occurs as the stream emerges at the lower level. A deposition of sediment is thereby forced, giving rise to *alluvial fans*. They differ from deltas in their location and in the character of their debris. Fan material often is gravelly and stony, more or less porous and, in general, well drained.

Alluvial-fan debris is found over wide areas in arid and semiarid regions. The soils therefrom, when irrigated and properly handled, often prove very productive. In humid regions, especially in certain glaciated sections, such deposits also occur in large enough areas to be of considerable agricultural importance.

Delta deposits.   Much of the finer sediment carried by streams is not deposited in the flood plain, but is discharged into the body of water to which the stream is tributary. Unless there is sufficient current and wave action, some of the suspended material accumulates, forming a delta. Such delta deposits are by no means universal, being found at the mouths of only a small proportion of the rivers of the world. A delta often is a continuation of a flood plain, its front so to speak, and is not only clayey in nature but is likely to be swampy as well. The deltas of the Nile and Po are good examples of this set of conditions.

Delta sediments, where they occur in any considerable acreage and are subject to flood control and drainage, become rather important agriculturally. The combination deltas and flood plains of the Mississippi, Ganges, Po, Tigris, and Euphrates rivers are striking examples. Egypt, for centuries the granary of Rome, bespeaks the fertility and productivity of soils originating from such parent material.

11:11. MARINE SEDIMENTS

Much of the sediment carried away by stream action is eventually deposited in the oceans, seas, and gulfs, the coarser fragments near the shore, the finer particles at a distance. Also, considerable debris is wrenched from the shore line by the pounding of the waves and the undertow of the tides. If there have been changes in shore line, the alternation of beds will show no regular sequence and considerable variation in topography, depth, and texture. These deposits have been extensively raised above sea level along the Atlantic and Gulf coasts of the United States and elsewhere, and have given origin to large areas of valuable soils. (See Fig. 11:6.)

Marine deposits have been worn and weathered by a number of

agencies. First, the weathering and erosion necessary to throw them into stream-suspension were sustained. These were followed by the sorting and solvent action of the stream itself. Next, the sediment was swept into the ocean to be deposited and stratified, possibly after being pounded and eroded by the waves for years. At last came the emergence above the sea and the final action of the forces of weathering. The latter effects are of great moment, since they determine the topography and, to a considerable extent, the chemical and physical nature of the resultant parent material.

Figure 11:6. Block diagram showing the location of marine sediments and their relation to the uplands. The emerged coastal plain has already suffered some dissection from stream action.

The marine sediments of the United States, although they have been subjected to weathering a shorter time than some of the residual debris, are generally more worn and usually carry less of the mineral nutrient elements. Their silica content is high, and they are often sandy, especially along the Atlantic seaboard. But in the Atlantic and Gulf coastal flatwoods and the interior pine lands of Alabama and Mississippi, clayey deposits are not uncommon. It is interesting to note that these marine clays may be dominated by kaolinite, illite, or montmorillonite.

In the continental United States, the marine deposits of the Atlantic and Gulf coastal provinces (See Fig. 11:4) occupy approximately 11 per cent of the country and are very diversified due to source of material, age, and the climatic conditions under which they now exist. Severe leaching as well as serious erosion occurs in times of heavy rainfall. In spite of this, however, their soils support a great variety of crops when adequately supplied with organic matter, properly cultivated and carefully fertilized.

11:12. THE PLEISTOCENE ICE AGE

During the Pleistocene,[6] northern North America, as well as northern and central Europe and parts of northern Asia, were invaded by a suc-

[6] For supplementary reading as to the Great Ice Age and its influence, see: R. F. Flint, *Glacial Geology and the Pleistocene Epoch* (New York: Wiley, 1947).

cession of great ice sheets. Certain parts of South America as well as areas in New Zealand and Australia were similarly affected. And Antarctica undoubtedly was capped with ice much as it is today.[7] The cause was a change in temperature and precipitation accompanied by other fluctuations. But just why the climate changes occurred is highly conjectural.

This change in climate that permitted the onset of the Pleistocene ice age evidently brought a lowering of temperature and an increase in precipitation. During this period the heat of summer did not by any means melt the winter accumulations of snow. Hence, great snow fields formed at certain centers. As the snow continued to thicken, the increasing pressure and the influence of summer-melting gradually changed the snow into ice. Thus, the great dome-shaped glaciers gradually came into being, 2 to 3 miles thick in their region of accretion.[8]

In North America, the major centers of ice accumulation were in central Labrador and the western Hudson Bay region, with a minor concentration in the Canadian Rockies. From the major centers, great continental glaciers pushed outward in all directions, but especially southward, covering, from time to time, most of what is now Canada and the northern part of the United States. The southernmost extension was down the Mississippi Valley, since here, due to the lower and smoother topography, the least resistance was met. (See Fig. 11:7.)

Central North America and Europe apparently sustained at least four [9] distinct ice invasions, separated, in each case, by long interglacial periods. So long, in fact, were these ice-free intervals that they are estimated to have covered in total a period considerably longer than the time that ice actually blanketed the country.[10] The existence of these interglacial periods

---

[7] It is estimated that the Pleistocene ice at its maximum extension covered perhaps 20 per cent of the land area of the world. In this connection, it is surprising to learn that present-day glaciers, which we consider as mere remnants of the Great Ice Age, occupy almost half as much land surface. The respective amounts of ice, however, are not in the same proportion, since our living glaciers are comparatively thin and are definitely on the wane.

[8] See R. A. Daly, *The Changing World of the Ice Age* (New Haven: Yale University Press, 1934). It is estimated that so much water was changed to glacial ice that, at maximum glaciation, the ocean level was perhaps 250 feet lower than at present. The melting of our present day glaciers would raise the ocean level possibly as much as 50 feet.

[9] The ice invasions of the central United States are recognized as four in number: Nebraskan, Kansan, Illinoian, and Wisconsin. The glacial debris of the eastern United States and Canada is practically all of Wisconsin age.

[10] The total length of the Pleistocene ice age is estimated at 700,000 to 1,000,000 years. According to recent studies using radioactive carbon (C^{14}), the glacial ice disappeared from northern Iowa and central New York possibly only about 12,000 years ago. We may be now enjoying the mildness of another interglacial period.

is conclusively proved by the presence of forest beds, the accumulation of peat between the glacial deposits of different ages, and by evidence of the prolonged erosion of the successive layers of glacial drift. In certain places, excavations yield clear evidence of fossil soils of mature age. Some of the interglacial intervals evidently were times of warm or even semitropical climate in regions that are now definitely temperate.

Figure 11:7. Sketch map of North America showing the maximum development of the continental glaciation. The three centers of ice accumulation are numbered. Apparently eastern and central United States were invaded from the Labradorian (1) and Hudson Bay (2) centers. Note the marked southernly advance of the ice in the Mississippi Valley where topography offered little resistance. To the eastward the Appalachian highlands more or less blocked the ice invasion.

As the glacial ice, coarsely crystalline and with a unique viscosity under this tremendous pressure, was pushed forward, it conformed itself to the unevenness of the areas invaded. It rose over hills and often over mountains with surprising ease. Not only was the existing regolith with its

---

Of the three major interglacial periods, the first (Aftonian) persisted perhaps 200,000 years, the second (Yarmouth) may have lasted for 300,000 years, while the third (Sangamon), which preceded the Wisconsin ice advance, possibly endured for 125,000 years. Assuming the Pleistocene age to have continued for not more than 1,000,000 years, it is obvious that glacial ice occupied what is now the north-central and northeastern United States less than half of the period designated as the Great Ice Age.

mantle of soil swept away, but also hills were rounded, valleys filled, and, in some cases, the underlying rocks were severely ground and gouged. Thus, the glacier became filled with rock wreckage, carrying much on its surface and pushing great masses ahead. Finally, when the ice melted away and the region again was free, a mantle of glacial drift remained—a new regolith and fresh parent material for soil formation.

The area covered by glaciers in North America is estimated as 4,000,000 square miles, while perhaps 20 per cent of the United States is either directly or indirectly influenced by the deposits. An examination of the maps of Figures 11:7 and 11:8 will make clear the magnitude of the ice invasion at maximum glaciation in this country.

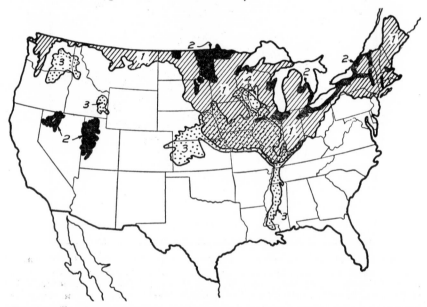

Figure 11:8. Areas in the United States covered by the continental ice sheet and the deposits either directly from, or associated with, the glacial ice. 1, till deposits of various kinds; 2, glacial-lacustrine deposits; 3, the loessial blanket—note that the loess overlies great areas of till in the Middle West; 4, an area, mostly in Wisconsin, that escaped glaciation. It is partially loess covered.

11:13. GLACIAL TILL AND ASSOCIATED DEPOSITS

The materials deposited directly by the ice are commonly spoken of as glacial till. Till is a mixture of rock debris of great diversity, especially as to size of particles. Boulder clay, which is so common in glaciated regions, is typical of the physical heterogeneity to be expected.

Glacial till is found mostly as irregular deposits called *moraines* of which there are various kinds. *Terminal* moraines, for instance, mark the southernmost extension of the various glacial lobes when the ice margin was stationary long enough to permit an accumulation of debris.[11] (See Fig. 11:9.) Many other moraines of a *recessional* nature are found to the northward, marking points where the ice front became stationary for a time as it receded by melting. While moraines of this type are generally outstanding topographic features, they give rise to soils that are rather unimportant due to their small area and unfavorable physiography.

Figure 11:9. Diagram showing the relationships between a terminal moraine, its outwash, and its associated ground moraine. Note the differences in topography and in the general nature of the three deposits. The ground moraine is the most widely distributed.

The *ground moraine,* a thinner and more level deposition laid down as the ice front retreated rather rapidly, is of much more importance. It has the widest extent of all glacial deposits and usually possesses a rather favorable agricultural topography. Associated with the moraine in certain places are such special features as *kames, eskers,* and *drumlins.*

An outstanding feature of glacial till materials discussed above is their variability. This is due to the diverse ways by which the debris was laid down, to differences in the chemical composition of the original materials, and to fluctuations in the grinding action of the ice. Till deposits cover wide areas and therefore have been subjected to markedly different climatic and vegetative conditions. Thus, over the glaciated portion of America, glacial till of all descriptions may be found, varying as to topography, color, texture, structure, depth, slope, and drainage. As might be expected, the soils derived from such soil material are most hetergeneous. Such variations serve to indicate that the term "glacial soil" is of value only in suggesting the mode, in general, of deposition of the parent ma-

[11] The position of the front of a glacier is determined by the relationship between the forward movement of the ice and rate of melting. When the former is dominant, the ice front advances. When melting is dominant, the ice front recedes. When these two forces are balanced, conditions are favorable for a stand of the ice and the building of a moraine.

terials. It indicates practically nothing as to the characteristics of a soil so designated.

11:14. GLACIAL OUTWASH AND LACUSTRINE SEDIMENTS

Great torrents of water were constantly gushing, especially during the summer, from the great Pleistocene ice sheets as their fronts advanced and retreated in response to their environment. The great loads of sediment carried by such streams were in part either dumped down immediately or carried to other areas for deposition. So long as the water had ready egress, it flowed rapidly away to deposit its load as outwash of various kinds.

Outwash plains.   A type of deposit of great importance is the *outwash* plain, formed by streams heavily laden with glacial sediment. (See Fig. 11:9.) This sediment is usually assorted and therefore variable in texture. Such deposits are particularly important in valleys and on plains where the glacial waters were able to flow away freely. Such valley fills are common in the United States, both north and south of the terminal moraine. For example, extensive outwash plains occur on Long Island, New York, and on the eastern side of the great Central Valley of California. The latter is a glacial wash from the Sierra Nevada. Even when such depositions are not of wide extent, their local importance is often very great. The small plains of New England are an instance of this as they offer ideal locations for villages and towns.

Glacial lake deposits.   In many cases, however, the ice front came to a standstill where there was no such ready escape for the water, and ponding due to the damming action of the ice occurred. (See Fig. 11:10.) Often, very large lakes were formed which existed for many years. Particularly prominent were those south of the Great Lakes in New York, Ohio, Indiana, Michigan, and in the Red River Valley. (See Fig. 11:8.) The latter lake, called Glacial Lake Agassiz, was perhaps 750 miles long and 250 miles wide at its maximum extension. The others, while individually much smaller, covered in total great stretches of country. Large lakes also occurred in the intermountain regions west of the Rockies as well as in the Connecticut Valley in New England and elsewhere.

With the glacial ice melting rapidly in the hills and higher valleys, these lakes were constantly fed by torrents from above which were laden with sediment derived not only directly from the ice but also from the unconsolidated till sheet over which they flowed. As a consequence, great deposits were made in these glacial lakes, ranging from coarse delta materials near the shore to fine silts and clay in the deeper and stiller waters. Such materials now cover large areas both in the United States and Canada, and their weathering has given rise to what are loosely designated as *glacial lake* soils. (See Fig. 11:8.)

Figure 11:10. When conditions of topography were favorable, the Wisconsin ice sheet acted as a great waning dam. The diagram shows a stage in the development of glacial lakes Chicago (C) and Warren (W). *(After Daly.)*

Glacial lake deposits probably present as wide a variation in physical and chemical characteristics as the soil materials of any of the physiographic provinces. Being deposited by water, they have been subject to much sorting and stratification. They range from coarse gravels, on the one hand, to fine clays on the other. There is also considerable variation in respect to lime content, pH, color, and structural characteristics. They are generally found in the lowlands, although they may occur well up on the hillsides if the shores of the old lakes encroached this far.

The soils developed from these lake sediments are most heterogeneous. Weathering, due to climatic differences, has been variable, and profile contrasts are great. Extending westward from New England along the Great Lakes until the broad expanse of the Red River Valley is reached, these deposits have produced some of the most important soils of the Northern states. They also occur in the intermountain regions of the United States where they have given rise to agriculturally important soils especially when irrigated.

11:15. GLACIAL-AEOLIAN DEPOSITS

During the glaciation, much fine material was carried miles below the front of the ice sheets by streams that found their source within the glaciers. This sediment was deposited over wide areas by the overloaded rivers. The accumulations occurred below the ice front at all points, but in the

United States seem to have reached their greatest development in what is now the Mississippi and Missouri valleys. Some of the debris found on the Great Plains probably had a similar origin, coming from glaciers debouching from the Rockies. All this, added to the great stretches of unconsolidated till in the glaciated regions and the residual material unclothed with vegetation on the Great Plains, presented unusually favorable conditions for wind erosion in dry weather.

Origin and location of loess.   It is generally agreed by glaciologists that a period of aridity, at least as far as the Great Plains and contiguous eastward areas were concerned, accompanied or immediately followed the retreat of the last ice sheet. The low rainfall of this period was accompanied by strong westerly winds. These winds, active perhaps through centuries, were instrumental in picking up and distributing fine material, both glacial and nonglacial in origin, over wide areas on the Great Plains and particularly in the Mississippi, Ohio, and Missouri valleys. These deposits cover the original soils and parent materials, both residual and glacial in origin. The situation was somewhat analogous to the wind erosion now experienced on the Great Plains, but was much more severe and occurred under somewhat different conditions.

This wind-blown material, called *loess*,[12] is found over wide areas in the United States, in most cases masking the unconsolidated materials below. It covers eastern Nebraska and Kansas, southern and central Iowa and Illinois, northern Missouri, and parts of southern Ohio and Indiana, besides a wide band extending southward along the eastern border of the Mississippi River. (See Figs. 11:8 and 11:11.) Extensive loessial deposits also occur in the Palouse region in Washington and Idaho and other areas in northwestern United States. In places, notably along the Missouri and Mississippi rivers, its accumulation has given rise to great bluffs which bestow a characteristic topography to the region. Farther from the rivers, the deposits, an upland type, are shallower and smoother in topography.

Nature of loess.   Loess is usually silty in character and has a yellowish-buff color, unless it is very markedly weathered or carries a large amount of humus. The larger particles are usually unweathered and

---

[12] Aeolian deposits, other than loess, occur, such as volcanic ash and sand dunes. Soils from volcanic ash occur in Montana, Idaho, Nebraska and Kansas. They are light and porous and not always of great agricultural value.

Sand dunes are of little value under any condition and become a menace to agriculture if they are moving. Examples of such deposits are found in the great Sahara and Arabian deserts. Smaller areas occur in this Country in, for example, Nebraska, Colorado and New Mexico and along the Eastern Seaboard.

angular. Quartz seems to predominate, but large quantities of feldspar, mica, hornblende, augite, and the like are found. The vertical walls and escarpments formed when this deposit is deeply eroded are one of its most striking physical characteristics.

In spite of the physical and chemical homogeneity of the loess as originally deposited, it has given rise in the central United States and elsewhere to soils of considerable diversity because of the climatic differences now existent in the various parts of the loessial area. A comparison of the loessial area of the Middle West (Fig. 11:11) with the map of the Great Soil

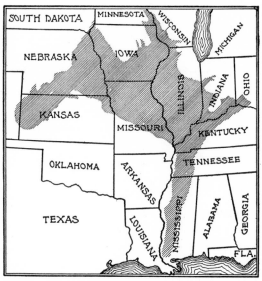

Figure 11:11. Approximate distribution of loess in central United States. The soil that has developed therefrom is generally a silt loam, often somewhat sandy. Note especially the extension down the eastern side of the Mississippi River and the irregularities of its northern extensions. Smaller areas of loess occur in Washington, Oregon, and Idaho. (See Fig. 11:8.)

Groups (Fig. 12:5) will show the presence of loess in six distinct soil regions. This situation, while indicating the probability of great differences in the fertility and productivity of loess soils, especially emphasizes the influence of climate as the final determinate of soil characteristics.

11:16. THE AGRICULTURAL SIGNIFICANCE OF THE GLACIATION

The Pleistocene glaciation, in most cases, has been a decided benefit, especially agriculturally. The leveling and filling actions, when drift was abundant, have given a smoother topography more suited to farming operations. The same can be said for the glacial lake sediments and loess deposits. Also, the parent materials thus supplied are geologically fresh, and the soils derived therefrom usually are, in general, not drastically leached. While it is difficult to show any consistent difference in total nutrients between the old residual and the younger glacial soils, it is generally admitted that glaciation has been a benefit to agriculture. Young soils generally are higher in available nutrients, and under comparable conditions they are superior in crop-producing power.

Soil Formation, Classification, and Survey

CHAPTER 12

To study satisfactorily any heterogeneous group in nature some sort of classification is necessary. This is especially true of soils. The value of experimental work of any kind is seriously restricted and may even be misleading unless the relation of one soil to another is known. Knowledge of crop requirements in any region is of uncertain value without some understanding of the formative processes of the soils in question and of their present profile similarities and differences.

In arriving at such an understanding three phases must be considered: (1) soil genesis or the evolution of a soil from its parent material; (2) soil classification, in this case especially as it applies to the United States; and (3) soil survey, its interpretation and utilization.

12:1. WEATHERING AND SOIL FORMATION

As shown in the last chapter mineral soils have originated from the unconsolidated materials that mask the country rock. This mantle of materials, the *regolith*, has in turn been differentiated from solid rock by the same agencies. The general trend of events as bedrock is disintegrated and in part decomposed to give parent material has already been sketched (p. 273).

Even a superficial examination will show that the weathering process seems in a broad way to be destructive. Thus, minerals present in the original unweathered rocks are continually subject to decomposition and disintegration. As weathering proceeds soluble constituents are lost in the drainage waters, leaving secondary minerals such as *iron oxide* and *silicate clays* as products of seemingly destructive processes.

At this point a very pertinent question logically arises. How can the

289

soil, a natural body resulting in part, at least, from synthesis, be developed by forces that are recognized the world over as wasteful and destructive? Why do not the original changes continue until the upper layer of the regolith is reduced to an inert mass, more or less free of soluble constituents, and hence incapable of supporting plant life?

Synthesis of clay and humus the answer. In the first place the disruption of the original silicate minerals paves the way for clay formation. The genesis of clay has already been discussed (p. 81) and its importance in relation to soil fertility fully emphasized. In fact, the natural fertility of mineral soils cannot be high without this particular synthesized product of weathering.

But this is by no means all. At very early stages of soil formation living organisms decisively intervene. Organic matter accumulates, especially at the surface, and the whole trend of the weathering is sharply modified. It now becomes *bio*chemical and *bio*colloidal. Colloidal humus supplements colloidal clay as a retainer of nutrients. Physically, particularly as regards structure, the soil mass becomes modified as a result of biotic influences.

Perhaps of even greater import is the fact that higher plants partially reverse the over-all downward movement of soluble constituents. Mineral elements are brought to the surface and deposited as part of organic residues. This retards their loss from the soil and encourages further biological activity. The activity and accumulation of organic matter together with clay synthesis, is the real secret of what may be termed *constructive weathering.*

Thus weathering, a *producer* of parent materials, and weathering, a *builder* of soils, operate simultaneously. Fundamentally the same processes are involved in both cases. These processes result in the destruction or alteration of parent materials and at the same time give rise to products which are essential for soil formation. Ultimately, therefore, the physical and biochemical forces are acting on a mixture of substances differing markedly from the parent material. Moreover, these weathering influences give rise to a horizontal layering within the soil mass and a *profile,* which is both characteristic and unique, is developed. As this differentiation progresses, a new natural body—a soil—comes into being.

12:2. DEVELOPMENT OF SOIL CHARACTERISTICS—SOIL AGE

In the early stages of soil formation, the characteristics of the weathering mass are almost entirely those of the parent material. These characteristics are lithological or *inherited.* As yet there has been no profile development in a soil sense. Any layering that may be evident is geological, that is, related to the deposition of the regolith. Sands and recent alluvium are good present-day examples.

As the influence of weathering becomes constructive in a soil sense and the presence of organic matter begins to exert its influence, a *young soil* gradually develops. *Acquired* [1] characteristics, that is, those induced largely by the environment, are noticeable but those inherited from the parent material are still dominant. The profile is only faintly developed, however, since the constructive agencies have not had time to impress their pattern.

However, as the environmental factors gradually attain the ascendancy, the new or acquired characteristics become dominant and the profile is much more fully developed. Inherited characteristics, although still in evidence, are definitely of minor importance in determining soil properties. The soil is now said to be *mature*. In other words, it has reached *dynamic equilibrium* with its particular environment.

This by no means indicates that soil forming processes do not continue to operate. On the contrary, they may be at the peak of their intensity when the soil reaches maturity. The over-all effect, however, is one which leaves the essential profile characteristics largely unchanged. Normal erosion at the surface and inclusions from the C horizon below tend to balance each other and thereby aid in maintaining these characteristics.

A relatively constant climatic environment is assumed when we speak of mature soils. As would be expected, however, changes in the environment do occur and these changes alter the characteristics of even mature soils. Under these conditions the soil that results is said to be *degraded*. The encroachment of a forest on a prairie is a good example, some of the characteristics induced by grass yielding to those of a wooded environment.

In the sequence of events described above it should be emphasized that *soil age* and *the length of time necessary for soil development* are not synonymous. Two soils may have been subjected to weathering forces for

---

[1] Examples of *inherited* and *acquired* characteristics are quite numerous. The presence of quartz is perhaps the most common example of the former, although the presence of any mineral, such as feldspar or mica, carried over unchanged into a soil, is a good illustration. Color also is often inherited, as in the case of a red parent sandstone or shale. Even clay, if originally a part of the parent material, may be rated as inherited.

Examples of *acquired* characteristics are as easily cited. Those due to organic matter, to clay formed as the soil developed, and to products of weathering such as red and yellow iron oxides are common. Certainly profile layering and the development of various structural forms within the various horizons are due largely to environmental influences. Acquired characteristics of a more local nature, such as imperfect drainage and the accumulation of alkali salts, should also be mentioned.

the same length of time and yet may *not* be of the same age. For example, the presence of $CaCO_3$ in the parent material will delay the maturing of a soil if its maturation is dependent upon leaching of bases. Thus, a soil developing from sandstone in such a climatic environment would reach maturity much more quickly than one developing from limestone. The real criterion of soil maturity is, therefore, not the weathering time, but rather the development and stabilization of a characteristic soil profile.

Briefly then, a *young* soil is one that is still in the process of adjustment to its environment. A *mature* soil, on the other hand, is in dynamic equilibrium with climatic and vegetative influences, and the profile horizons are not appreciably changing either physically or chemically. We are now ready to consider the nature of the profile that a well-drained mature soil is likely to present.

12:3. THE SOIL PROFILE

As parent material is molded into a soil by the biochemical means described above, a more or less definite layering develops, especially if drainage is adequate. This zoning is particularly noticeable near the soil surface. Here, climatic agencies are more intense and there has been an opportunity for the accumulation of organic matter. A section down through the various layers to, or into, the less weathered parent material is the *profile* already so frequently mentioned. The texture, depth, color, chemical nature, and sequence of the various horizons characterize a soil and determine its agricultural value. Profile study is, therefore, of prime importance.

Soil horizons.   For convenience in study and description, the layers resulting from soil forming processes are grouped under three heads: A, B, and C. (See Fig. 12:1.) The subdivisions of these are called *horizons*. The A group (eluvial)[2] lies at the surface and is characterized as a zone of maximum leaching. Beginning at the surface of the mineral matter the horizons are designated as A_1, A_2, etc. If a layer of organic matter covers the surface, as is often the case in forests, it is referred to in mass as A_0. If it is thick enough to exhibit distinct layers, however, the terminology is extended to A_{00}. (See Fig. 12:1.)

The B group (illuvial)[3] comes next and includes the layers in which

---

[2] Eluvial from *ex* or *e* meaning out and *luv,* washed.

[3] Illuvial from *il* or *in,* meaning in and *luv,* washed. Although the B horizon is often referred to as the *subsoil,* this terminology may be technically incorrect. In some eroded soils and in soils with shallow A layers, the B horizon makes up at least part of the surface or plow layer. Also since the A horizon of certain soils is deep (24 inches or more) the subsoil may include a part of A in addition to B.

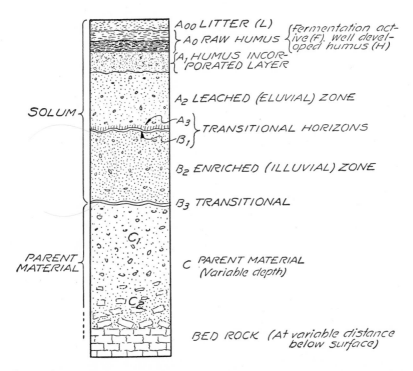

Figure 12:1. A theoretical soil profile showing all of the horizons usually distinguished. Any particular individual profile, however, generally exhibits clearly only part of these. Further details are as follows:

A₀₀. This horizon consists of loose relatively undecomposed organic debris. It is usually absent on grass lands but present on forest soils, especially those of temperate regions, and very abundant at certain times of the year.

A₀. A partially or fully humified organic horizon. It may be matted, fibrous, or granular. On grass land it is usually absent. On forest soils two distinct layers often may be distinguished—F, the zone of fermentation and H, a markedly humified zone.

A₁. A dark colored mineral horizon containing a relatively large amount of humified organic matter thoroughly mixed with the inorganic layer. In chernozems this layer is very thick; in podzols very thin or absent; and in other soils variable.

A₂. A light-colored mineral horizon resulting from a leaching and bleaching action *(eluviation)*. It is well developed and very noticeable in true podzols—the gray layer or *bleicherde* of these soils. It is absent from chernozems and certain other soils especially those of arid and semiarid regions.

A₃. A transition layer, often absent. When it is present, it is more like A than B.

B₁. Also a transitional horizon and absent from many soils, more like the B than A.

B₂. A zone of accumulation *(illuviation)* especially of silicate clays and iron and aluminum compounds. It is particularly prominent in true podzols as a *reddish-brown* horizon. The hardpan *(orstein)* of the podzol occurs here when present as does the *clay pan* of certain other soils. In arid region soils the B₂ is often characterized by special structural forms, frequently columnar or prismatic.

B₃. A transitional layer. It may or may not be present.

C. Unconsolidated parent material similar to that from which the solum has developed. This may come from the bedrock below or it may have been transported from elsewhere and deposited on the bedrock.

293

deposition from above, or even from below, has taken place. It is the region of maximum accumulation of materials such as iron and aluminum oxides and the silicate clays. These materials may have washed downward from the surface layers or they may have formed in the B horizon. In arid regions calcium carbonate, calcium sulfate, and other salts may accumulate in the lower B. Its horizons are labeled in order downward as B_1, B_2, etc. The A and B horizons together are called the *solum,* that is, the portion of the profile developed by soil building processes as distinguished from the parent material immediately below.

The C horizon, or parent material,[4] is noticeably less weathered and is usually similar to or more or less identical with that from which the A and B horizons are derived. As yet it has not been subjected to soil building but its upper layers will in time become a part of the solum. Since the C horizon, especially the upper part, may show considerable chemical weathering, several zones may be distinguished. Generally, however, little attempt is made to differentiate within this horizon. For further details of the profile see the notes accompanying Figure 12.1.

Horizons in a given profile.   It is at once evident that the profile of any one soil probably will not show all of the horizons that collectively are cited in Figure 12:1. The profile may be immature or may be overly influenced by some local condition such as poor drainage, texture, or topography. Again some of the horizons are merely transitional and may at best be very indistinct. With so many factors involved in soil genesis, a slight change in their coordination may not encourage the development of some layers. As a result, we can be sure of finding in any well-drained and uneroded mature soil only certain horizons. They are: A_0, if the land is forested; A_1 or A_2 depending on circumstances; B_2; and C. (See Fig. 12:1.) Conditions of soil genesis will determine which others are present and their clarity of definition.

When a virgin soil is put under cultivation, the upper horizons become the furrow-slice. The cultivation, of course, destroys the original layered

---

[4] *Parent material* in a broad, *geological* way refers to the unconsolidated mineral mass from which the solum has been developed. The past tense is implied since the parent has lost its identity in soil formation.

In a narrow and *contemporary* sense, however, the term is used to designate the unconsolidated material lying directly below the soil solum. This terminology can only be used when there is sufficient evidence that an appreciable proportion of the solum has been synthesized from mineral matter more or less identical with this basal horizon. The letter C, which is applied to the latter, connotates *parent material* in this *particular* present day *sense.* Any unconsolidated material below the solum that cannot be so characterized is referred to as D.

condition of this portion of the profile, and the furrow-slice becomes more or less homogeneous. In some soils the A horizons are of sufficient depth so that not all of the A is included in the furrow-slice (Fig. 12:2). In other cases where the A is quite thin, the plowline is just at the top of or even down in the B.

Figure 12:2. Generalized profile of the Miami silt loam, one of the gray-brown podzolic soils of eastern United States. A comparison of the profile of the virgin soil with its arable equivalent shows the changes that may be expected from cultivation. If erosion occurs, the original A horizon may disappear, at least in part, and some of the B horizon will be included in the furrow-slice. (*After M. Baldwin, "The Gray-brown Podzol Soils of Eastern United States,"* Proc. and Papers of the First Internat. Cong. of Soil Sci., 4: 276–82, 1927.)

Many times, especially on cultivated land, serious erosion has occurred and as a result a *truncated* profile is encountered. As the surface soil was swept away, the plowline was gradually lowered in order to maintain a sufficiently thick furrow-slice. Hence the furrow, in many cases, is almost entirely within the B zone and the C horizon is correspondingly nearer the surface. Many farmers, especially in our Southern States, are today cultivating the subsoil without realizing the ravages of erosion. In profile study and description such a situation requires careful analysis.

12:4. FACTORS INFLUENCING SOIL CHARACTER [5]

So far, we have concerned ourselves primarily with the effects of weathering, both constructive and destructive, on soil formation. Forces of weathering, however, are but active expressions of a number of factors which largely control the kind of soil that finally develops. At least five such factors are apparent.

1. *Climate* (particularly temperature and precipitation)
2. *Living organisms* (especially the native vegetation)
3. *Nature of parent material* ⟨Texture and structure / Chemical and mineralogical composition⟩
4. *Topography of area*
5. *Time* that parent materials are subjected to soil formation

Climate.   From an over-all standpoint, climate is perhaps the most influential of these factors. In the first place, it determines in no small degree the nature of the weathering that occurs. It has already been pointed out that temperature and precipitation exert profound influences on the rates of chemical and physical processes. These processes are in turn the essential means by which profile development is effected. Consequently, if allowed ample opportunity, climatic influences eventually tend to dominate the soil formation picture.

The effectiveness of climate is not altogether independently exerted, however. In fact, climatic influences are usually expressed through or in combination with the other factors. For example, much of the influence of climate is due to the measure of control which it exercises over vegetation. Thus, in humid regions, plentiful rainfall not only encourages rapid chemical changes but at the same time provides an environment favorable for the growth of trees. The influence of these two factors on the kind of soil that develops cannot be overemphasized.

Vegetative cover.   The vegetative cover native to a given region acts as a modifier of climatic influences. The role of the organic fraction of plant residues has already been emphasized (p. 155). Inorganic salts associated with plants also play a vital part. The continual deposition at the

---

[5] For a thought-provoking treatise on this subject, see H. Jenny, *Factors of Soil Formation* (New York: McGraw-Hill, 1941).

surface of mineral elements brought up by plants from various depths within the soil is a part of what is essentially a cyclical process. These nutrients are released at or near the surface by the decomposition of plant residues and are then moved downward in the soil by leaching. Later they may be reabsorbed by higher plants and finally returned to the surface where the cycle starts again. Obviously, the kind of plants concerned in this process, their rooting habits, mineral composition, etc., will play a vital role in the type of soil which eventually develops.

Parent material. The nature of the parent material, even in humid regions, may still profoundly influence the characteristics of even fully mature soils. For example, the downward movement of water is controlled quite largely by the texture of the soil. Its chemical and mineralogical compositions often not only determine the effectiveness of the weathering forces, but in some instances partially control the natural vegetation. For example, the presence of limestone in a humid region soil will delay the development of acidity, a process which the climate encourages. In addition, the species of trees usually found on limestone materials are relatively high in metallic cations or bases. By continually bringing these bases to the surface the vegetation is responsible for a further delay in the process of acidification, or in this particular case, the progress of soil maturity.

Topography. The topography of the land may be such as to hasten or delay the work of climatic forces. Thus, in smooth flat country the rapidity with which excess water is removed is much less than if the landscape were rolling. The latter topography encourages some natural erosion of the surface layers, which, if extensive enough, may eliminate the possibility of a deep soil. On the other hand, if water stands for part or all of the year on a given area, the climatic influences become relatively ineffective in regulating soil development. Topography, therefore, is significant not only as a modifier of climatic effects, but often as a major control in local areas.

Time. The actual length of time that materials have been subjected to weathering plays a significant role in soil formation. Perhaps the best evidence of the importance of time may be obtained by a comparison of the soils of a glaciated region with those in a comparable area that was untouched by the ice sheet.[6] As a general rule, the influence of parent material is much more apparent in the soils of glaciated regions. This is due

---

[6] It is recognized that such a comparison is not entirely valid because of climatic differences. But if the comparison is made near the boundary of the southernmost glacial advance, these climatic differences may not be great.

primarily to the fact that in many cases insufficient time has lapsed since the disappearance of the ice to permit the changes in the composition of the glacial deposit that are necessary for full maturity of soils.

It should not be inferred from the above, however, that mature soils are not found in glaciated regions. In fact, they are quite numerous in certain areas. If other conditions, such as the nature of the parent material, topography, slope, etc., are favorable, climatic influences dominate and the time of weathering in years becomes relatively less significant.

12:5. SOIL CLASSIFICATION [7]—SOIL ORDERS

The concepts in the preceding section have become the foundation of a system of soil classification now used in the United States and elsewhere. By means of this classification soils are grouped in three orders: (1) Zonal, (2) Intrazonal, and (3) Azonal. (See Table 12:1.) A brief description of each follows:

The characteristics of *zonal* soils are determined primarily by the climate in which they have developed. Differences in rock formation and geological origin are largely masked, or have been rendered subordinate by dominating climatic influences. Local features such as drainage, topography, etc., are such as to permit or even encourage the maximum influence of climate and vegetation. As the name *zonal* indicates these soils are of such wide expanse as to be thought of as more or less regional in extent.

Associated with zonal soils are the two other groups—*intrazonal* and *azonal*. The former includes those soils that, in spite of climate and vegetation, reflect the influence of some local condition such as poor drainage, alkali salts, or some other local characteristic. Many of their properties are, of course, similar to those of the zonal soils with which they are associated but the characteristics resulting from local condition are dominant. Since such soils cross zonal boundaries, they are termed intrazonal. Azonal soils in marked contrast are those that are without horizon differentiation. Profile layers resulting from soil development are not apparent. Most soils developed on recent alluvial and colluvial deposits belong in this group.

12:6. ZONAL SOILS—A GENERAL SURVEY

As the classification of soils is followed still further, it seems logical to first consider the zonal soils because of their wide expanse and world im-

[7] The subject of soil classification is quite thoroughly reviewed by a number of authors in *Soil Science,* Vol. 67, February, 1949. Even a casual examination of these articles will reveal not only the complexity of soil classification but also its evolutionary incompleteness.

A Classification of Soils into Orders, Suborders and Great Soil Groups [a]
Each Great Soil Group is Subdivided into Numerous Soil Series and Soil Types. (See Sec. 12:19.)

Order	Suborder	Great Soil Groups
Zonal Soils	1. Soils of the cold zone	Tundra
	2. Light-colored podzolized soils of timbered regions	Podzol Soils Brown Podzolic Soils Gray-Brown Podzolic Soils Red-Yellow Podzolic Soils Gray Podzolic or Gray Wooded Soils
	3. Soils of forested warm-temperate and tropical regions	A variety of Latosols are recognized. They await detailed classification
	4. Soils of the forest-grassland transition	Degraded Chernozem Soils Noncalcic Brown or Shantung Brown Soils
	5. Dark-colored soils of semiarid, subhumid, and humid grasslands	Prairie Soils (semipodzolic) Reddish Prairie Soils Chernozem Soils Chestnut Soils Reddish Chestnut Soils
	6. Light-colored soils of arid regions	Brown Soils Reddish-brown Soils Sierozem Soils Red Desert Soils
Intrazonal Soils	1. Hydromorphic soils of marshes, swamps, flats, and seepage areas	Humic-glei Soils (includes wiesenboden) Alpine Meadow Soils Bog Soils Half-bog Soils Low-humic Glei Soils Planosols Ground-water Podzols Ground-water Latosols
	2. Halomorphic (saline and alkali) soils of imperfectly drained arid regions, littoral deposits	Solonchak Soils (saline soils) Solonetz Soils (alkali soils) Soloth Soils
	3. Calcimorphic soils	Brown Forest Soils (Braunerde) Rendzina Soils
Azonal Soils	(No suborders)	Lithosols Regosols (includes dry sands) Alluvial

[a] Modified from J. Thorp and G. D. Smith, "Higher Categories of Soil Classification: Order, Suborder, and Great Soil Groups," *Soil Sci.,* 67: 117–26, 1949.

portance. As seen in Table 12:1 the *order* of zonal soils is further broken down into *suborders* on the basis of specific climatic and vegetative regions. Each of these suborders in turn is divided into *great soil groups* such as the *podzol, prairie,* etc. These great soil groups, because they are an expression of more specific conditions, will be the subject of much of the discussion that follows.

The classification of zonal soils, outlined in Table 12:1, is presented somewhat more simply by the drawings in Figure 12:3. Here the relation-

Figure 12:3. *Above*—a simplified diagram showing how the natural vegetation varies with climate. *Below*—a similar diagram indicating the relationship of zonal soils to climate. Note that soil boundaries correspond rather closely to those of the natural vegetation.

The right to left successions of soils and vegetation shown in the diagrams approximate those that will be encountered when travelling from the east coast of North America to the Sierra Nevada and Cascade Mountains. Typical desert conditions occur in the intermountain regions west of the Rockies.

ship among climate, vegetation, and some of the important zonal soils is illustrated. The diagrams are particularly helpful in the study of the soils of the United States since the general climatic differences shown in Figure 12:3 approximate those found in this country when going from the Rocky Mountain area eastward. It would be advisable to observe this figure carefully before considering the specific properties of the zonal soils.

In regions too cold for the growth of trees or grass and yet warm enough for some plant life, the vegetation which develops is known as *tundra*. (See Fig. 12:3.) This consists primarily of mosses, lichens, and shrubs. The tundra is found under both humid and arid conditions and the soils which develop are of little agricultural value.

In humid regions the native vegetation of zonal soils is predominantly forests. Within forested areas *podzols* or *podzolic* soils develop if the climate is temperate and moist, whereas *latosols* are formed in wet tropical or semitropical regions. These mature forest soils, as you would expect, are quite thoroughly leached. Consequently, they are usually definitely acid in the surface and there is no $CaCO_3$ remaining in the solum. An accumulation of iron and aluminum as well as silicate clays is common in the lower horizons. As the intensity of their weathering would suggest, profile layering in mature forest soils is quite distinct. Their native fertility as a result of leaching is low compared to that of soils of drier regions.

In addition to the forest soils of humid regions, a second group of soils under forest cover should be mentioned. This group is the *Gray wooded* soils of western United States and Canada and certain other countries. Having developed under subhumid to semiarid cool climates, their characteristics resemble somewhat those of the podzols. They are, however, less drastically leached and hence are much less acid than the latter soils.

As one moves from eastern United States to regions of lower rainfall further west, the humid-region forests are gradually replaced by grasslands. (See Fig. 12:3.) The so-called tall grasses which cover the *prairie soils* are found under climatic conditions which, although drier than those of some forested areas, are still considered humid. Consequently, these soils have some properties in common with forest soils and others in common with soils of the semiarid grasslands. They have been subjected to considerable leaching, but their color and organic matter content and distribution resemble that of other grassland soils.

The *Chernozem* and *Chestnut* groups are developed under semiarid conditions while the *Brown* and *Desert* soils are zonal representatives of arid regions. (See Fig. 12:3.) All these soils have developed under an annual rainfall of 25 inches or less. Due to the consequent lack of leaching there is usually a $CaCO_3$ accumulation at some point in the profile, usually in the upper C horizon. (See Fig. 12:7.) As the rainfall decreases this layer of calcium carbonate, underlain by more soluble salts such as $CaSO_4$, is found nearer and nearer the surface. Unlike humid-region soils, there is little translocation of iron and aluminum. These soils are variable in color primarily due to differences in organic matter content as well as differences in the processes of decay. As the annual precipitation becomes progressively less, grayish colors become more and more pronounced. Where the temperature is high, shades and tints of yellow and red occur. This accounts for such names as *reddish chestnut* and *red desert*.

In summary, it can be said that the properties of the zonal soils of the drier regions differ from those of humid region forest soils in the following major respects.

1. Their surface soil pH values are higher (usually near 7 or above).
2. Their nutrient status, particularly in respect to bases, is higher.
3. These soils are (except for the Chernozems) lower in organic matter and nitrogen in the surface horizons.
4. They nearly always contain a $CaCO_3$ accumulation at some point in the profile.
5. They usually exhibit a less distinct profile development.
6. Biologically, organisms are active at greater depths, but because of moisture deficiencies, less over-all microbial activity occurs in the profile of aridic zonal soils.

12:7. TUNDRA SOILS [8]

The zonal great soil groups will now be considered in order beginning with the tundra. (See Table 12:1.) The soils of this category are of little agricultural importance except as pasturage for reindeer and caribou. Consequently, they deserve hardly more than passing mention in spite of their tremendous expanse in northern Europe, Asia, and North America. Roughly 40 per cent of the Soviet Union is thus covered, an area equal to that of the whole United States.

These soils lie just north of the *podzolic* and *gray wooded* groups and, as might be expected, the transition from forests to the mosses, lichens, and shrubs of the northlands is most irregular. The accumulation of such

[8] See I. C. Fuestel; A. Dutilly; and M. S. Anderson, "Properties of Soils from North American Arctic Regions," *Soil Sci.,* 48: 183–98, 1939.

organic matter gives a peaty surface covering over a bluish-gray, sticky and compact subsoil. Since the substratum, and sometimes even the subsoil, of the tundra remains frozen most of the year, a poorly drained boggy condition is sure to be the rule at certain seasons. Much heaving takes place with the alternate freezing and thawing, and explosive blisters sometimes occur. With the tundra soils are associated the muskeg peats, often with perpetually frozen subhorizons.

12:8. PODZOLIZATION [9]

Since, in addition to the true *podzols*, several of the other great soil groups are *podzolic* in nature, the process of podzolization should be thoroughly understood before proceeding further. This process, in its greatest intensity, requires certain conditions. Firstly, temperature, rainfall, vegetation, and other factors must favor an abundant surface accumulation of organic matter called duff or *mor*. (See Figs. 12:4 and 12:6.) Forests are therefore the most common vegetation, although mild podzolization sometimes occurs with grasses. Coupled with this there must be a type of organic matter decomposition that will develop *acids* and other substances of great solvent capacity. When podzolization is intense, fungi seem to be the major microorganisms engaged in the production of humus, bacterial activity being at a minimum. (See Fig. 14:5.) In such an acid, low-calcium organic medium, earthworms are practically absent. pH values as low as 3.5 are often found in this accumulation, especially that of the H layer. (See Fig. 12:4.)

Acid leaching. If vigorous podzolization is to occur, sufficient moisture must be present to promote marked leaching. This process is greatly speeded up if the parent material is loose and open. Leaching carries the acids of the organic horizons downward through the mineral layers below, dissolving and entirely removing carbonates of all kinds. The colloidal complex of the A horizon thus becomes more or less saturated with hydrogen and hence it is rendered extremely acid. pH values of 4.0 to 4.5 are common in this leached layer.

Under the conditions described above, the colloidal complexes of the A horizon become unstable and break up. The iron and aluminum not already removed are carried away, probably in the sol condition. No doubt humic substances, other than organic acids, have something to do with this

[9] J. S. Joffe, *Pedology* (New Brunswick, N. J.: Rutgers University Press, 1936), Chap. 9; and C. E. Kellogg, *The Soils That Support Us* (New York: Macmillan, 1941), pp. 138–49.

chemical eluviation. The A_2 horizon, thus drastically leached, assumes a bleached, gray appearance and is left in a highly acid, siliceous condition. Because of its gray color and ashy appearance the term *podzol* [10] has been applied, and *podzolization* is used to designate collectively the processes that tend to develop such a layer. (See Fig. 12:4.)

Figure 12:4. A well-developed podzol profile at White Lake Lodge, New York, on the southwestern edge of the Adirondack Mountains. The soil is a stony loam, forested with birch, hemlock, and spruce. Note the thickness of the organic layers (mor or duff), the depth of the gray silicious horizon (A_2), and the marked acidity of the whole profile, even the C_1. The layer of precipitated humus (B_2) is quite distinct. The letters L, F, and H refer to *litter*, zone of *fermentation* and *humus* layer.

Accumulations in the B horizon. While the carbonates, sulfates, and other soluble salts are in large degree carried entirely out of the solum by the podzolic process, colloidal humus which has been leached from above accompanied by part of the iron and aluminum oxides is deposited in the B horizon. Just why the humus and these oxides should precipitate is difficult to explain satisfactorily. Perhaps the somewhat increased base content

[10] From the Russian *pod,* meaning "under" and *zola,* "ash."

may finally force them into a gel condition. Also the upward movements of capillary water in summer may carry these oxides back up into the zone of concentration. But whatever the cause, a typical and mature podzol profile may exhibit in the B zone three distinct horizons in order: a precipitated humus (B_{2_1}), a reddish-brown layer due to a concentration of the sesquioxides with some humus (B_{2_2}), and a yellowish horizon (B_3) below, which gradually merges with the parent material (see Fig. 12:4).

Podzols and podzolic soils. The preceding presentation has dealt with podzolization in its greatest intensity. This gives rise to a true *podzol* soil, the essential profile characteristics of which are shown in Figure 12:4. With the exception of the A_1, all the horizons associated with an ideal profile (Fig. 12:1) are found in a well-developed podzol.

The podzol soils gradually merge to the southward with those having a brown or gray-brown surface layer and an admixture of the organic matter with the A horizon. Under such conditions the gray siliceous layer becomes thinner and thinner until it disappears. The precipitated humus zone is no longer evident, and the accumulation of iron and aluminum in the B horizon is less prominent but silicate clays are more apt to occur. The organic layer becomes more and more mixed with the mineral soil below until the A_0 is very thin, most of the organic matter being a part of the A_1. This layer, now called a *mull*, thus becomes very prominent at the expense of the A_0 and A_2, the latter changing from a gray to a brown color. We now have a mildly podzolized soil, very much higher in fertility than the drastically leached profile with its gray and acid A_2 horizon. (See Fig. 12:6.)

Under still warmer humid conditions podzolization effects are further modified. In the B horizons red and yellow colors begin to dominate. These colors are due primarily to oxidized and hydrated forms of iron. Apparently such soils, although definitely podzolized, have experienced the modifying influence of latosolization so characteristic of soils of warmer regions.

A marked change in profile also is found as progress is made toward a more arid climate. Forest gives way to grass and the podzolic characteristics gradually fade. Carbonates become evident in the profile and, as the rainfall lessens still more, they are found nearer and nearer the surface. In the United States the podzolic soils grade westward into prairie soils, then into chernozems, and finally into more pronounced aridic region types. (See Fig. 12:3.)

12:9. PODZOLIC SOIL REGIONS OF THE UNITED STATES

The soils of northeastern United States, as already emphasized, show conclusive gradations from podzolic to latosol conditions southward, and from podzolic to aridic in a westerly and southwesterly direction. This merging is inevitable. As a result, six podzolic soil regions may definitely be distinguished. (See Table 12:1.)

True podzols.[11]   The first, drastically podzolized, is designated as the region of typical *podzol soils* because of the characteristic color of the A_2 horizon. These soils occur mostly in northern and northeastern United States. (See Fig. 12:5.) Their profile characteristics already have been explained. It need only be said further that the parent material is so drastically leached during soil formation and the upper layers are left so acid, that such soils are rather low in agricultural value except in certain cases. Once the organic matter is gone the slump in productivity is rapid. Most of these soils are best left in woodland. Only with certain crops, such as potatoes in Aroostock County, Maine, is their cultivation advisable.

Brown podzolic soils.   Just south of the typical podzols in New England, New York, and elsewhere in northern United States is found a less drastically podzolized soil group of considerable importance in spite of its comparatively small area—the *brown podzolic*.[12]

Most of the properties of these soils are such that they can almost be considered as weak podzols. There is only a small amount of organic matter (A_0) on the surface of virgin soils. The infertile siliceous layer of the podzol (A_2) is absent or very faint. Consequently, the thin A_1 (2–3 inches) which contains a considerable amount of organic matter lies directly on the B horizon. Moreover, there is little evidence of cementation or clay accumulation in the B. Consequently, the brown podzolic soils are loose and well drained and, in spite of their acidity, are much better suited for agriculture than are the typical podzols. They are a transitional group

[11] As might be expected, various degrees and gradations of podzol formation occur. For instance, in many podzols the A_2 apparently rests directly on the B_2, which is especially high in iron. Such a profile is called an *iron podzol*. When there is a distinct layer of precipitated humus (B_{2_1}) this profile is called a *humus podzol*. In either case the B_{2_2} below is a more compact layer, comparatively high in precipitated iron and aluminum and reddish-brown or yellowish-brown in color. Sometimes this zone is very hard and impervious to water, a true hardpan. It is then known as an *Ortstein* layer. Such conditions favor poor drainage which produces a *half-bog* and finally a *bog* soil whose solum is almost entirely organic.

[12] See W. H. Lyford, "The Morphology of the Brown Podzolic Soils of New England," *Proc. Soil Sci. Soc. Amer.*, 11: 486–92, 1946.

of great importance in New England and play an important role in the agriculture of this section.

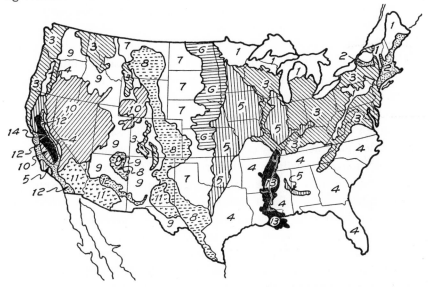

Figure 12:5. A simplified map showing the major Great Soil Groups of the United States. *(After Marbut and Kellogg.)* The poorly drained soils in most cases are included with their zonal associates. The regions located are as follows:

1. Podzol.
2. Brown podzolic.
3. Gray-brown podzolic.
4. Red and yellow podzolic
5. Prairie and reddish-prairie (Includes some Planosols & Rendzinas).
6. Chernozem.
7. Chestnut and reddish-chestnut.
8. Brown and reddish-brown.
9. Shallow soils (lithosols), mountain, upland, and valley.
10. Gray desert (Sierozem).
11. Reddish desert.
12. Non-calcic brown.
13. Mississippi alluvium.
14. Alluvium and outwash of the central valley, California.

Gray-brown podzolic soils.   The gray-brown podzolic soils which lie still further southward (Fig. 12:5) are also mildly podzolized. Due to differences in climate, vegetation, and parent materials, however, they present a profile somewhat different from the brown podzolic. The organic matter, mostly from deciduous trees, does not accumulate on the forest floor as a mat (mor or duff). It has largely become incorporated with the mineral soil (A_1) giving a *mull* layer several inches thick, within which a mild decomposition is occurring. The gray siliceous layer of the podzol is replaced by a gray or yellowish-brown horizon (A_2) from 5 to 12 inches thick. This horizon is characterized by a horizontal, platy structure, and as with the podzol, it is the zone of eluviation. In spite of this, however, considerable exchangeable calcium still occupies the colloidal complex. Consequently, these layers, especially the A₁, are not excessively acid. In fact, at times they are only mildly so. Bacteria and actinomyces are active as well as fungi, and earthworms are numerous.

The B horizons of these soils show some accumulation of silicate clays and often possess a blocky structure that does not always facilitate drainage. Oxides of iron and aluminum also accumulate in this horizon. All in all, the gray-brown podzolic soils constitute a zonal group of great agricultural value. For further profile details see Figs. 12:2 and 12:6.

Although the fertility of the gray-brown podzolic soils is only medium, the climate under which they occur favors crops that assure stable agricultural conditions, especially in the United States. Opportunities for making a livelihood are such as to render the gray-brown podzolics, covering a great strip from the Middle Atlantic states westward to Iowa and Missouri (see Fig. 12:5), one of the bulwarks of American agriculture. Great areas of this soil group also occur in western Montana and northern Idaho. Besides, a wide belt extends down the coastal and valley regions of western Washington and Oregon and into California as far south as San Francisco.

Red-yellow podzolic soils. The red-yellow podzolic soils of the Southern States (see Fig. 12:5) indicate clearly that the modifying influence of latosolization has been at work. These soils have originated under a mild climate, an abundant rainfall, and a mixed forest, often markedly deciduous. As a result, podzolic influences have been most genial.

Virgin soils of this group have a thin layer of unincorporated organic matter, underlain by 2 to 3 inches of A₁. The *red podzolic* soils have a yellowish-gray A₂ several inches in thickness over a red or brownish-red B horizon. Having developed under slightly greater effective moisture conditions, the iron oxides in the *yellow podzolics* are more highly hydrated. Consequently, the colors are somewhat less brilliant. The A₂ is light yellow and is somewhat thicker than the corresponding horizon of the red podzolics. The heavy-textured B horizon is yellow to light yellow, an indication of the hydrated state of the iron.

These red and yellow soils have been developed from all sorts of parent materials, ranging from granites to limestones and from residual debris to marine sediments. Yet they have many attributes in common. It is remarkable that climate and its accompanying vegetation has been able to mold them into such noticeable uniformity. As progress is made southward these soils merge so gradually into the semi-latosols as to make the line of demarcation very vague. In eastern United States they stand next to the gray-

Figure 12:6. Monoliths of soil profiles representing four great soil groups. The process of podzolization is much more intense with the podzol than with the gray-brown podzolic soil even though both have developed under forest vegetation. Note the precipitated humus in the B_{2h} horizon of the podzol, below which iron and aluminum oxides have accumulated (B_{2ir}).

In the case of the gray-brown podzolic soil, the A_2 is subdivided into two layers (A_{21} and A_{22}). Mild acid leaching has resulted in the formation of silicate clays which have accumulated in the B horizon (B_{2t}) of this soil.

The chernozem and chestnut have been subjected to calcification under grass vegetation. This accounts for the high organic content, noticeably present in the chernozem, and for the deep A_1 horizons. Note that the zone of $CaCO_3$ accumulation (C_{ca}) is found nearer the surface in the chestnut than in the chernozem.

309

brown podzolics in importance. But, because of their climate, they balance rather than compete with the latter in agricultural production.

Prairie soils.[13] The fifth podzolic or perhaps semipodzolic soil region in the United States is that of the *prairie* whose soils are classified as dark-colored grass lands. (See Table 12:1 and Fig. 12:5.) Its climate is much the same as that operative in the gray-brown podzolic soil region to the eastward. But because the native vegetation was tall grass instead of forest the soils are strikingly different. Under such a cover the organic matter, thoroughly mixed with the A horizon, is especially high. The leaching, while sufficient to remove the calcium carbonate from the solum, has not seriously impaired the natural fertility. This is the only large area of such soils in the world. Just why they are free of woods and whether they would become partially forested in time if undisturbed by man are mooted questions.

The abundant native grass cover of the prairie soil area has resulted in a deep, rich, dark-brown A horizon with a varied and active microorganic flora. Southward, the color changes to reddish brown and the soils are spoken of as *reddish prairie* soils. The structure of the surface soil is decidedly granular, due to the influence of the grass cover. The exchangeable calcium is high, in spite of the definite acidity, and little downward movement of iron and aluminum has occurred. In places the presence of clay pans indicates considerable translocation of clay. The B horizon is brownish and grades into a parent material that often is rich in lime. Podzolic influences, modified by climate and vegetation, have been decidedly beneficial. The marked accumulation of humus and its dark color, both extremely noticeable to eastern eyes, are probably due, in part at least, to the hot dry summers which have impeded and modified microbial activities, so marked in spring and autumn.

This belt of prairie soils, extends latitudinally through the heart of the country, with the chernozems on the one hand and with the gray-brown podzolics on the other. They are uniformly fertile and, with the red and yellow soils of the South and the gray-brown forest soils of the East, control the agriculture of central and eastern United States.

Gray wooded soils. The sixth podzolic soil to be considered is the *gray wooded* or *gray podzolic* group of western United States and Canada. These soils are developed under forest cover, and a cool, subhumid to semi-

---

[13] For an excellent discussion of these soils, see G. D. Smith; W. H. Allaway; and F. F. Riecken, "Prairie Soils of the Upper Mississippi Valley," *Advances in Agronomy,* II: 157–205, 1950.

arid climate. A semidecomposed organic matter layer (A_0) is found and a very thin A_1 of mixed mineral and organic matter is present. The A_2 horizon like that of the gray-brown podzolic soils is somewhat leached and platy.

These soils, although definitely podzolized, are not so thoroughly leached as their humid region equivalents. Consequently, the soils usually are not as acid, pH values as high as 7.0 in the B horizon frequently being encountered.

12:10. FORMATION OF LATOSOLS [14]

Under the abundant rainfall and high temperatures of the tropics and semitropics, weathering forces work faster and carry their influence to greater extremes than in temperate regions. Here there has been no glaciation to interrupt the process and the country rock and the regolith have been subjected to drastic decomposition. Hydrolysis, as well as oxidation, has been extremely intense and silicate minerals have quickly succumbed. In many parts of the tropics wet and dry seasons alternate, which no doubt greatly intensifies chemical activities, especially those of the organic matter. The process which is responsible for the formation of these soils is termed *latosolization*.

The process and its results. In the genesis of latosols the soluble bases, such as calcium, magnesium, potassium, and sodium, are quickly released. Due to the mobility of these cations the pH is near 7. This condition of low acidity is furthered by the rapid decay of organic residues and the immediate release of the bases in organic combination. As a result, the solubility of the *silica* is encouraged and that of the *iron, aluminum,* and *manganese* retarded. If drainage is at all satisfactory, intense oxidation occurs. Thus, as weathering proceeds, red or yellow parent materials, high in the sesquioxide and low in silica, result. The extent of silicon removal and sesquioxide accumulation is remarkable. In Cuba, for example, a soil containing 1.8 per cent of SiO_2 and 71.1 per cent of Fe_2O_3 has developed from parent material showing 41.9 per cent of SiO_2 and only 7.8 per cent Fe_2O_3.[15]

Because of the intensity of tropical weathering the regolith often becomes very deep and when a soil develops the B horizon usually extends

[14] See R. P. Humbert, "The Genesis of Laterite," *Soil Sci.,* 65: 281–90, 1948; and E. C. J. Mohr and F. A. Van Baren, *Tropical Soils* (New York: Interscience, 1954).

[15] H. M. Bennett, and R. V. Allison, "The Soils of Cuba," *Tropical Plant Research Foundation,* Washington, D. C., 1928, p. 2.

many feet below the surface. Original differences due to the character of the country rock are often practically eliminated by the vigor of the chemical processes. The oxidation of iron and the hydration of iron and aluminum during latosol formation is, of course, intense above the water table and red and yellow hydrous oxide clays are the final product. Iron concretions are found which are indicative of some translocation of the sesquioxides. In fact, where drainage is restricted soft deposits of these compounds often occur at or near the water table. In some countries these are cut out in conveniently sized blocks, which harden when dry and thus make excellent building material. These cemented horizons in certain latosols are termed *laterites*.[16]

The process of latosolization is so intense and leaching is so thorough that the *hydrous oxide* clays that develop are very low in exchangeable bases. In spite of this, however, the resulting latosols under natural vegetation usually are not extremely acid. Due to the exceedingly low cation exchange capacity of the hydrous oxide clays, the bases present, even though small in amount, are able to maintain a relatively high percentage base saturation. The pH is therefore held at a comparatively high level, often between 6 and 7.

12:11. LATOSOLS[17]—CHARACTERISTICS OF

It is not difficult to forecast some of the characteristics of a zonal and well-developed latosol. A red or yellow color, especially in the B horizons, is a foregone conclusion. However, the surface soil, if uneroded, often is brown or gray. In other cases the red or yellow color dominates the surface soil. This is likely to be the case when the parent material was basaltic. Also, enough erosion may have occurred, especially on cultivated lands, to bring some of the bright red or yellowish subsoil into the furrow-slice.

Another latosolic characteristic of outstanding importance is the peculiar granular condition that is developed and which promotes excellent internal drainage. Moreover, hydrous oxide clays do not possess the plasticity

[16] A *laterite* soil is therefore only one of the varieties of *latosols* found in humid tropical regions.

[17] *Latosol* is the term applied to the suborder which includes soils of "tropical and equatorial regions having their dominant characteristics associated with low silica-sesquioxide ratios of clay fractions, low base-exchange capacities, low activities of clay, low content of most primary minerals, low content of soluble constituents, a high degree of aggregate stability and (perhaps) some red colour." See C. E. Kellogg, *Preliminary Suggestions for the Classification and Nomenclature of Great Soil Groups in Tropical and Equatorial Regions,* Commonwealth Bur. of Soil Sci., Tech. Communication No. 46, 1949, p. 79.

and cohesion that characterize the silicate clays of temperate regions. This allows the cultivation of typical latosols immediately after a heavy rain with little danger of generating an unsatisfactory physical state. In fact, latosols are utilized for agriculture under a weight of rainfall that would render siliceous soils utterly unworkable.

Typical latosols, as already stated, are low in cation exchange capacity compared to representative temperate-region soils. This is due in part to their lack of organic matter and in part to the nature of their hydrous oxide clays. They are extremely deficient in exchangeable bases and in available nutrients in general. This means that their fertility level is very low. Hence, virgin soils, unless precautions are taken, are soon depleted in fertility when put under cultivation. Such soils usually require liberal fertilization if plant culture is to be at all intensive.

One disadvantage of the high content of sesquioxides is in respect to the efficiency of superphosphate. The iron and aluminum tend to render the phosphates of the fertilizer not only insoluble but very unavailable to crops. (See p. 438.) Some latosols are moderately or even strongly acid but not so intensely so as a silicate clay would be at the same percentage base saturation. These soils usually respond to lime even when applied in small amounts, as well as to commercial fertilizers.

Since humid-tropical and humid-semitropical climates merge more or less gradually into arid as well as into humid-temperate conditions, latosolization varies accordingly. All sorts of profile types may thus be found corresponding to climatic gradations. Indeed, it is often difficult to decide whether a given soil is essentially latosolic or podzolic. Thus, the red earths and red loams of the Mediterranean regions are considered by some to be progressively transitional. Without a doubt this is true for the red and yellow soils of our Southern States.

It is not to be inferred, however, that all soils in the tropics are latosols. Alluvial soils of all kinds occur as well as colluvial and fan debris. These may show very little latosolization. Moreover, at the higher elevations podzolization is often the dominant type of soil genesis.

In Europe, latosols are found in southern France, Spain, Italy, and Greece. They also are typically developed in Central America, Mexico, Puerto Rico, Cuba, and other islands in the Caribbean Sea. In northern South America, India, Burma, Thailand, Java, Borneo, Sumatra, and contiguous regions, latosols are common, while on the islands of the central Pacific, red earths are abundant. The latosols of Hawaii have received especially careful study. Originally forested, latosols will grow many kinds of tropical and semitropical crops—sugar cane, rubber, coffee, bananas, and pineapples being common products.

12:12. CALCIFICATION

As one moves westward from forested regions to areas of lower rainfall, the process of podzolization is gradually replaced by that of *calcification*. The prairie soil area represents very well the transition zone in which both of these processes have been and still are active.

As suggested by the term calcification, this process yields a soil sufficiently high in calcium to give a fairly high percentage base saturation. Climate and its resulting vegetation are largely responsible for this situation. (See Fig. 12:7.) The rainfall in these areas is insufficient to leach much of the calcium and other divalent cations from the soil profile. Only in the upper horizons are the soils even mildly affected in this way.

Moreover, soluble constituents leached from the surface horizons are not removed from the profile. They are only moved to the lower horizons. Thus, a zone of accumulation of $CaCO_3$ occurs at a depth approximating the average penetration of the rain waters. On the drier soils, the more soluble calcium sulfate will also accumulate, usually below the zone of carbonate concentration. Even soluble salts of sodium and potassium may be present at the lower depths of the zonal soils of the arid regions.

It should be emphasized that even a considerable removal of soluble salts from the upper horizons of these soils does not yield excessively acid conditions. In fact, the surface horizons are at most mildly acid. In the drier regions the surface soils are commonly neutral or mildly alkaline. The percentage base saturation, even in the surface of such soils, is very high, due primarily to the large quantities of adsorbed calcium present.

The native vegetation, which ranges from grasses to desert shrubs, has contributed to the progress of calcification. The grasses are particularly effective in returning bases to the surface of the soil. The extensive root systems of these plants also supply large amounts of organic matter. The humus that develops seems to be effective in stabilizing the soil colloids when adequate calcium is present. This prevents the downward movement of the finer materials, a process so characteristic of podzolization.

12:13. SOILS OF SEMIARID AND ARID REGIONS OF THE UNITED STATES

Chernozems.   Moving westward from the prairie soils of the United States the first great soil group to be encountered is that of the *chernozems*.

(See Figs. 12:3 and 12:7.) Here calcification is dominant. The rainfall ranges from 15 to 25 inches annually and the native vegetation is mixed grass. While the precipitation is sufficient to support a vigorous growth of herbaceous plants, it is not heavy enough to leach through the profile. As a result, calcium carbonate accumulations usually occur in the upper C horizon which, therefore, is mildly alkaline and usually grayish or yellowish-brown with white spots or blotches of precipitated calcium carbonate. Under this lime accumulation lenses of gypsum are often found.

The A_1 horizon of a typical northern chernozem is black [18] due to the accumulation and decay of organic matter under scanty rainfall and hot dry summers. This horizon is surprisingly deep, often 12 to 15 inches. (See Fig. 12:6.) In reaction it usually is neutral to somewhat acid. Its granular structure is one of its outstanding physical characteristics. The depth to which the organic matter has penetrated possibly is related to the high-percentage base saturation, and the type of vegetation. The amount of extremely black pigment present may also be related to the percentage base saturation.

A typical chernozem surface soil is surprisingly high in mineral nutrients as well as in nitrogen and sulfur. A chemical analysis has already been cited (see p. 28) which fully supports these statements. On the basis of nutrient content the chernozems are the most fertile soils of large area in the United States. Because of low uncertain rainfall, however, they do not consistently produce so much as the corresponding prairie soils. The southern chernozems are usually lower in organic matter, lighter in color, and have reddish or yellowish subsoils. (See Fig. 12:6 for contrast with a typical podzol.)

Chestnut and brown soils. The *chestnut* and *brown* soil groups lie, in the order named, between the chernozem belt and the Rocky Mountains. They are the principal soils of the Great Plains. (See Fig. 12:5.) With a rainfall of only 10 to 15 inches annually, the vegetation is mostly of a steppe type. Due to the scanty precipitation such soils are much lower in organic matter than are the chernozems and the layer of carbonates is nearer the surface. Thus, the surface layers are neutral or even alkaline. Gypsum also is likely to be present in the subsoil. These soils, as well as the chernozems, are used for cereal production but nonirrigated agriculture is hazardous because of the low and variable rainfall. The plowing of such soils has increased wind erosion and has magnified the dust storms that in recent years have menaced the agriculture of the Middle West. The dust

[18] *Chernozem* means black earth.

bowls of Texas, Oklahoma, Colorado, and Kansas, and of the Dakotas and Nebraska lie in these soil regions. (See Fig. 9:7.) Much of this extensive area should be in range and again under the protection of native vegetation.

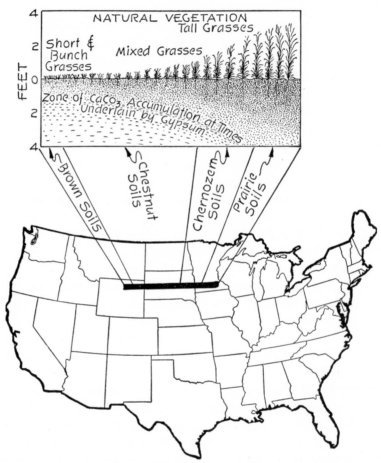

Figure 12:7. The correlation between natural vegetation and certain zonal soil groups is graphically shown for a strip of territory in north central United States. The control, of course, is climate. This figure is a field illustration of the concept carried by Figure 12:3. Note the greater organic content and deeper zone of calcium accumulation as one proceeds from the drier areas in the west toward the more humid region where prairie soils are found.

The comparative characteristics of the *chestnut, brown,* and *chernozem* soils are illustrated in Figure 12:7. All three great soil groups have developed under grasses. With decreasing rainfall, however, the shorter grasses dominate the vegetation. Profile development is less marked and organic matter content becomes more scanty as the annual precipitation decreases. The depth at which carbonate accumulations are encountered is much less in the soils of arid regions. For a *chestnut* profile see Figure 12:6.

Under warmer conditions, the characteristics of grassland soils, and particularly their colors, are somewhat different from their temperate region equivalents. The black and brown colors so common in the nothern plain soils in this country give way to browns and reddish browns as one moves southward. The higher temperature apparently encourages the oxidation of iron and at the same time results in a lower organic matter content of the surface layers. The names associated with the great soil groups in these warmer regions—*Reddish-prairie, Reddish-chestnut,* and *Reddish-brown* (see Fig. 12:3 and Table 12:1)—reflect this color change.

Desert soils. When climatic conditions are so arid that grasses will not persist, desert shrubs become the natural vegetation. Under these conditions three zonal great soil groups are found: (1) *Sierozem* (Gray Desert), (2) *Desert,* and (3) *Red Desert.* The Sierozems develop under slightly higher moisture conditions than the desert soils, and are found quite extensively in the intermountain region west of the Rockies. The vegetation on the desert soils is even more scanty than that of the sierozems and consequently much wind erosion occurs.

The *red desert* soils are found in southwestern United States under a warm to hot arid climate. As is the case with the Sierozem and desert soils, there is a layer of $CaCO_3$ accumulation under the surface horizon. This $CaCO_3$ layer is frequently cemented, giving rise to a hardpan. Except when irrigated, such desert soils are of little agricultural value.

12:14. INTRAZONAL SOILS

Associated with each of the zonal soils already considered are those soils of the *intrazonal* order. (See Table 12:1.) The major characteristics of the latter are largely determined by some local feature rather than by climate. Three major suborders of intrazonal soils are recognized: (1) *Hydromorphic,* (2) *Halomorphic,* and (3) *Calcimorphic.* They will be considered in order.

12:15. HYDROMORPHIC SOILS

Hydromorphic soils are characterized by an excess of soil moisture. Drainage is usually poor either because of profile characteristics which prevent normal water filtration, or because the soil is located in a low-lying area. The *ground water podzol, half-bog,* and *bog* soils are typical examples of great soil groups belonging to this suborder in temperate forested regions.

These soils, in the order named, become progressively more poorly drained. The ground water podzol has developed under a high water table. It has an exceptionally deep mat of undecomposed organic matter and is characterized by a cemented B_2 (ortstein). Progressing to the half-bog we find an increasingly high water table which in a bog is at or very near the surface during most of the year. The latter soils include the peats and mucks so important in vegetable production when properly drained. (See Chapter 13.)

One characteristic common to many poorly drained mineral soils is the presence of so-called *glei* horizons. (See Fig. 12:9.) Due to alternate periods of dry and moist conditions these horizons have become mottled with irregular colorations. Red, yellow, and brown streaks or spots are indicative of the oxidized forms of iron and manganese. Mixed with these are blue and gray colors which are characteristic of reduced compounds. This mottled condition is looked for in the diagnosis of poorly drained soils.

Two hydromorphic soil groups found in *humid grasslands* are of special interest and importance. These are the *Wiesenboden* [19] and the *planosol* groups. Although the Wiesenboden group is found only under grass or sedges, planosols occur frequently in forested areas as well.

The Wiesenboden group is encountered primarily in association with the zonal prairie soils, which they resemble in many respects when properly drained. These soils occur in relatively flat areas of restricted drainage and have a dark colored surface horizon which is usually near neutrality. When drained, the productivity of the Wiesenbodens is high since their poor drainage is due to location rather than to clay pan development. The contrast between a Wiesenboden and a prairie profile can be seen by referring to Figure 12:8.

The *planosols,* which are poorly drained upland soils, occupy great stretches of prairie in southern Illinois and Iowa and northern Missouri as well as scattered areas in humid forest regions. These soils have been subjected to podzolization and are characterized by a heavy clay pan.

[19] These are included in the humic-glei soil group in Table 12:1 and are sometimes referred to as meadow soils.

Their surface is strongly leached and, due to their profile restrictions, they are not nearly as productive, even when artificially drained, as are their zonal associates.

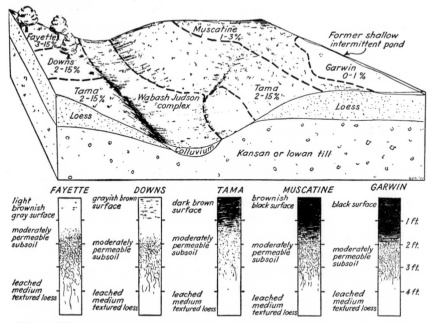

Figure 12:8. A block diagram showing an *association* of soils in Iowa. Note the relationship of soil type to (1) parent material, (2) vegetation, (3) topography, and (4) drainage. In this diagram two gray-brown podzolic soils (Fayette and Downs), two prairie soils (Tama and Muscatine), and a hydromorphic soil, or Wiesenboden (Garwin) are shown. *(From F. F. Riecken and G. D. Smith, "Principal Upland Soils of Iowa, Their Occurrence and Important Properties," Iowa Agr. Exp. Sta. Agron., 49, Revised.)*

12:16. HALOMORPHIC SOILS [20]

Soils developed under imperfect drainage conditions in arid regions are often characterized by abnormal salt concentrations in the upper horizons. Because of the effects of salts on their properties, these soils are termed *halomorphic*. They are most generally found in association with the cher-

---

[20] The classification presented here is used by the United States Department of Agriculture, Soil Survey Division. A newer and somewhat modified classification designed to evaluate soils in terms of plant response has been proposed by the United States Salinity Laboratory. This is discussed by H. E. Haward and C. H. Wadleigh, "Plant Growth on Saline and Alkali Soils," *Advances in Agron.,* 1: 1–38, 1949. This classification is discussed on page 379 and ff. of this textbook.

nozems, chestnuts, browns, and desert soils, and as a group are commonly, though perhaps incorrectly, referred to as "alkali soils."

Solonchak or *saline* soils result when there is an accumulation of soluble salts of sodium, calcium, magnesium, and potassium in the upper horizon. The process operative is known as salinization. The anions found are mostly the chloride and sulfate with some carbonate and bicarbonate. The surface of a solonchak often is irregularly covered with a white crust of salts. (See Fig. 14:8.) These salts have been carried upward by capillarity and have remained when the water evaporated. As a result, solonchaks are commonly called *white alkali* soils.

Since the exchangeable ions of solonchaks are dominantly calcium and magnesium with relatively low amounts of adsorbed sodium, these soils are only slightly alkaline, their pH seldom rising much above 8. Their high salt concentration prevents dispersion of the soil granules, giving a physical condition that is not unfavorable for agricultural utilization. In spite of this, however, crop production on these soils is possible only after drainage is installed and the salt concentration lowered.

Under conditions which have allowed a high concentration of sodium to become associated with the colloids, a *solonetz* soil is formed. The pH of this soil is high due to the adsorbed sodium and to the presence of sodium carbonate. The soil colloids, both inorganic and organic, become dispersed and tend to move slowly down the profile. The dark color of the salty surface crust that often is observed is due to the dissolved organic matter. This accounts for the common name "black alkali" applied to these soils. The process of the formation of solonetz soils is aptly termed *solonization*.

The profile which develops as a result of this process is quite unique. Underneath a very thin friable surface horizon is found a dark horizon of hard clay. This zone has a characteristic columnar structure (see p. 57) and makes a solonetz easy to identify. Solonetz soils are very unproductive due to their toxic chemical properties and poor physical condition. They can often be reclaimed, however, by proper management.[21]

If improved drainage is maintained in the case of a solonetz it may eventually become leached thoroughly enough to allow the formation of a *soloth*. This soil has an acid light-colored surface horizon over a heavy dark brown B. Moreover, the excess colloids have been removed from the A horizon. These soils can be used essentially in the same way as their zonal associates.

[21] Methods of managing alkali soils are considered in Chapter 14, page 382 and ff.

12:17. CALCIMORPHIC SOILS

The characteristics of *calcimorphic* soils are largely due to the high lime content of their parent materials. *Brown forest soils* of the humid east and their grassland equivalents, the *Rendzinas*, are the two soil groups commonly recognized. (See Table 12:1.) The surface soils of both are at least neutral if not alkaline. Brown forest soils are dark brown in the surface and gradually grade into the gray calcareous parent material. There is little profile layering compared to zonal soils in the same region. Brown forest soils apparently are of much greater importance in Europe than in America.

Rendzinas are rather thin dark-colored grassland soils developed from soft lime rocks. The blacklands of north central Texas is a well-known area of these soils in the United States. These soils are often subject to erosion damage, which is particularly serious due to their shallow depth.

12:18. AZONAL SOILS

The characteristics of azonal soils are determined, not by the climate or any particular soil forming process but rather by the nature of their parent material. Three groups are commonly recognized—*lithosols, regosols,* and *alluvial.* (See Table 12:1.) The first give rise to thin surface soils over bedrock. They are commonly found on steep slopes, show little soil development, and in general are not of significance agriculturally.

Regosols are also very young soils and are located on deep unconsolidated soft mineral deposits. They differ from lithosols in that they are usually not stony. They are largely confined to areas of sand dunes, loess, and steeply sloping glacial drift.

Alluvial soils are of much greater agricultural importance than the azonal soils already mentioned. Large areas are found along rivers such as the Mississippi and Ohio wherever recent alluvium occurs. Valley bottoms throughout the country commonly contain alluvial soils. When properly drained such soils are very productive. The rich lands of the Mississippi delta and floodplain are good examples.

12:19. THE SUBDIVISION OF A SOIL GROUP—SOIL SERIES

The first concept in soil classification is a comprehensive one—the decision as to whether a soil is *zonal, intrazonal,* or *azonal* and to what great *soil group* it belongs. These groups already have been discussed, but in passing it is well to emphasize again that a great soil group is a very broad subdivision based on the recognized tendency of soils under a given set of climatic conditions to assume a general similarity as to profile and other characteristics. And, as may be expected, there are many varieties of soils within each great group. The reasons are not difficult to discover.

In the United States, as elsewhere, many of the soils are young and the original geological characteristics of the parent materials are much in evidence. Also, topography, depth, drainage, aeration, and organic accumulation are variable. Thus, even if climate were uniform, a great miscellany of soils would still occur within any particular region. Indeed the layman is likely to be impressed by the unlikenesses within a great soil group rather than by the similarities that make it possible to establish such a broad division.

Soil series defined.   Obviously then, the next step is a subdivision within each great soil group. This is necessary if any detailed study is contemplated or any agricultural evaluation is to be made. This separation is accomplished by subdividing the great soil groups into lesser groups called *series*. These units are quite distinct. The soils of any one series have similar profile characteristics except for the texture of the surface layer. In more precise terms, a *series* is a group of soils developed from the same kind of parent material, by the same genetic combination of processes, and whose horizons are quite similar in their arrangement and general characteristics. Ideally, the only differences of agricultural importance that should exist between the various soils of any given series are in the textures of the surface layer and even here the range should not be great.

Differentiating and naming of series.   Series are of course established on the basis of profile characteristics. This requires a careful study of the various horizons as to number, order, thickness, texture, structure, color, organic content, and reaction (acid, neutral, or alkaline). Such features as hardpan at a certain distance below the surface, a distinct zone of calcium carbonate accumulation at a certain depth, or striking color characteristics greatly aid in series identification.

In the United States each series is given a name, usually from some city, village, river, or county, such as Fargo, Muscatine, Cecil, Mohave, Ontario, and the like. Members of the Ontario series include Ontario sandy loam, Ontario fine sandy loam, and Ontario loam. These soils are quite similar except for the texture of their A horizons.

It is well to state at this point that similar series are grouped together to give soil families.[22] Thus, the classification so far runs as follows: (1) the

---

[22] The family grouping is not as yet well worked out and is of interest only to the specialist.

order, that is, whether zonal, intrazonal, or azonal; (2) the *suborder,* such as light-colored soils of the arid regions; (3) the *group,* as, for example, the gray-brown podzolic or chernozem; (4) the *family;* and finally (5) the *series* just considered.

12:20. SOIL TYPES, PHASES, AND CATENAS

The subdivision of the series on the basis of the texture of the A horizon gives the soil *type.* It is well to emphasize, however, that differences in texture between the various soil types in any given series cannot be great. For instance, a soil with a sandy surface layer could hardly have the same profile otherwise that a soil with a clayey A horizon would possess. A series generally consists of a dominant type or types with several minor types varying somewhat as to the texture of the surface horizons.

Any particular soil is designated for simplicity by the textural name of its surface layer, such as sandy loam, gravelly loam, clay loam, and so on. To this is prefixed the series name in designating the soil type. Mohave sandy loam, Carrington silt loam, Norfolk sandy loam, Miami silt loam, Houston clay and Fort Collins loam are examples. The type name, therefore, consists of two parts, the first designating the series, and the second indicating the particular individual within the series. This designation is especially valuable as it implies very specifically a great number of characteristics which otherwise would require detailed explanation. It also lends itself to mapping and description.

All areas of the same soil type in the same general locality are alike (within limits) as to profile characteristics, including the texture of the surface horizon, and were originally similar in fertility. Methods of farming have, of course, developed differences in immediate productivity. This sometimes leads to confusion in comparing soils of different farms.

Areas of the same soil type at some distance from each other usually show certain minor variations. For example, Knox silt loam soils 50 or 60 miles apart exhibit certain well-recognized deviations that must be considered in making fertility recommendations. Again variations are to be expected as one soil type grades into another. Thus, the heterogeneity of the soil type as to minor characteristics must constantly be kept in mind.

Soil phase. A soil type is not quite the ultimate subdivision of a series since *phases* are often mapped within types. A *phase* is a subdivision on the basis of some important deviation such as erosion, slope, stoniness, or soluble salt content. It really marks a departure from the normal, or key type, already established. Thus, a Cecil sandy loam, eroded phase, or a

Hagerstown silt loam, stony phase, are examples of soils where distinctions are made in respect to the phase.

Soil associations and catenas.   Before proceeding with a consideration of soil survey methods, two more means of classifying associated soils should be mentioned. In the field, soils of different kinds are commonly found together. Such an *association* of soils may consist of zonal soils, intrazonal soils, azonal soils, or a combination of members of one or more of these soil orders. Thus, a shallow regosol on steep uplands may be found alongside a well drained gray-brown podzolic or a soil developed from recent alluvium. The only requirement is that the soils be found together in the same area. Soil associations are important in a practical way since they help determine combinations of land-use patterns which must be used to support a profitable agriculture.

Zonal soils and imperfectly or poorly drained intrazonal soils, all of which have developed from the same parent materials under the same climatic conditions, are often found closely associated under field conditions. This association on the basis of drainage or of differences in relief is known as a *catena* and is very helpful in practical classification of soils in a given region. The relationship can be seen by referring to Figure 12:9 where the Bath-Mardin-Volusia-Chippewa catena is shown. Although all four or five members of a catena are seldom found in given area, the diagram illustrates the relationship of drainage to topography.

12:21. SOIL SURVEY AND ITS UTILIZATION [23]

The classification as outlined in the preceding pages is susceptible to enough detail and precision to make it valuable in soil survey. In fact, it was developed for just such a purpose. The function of a soil survey is to classify, locate on a base map, and describe the nature of soils as they occur in the field. The soils, if the system utilized in the United States is followed, are classified into *series* and *types* on the basis of their profile characteristics. The field man, since his work is localized, concerns himself mostly with series and type separations, giving the broader regional distinctions only general consideration.

Field mapping.   As the series and type identification progresses in the survey of any area, the location of each individual soil is shown on a suit-

---

[23] For an authoritative discussion of soil survey procedures and related features see "Soil Survey Manual," Agricultural Handbook No. 18, by Soil Survey Staff, Bur. of Plant Industry, Soils and Agr. Engineering, Wash., D. C., 1951. See also a series of articles on soil survey interpretation, *Proc. Soil Sci. Soc. Amer.* 22: 152–70, 1958.

able base map. The maps often used in the United States are aerial base maps such as the one shown in Figure 12:10. In many respects they have considerable advantage over the ordinary contour maps in that land cover

Figure 12:9. Monoliths showing four soils of a drainage *catena* (below) and a diagram showing their topographic association in the field (above). Note the decrease in the depth of the well aerated zone (indicated by arrows) from the Bath soil (left) to the Chippewa (right). The latter remains poorly aerated throughout the growing season. These soils are all developed from the same parent material, differing only in drainage and topography. The Volusia soil as pictured was cultivated (note Ap = plowed) while the others were located on virgin sites. Other symbols are as follows: ir = iron; g and G = gleyed, a mottled layer indicative of poor aeration, G being more intensely gleyed; m = massive compact layer.

and field boundaries show very clearly. Thus, the surveyor can quickly locate his position on the map and can indicate in great detail the soil boundaries.

Using the procedure outlined above, a field map is thus obtained which

Figure 12:10. An aerial photograph of an area in Boone County, Iowa. Such maps are invaluable in making soil surveys since the field man is able to visualize quickly the topographical features of the section in which he is working.

Note the contrast between cropped areas and those in woods. The roads, farm buildings, and individual fields are plainly visible. Alternate, irregular light and dark streaks are seen where surface erosion has taken place.

The area shown is representative of the forest-grassland transition zone where gray-brown podzolic (forest) soils and prairie (grassland) soils are prevalent. (*U. S. Soil Conservation Service photo.*)

not only gives the soil type and phase, but also often furnishes information as to slope and severity of erosion. Thus, the map becomes of even greater practical value.

The field map, after the separations have been carefully checked and correlated, is now ready for reproduction. In the past, this reproduction was made in color. (See Fig. 12:11.) For maps made in recent years a reproduction is made of the aerial photograph with the appropriate soil symbols shown. When published the map accompanies a bulletin containing a discussion of the topography, climate, agriculture, and soils of the area under consideration. Each soil type is minutely described as to profile and suggestions as to practical management are usually made. Such a field map is shown in Figure 12:11 where the relationship of topography to soil associations can be readily seen.

Use of soil surveys.   Soil-survey bulletins and maps perhaps attain their greatest usefulness as a basis for other scientific work. Profile studies, whether physical, chemical, or biological, must be preceded by some sort of a survey or classification. Crop research of all kinds is facilitated if a soil survey has previously been made. Land evaluation and appraisal, statistical studies, and sociological investigations are other interests served.

There is a growing tendency to make use of soil survey maps and bulletins in a more practical way. The extension specialist and the county agricultural agent find the survey maps and bulletins a guide in making suggestions and recommendations. They afford information that it would be impossible to obtain elsewhere, and for a broad, over-all concept of an area nothing better can be consulted. In some cases simpler and more practical bulletins follow the rather technical ones. Opportunity is thus given for the effective presentation of information and up-to-date recommendations that cannot be included in the soil-survey bulletin itself.

The value of an illustrative means of showing the relationships among soil types within a given region can be seen by referring to Figure 12:8. A glance at this diagram shows the meaning and need for classification. It also suggests that soil management must be accommodated to the soil type insofar as possible.

Engineers and hydrologists also use soil survey information in a practical way. Prospective road beds can be selected from soil survey maps. Estimates of water runoff and infiltration can be made on the basis of soil characteristics enumerated in soil-survey bulletins. Predictions can be made of hydrologic changes in relation to modifications in land-use patterns.

The soil survey in a practical way is perhaps of greatest value in land

Figure 12:11. Part of the Madison County, New York, soil map showing the topography and drainage and the relation of the various soil types to one another. The Volusia series has been formed from ground moraine, the Palmyra from glacial outwash, while the Genesee and Holly are alluvial. Note the varying elevations of the peat (called muck) deposits.

classification for agricultural and other uses. The classification which is of most concern to agriculturists is that in use by the United States Soil Conservation Service. Because of its widespread application it should be of some interest.

12:22. LAND—CAPABILITY [24] CLASSIFICATION

Soil-survey maps and reports have become two of the bases for a system of land-capability classification. This system requires that every acre of land be used in accordance with its *capability* and *limitations*. Land is classified according to the most suitable sustained use that can be made of it while providing for adequate protection from erosion or other means of deterioration. Thus, an area where the soils are deep, well drained, and have a stable surface structure, and where the slope is only 1 to 2 per cent may be cropped intensively almost indefinitely with little danger of erosion or loss in productivity. Such an area has great capabilities and few limitations in the use to which it can be put. In contrast, an area on which shallow or poorly drained soils are found or wherein steep slopes are prevalent, has limited capabilities and many limitations as to its use. One can easily see how the characteristics of soils would be one of the criteria for identifying the best land use.

Capability classes.[25]   Under the system set up by the United States Soil Conservation Service, eight land-capability classes are recognized. These classes are numbered from I to VIII. Soils having greatest capabilities for response to management and least limitations in the ways they can be used are in class I. Those with little capabilities and great limitations are found in class VIII. (See Figs. 12:12 and 12:13.) A brief description of the characteristics and safe use of soils in each class follows:

Class I.   Soils found in this land class have few limitations that restrict their use. They can be cropped intensively, used for pasture, range, woodlands, or even for wildlife preserves. The soils are deep, well drained

---

[24] At this point it may be well to point out the difference between *soil* and *land*. Soil is the more restrictive term, referring to a collection of natural bodies with depth as well as breadth, whose characteristics may be only indirectly related to their current vegetation and use. Land is a broader term which includes among its characteristics, not only the soil, but other physical attributes such as water supply, existing plant cover, and location with respect to cities, means of transportation, etc. Thus, we have *forest land, bottom land,* and *grasslands* which may include a large variety of soils.

[25] For a brief review of this subject see A. A. Klingebiel, "Soil Survey Interpretation —Capability Groupings," *Proc. Soil Sci., Soc. Amer.* 22: 160–63, 1958. A somewhat more detailed discussion is given in *Administrator Memorandum SCS 136,* U.S. Dept. of Agric., May 19, 1958. These publications are the source of the descriptions of land capability classes used in this text.

and the land is nearly level. They are either naturally fertile, or have characteristics which encourage good response of crops to applications of fertilizer.

Figure 12:12. Diagram showing the intensity with which each land-capability class can be used with safety. Note the increasing limitations for which the land can be safely used as one moves from land-capability class I to class VIII. (Modified from R. D. Hackensmith, and J. G. Steele, "Recent Trends in the use of the Land-Capability Classification," *Proc. Soil Sci. Soc. Amer.*, 14; 383–88, 1949.)

The water-holding capacity of soils in class I is high. In arid and semi-arid areas soils having all the other favorable characteristics mentioned above may be in class I if they are irrigated by a permanent irrigation system.

The soils in class I need only ordinary crop-management practices to maintain their productivity. These include the use of fertilizer and lime and the return of manure and crop residues, including green manures. Crop rotations are also followed.

Class II. Soils in this class "have some limitations that reduce the choice of plants or require moderate conservation practices." [25] These soils may be used for the same crops as class I. However, they are capable of sustaining less intensive cropping systems, or, with the same cropping systems, they require some conservation practices.

The use of soils in class II may be limited by one or more factors such as: (1) gentle slopes; (2) moderate erosion hazards; (3) inadequate soil depth; (4) less than ideal soil structure and work ability; (5) slight to moderate alkali or saline conditions; and (6) somewhat restricted drainage.

Figure 12:13. A photograph showing several land-capability classes in San Mateo County, California. A range is shown from the nearly level land in the foreground (class I) which can be cropped intensively, to that of the badly eroded hillsides (classes VII and VIII). Although topography and erosion hazards are emphasized here, it should be remembered that other factors such as drainage, stoniness, droughtiness, etc., also limit soil usage and help determine the land-capability class. *(Photo by U.S. Soil Conservation Service, U.S. Dept. of Agric.)*

The management practices that may be required for soils in class II include terracing, strip cropping, contour tillage, rotations involving grasses and legumes, and grassed waterways. In addition, those practices which are used on class I land are also generally required for soils in class II.

Class III. "Soils in class III have severe limitations that reduce the choice of plants or require special conservation practices or both." [25] The same crops can be grown on class III land as on classes I and II. The amount of clean, cultivated land is restricted, however, as is the choice of the particular crop to be used. Crops which provide soil cover, such as grasses and legumes, must be more prominent in the rotations used.

Limitations in the use of soils in class III result from factors such as: (1) moderately steep slopes; (2) high erosion hazards; (3) very slow water permeability; (4) shallow depth and restricted root zone; (5) low water-holding capacity; (6) low fertility; (7) moderate alkali or salinity; and (8) unstable soil structure.

Soils in class III often require special conservation practices. Those mentioned for class II land must be employed, frequently in combination with restrictions in kinds of crops. Tile or other drainage systems may also be needed.

Class IV. Soils in this class can be used for cultivation but there are very severe limitations on the choice of crops. Also, very careful management may be required. The alternative uses of these soils are more limited than for class III. Close-growing crops must be used extensively and row crops cannot be grown safely in most cases. The choice of crops may be limited by excess moisture as well as by erosion hazards.

The most limiting factors on these soils may be one or more of the following: (1) steep slopes; (2) severe erosion susceptibility; (3) severe past erosion; (4) shallow soils; (5) low water-holding capacity; (6) poor drainage; and (7) severe alkali or salinity. Soil conservation practices must be applied more frequently than on soils in class III. Also, they are usually combined with severe limitations in choice of crop.

Class V. Soils in class V to VIII are generally not suited to cultivation. Those in class V are limited in their safe use by factors other than erosion hazards. Examples of such limitations follow: (1) subject to frequent stream overflow; (2) growing season too short for crop plants; (3) stony or rocky soils; and (4) ponded areas where drainage is not feasible. Oftentimes, pastures can be improved on this class of land.

Class VI. Soils in this class have severe limitations that restrict their use largely to pasture or range, woodland, or wildlife. The limitations are the same as those for class IV land but they are more severe.

Class VII. Soils in class VII have very severe limitations which restrict their use to grazing, woodland, or wildlife. The physical limitations are the same as VI except they are so severe that pasture improvement is impractical.

Class VIII. In this land class are soils that should not be used for any kind of commercial plant production. Their use is restricted to "recreation, wildlife, water supply, or aesthetic purposes." [25] Examples of kinds of soils or land forms which are included in class VIII are: sandy beaches, river wash, and rock outcrop.

Subclasses. In each of the land capability classes are *subclasses* which have the same kind of dominant limitations for agricultural use. The four kinds of limitations recognized in these subclasses are: risks of erosion (e), wetness, drainage, or overflow (w), root zone limitations (s), and climatic limitations (c). Thus, a soil may be found in class III (e), indicating that it is in class III because of risks of erosion.

This land-classification scheme illustrates the use which can be made of soil surveys in a practical way. The many soils delineated on a map by the soil surveyor are viewed in the light of their safest and best long-time use. The eight land capability classes have become the starting point in the development of farm plans so useful to thousands of American farmers.

Organic Soils—Nature, Properties, and Utilization

CHAPTER 13

On the basis of organic content, two general groups of soils are commonly recognized—mineral and organic. The so-called mineral soils vary in organic matter from a mere trace to as high as 15 or even 20 per cent. Those soils, the organic content of which ranges from 20 or 25 to as high in some cases as 90 or 95 per cent, are arbitrarily termed organic soils. For those that are cultivated, perhaps 80 per cent of organic matter is a good average figure.

Organic soils are by no means so extensive as are mineral soils, yet their acreage in the aggregate is quite large. Their use in favored localities for the intensive production of crops, particularly vegetables, has become very important. As the development of such lands goes on, more and more attention will be given to their investigation. In the past organic soils have not received the study that they deserve. As a result, less exact knowledge regarding their physical, chemical, and biological characteristics is available than for mineral soils. In general, however, the same edaphological principles hold in a broad way for both.

13:1. GENESIS OF ORGANIC DEPOSITS

Marshes, bogs, and swamps provide conditions suitable for the accumulation of organic deposits. The highly favorable environment in and adjacent to such areas has encouraged the growth of many plants, such as pondweed, cattails, sedges, reeds and other grasses, mosses, shrubs, and also trees. These plants in numberless generations thrive, die, and sink down to be covered by the water in which they grew. The water shuts out the air, prohibits rapid oxidation, and thus acts as a partial preservative. The decay that does go on is largely through the agency of fungi, anaerobic

334

bacteria, algae, and certain types of microscopic aquatic animals. They break down the organic tissue, liberate gaseous constituents, and aid in the synthesis of humus.

As the process continues, the organic mass becomes brown or even black in color. If decomposition proceeds far enough, this mass of organic soil-material acquires such profile characteristics as to justify its designation as a true organic soil. Apparently the humus now present is the result of ligno-protein unions and polyuronide formation much like the processes prevalent in mineral soils. (See p. 141.)

The layering of peat beds. As one generation of plants follows another, layer after layer of organic residue is deposited in the swamp or marsh. The constitution of these successive layers changes as time goes on since a sequence of different plant life is likely to occur. Thus, deep-water plants may be supplanted by reeds and sedges, these by various mosses, and these in turn by shrubs, until finally forest trees, either hardwoods or conifers, with their characteristic undergrowth, may gain a foothold. The succession is by no means regular, or definite, as a slight change in climate or water level may alter the sequence entirely.

The profile of an organic deposit is, therefore, characterized by layers, differing not only as to their degree of decomposition but also as to the nature of the original plant tissue. In fact, these layers later may have become soil horizons. Their final character is determined in part by the nature of the original materials and in part by the type and degree of decomposition. Thus, the profile characteristics of organic soils, as with those dominantly mineral in nature, are in part inherited and in part acquired.

13:2. AREA AND DISTRIBUTION OF PEAT ACCUMULATIONS

As might be expected, peat deposits are found all over the world wherever the conditions are favorable. But only in certain countries are these accumulations utilized in any intensive way. In Germany, Holland, Norway, Sweden, Russia, Poland, Ireland, England, and Scotland, economic use has long been made of peat and peat products. Organic deposits in Germany occupy perhaps 5,000,000 acres, in Sweden 12,000,000 and in Ireland 3,000,000 acres. Canada possesses approximately 12,000,000 acres of peat, mostly undeveloped.

In nonglaciated United States. Organic deposits of the nature described occur in many parts of the United States.[1] In Florida the Ever-

---

[1] For tabular information as to acreages see A. F. Gustafson, *Soils and Soil Management* (New York: McGraw-Hill, 1941), p. 395.

glades, spread out over an extensive plain, contain considerably over 2,000,000 acres of saw-grass (sedge) accumulations. Along the Atlantic coastal plain great marsh deposits are found, especially in North Carolina. In California there are the tule-reed beds of the great central valley, approximately 300,000 acres in extent. Louisiana alone possesses about 3,000,000 acres of organic accumulations of various kinds. All of these are southward and outside of the glaciated areas of the United States. They are related only indirectly to the glaciation through a change in climate and a rise in ocean level due to the melting of the continental ice sheet.

In glaciated United States.   Northward in the regions covered by glacial debris of various kinds, organic deposits are even more extended. In fact, about 75 per cent of the peat deposits of continental United States occur in the glaciated areas. Minnesota, Wisconsin, and Michigan are especially favored in this respect, their combined acreage running well above 12,000,000 acres. Washington, with about 2,000,000 acres, ranks highest of all the Western states. Indiana, Massachusetts, New York, and New Jersey fall into the 300,000- to 500,000-acre class. Other states, especially Iowa, Illinois and Maine, contain smaller but often very important areas.

The total acreage of peat deposits in the United States proper is in the neighborhood of 25,000,000 acres. In Alaska and northern Canada, and in northern Asia and Europe as well, there occur great areas of peat derived from sedges and mosses called *muskeg*. In many cases the subhorizons of such accumulations are perpetually frozen. They are an important feature of the tundra soils that characterize these regions. (See p. 302.)

The Pleistocene glaciation by impeding drainage led to the formation of swamps and bogs. As the climate became milder and gradually attained its present status, conditions were ideal for swamp vegetation to flourish. As a result, certain parts of the glaciated region are liberally dotted with organic accumulations ranging from a few inches to 50 feet in depth. Some areas, a number of square miles in extent, are solidly occupied as in Minnesota, while in other localities the peat lies in isolated patches or in long ribbons as in southeastern Wisconsin and in central New York. Both of the latter accumulations are in many cases associated with drumlins. (See p. 283.) These long, cigar-shaped hills when parallel often alternate with narrow swamps several miles in length that are filled with organic matter in various stages of decay.

13:3. CLASSIFICATION OF PEAT—
DESCRIPTION OF THE VARIOUS TYPES

Peat, regardless of its stage of decomposition, may conveniently be classified according to its parent materials and under three general heads as follows:

Classification of Peat [2]

1. Sedimentary peat — mixtures of water lilies, pondweed, hornwort, pollen, plankton, etc.

2. Fibrous peat — sedges of various kinds, mosses—sphagnum, hypnum, and others, reeds and other grasses, cattails, both latifolia and angustifolia — and their mixtures

3. Woody peat — deciduous and coniferous trees — and their undergrowth

Sedimentary peat. Sedimentary peat usually accumulates in comparatively deep water and, therefore, generally is found well down in the profile. Sometimes, however, it is intermixed with the other types of peat nearer the surface. Sedimentary peat seems to be derived from plant materials that humify rather freely and rather completely. Due to the nature of the original tissue and perhaps also to the type of decay, a highly colloidal and characteristically compact and *rubbery* substance develops. This material is unique and so different from the other types of peat commonly found in the profile that it always attracts considerable attention when encountered.

Not only is sedimentary peat rubbery in character but it is usually olive-

[2] In Germany peats are classified in a general way into *high-moor* and *low-moor* in reference to the shape of the deposits. The high-moors are convex, that is, raised in the center, while the low-moors are concave. The former is usually quite acid and low in calcium, the latter less acid and quite high in exchangeable calcium.

In England the corresponding terms are *moor* and *fen*. The term *heathland* refers to a shallow acid peat.

For a discussion of American peats and their classification, see A. P. Dachnowski-Stokes, and V. Auer, "American Peat Deposits," *Handbuch der Moorkunde*, Gebrüder Borntraeger, Berlin, 1933, Band 7.

green in color when in its natural position. On exposure to the atmospheric air it darkens rapidly, sometimes becoming almost black. Due to its highly colloidal nature, its moisture capacity is high, perhaps four or five times its dry weight. Water thus imbibed is held tenaciously and therefore this peat dries out very slowly. The colloidal materials of sedimentary peat are largely irreversible—that is, when once dry, this peat absorbs water very slowly and persistently remains in a *hard* and *lumpy* condition.

Sedimentary peat is thus very undesirable as a soil, because its unfavorable physical condition renders it unsatisfactory for use in the growing of plants. Even small amounts in the furrow-slice lower the desirability of the peat for agricultural purposes. Fortunately, in most cases, it occurs well down in the profile and ordinarily does not appear above the plowline. Therefore, its presence usually is unnoticed or ignored unless it obstructs drainage or otherwise interferes with the agricultural utilization of the peat deposit.

Fibrous peats.   As indicated by the classification just presented, a number of fibrous peats occur, often in the same swamp deposit. They are all high in water-holding capacity, and may exhibit varying degrees of decomposition. They differ among themselves especially as to their filamentous or fibrous physical nature. Undecomposed moss and sedge are fine enough to be used in greenhouses and nurseries and as a source of organic matter for gardens and flower beds. Reed and cattails, however, are somewhat coarse, especially the latter.

All of the fibrous materials as they decay may make satisfactory field soils although their productivity will vary. Moss peats are almost invariably quite acid and relatively low in ash and nitrogen. The sedges are intermediate in these respects, while cattail peats are not so acid and have a better nutrient balance. Fibrous peats may occur at the surface of the organic accumulation of which they are a part or well down in the profile. They usually lie above the sedimentary deposit when this type of peat is present. Nevertheless, if just the right fluctuation of conditions has occurred a stratum of sedimentary peat may lie imbedded within the fibrous-peat horizons and rather near the surface.

Woody peat.   Since trees are the vegetation present in many swamp deposits, woody peat is usually at the surface of the organic accumulation. This is not an invariable rule, however, since a rise in water level might kill the trees and so favor reed, sedge, or cattail as to give a layer of fibrous material over the woody accumulation. It is not particularly surprising, therefore, to find subhorizon layers of woody peat.

Woody peat is brown or black in color when wet, according to the degree of humification. It is loose and open when dry or merely moist, and decidedly nonfibrous in character. Virgin deposits often are notably granular. It is thus easily distinguished from the other two types of peat unless the samples are unusually well disintegrated and decomposed.

Woody peat develops from the residues not only of deciduous and coniferous trees but also from the shrubs and other plants that occupy the forest floor of the swamp. Maple, elm, tamarack, hemlock, spruce, cedar, pine, and other trees occur as the climax vegetation in swamps of temperate regions. In spite of the great number of plants that contribute to its accumulation, woody peat is rather homogeneous unless it contains admixtures of fibrous materials.

The water capacity of woody peat is somewhat lower than that of sedge peats, which in turn is much less than that of moss peats. For that reason woody peat is less desirable than the others for use in greenhouses and nurseries where such materials are used as a means of moisture control and a compost conditioner. Woody residues produce a field soil, however, that is quite superior and much prized for the growing of vegetables and other crops. Such woody peats, unfortunately, are confined in general to Wisconsin, Michigan and New York.

13:4. VARIOUS USES OF PEAT [8]

Nurseries, greenhouses, and lawns. Peat is utilized in a number of ways, depending on the nature of the material. In the United States, Canada, and Europe the more or less undecomposed products are very commonly employed as a source of organic matter. This is true of moss and sedge peat. When incorporated with mineral soil in sufficient quantities, peat not only insures a good physical condition but markedly increases the water capacity of the mixture. Soils for potting and other purposes are greatly benefited physically by its use. It is thus valuable in greenhouses, gardens, flower beds, and nurseries both as a soil amendment and as a mulch around growing plants of all kinds.

Peat is likewise useful in the preparation of lawn soils, of golf greens, and in numerous other ways where tilth and organic matter are important factors. While the undecayed materials are generally utilized for such pur-

[8] I. C. Feustel, "The Present Status of Research Relating to the Use of Peat and Muck as Soil Amendments," *Proc. Soil Sci. Soc. Amer.*, 4: 271–74, 1939. This article carries an excellent bibliography.

A. R. Albert, "Status of Organic Soil Use in Wisconsin," *Proc. Soil Sci. Soc. Amer.*, 10: 275–78, 1945.

L. A. Jones, *et al., Soils, Geology and Water Control in the Everglades Region,* Bul. 442, Univ. Florida Agr. Exp. Sta., 1948.

poses, the humified products are on occasion also employed. They are often just as satisfactory and in some instances even superior to the less decayed types.

As bedding, litter, and packing.   Peat, especially the sedge and moss types, may be used in stables as bedding and litter. Such material readily absorbs and conserves the liquid manure, and when the mixture is applied to the soil, the peat contributes a considerable amount of slowly decomposing organic matter. However, the presence of the liquid and solid manure activates the organic matter of the peat and renders its decomposition more rapid than otherwise would be the case. Peat is likewise utilized in poultry houses as a litter under the roosts and in the runways. Sphagnum and other suitable forms of fibrous peats even serve as packing materials in place of excelsior and the other substances commonly employed. They also are good insulating materials.

As fuel.   In Holland, Germany, Belgium, Ireland, and other countries of Europe, peat is dug out in brickette form, dried thoroughly, and used as fuel. Thus, vast amounts of Dutch and German peat have not only been used locally, but also were shipped considerable distances for industrial purposes. In lands where wood is scarce and coal expensive, peat deposits are an exceedingly valuable natural resource. In Holland the excavation of peat has been so regulated as to leave the site well drained and in such a condition that field crops can be grown, aided by the portions of the organic matter that, by law, must be left behind. Some of the most productive agricultural areas in Holland lie on the site of these reclaimed and properly exploited bogs. Such soils must be heavily treated, of course, with commercial fertilizer.

Field soils.   In the United States the most extensive use of peat is as a field soil, especially for vegetable production. Thousands of acres are now under cultivation, often producing two crops a year. In some respects the vegetable industry has been revolutionized by the exceedingly favorable nature of these organic soils when adequately drained and properly fertilized. Peats for such use should be well decomposed, the decay often having gone so far as to make it almost impossible to identify with certainty the various plants that have contributed to the accumulation. As the following pages indicate, the edaphological interest in peat relates mainly to its use as a natural soil and not as an artificial and commercial product for greenhouse, nursery, or factory consumption.

However, more and more of the processed peat is appearing on the market both in Canada and the United States. Such material is mostly sedge and moss, undecomposed or only slightly decayed. With great quantities of suitable material available, there is no reason why the demand within the United States should not be met with a domestic product, rather than, as heretofore, with imports.

13:5. MUCK VERSUS PEAT—MUCK SOILS

Organic deposits are generally classified on the basis of their state of decomposition.[4] Those deposits that are slightly or nondecayed are termed *peat*, while those that are markedly decomposed are called *muck*. In peat deposits, one is able to differentiate the kinds of plants which were deposited, especially in the upper horizons. By contrast, muck is generally decomposed to the point where the original plant parts cannot be identified.

Peat may be quite coarse- or fine-structured depending on the nature of the plant residues which were deposited. Well-decomposed mucks on the other hand, are often quite fine since the original plant structure has broken down. When dry, they may be quite powdery and subject to wind erosion.

13:6. PEAT SOILS—THEIR CLASSIFICATION AND PROFILE SEQUENCE

Since the parent materials influence so definitely the physical and chemical properties of the resultant peat soils, any classification must take these original substances into account. The following grouping is simple and, to anyone familiar with peat soils, very convenient as well. Since sedimentary peat is seldom near the surface on good peat land, and when so located is physically very undesirable, it is not included in the peat soil classification presented below:

*Classification of Peat Soils
Based on Parent Materials*

Fibrous peat soils
$\begin{cases} (1) & \text{sedges of various kinds} \\ (2) & \text{mosses—sphagnum, hypnum} \\ & \text{and others} \\ (3) & \text{reeds and other grasses} \\ (4) & \text{cattails—latifolia and} \\ & \text{angustifolia} \end{cases}$ $\begin{cases} (5) & \text{and their} \\ & \text{mixtures} \end{cases}$

[4] In previous editions of this textbook, the distinction between muck and peat was on the basis of their content of mineral matter. Deposits which contained from 20 to 50 per cent organic matter were called *muck* while those containing more than 50 per cent were classed as peats. Since the more dominant usage in the literature is as indicated above, the distinction based on degree of decomposition will be adhered to.

Woody peat soils $\left\{\begin{array}{l}\end{array}\right.$ (1) deciduous and (2) coniferous trees and (3) undergrowth. In some cases, unfortunately, woody peats sometimes carry an admixture of rubbery material.

Inherited vs. acquired characteristics.   It is to be especially noted that the classification of peat soils is almost identical with the grouping of the original soil materials. (See p. 337.) This is because the parent substances so definitely determine the nature of the profile that no other scheme of classification is nearly so satisfactory. With mineral soils the situation is quite different. Although parent materials are very important, the profile characteristics of a well-developed zonal mineral soil are a reflection in large degree of climate. In other words, *acquired* characteristics rather than those *inherited* from the original materials dominate the profile (p. 291). The contrast presented by peat soils is noteworthy and of great practical significance.

It was found in the consideration of mineral soils that their genesis, their outstanding characteristics, and their plant relationship could not be clearly understood without some knowledge of their profiles. The same is true of peat soils. The next logical step, therefore, is to inquire into the profile sequence of organic soils.

Peat profiles.   Ideally, one might expect that the profile succession of peat soils would be rather definite for any region and especially for any particular bog. In many plots of Michigan, Wisconsin, and central New York, for instance, sedimentary peat is found mostly near the bottom of the profile, fibrous material of some kind comes next with woody peat, if the climax vegetation is attained, at the surface. (See Fig. 13:1.) These materials have been laid down through so-called *progressive* development under conditions of relatively stable water table. But if there has been radical changes in the water table, the succession ultimately attained may be quite different. Thus, woody peat is sometimes found below the surface of accumulation, covered by deposits that ideally should be encountered beneath. Admixing of the layers may further obscure the sequence. Hence, it sometimes is difficult to forecast, except in a broad way, the horizon order of the peat soils of any particular bog.

Again the profile may be immature, the possible succession of plants and their resultant accumulation having only well begun. Thus in New York, Michigan, and Wisconsin, the climax vegetation, as already suggested, is forest. Yet the surface peat in many beds may be derived from the decomposition of mosses or sedges or cattail or their intermixture, with a limited sequence or even no other organic horizons below. Thus, the arrangement of the profile layers in a peat bed are not always predictable. As a result, Figures 13:1 and 13:2 only suggest in a tentative way what actually may be encountered under field conditions.

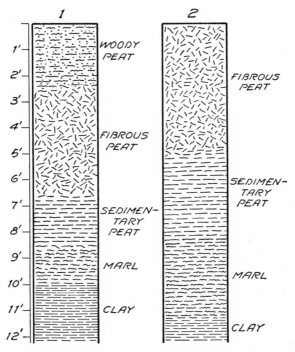

Figure 13:1. Representative profiles of woody peat soil (1) and a fibrous peat soil (2). The woody peat is, of course, the more desirable as a field soil. Note the presence in both profiles of rubbery sedimentary peat and of marl. *(After Wilson and Staker.)*

13:7. PHYSICAL CHARACTERISTICS OF FIELD PEAT SOILS

In spite of the many kinds of peat soils that are encountered in various parts of the United States, a generalized description will be ventured in respect to their outstanding physical characteristics. Such statements will apply merely to that portion of the organic accumulation that normally occurs in the furrow-slice of cultivated peats. This layer determines in part the suitability of the deposits for successful crop production. For a view of peat under cropping see Figure 13:3.

Color. The color of a typical cultivated peat soil, dark brown or intensely black when it is wet, is perhaps the first physical characteristic that attracts the attention. Although the original materials may be gray, brown, or reddish-brown, dark-colored humic compounds appear as decomposition advances. In general, the changes that the organic matter undergoes seem to be somewhat similar to those occurring to the organic residues of mineral soils in spite of the restricted aeration of the peat.

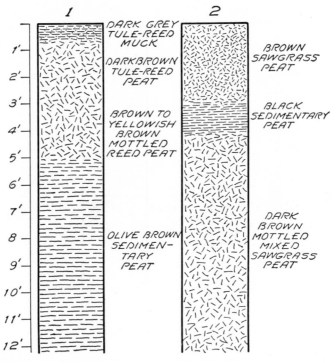

Figure 13:2. Generalized profiles of (1) San Joaquin tule-reed peat soil of the Mandeville type, and (2) Florida saw-grass peat soil of the Okeelanta type. *(After Dacknowski-Stokes' description.)*

Bulk density. The second outstanding characteristic that is likely to be noted is the light weight of the representative peat soil when dry. The bulk density (volume weight) compared with mineral surface soils is surprisingly low, 0.20 to 0.30 perhaps being a fair estimate. A cultivated surface mineral soil will usually fall within the limits of 1.25 to 1.45. A cubic foot of peat soil will contain from 8 to 20 pounds of dry matter, depending on its original source, the condition of the layer and the admixture of mineral materials. An acre-furrow-slice of the depth common in mineral soils, while variable, may be considered to weigh 400,000 or perhaps 500,-000 pounds when dry. Compared with the 2,000,000 or 2,500,000 pounds ordinarily considered as the dry weight of an acre-furrow-slice of a representative mineral soil, such figures seem small indeed.

Figure 13:3. Harvesting onions on a peat soil. Note the dark color of the soil, the level topography, and the uncleared wooded area in the rear. The production of high valued vegetable crops makes the use of mechanized equipment desirable. *(N. Y. State College of Agriculture photo.)*

Water capacity. A third important property of peat soil is its high water-holding capacity, one of the characteristics of highly colloidal solids and especially developed by organic matter in such a state. While a dry mineral soil will adsorb and hold from one fifth to two fifths its weight of water, a peat soil will retain two or perhaps three or four times its dry weight of moisture, depending on conditions.[5] This water-holding capacity, possibly ten times greater by weight than that of mineral soils, is very important in the growing of vegetables. With such crops the presence of an abundant water supply is essential.

It must not be hastily assumed, however, that peats in the field greatly surpass mineral soils in their capacity to supply plants with water. Two conditions militate against the organic soils. In the first place, their

[5] Undecayed or only slightly decomposed moss or sedge peat in contrast with their soils have a much greater water-holding capacity. Not uncommonly such materials can hold water to the extent of twelve, fifteen, or even twenty times their dry weights. This explains in part their value in greenhouse and nursery operations.

amounts of unavailable water are much higher proportionately than that of mineral soils. Again, since the comparative figures quoted are on the basis of dry weight, the peat soils with their low bulk densities are at a considerable disadvantage. When considered on the volume basis, a given layer of peat soil at optimum moisture will supply somewhat more water to plants than a representative mineral soil also at optimum. But not in such excess as the figures quoted in the preceding paragraph might lead one to expect.

Structure.   A fourth outstanding characteristic of a typical woody or fibrous peat soil is its almost invariably good physical condition. While decayed organic matter is, in large degree, colloidal and possesses high adsorptive powers, its cohesion and plasticity are rather low. A peat soil of good quality is therefore porous, open, and easy to cultivate. These characteristics make it especially desirable for vegetable production. However, during dry periods, the lightness and looseness of peat, the granular condition of which has been reduced by cultivation, may drift badly in a high wind and extensive crop damage may result. It may also become ignited when dry and support a smoldering fire to such an extent as greatly to decrease or even destroy its usefulness. Such a fire often is difficult to put out and may continue for several years.

In suggesting that the surface layer of an arable peat soil is likely to be granular, it is not to be inferred that the whole profile is in this structural condition also. Far from it. All sorts of physical arrangements are encountered in the subhorizons, such as laminated, vertical, fragmental, fibrous, and rubbery. The variability from horizon to horizon is determined not only by the character of the original materials, but also by the nature and degree of decomposition.

13:8. THE COLLOIDAL NATURE OF PEAT SOILS [6]

Because of the very high content of organic matter and the particular type of humification that occurs, the colloidality of peat soils is strikingly beyond that exhibited by most mineral soil colloids. Their surface area exceeds even that of montmorillonite clay perhaps two, three, or even four times, and cation-exchange capacities are correspondingly greater. How-

[6] B. D. Wilson and M. J. Plice, *The Buffer Capacity of Peat Soils*, Memoir 146, Cornell Univ. Agr. Exp. Sta., 1933.

H. C. Millar; F. B. Smith; and P. E. Brown, "The Base Exchange Capacity of Decomposing Organic Matter," *Jour. Amer. Soc. Agron.*, 28: 753–66, 1936.

I. C. Fuestal, *The Acidic Properties of Peat and Muck*, Technical Bulletin 690, U.S. Dept. of Agriculture, 1939.

ever, in spite of differences as to original tissue and conditions of genesis, the humus of peat soils greatly resembles that of mineral soils except for the intensity of the colloidal properties. For instance, it has been suggested that the cation-exchange capacity of a mineral soil is enhanced approximately 2 milliequivalents for every gram increase in humus (p. 93). The figure for peat soils, especially if they are woody in origin, is somewhat higher in general, perhaps in the neighborhood of 3 milliequivalents for every gram of dry organic matter.

Formula and calcium content. Not only can the same graphic formula employed for mineral soils— $\begin{matrix} Ca \\ H \\ B \end{matrix}$ $\boxed{\text{Micelle}}$ —be used to represent the colloidal complex of peat, but it is noteworthy that the same metallic cations are adsorbed by the two types of soil, and in the same order of magnitude, namely, $Ca > Mg > K$ or Na. (See p. 73.) This important difference is to be noted, however. The amount of adsorbed calcium is very much greater than is the case with mineral soils. That this is likely to be true, whether the peat is comparatively low lime or high lime, is apparent from the data of Table 13:1. The two soils in question are New York

TABLE 13:1

Cationic Condition of Two New York Woody-peat Soils—One Low and the Other High in Lime [a]

Exchange Characteristics	Ca	Mg	K	Na
Exch. metallic cations, m.e. 100 gms.:				
Low-lime peat	39.8	9.7	0.87	0.80
High-lime peat	159.7	12.0	1.16	0.87
Percentage of each cation in exchangeable condition:				
Low-lime peat	80	100	34	...
High-lime peat	75	51	27	...

[a] Calculated from B. D. Wilson and E. V. Staker, *Ionic Exchange of Peat Soils,* Memoir 172, Cornell Univ. Agr. Exp. Sta., 1935.

woody peats. The total calcium content of the low-lime peat is 1.40 per cent of CaO and its cation exchange capacity is 184 milliequivalents. The corresponding figures for the high-lime soil are 6.00 per cent of CaO and 265 milliequivalents cation-exchange capacity.

The data of Table 13:1 show that most of the calcium present in peat soils and a very large proportion of the magnesium are in an exchangeable condition. Moreover, approximately one third of the total potassium is exchangeable. All this is strikingly in contrast with a mineral soil where usually less than 35 per cent of the calcium, less than 10 per cent of the magnesium, and less than 1 per cent of the total potassium are exchangeable. (See Fig. 2:4.)

Strength of acids. The pH of peat soils, as with mineral soils, is controlled by the colloidal complex, its percentage base saturation being a major factor (p. 97). The ratio of the metallic cations and the nature of the micelle also exert an influence, the latter being especially important. In general, the colloidal complex of peat when saturated with hydrogen will develop a lower soil pH than will acid mineral clays similarly charged. In other words, the peat complex is the stronger acid. This means that at the same percentage base saturation peats will be somewhat more acid than mineral soils.

Buffering. Since the buffering [7] of a soil is determined in large degree by the magnitude of its cation exchange capacity, peat soils in general show an unusually marked resistance to a change in pH, much greater, of course, than do mineral soils. As a consequence, considerably more sulfur or lime is necessary to change the pH of a peat soil than to effect a similar modification in a mineral soil at a corresponding buffer level. However, the buffer curve obtained by plotting pH against percentage base saturation is of the same general order as that for mineral soils (p. 366), except that the pH at 50 per cent base saturation is somewhat less.

Lime loss. Because of the large amount of exchangeable calcium and magnesium in representative peat soils and the marked evolution of carbon dioxide if such soils are drained and under cultivation, cation exchange is even more active than in mineral soils. As a consequence, the drainage waters from peat swamps and bogs usually not only carry large amounts of lime, but they are likely to be alkaline also. However, the loss of lime from most peat bogs is not serious, because of the high initial content of this constituent. Moreover, a rise of the water table that often occurs in the spring may tend to restore somewhat the bases carried downward during the previous season. In general, the lime content of cultivated peat soils is reduced to the point where this constituent is critical only in special cases.

Exchange data. In order that the cation exchange properties may be visualized a little more concretely, further data are offered respecting the two woody-peat surface soils already discussed, one comparatively low in lime, the other rather high. The exchange data, already quoted on page

---

[7] A simple explanation of soil buffering will be found on page 364 and ff.

98, for a representative humid-region mineral soil, are offered in contrast. (See Table 13:2.)

TABLE 13:2

**Exchange Data for Two Woody-peat Surface Soils [a] and for a
Representative Humid-region Mineral Surface Soil
(Expressed in Milliequivalents per 100 Gms.)**

	Woody Peats		Humid-region
Exchange Characteristics	*Low Lime*	*High Lime*	*Mineral Soil*
Exchangeable Ca	39.8 m.e.	159.7 m.e.	6 to 9 m.e.
Other exch. bases, *B*	21.7 "	43.4 "	2 to 3 "
Exchangeable H	122.3 "	62.0 "	4 to 6 "
Total exch. capacity	183.8 "	265.1 "	12 to 18 "
Percentage base saturation	33.5	76.6	66.6
pH	4.0	5.1	5.6–5.8

[a] Calculated from B. D. Wilson and E. V. Staker, *Ionic Exchange of Peat Soils,* Memoir 172, Cornell Univ. Agr. Exp. Sta., 1935.

13:9. CHEMICAL COMPOSITION OF ORGANIC SOILS

While organic soils are even more variable chemically than mineral soils, as the data below [8] indicate, certain outstanding and fairly constant char-

[8] Chemical analyses of certain representative peat soils in percentage based on dry matter are shown in the following table:

Source	*Nature*	*Organic Matter*	N	P_2O_5	K_2O	CaO
Minnesota	(low lime)	93.0	2.22	0.18	0.07	0.40
Minnesota	(high lime)	79.8	2.78	0.24	0.10	3.35
Michigan	(low lime)	77.5	2.10	0.26	...	0.16
Michigan	(high lime)	85.1	2.08	0.25	...	6.80
German	(low lime)	97.0	1.20	0.10	0.05	0.35
German	(high lime)	90.0	2.50	0.25	0.10	4.00
Austria	(low lime)	93.3	1.40	0.10	0.06	0.45
Austria	(high lime)	83.8	2.10	0.18	0.13	2.38
New York	(low lime)	94.2	1.26	0.15	0.10	0.60
New York	(high lime)	81.5	2.56	0.19	0.28	6.51
Minnesota	(low organic)	59.7	2.35	0.36	0.17	2.52
Minnesota	(high organic)	94.0	1.70	0.16	0.04	0.31
Florida	(sawgrass peat)	87.1	2.79	0.41	0.04	5.20
Canada	(peat soil)	74.3	2.19	0.20	0.16	...
Washington	(woody sedge peat)	89.2	3.52	0.43	0.09	1.29

These data were gathered from a number of sources. See T. L. Lyon; H. O. Buckman; and N. C. Brady, *The Nature and Properties of Soils* (New York: Macmillan, 1952), p. 381.

acteristics are in evidence. In order to present these more clearly, a representative analysis of the surface layer of an arable peat soil is given (Table 13:3), but with the understanding that it is merely suggestive. The chemical analysis of the upper layer of a representative humid-region mineral soil (see p. 22) is cited for comparison and contrast.

TABLE 13:3

Suggested Analysis for a Representative Peat and a Mineral-surface Soil Respectively, Expressed in Per Cent Based on Dry-matter

Constituent	Peat Surface Soil	Mineral Surface Soil
Organic matter	80.00	4.00
Nitrogen (N_2)	2.50	0.15
Phosphoric acid (P_2O_5)	0.20	0.10
Potash (K_2O)	0.10	2.00
Lime (CaO)	4.00	0.60
Magnesia (MgO)	0.50	0.50
Sulfur trioxide (SO_3)	1.50	0.10

Nitrogen and organic matter.   The high nitrogen and organic content of peat soils are self evident and need no further emphasis here. But there are two interrelated features in respect to these constituents that do justify further consideration. *First,* peat soils have a wide carbon-nitrogen ratio, the minimum being in the neighborhood of 20. In contrast, this equilibrium ratio for a cropped mineral soil is usually around 10 to 12.

Second, peat soils, in spite of their wide carbon-nitrogen ratio, generally show exceedingly vigorous nitrification. In fact, the nitrate accumulation, even in a low-lime peat, is usually greater than that of a representative mineral soil. This can only be explained on the basis of the large amount of nitrogen carried by the peat, the presence of adequate calcium, and the inactivity of part of the carbon. Thus, the *effective* carbon-nitrogen ratio of peats may be as narrow as that of mineral soils. As a result, the multiplication of the competitive general-purpose heterotrophic organisms is not excessively encouraged. The nitrifiers, therefore, are given ample opportunity to oxidize the ammoniacal nitrogen.

Phosphorus and potassium.   The phosphorus and potassium of peat are both low, the latter exceedingly so in comparison with a mineral soil. Even the phosphoric acid is actually less in pounds per acre-furrow-slice. On this basis, the representative mineral soil is cited as containing 2,000 pounds of P_2O_5. An equivalent layer of peat soil (say 500,000 pounds) would furnish only 1,000 pounds of P_2O_5 or one-half as much. This explains why, in the growing of crops on a peat soil, phosphorus as well as potash must be applied in large amounts.

Calcium and pH. The high calcium content of peat soils is easily explained. Much of the water entering swamps is from seepage and has had ample opportunity of dissolving lime in its passage through the subsoil and substratum of the surrounding uplands. Since decaying organic matter is highly adsorptive and calcium ions plentiful, the resultant peat horizons cannot avoid the presence of large amounts of exchangeable calcium ions. Nor is leaching, as with mineral soils, such an important factor in robbing the surface layers of lime. High lime, most of which is exchangeable, is an outstanding characteristic of many peat soils, especially those of woody origin.

In spite of this high lime content, the majority of peat soils are distinctly acid, often very markedly so. For instance, the average pH of twelve woody-peat soils from Oswego County, New York, was 5.3 in spite of an average CaO content of 3.74 per cent.[9] So great are the cation adsorption capacities of peat soils that they may be at a low percentage base saturation and yet be carrying exceptionally large amounts of exchangeable calcium. At the same time the percentage base saturation (see p. 349) is such as to assure a markedly acid condition.

Magnesium and sulfur. The percentage of magnesium in peat soil is usually no greater than that of a mineral soil. The actual amount, however, is much less due to the low dry-weight of peat by volume. (See p. 344.) The situation is thus much the same as that of phosphoric acid, although it is alleviated somewhat by the high proportion of the magnesium that is held in an exchangeable condition. Peat soils, long intensively cropped, may possibly develop a magnesia deficiency unless fertilizers carrying this constituent have been used. Since most peats are seldom limed, there is little chance of adding magnesium in this particular way.

The abundance of sulfur in peat soils is not at all surprising. Plant tissue always contains considerable sulfur, and as a consequence, organic deposits such as peat should be comparatively high in this constituent. When sulfur oxidation is vigorous, as is usually the case with arable peat soils, sulfates may accumulate. At times a white incrustation, probably calcium sulfate (gypsum), can be observed along ditches and at other places on the

[9] B. D. Wilson, and E. V. Staker, *The Chemical Composition of the Muck Soils of New York*, Bulletin 537, Cornell Univ. Agr. Exp. Sta., 13, 1932.

surface of peat deposits where the upward movement and the evaporation of moisture is taking place. Sulfur is abundant enough in most peat soils as to reduce the possibility of this element being a limiting factor in plant growth.

Anomalous features.   Peat soils in comparison with mineral soils have been shown to exhibit three somewhat anomalous features. They are worthy of restatement. *First,* the representative peat soil possesses a wide carbon-nitrogen ratio and yet in spite of this it supports a very vigorous nitrification. *Second,* peat soils are usually comparatively high in lime and yet may be definitely acid, often highly so. And *third,* in the presence of a high H-ion concentration, nitrate accumulation takes place far beyond that common in mineral soils with the same low pH. This last feature indicates that in many peat soils the H ion concentration does not impede, in itself, this very important biochemical transformation. Apparently, the high calcium content and the low content of iron, aluminum and manganese in peats account for this anomaly.

13:10. BOG LIME—ITS IMPORTANCE

In many cases peat soils are underlain at varying depths by a soft impure calcium carbonate called *bog lime* or *marl.*[10] Its probable position in the profile is indicated by Figure 13:1. Such a deposit may come from the shells of certain of the Mollusca, which have inhabited the basin, or from aquatic plants, such as mosses, algae, and species of Chara. These organisms have the power of precipitating the calcium as insoluble calcium carbonate. It seems that these plants and animals occupied the basin before or in some cases during the formation of the peat, the marl resulting from the accumulation of their residues on the bottom of the basin or farther up in the profile.

Marl is a white or gray, soft, crumbly material, often full of shells. It effervesces freely with dilute hydrochloric acid which suggests that it is largely calcium carbonate. When the deposit is extensive enough and the presence of water or the thickness of the overburden do not interfere too much, marl may be dug out, dried and pulverized, and used as agricultural lime. In general, however, it cannot compete in price with ground limestone, although on the basis of calcium content it is often just as satisfactory a form of lime.[11]

---

[10] Bog lime is usually spoken of agriculturally as *marl.* Marl, as correctly used by the geologist, refers to a calcareous clay of variable composition. Bog lime, when it contains numerous shells, is often termed *shell marl.*

[11] S. G. Bergquist, *et al., Marl—Its Formation, Excavation, and Use,* Special Bul. 224, Mich. Agr. Exp. Sta., 1932.

In cases in which marl is present, it may not only supply calcium to the circulating waters, but if high in the profile, may actually become mixed with the surface peat. As a result, such peats are likely to be low in acidity or even alkaline. In general, an alkaline peat is not considered as highly desirable for intensive culture, especially the growing of vegetables, as are moderately acid peats.

13:11. FACTORS THAT DETERMINE THE VALUE OF PEAT AND MUCK SOILS

Drainage and water table. The value of peat agriculturally will depend on a number of factors. Of first consideration is the possibility of drainage, that is, a more or less permanent lowering and control of the water table sufficient to allow an adequate aeration of the root zone during the growing season. Oftentimes, however, such drainage is expensive and may require the co-operation of a number of landowners, some of whom may have no interest in the utilization of the peat.

Moreover, it may be advantageous to raise or lower the water table of peat soils at various times during the season. For instance, celery at setting is benefited by plenty of moisture. As the crop develops, the water table should be gradually lowered to accommodate the root development. The probable cost of drainage and of the seasonal control of the moisture may be such as to make the reclamation of a peat bed economically unwise. Since peat is very often covered with a forest growth, the cost of clearing also must be reckoned with. In some cases this cost may be rather high.

Depth and quality. Peat settles considerably during the first few years after drainage and cultivation have become operative, and may continue to shrink appreciably in after years.[12] If a depth adequate for cropping does not remain, the expense of reclamation is more or less thrown away. Three or 4 feet of organic material are desirable, especially if calcareous clay or marl underlies the deposit.

The quality of the peat is of special importance, not only as to the degree of decay, but also as to the nature of the original plant materials. The presence of the rubbery sedimentary type in the furrow-slice is especially deplorable. (See p. 337.) Woody peat, on the other hand, is generally considered as more desirable than that coming from cattails, reeds and other plants and it usually is highly prized wherever it occurs. Much of the

[12] See N. K. Ellis and R. Morris, "Preliminary Observations on the Relation of Yield of Crops Grown on Organic Soils with Controlled Water Table and the Area of Aeration in the Soil and Subsidence of the Soil," *Proc. Soil Sci. Soc. Amer.*, 10: 282–83, 1945. These authors report a shrinkage in general of 1 inch in 10 years. See also J. E. Dawson, "Organic Soils," *Advances in Agronomy*, 8: 378–401, 1956.

United States acreage of this type of peat soil lies in Wisconsin, Michigan, and New York.

13:12. PREPARATION OF PEAT FOR CROPPING

Since peat soils are often forested or covered with shrubs and other plants, the first step is to clear the land. Drainage may then be facilitated further, and the water table lowered and brought under control. The utilization of the area as pasture for a few years is sometimes practiced. The roots and stumps are thus given time to decay, their removal being relatively easy when the land is finally fitted for cultivation.

If the peat area is burned over to remove the brush and other debris, it should be done early in the season while the land is wet and not likely to catch fire. Such a fire is often difficult to extinguish and may ruin the deposit by destroying the more fertile surface layer. Moreover, the acrid smoke may seriously impair the quality of certain neighboring crops. Tokay grapes in central California are a case in point. If, however, the surface soil is fibrous with a more desirable layer below, it may be of advantage to burn this part, the resultant ash serving to mineralize the newly exposed layers.

After breaking the peat soil, preferably with heavy plows drawn by a tractor powerful enough to mash down second growth brush or sapling trees, it is advisable to grow such crops as corn, oats, or rye for a year or two, as they do well on raw and uneven peat lands. Once the peat is adequately weathered, freed of roots and stumps, and all hummocks eliminated, it is ready for vegetable production. More thorough drainage is now required and is usually obtained by a system of ditches. Sometimes tile drains or even mole drains are used.

13:13. MANAGEMENT OF PEAT SOILS [13]

All sorts of vegetable crops may be grown on peat soils—celery, lettuce, spinach, onions, potatoes, beets, carrots, asparagus, and cabbage perhaps being the most important as well as such specialized crops as peppermint. In some cases, peat is used for field crops, a more or less definite rotation being followed. Sugar beets, corn, oats, rye, buckwheat, flax, clover, tim-

[13] A few of the many important publications dealing with the management of peat soil are: J. E. Knott, *Fertilizing Onions on Muck Soils,* Bulletin 650, Cornell Univ. Agr. Exp. Sta., 1930; S. R. Breckenbach, *A Fertility Program for Celery Production on Everglades Organic Soils,* Bulletin 333, Fla. Agr. Exp. Sta., 1939; P. M. Harmer, *The Muck Soils of Michigan, Their Management and Uses,* Special Bulletin 314, Mich. Agr. Exp. Sta., 1941.

othy, and other field crops give good yields when suitable fertilization is provided. Moreover, certain nursery stocks do well on peat. In many cases, specially in Europe, peat soils are used extensively for pasture and meadows. In fact, almost any crop will grow on peat soil if properly managed. For a view of peat under cropping see Figure 13:3.

Structural management. Plowing is ordinarily unnecessary every year, as the peat is porous and open, unless it contains considerable silt and clay. In fact, a cultivated peat soil generally needs packing rather than loosening. The longer a peat has been cropped the more important compaction is likely to be. Cultivation tends to destroy the original granular structure, leaving the soil in a powdery condition when dry. It is then susceptible to wind erosion, a very serious problem in some sections.

For this reason, a roller or packer is an important implement in the management of such land. The compacting of the peat allows the roots to come into closer contact with the soil and facilitates the rise of water from below. It also tends to reduce the blowing [14] of the soil during dry weather, although a windbreak of some kind is much more effective. The cultivation of peat, while easier than for mineral soils, is carried on in much the same way and should be shallow, especially after the root development of the crop has begun.

Use of lime. Lime, that so often must be used on mineral soils, ordinarily is less necessary on peat, since this soil, as already noted, usually is adequately supplied with calcium. On acid mucks containing appreciable quantities of inorganic matter, however, the situation is quite different. The highly acid conditions result in the dissolution of iron, aluminum, and manganese to the extent that they become present in toxic quantities. Under these conditions, large amounts of lime may be necessary to obtain normal plant growth.

Commercial fertilizers. Of much greater importance than lime are commercial fertilizers. In fact, complete reliance is placed on these materials in the production of most crops, especially vegetables. As organic soils are very low in phosphorus and potassium, these elements must by all means be added. Since vegetables usually are rapid-growing plants, succulence often being an essential quality, large amounts of readily available nitrogen are necessary. The nitrogen of newly broken peat is often available rapidly enough to supply this need, especially for oats, rye, corn, wheat, and similar crops. Such peat land, therefore, frequently requires at the beginning only a small amount of nitrogen with the phosphoric acid

[14] For a brief discussion of the control of wind erosion on peat soils, see page 240.

and potash. This is especially true of woody peats and is taken advantage of in the fertilization of such soils. After peat soils have been cropped for a few years, decay and nitrification are frequently too slow to meet the crop demand for nitrogen. Under such conditions this element is needed in larger amounts and a fertilizer containing nitrogen as well as phosphoric acid and potash is usually recommended. The amount of any given fertilizer applied will depend upon the kind of crop to be grown, the chemical and physical nature of the peat, its drainage, its previous fertilization and the length of time it has been under cultivation.

Trace elements. Peat soils not only are in need of potassium, phosphorus, and nitrogen, but often some of the trace elements as well. Just what function the trace elements perform is not definitely known, but their fertilizer value is now well established on such soils, and they must be considered in any well-balanced fertilizer program.[15] On New York woody peats, copper sulfate has given good results in the control of certain diseases of lettuce and has aided in the coloration of onions. In fact, the application of this salt at the rate of 100 to 200 pounds to the acre is becoming a recognized treatment for these soils when they are first put under cultivation.

In Florida and elsewhere not only copper sulfate, but salts of manganese and zinc, are used to better the physiological condition of both peat and muck soils. Boron deficiencies are also becoming evident. Michigan peats, in general, need both boron and copper, compounds of these trace elements being mixed with the ordinary fertilizer at the rate of 50 to 100 pounds of borax and 100 to 200 pounds of copper sulfate per ton of fertilizer. Common salt in addition seems to give good results on Michigan peats, especially for beets, celery and cabbage. Perhaps both the sodium and the chlorine play important roles in crop nutrition on these soils.

13:14. PEAT VS. MINERAL SOILS

In assigning peat soils to a separate chapter, one is encouraged to think of them as distinctly and even radically different from most mineral soils. In many respects this certainly is true. Yet, fundamentally, the same types of change occur in the two groups; nutrients become available in much the same way and their management is based upon the same principles of fertility. In recognition of this, peat appears in the world classification of soils (Table 12:1) as *bog* soils, subject, of course, to such subdivisions as best show their differences in agricultural value.

[15] The use of trace elements as fertilizers is discussed more fully on page 488.

The Soil Reaction;
Soil Acidity and Alkalinity

CHAPTER 14

One of the outstanding physiological characteristics of the soil solution is its reaction. Since microorganisms and higher plants respond so markedly to their chemical environment, the importance of soil reaction, and of the factors associated with it, has long been recognized. Three conditions are, of course, possible: *acidity, neutrality,* and *alkalinity.*

Soil acidity is common in all regions where precipitation is high enough to leach appreciable amounts of exchangeable bases from the surface layers of soils. So widespread is its occurrence and so marked is its influence on plants that it has become one of the most discussed properties of soils. Because of the large area of arable acid soils the importance of soil acidity in a practical way surpasses that of soil alkalinity.

Alkalinity occurs when there is a comparatively high degree of base saturation. The presence of salts, especially calcium, magnesium, and sodium carbonates, also gives a preponderace of OH ions over H ions in the soil solution.[1] Under such conditions the soil is alkaline and sometimes, very strongly so, especially if sodium carbonate is present, a pH of 9 or 10 being not uncommon. Alkaline soils are, of course, characteristic of most arid and semiarid regions. Their discussion will follow that of acid soils.

Sections 14:1 and 14:2 may be omitted by the reader interested in only a very general coverage of soil acidity.

[1] When salts of strong bases and weak acids, such as Na_2CO_3, K_2CO_3, and $MgCO_3$ go into solution they undergo hydrolysis and develop alkalinity. For Na_2CO_3 the reaction is as follows:

$$2\ Na^+ + CO_3^= + 2\ HOH \rightleftharpoons 2\ Na^+ + 2\ OH^- + H_2CO_3$$

Since the dissociation of the NaOH is greater than that of the weak H_2CO_3, a domination of OH ions results.

357

14:1. THE COLLOIDAL CONTROL OF SOIL REACTION

A feature of fundamental importance must be examined before considering the practical problems of soil acidity. The trait referred to is the control mechanism of the pH of the soil solution which lies largely in the soil colloidal complex.

Source of hydrogen ions. It has already been explained (p. 88) that the colloidal complex of the soil may be considered as a mixture of rather insoluble acids and salts of these acids. The adsorbed hydrogen and metallic cations which surround the insoluble micelles tend to be in dynamic equilibrium with the soil solution. Consequently, the pH of the soil solution is markedly affected by these adsorbed cations as dissociation takes place.

There are two major colloidal sources of H ions for the soil solution: (1) adsorbed Al ions, and (2) adsorbed H ions. Under very acid conditions much aluminum becomes soluble and is present as Al^{+++} ions. Being trivalent in charge, these ions are adsorbed by the soil colloids even more tightly than are the hydrogen ions. Thus, a very acid soil is dominated by Al and H ions. The adsorbed aluminum is in equilibrium with Al ions in the soil solution. The latter contribute to soil acidity through their tendency to hydrolize. A simplified reaction may be used to illustrate how adsorbed aluminum can increase acidity in the soil solution.

$$\boxed{\text{Micelle} \mid \text{Al}} \rightleftharpoons \underset{\text{Soil Solution}}{Al^{+++}}$$
$$\text{Adsorbed}$$

The Al ions in the soil solution are then hydrolyzed as follows: [2]

$$Al^{+++} + 3H_2O \longrightarrow Al(OH)_3 + 3H^+$$

The $Al(OH)_3$ is not ionized so the H ions thus released give a very low pH value in the soil solution.

Adsorbed hydrogen, since it is in equilibrium with the soil solution, is another important source of H ions. (See Fig. 14:1.) Thus, the higher the adsorbed hydrogen saturation in a given soil the larger will be the concentration of H ions in the soil solution and the lower the pH. A perhaps oversimplified equation to show the release of adsorbed hydrogen to the soil solution is as follows:

$$\boxed{\text{Micelle} \mid \text{H}} \rightleftharpoons \underset{\substack{\text{Soil Solution} \\ \text{Hydrogen}}}{H^+}$$
$$\underset{\text{Hydrogen}}{\text{Adsorbed}}$$

The effect of both adsorbed hydrogen and aluminum is to increase the H ion concentration in the soil solution. The Al ions seem to dominate the situation under very acid conditions, but as the pH is raised to the range common for agricultural soils, the adsorbed H ions become more important. Since we are most concerned with soils on which crop plants can be grown, our interest will be concentrated on the

[2] The reaction may take place stepwise, with $Al(OH)^{++}$ and perhaps $Al(OH)_2^+$ being formed or it may occur as indicated. In any case a hydroxide-containing Al compound and H ions result from the hydrolysis.

adsorbed hydrogen and its influence on the pH of the soil solution. In the discussion which follows we shall assume that the adsorbed H ions are the major source of soil solution hydrogen, recognizing that this is technically in error for those acid soils in which Al ions may also play a dominant part.

Source of OH ions. If adsorbed hydrogen and aluminum are replaced from acid soils by cations such as Ca, Mg, and K, the H ion concentration in the soil solution will decrease. The concentration of OH ions will simultaneously increase since there is an inverse relationship between the H and OH ions. Thus, the so-called base-forming cations become sources of OH ions merely by replacing the adsorbed hydrogen.

The metallic cations such as Ca, Mg, and K also have a more direct effect on the OH ion concentration of the soil solution. A definite alkaline reaction results from the hydrolysis of colloids saturated with these cations. An example of such a reaction is as follows:

$$\text{Ca} \boxed{\text{Micelle}} + H_2O \rightleftarrows \begin{matrix} H \\ H \end{matrix} \boxed{\text{Micelle}} + Ca^{++} + 2OH^-$$

In a Ca-saturated soil, the tendency for the metallic cations to encourage OH ion formation is obvious. In a soil containing both H and Ca ions the same tendency is there, but its effect is not so obvious since it is countered by the effect of the adsorbed H ions. It should be kept in mind that under natural conditions the reactions to furnish H and OH ions to the soil solution occur simultaneously. That is, H ions and metallic cations are held at one time by the same micelle. (See Fig. 4:3.) The pH of the soil solution, therefore, will depend upon the relative amounts of adsorbed hydrogen and adsorbed metallic cations. Where the effect of the hydrogen is dominant, acidity results. Excess bases yield alkalinity, while at just the right balance the pH of the soil solution will be 7. (See Fig. 2:6.)

Percentage base saturation. The relative proportions of the adsorbed hydrogen and the exchangeable bases of a colloidal complex are shown by the *percentage base saturation.* (See p. 97.) Obviously, a low percentage base saturation means acidity while a percentage base saturation approaching 100 will result in neutrality or alkalinity. In general, humid-region soils dominated by *silicate clays* and *humus* are acid if their percentage base saturation is much below 90. When such soils have a percentage base saturation of 90 or above they usually are neutral or alkaline. The exact pH value in any case, however, is determined by at least two other factors in addition to the percentage base saturation: (1) the nature of the micelle, and (2) the kind of adsorbed bases.

Nature of the micelle. At the same percentage base saturation different types of colloids will have different pH values. This is due to the fact that the various colloidal materials differ in the degree of dissociation of their adsorbed hydrogen. For example, the adsorbed hydrogen of the organic complex dissociates into the soil solution with comparative ease. For that reason, the pH value of organic soils at a given degree of base saturation is lower than that of comparable mineral soils.

In contrast, the dissociation of the adsorbed hydrogen from the iron and aluminum hydrous oxides is relatively low. Consequently, soils dominated by this type of colloid have relatively high pH values for a given percentage base saturation. The dissociation of adsorbed hydrogen from silicate clays is intermediate between that from humus and from the hydrous oxides.

The relative degrees of dissociation of the adsorbed hydrogen can be seen by comparing the pH values which are found when the various colloids are about 50 per cent saturated with bases. The organic colloids would have pH values of 4.5 to 5.0, the silicate clays of 5.2 to 5.8 and the hydrous oxides of 6.0 to 7.0. These figures verify the importance of type of colloid in determining the pH of a soil.

It should be noted that the different acid silicate clays—the kaolinite, montmorillonite, and hydrous mica types—apparently dissociate in somewhat different degrees, the kaolinite least and the montmorillonite greatest. (See p. 367.) Likewise, the organic colloids exhibit considerable variety among themselves. In spite of this, however, the organic group apparently has a lower pH value than any of the clays when at corresponding percentage base saturations.

Kind of adsorbed bases. Another factor which influences the pH of a soil has to do with the comparative amounts of the *particular* bases present in the colloidal complex. Sodium saturated soils have much higher pH values than those dominated by Ca and Mg. Thus, at a percentage base saturation say of 70, the presence of Ca, Mg, K, and Na ions in the ratio of 10–3–1–1 would certainly result in a lower pH than if the ratio were 4–1–1–9. In the one case calcium is dominant, in the other we are dealing with a sodium-calcium complex dominated by sodium.

With the reaction of the soil solution influenced by three distinct and unco-ordinated factors—percentage base saturation, nature of the micelle, and the ratio of the exchangeable bases—one would hardly expect to find a close correlation between percentage base saturation and pH when comparing soils at random. Yet with soils of similar origin, texture, and organic content, a rough correlation does exist. Nevertheless, it should not be relied on with any great degree of certainty. Two soils with the same pH seldom possess exactly the same percentage base saturation and vice versa.

14:2. MAJOR CHANGES IN SOIL pH

There are two major groups of factors which bring about large changes in soil pH: (1) those which result in increased adsorbed hydrogen; and (2) those which increase the content of adsorbed bases. Each group will be considered briefly.

Acid forming factors. In the process of organic matter decomposition both organic and inorganic acids are formed. The simplest and perhaps the most widely found is carbonic acid (H_2CO_3) which results from the reaction of CO_2 and water. The solvent action of H_2CO_3 on the mineral constituents of the soil is exemplified by its dissolution of limestone or calcium carbonate (p. 396). The long-time effects of this acid have been responsible for the removal of large quantities of bases by solution and leaching. Because carbonic acid is relatively weak, however, it cannot account for the low pH values found in many soils.

Inorganic acids such as H_2SO_4 and HNO_3 are potent suppliers of hydrogen ions in the soil. In fact, these acids along with the stronger organic acids account for the development of moderately and strongly acid conditions. Sulfuric and nitric acids are formed, not only by the organic decay processes but also from the microbial action on certain fertilizer materials such as sulfur and ammonium sulfate. In the latter case, both nitric and sulfuric acids are formed. (See p. 491.)

A good example of a process by which strong *organic* acids are formed is that of podzolization. The organic debris is attacked largely by fungi which have among their important metabolic end products relatively complex but strong organic acids. As these are leached into the mineral portion of the soil, they not only supply hydrogen for adsorption, but also they replace bases and encourage their solution from the soil minerals.

Another process which encourages acidity is that of leaching. Thereby, bases which have been replaced from the colloidal complex or which have been dissolved by percolating acids, are removed in the drainage waters. This process encourages the development of acidity in an indirect way by removing those metallic cations which might compete with hydrogen on the exchange complex.

Base forming factors. Any process which will encourage the maintenance or buildup of the exchangeable bases such as Ca, Mg, K, and Na will contribute toward a reduction in acidity and an increase in alkalinity. Of great significance are the weathering processes which release these exchangeable cations from minerals and make them available for adsorption. The addition of base-containing materials such as limestone is a common procedure which man uses to furnish metallic cations in order to augment nature's supply. Irrigation waters also frequently contain salts of various kinds, the cations of which are adsorbed by soil colloids. They may increase soil alkalinity, sometimes excessively so.

Conditions which permit the exchangeable bases to remain in the soil will encourage high pH values. This accounts for the relatively high pH of soils of the semiarid and arid regions. Leaching waters do not remove most of the metallic cations as they are weathered from soil minerals. Consequently, the percentage base saturation of these soils remains high. In general, this situation is favorable for crop production. Only when the pH is too high or when sodium is the dominant cation is plant growth unfavorably affected.

14:3. MINOR FLUCTUATIONS IN SOIL pH

Not only do soil solutions suffer major and often drastic changes in H ion concentration (as indicated above) but also they exhibit minor fluctuations as well. For instance, the drying of soils, especially above field temperatures, will often cause a noticeable increase in acidity. This is probably due to a change in the organization of the colloidal matter and should be kept in mind in preparing soil samples for pH determination.

The pH of mineral soils tends to decline during the summer, especially if under cultivation, due to acids produced by microorganisms. The activities of the roots of higher plants, especially with regard to acidic exudates, may also be a factor. In winter and spring an increase in pH often is noted, possibly because biotic activities during this time are considerably slower. As a result, the alkalizing influence of the solution of minerals will tend to raise soil pH.

14:4. H ION HETEROGENEITY OF THE SOIL SOLUTION

In considering the H ion concentration of the soil solution it is not to be inferred that one is dealing with an ordinary homogeneous solution. In fact, because of adsorption, the exact opposite is true. (See Fig. 14:1.) For example, the H ions are concentrated near the colloidal interfaces and become less numerous as the distance from the micelle is increased. Thus, differences in H ion concentration between the inner and outer layers of the capillary water are to be expected. Also, differences in pH are noted from one portion of soil to that only a few inches away. This is due to local microbial action and to the uneven distribution of organic residues in the soil.

Figure 14:1. Diagram showing the equilibrium relationship between *reserve* and *active* acidity. Note the large number of adsorbed H ions compared to those in the soil solution. Obviously, neutralizing only the H ions in the soil solution will be of little consequence since they will quickly be replenished by some of the numberless H ions adsorbed at the colloidal surfaces. This means high buffering.

The variability of the soil solution is important in many respects. For example, it affords microorganisms and plant roots a great variety of solution environments. Organisms that are unfavorably influenced by a given H ion concentration may find, at an infinitesimal distance away, another that is more satisfactory. This may account in part for the many different floral species present in normal soils.

14:5. ACTIVE VERSUS EXCHANGEABLE ACIDITY

In an acid soil two groups of hydrogen ions are involved—those of the soil solution itself and those held as adsorbed cations by the colloidal complex. These groups are in dynamic equilibrium and consequently both must be considered in any attempt to alter the H^+ to OH^- ratio of the soil solution.

For convenience of distinction the H ion concentration of the soil solution is designated as *active acidity*. Those exchangeable H ions held on the soil colloids are referred to as the *reserve* or *potential acidity* [2] of the soil. This situation is shown graphically by Figure 14:1 and by the following equation:

$$\text{Adsorbed H ions} \quad \rightleftharpoons \quad \text{Soil solution } H^+$$
$$\text{(Reserve acidity)} \qquad\qquad \text{(Active acidity)}$$

Since the adsorbed hydrogen tends to move outward and become active when the acidity of the soil solution is reduced, the term reserve is particularly significant. Distinct as the two groups apparently are, they grade into each other as progress outward from the colloidal interface is made.

Amounts of active and reserve acidity. The relative magnitude of the two types of acidity—active *vs.* exchangeable—is not only interesting but is of vital practical importance as well. In referring to the acidity of a soil as high or very high, the impression may be given that the active acidity under certain conditions may be exceedingly great, even dangerously so. Actually, however, the reverse is true. For example, only about *1/50* of a *pound* of calcium carbonate would be required to neutralize the active acidity in an acre-furrow-slice of an average mineral soil having a pH of 6.[3] If the same soil should possess a pH of 5, 1/5 pound of calcium carbonate would be adequate, while if the pH should be lowered to 4, two pounds would be ample. Thus, the *active* acidity is evidently ridiculously small even at its maximum.

Since limestone at the rate of 1, 2, or even 3 tons to the acre is often recommended, this neutralizing agent is obviously applied in amounts hundreds of times in excess of the active acidity. The reason for such heavy applications is largely due to the magnitude of the exchangeable hydrogen. These adsorbed hydrogen ions move into the soil solution when the H ion concentration thereof becomes depleted. The potential acidity thus supplies

---

[3] This assumes that the $CaCO_3$ could be brought in contact with the soil solution and that only the hydrogen ions actually in this solution would react with the $CaCO_3$. A soil moisture content of 20 per cent was assumed in making this calculation.

hydrogen ions which must be neutralized before the pH of the soil solution can be changed appreciably.

Conservative calculations indicate that the reserve acidity may be perhaps 1,000 times greater than the active acidity in the case of a sandy soil, and 50,000 or even 100,000 times greater for a clayey soil high in organic matter. The figure for a peat soil is likely to be even greater. The practical significance of this tremendous difference in magnitude of the active and reserve acidities of soils should be apparent after reading the next section.

14:6. THE BUFFERING OF SOILS

As pointed out above, there is a distinct resistance to a change in soil pH other than that offered by the soil solution itself. (See Fig. 14:2.) This resistance, called *buffering,* is generally characterisitc of mixtures of weak acids and their salts. While such weak acid anions as the carbonate and bicarbonate, are present in soils, the important ones from the standpoint of this phenomenon are those of the colloidal complex. In short, the average soil is colloidally buffered by the clay and humus present.

Figure 14:2. The buffering action of a soil can be likened to that of a coffee dispenser depicted above. A. The active acidity, which is represented by the coffee in the indicator tube on the outside of the urn, is small in quantity. B. When hydrogen ions are removed, this active acidity falls rapidly. C. The active acidity is quickly restored to near the original level by movement from the potential or adsorbed acidity. By this process there is considerable resistance to the change of active acidity.

The mechanics of soil buffering can be explained rather simply if we first consider the dissociation of H ions from the weak colloidal acids. (See Fig. 14:1.) This can be represented as before (see p. 358) for a single hydrogen ion as follows:

$$\text{Adsorbed H ions} \quad \rightleftharpoons \quad \text{Soil solution H}^+$$
$$\text{(Reserve acidity)} \qquad\qquad \text{(Active acidity)}$$

Note that this characteristically weak acid dissociates only sparingly and that most of the hydrogen remains in an undissociated, adsorbed form.

Now let us consider what would happen if we were to add just enough liming material to neutralize the H ions in the soil solution. Immediately the above reaction would be shifted to the right, resulting in more hydrogen ions moving out into the soil solution. As a consequence, the pH rise which results would be negligibly small and would remain negligibly small until enough lime has been added to appreciably deplete the exchangeable (reserve) hydrogen.

This resistance to pH change is equally important in preventing a rapid lowering of the pH of soils. For example, consider the case where H ions are added to a soil or where they result from certain biochemical changes. This would give a temporary increase in the H ions in the soil solution. In this case the equilibrium reaction above would immediately shift to the left and more H ions would become adsorbed on the micelle. Again, the resultant pH change, this time a lowering, in the soil solution would be very small.

These two examples point out rather clearly the principles involved in buffering. In addition, they show that the basis of buffer capacity lies in the adsorbed cations of the complex. Hydrogen ions, together with the adsorbed metallic cations, not only indirectly control the pH of the soil solution, but also determine the quantity of lime or acidic constituents necessary to bring about a given pH change.

14:7. BUFFER CAPACITY OF SOILS AND RELATED PHASES

The higher the exchange capacity of a soil the greater, other factors being equal, will be its buffer capacity. This is because more H ions and metallic cations must be interchanged to effect a given rise or lowering of the percentage base saturation. In practice this is fully recognized in that the heavier the texture of a soil and the higher its organic content, the larger must be the application of lime to force a given change in pH.

Buffer curves. Another phase of buffering, less understood but equally important, logically presents itself at this point. Is the buffer capacity of soils the same throughout the percentage base saturation range? This is best answered by reference to an average theoretical titration curve presented by Peech [4] for a large number of Florida soils. (See Fig. 14:3.)

[4] M. Peech, "Availability of Ions in Light Sandy Soils as Affected by Soil Reaction," *Soil Sci.,* 51: 473–86, 1941. This author finds that the same type of composite curve also holds for New York mineral soils.

Three things are clearly obvious from the curve. First, there is a rather definite correlation, in general, between the percentage base saturation of these soils and their pH. This has already been suggested (p. 97) and therefore is not wholly unexpected.

Figure 14:3. Theoretical titration curve for a large number of Florida soils. *(After Peech.)* The dotted line indicates the zone of greatest buffering. The maximum buffering should occur at approximately 50 per cent base saturation.

Second, the generalized curve indicates that the degree of buffering varies, being lowest at the extreme base saturation values. Between these extremes where the curve is flatter, the buffering reaches a maximum. Theoretically, the greatest buffering occurs at about 50 per cent base saturation. This situation is extremely important both technically and practically.

Third, the buffering, as indicated by the curve, is more or less uniform over a pH range of say 4.5 to 6.5. This is vitally significant as it indicates, for example, that under field conditions about the same amount of lime will be required to change the soil pH from 5.0 to 5.5 as from 5.5 to 6.0.

Before leaving this phase it is well to remark that the curve of Figure 14:3 is a composite and represents the situation in respect to any particular soil only in a general way. That the titration curves for individual soils will deviate more or less widely is to be expected since the colloidal complex of different soils varies with the kinds and amounts of clay and humus present.

Variation in titration curves. As an instance of the difference between the clay groups, Mehlich's [5] results are especially significant. He found the pH values of montmorillonite and the hydrous micas to lie be-

[5] A. Mehlich, "Base Unsaturation and pH in Relation to Soil Type," *Proc. Soil Sci. Soc. Amer.*, 6: 150–56, 1941.

tween 4.5 and 5.0 when these clays were at 50 per cent base saturation. The pH values of kaolinite and halloysite under comparable conditions were found in general to lie within a range of 6.0 to 6.5.

The influence of the different clays upon the titration curves of individual soils is nicely shown by the data in Figure 14:4. Samples from the B horizon were used to avoid the complicating effects of organic matter. In light of the figures quoted from Mehlich in the preceding paragraph, it is easy to see from these curves that the Cecil subsoil with a pH of about 6.4 at 50 per cent base saturation must be highly kaolinitic. The corresponding pH for the Iredell is about 4.4, indicating that clays of the montmorillonite or similar types are dominant in this soil. Obviously, the clays of the Iredell develop stronger acids than those of the Cecil and, under comparable conditions, exhibit a higher buffer capacity.

Figure 14:4. Titration curves for the B horizon of two North Carolina soils. The Cecil is dominated by kaolinitic minerals (1 to 1 types) and the Iredell by montmorillonitic clays (2 to 1 types). Note the difference in the trends of the two curves and how they in turn differ from the composite ideal as set up by Peech (Fig. 14:3). This is to be expected.

At 50 per cent base saturation, the Cecil shows a pH near 6.4. The corresponding figure for the Iredell is about 4.4. Obviously the Iredell presents a stronger acid and hence is more highly buffered. Since the samples from the two came from the subsoils, the trend of their curves is not influenced to any degree by humus. *(The Cecil and Iredell curves are from Mehlich's paper cited on p. 366.)*

14:8. IMPORTANCE OF BUFFERING

Stabilization of soil pH.   A marked change in pH undoubtedly indicates a radical modification in soil environment, especially in respect to the availability of plant nutrients. And if this environment should fluctuate too widely higher plants and microorganisms undoubtedly would suffer seriously before they could make adequate adjustments. Not only would they be affected directly by the change in H ion concentration but also the indirect influences on nutrient elements might prove to be exceedingly unsatisfactory. (See Figs. 14:5 and 14:6.) The stabilization of soil pH through buffering seems to be an effective guard against these difficulties.

Quantities of amendments required. Obviously, the greater the buffering capacity of a soil, the larger must be the amounts of lime or sulfur used to effect a given change in pH. Hence, in deciding as to the amount of lime to apply to a soil of known pH, texture and organic content are among the important soil factors to be considered. These properties give a rough idea as to the adsorptive capacity of a soil and hence of its buffering. (See p. 365.) Chemical tests, such as a determination of cation exchange capacity, are also helpful in a practical way.

14:9. SOIL-REACTION CORRELATIONS [6]

Certain correlations have been established in respect to soil pH that are of considerable practical as well as scientific interest. The interrelations between pH values and (1) exchangeability of *calcium* and *magnesium*, (2) the solubility of *aluminum, iron,* and the *trace elements,* (3) the availability of *phosphorus,* and (4) the activity of *soil microorganisms* are discussed in the following paragraphs.

Exchangeable calcium and magnesium. It has already been shown that as the exchangeable calcium and magnesium are lost by leaching, the acidity of the soil gradually increases. Consequently, in humid region soils there is a fairly definite correlation between the pH and the amounts of these two constituents present in exchangeable form. (See Fig. 14:5.) In arid regions, the same general relationships hold except under conditions where an appreciable amount of sodium is adsorbed. (See p. 379.)

Aluminum, and the trace elements. The relationships between soil reaction and the activity of aluminum, iron, and manganese are shown in Figure 14:5. When the pH of a mineral soil is low, appreciable amounts of these three constituents are soluble, so much so in fact that they may

---

[6] See N. A. Pettinger, *A Useful Chart for Teaching the Relation of Soil Reaction to the Availability of Plant Nutrients to Crops,* Bulletin 136, Va. Polytec. Inst., 1935; and E. Truog, "Lime in Relationship to Availability of Plant Nutrients," *Soil Sci.,* 65: 1–7, 1948.

become extremely toxic to certain plants.[7] However, as the pH is increased, precipitation takes place and the amounts of these ions in solution become less and less until at neutrality or somewhat above certain plants may suffer from a lack of available manganese and iron. This is especially likely to be the case if a markedly acid sandy soil is suddenly brought to a neutral or alkaline condition by an over application of lime.

While deficiencies of manganese, and especially iron, are not widespread, they do occur in certain areas, particularly on overlimed sandy soils or alkaline arid region soils. If the soil reaction is held within a soil pH range say of 6.0 to 7.0, the toxicity of the aluminum, iron, and manganese may satisfactorily be suppressed. At the same time their unavailability will be avoided unless these elements are decidedly lacking in the soil. Copper and zinc are affected in the same way by a rise in pH, the critical point being near 7 pH, above which their availability definitely declines. (See Fig. 14:5.)

With boron,[8] the situation is somewhat different and probably is more complicated. Although neither the soil untreated nor the lime alone appreciably precipitate boron, some authors feel that the two, when in combination, fix it markedly. Possibly also the excess of calcium hinders in some way the movement of boron into the plant, in spite of its solubility. Too much calcium in the plant cells might even interfere with boron metabolism even though plenty of the latter should be present. It has also been suggested that lime may create a serious competition for boron by a stimulation of soil microorganism activity.

Available phosphorus. The kind of phosphate ion present varies with the pH of the soil solution. When the soil is alkaline, the HPO_4 ion apparently is the commonest form. As the pH is lowered the soil becomes slightly to moderately acid, both the HPO_4 ion and the H_2PO_4 ion prevail. At higher acidities H_2PO_4 ions tend to dominate. Because of the formation of insoluble compounds, a soil reaction which yields a mixture of HPO_4 and H_2PO_4 ions is usually preferred.

The activity of the soil phosphorus is related to pH in another way, in this case indirectly. It has already been explained that as soil acidity in-

---

[7] H. D. Morris and W. H. Pierre, "The Effect of Calcium, Phosphorus and Iron on the Tolerance of Lespedeza to Manganese Toxicity in Culture Solution," *Proc. Soil Sci. Soc. Amer.,* 12: 382–86, 1947. C. K. Fujimoto and G. D. Sherman, "Behavior of Manganese in the Soil and the Manganese Cycle," *Soil Sci.,* 66: 131–45, 1948.

[8] K. C. Berger, "Boron in Soils and Crops," *Advances in Agronomy,* Vol. 1: 321–48, A. G. Norman (ed.) (New York: Academic Press, 1949).

creases there is an enhancement in the activity of the iron, aluminum and manganese. Under such conditions soluble phosphates are markedly fixed as very complex and insoluble compounds of these elements. This fixation is most serious when the soil pH is below 5.0. The situation is shown graphically in Figure 17:2.

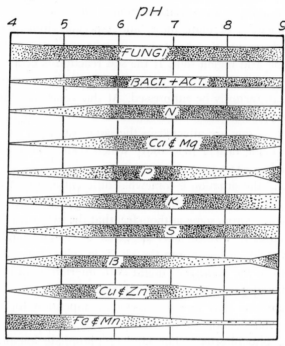

Figure 14:5. Diagram showing the relationships existing in mineral soils between pH on the one hand and the activity of microorganisms and the availability of plant nutrients on the other. The width of the bands and the degree of shading indicate the zones of greatest microbial activity and the most ready availability of nutrients.

Apparently the availability of nitrogen depends in large degree upon the activity of microorganisms and the mobility of calcium and magnesium. Note that the satisfactory availability of phosphorus is restricted to a pH range of approximately 6 to 7. The wide ranges for potassium and sulfur are noticeably in contrast with that of the phosphorus. Also it is evident that the soil must be somewhat acid, say pH 6, if the trace elements, even if present in suitable amounts, are to show satisfactory availability.

Considering the correlations as a whole, a pH range of approximately 6 or 7 seems to promote the most ready availability of plant nutrients. In short if soil pH is suitably adjusted for phosphorus, other plant nutrients, if present in adequate amounts, will be satisfactorily available in most cases.

If the pH of a mineral soil is raised much above 7, the phosphate nutrition of higher plants is disturbed in other ways. In the first place, at these high pH values, complex insoluble calcium phosphates are formed. Thus, the solubility of both the native and applied phosphorus may be very seriously impaired. Furthermore, at pH values above 7, the excess calcium may hinder phosphorus absorption and utilization by plants.[9]

The correlation of phosphorus availability and soil reaction would be sadly incomplete without an examination of the situation in the intermediate pH range of mineral soils, say from 6 to 7. Between these two pH limits phosphorus fixation seems to be at a *minimum* and conversely phosphorus availability as far as most plants are concerned, is at a maximum. (See Fig. 14:5.) In the regulation of the phosphorus nutrition of crops it is rather important, therefore, that soil pH be kept within the conservative limits of 6 to 7 or very near thereto. Even then higher plants often do not absorb one half or even one third of the available phosphoric acid currently supplied by the application of superphosphate or other fertilizers carrying phosphorus.[10] (For further consideration of phosphorus fixation and availability in soils, see Chapter 17, p. 437 and ff.)

Soil organisms and pH.   It is well known that soil organisms are influenced by fluctuations in the reaction of the soil solution. This may be due in extreme cases to the H ion itself but in most soils it must be ascribed to the factors correlated with soil pH and already discussed in the preceding paragraphs.

In general, it is recognized that bacteria and actinomycetes function better in mineral soils at intermediate and higher pH values, the activity being markedly curtailed when the pH drops below 5.5. Fungi, however, are particularly facultative, flourishing more or less satisfactorily at all soil reactions. In normal soils, therefore, fungi predominate at the lower pH values but at intermediate and higher ranges they meet strong competition from the bacteria and actinomycetes and, hence, must yield the field to some degree. (See Fig. 14:5.)

Nitrification and nitrogen fixation take place vigorously in mineral soils only at pH values well above 5.5. However, decay, aminization, and ammonification, although curtailed, will still proceed with considerable intensity at lower pH values because most fungi are able to effect these enzymic transfers at high acidities. This is, indeed, fortunate since higher plants growing on very acid soils are provided with at least ammoniacal nitrogen.

[9] W. H. Pierre and G. M. Browning, "The Temporary Injurious Effects of Excessive Liming of Acid Soils and Its Relation to the Phosphate Nutrition of Plants," *Jour. Amer. Soc. Agron.,* 27: 742–59, 1935.

[10] G. Stanford; C. McAuliffe; and R. Bradfield, "The Effectiveness of Superphosphate Top-dressed on Established Meadows," *Agronomy Journal,* 42: 423–26, 1950.

All in all, a soil in the intermediate pH range, say from 6 to 7, perhaps presents the most satisfactory biological regime. Here nutrient conditions are favorable without being extreme and phosphorus availability is at a maximum.

One very significant exception to the generalized correlation of bacteria with soil reaction should be mentioned. The organisms that oxidize sulfur to sulfuric acid (p. 139) seem to be markedly facultative. Apparently they not only function vigorously in soils at medium to higher pH values but under markedly acid conditions as well. This is extremely important as it is therefore possible to apply sulfur to soils and develop, through the activity of these bacteria, highly acid conditions. If these organisms were at all sentitive to low pH and its correlated factors, their activity would soon be retarded and finally brought to a halt by their own acidic products. Under such conditions sulfur would be relatively ineffective as a soil acidifier.

14:10. THE RELATION OF HIGHER PLANTS TO SOIL REACTION

On the basis of the preceding correlations it is possible to distinguish, more or less clearly, three physiological setups in respect to arable soils: (1) the conditions presented by a very acid soil; (2) those of a mildly alkaline soil; and (3) the physiological complex of a soil intermediate in reaction.

A very acid soil will, of course, present a low pH (say 4.5), with low exchangeable calcium and magnesium, and a high solubility of aluminum, iron, manganese and boron and a low solubility of molybdenum. Besides there is the possibility of organic toxins and certainly there will be a low availability of nitrogen and phosphorus. (See Fig. 14:5.)

At the other extreme will be an arable alkaline soil with a pH perhaps of 7.5. Here will be found plenty of active calcium, magnesium and molybdenum, little or no toxic aluminum, a mild yet active humus, and a ready availability of nitrogen. However, if the pH is too high, an inadequate availability of iron, manganese, copper, zinc, and especially of phosphorus and boron may occur.

The third and intermediate physiological setup is presented by a moderately to slightly acid soil. This seems for the average plant to be quite satisfactory since the chemical and biological agencies are well in balance. Nutrient availability and microorganism activity seem to be most satisfactory under these conditions. (See Fig. 14:5.)

Because of the many physiological factors involved, it is very difficult to correlate with any exactitude the optimum growth of plants on mineral soils with their pH. On the other hand, the relationship of higher plants to the three physiological setups described above can be established and in a practical way are just as significant. On this basis some of the important plants are tentatively rated. (See Fig. 14:6.)

Crop ratings. With such crops as alfalfa and sweet clover abundant, calcium seems to be a very important factor.[11] These plants are calcium-loving and are adjusted to the physiological conditions of a high-lime soil. Except under especially favorable conditions, humid-region mineral soils must, sooner or later, be limed in order to grow crops of this group satisfactorily.

Native rhododendrons and azaleas are at the other end of the scale and apparently require a considerable amount of iron. This constituent is copiously available only at low pH values and consequently at low percentage base saturations. Undoubtedly highly acid soils also present other conditions physiologically favorable for this type of plants. Incidentally, soluble aluminum apparently is not detrimental as it is to certain plants higher up the scale. If the pH and the percentage base saturation are not low enough, plants of the low-lime type will show chlorosis and other symptoms indicative of an unsatisfactory nutritive condition.

As arable soils in a humid region are usually somewhat acid, it is indeed fortunate that most cultivated crop plants not only grow well on moderately to slightly acid soils but seem to prefer the physiological conditions therein. (See Fig. 14:6.) Since pasture grasses, many legumes, small grains, intertilled field crops, and a large number of vegetables are included in this broadly tolerant group, soil acidity is not such a calamity as it was once considered. In terms of pH, a range from 5.8 or 6.0 to slightly above 7.0 is most suitable for this group. (The significance of this as it relates to liming is presented in Chap. 15, p. 404.)

14:11. THE DETERMINATION OF SOIL pH [12] AND THE LIMITATIONS OF THE VALUES OBTAINED

The importance of pH measurements as a tool in liming and similar problems should be obvious from the previous sections. In fact, pH is a diagnostic figure of unique value and as a result its determination has be-

[11] *Soil Sci.,* Vol. 65, No. 1, January, 1948, carries a symposium of eleven articles on calcium. Several bear on the phases under consideration.
[12] See M. L. Jackson, *Soil Chemical Analysis* (Englewood, N. J.: Prentice-Hall, 1958), Chap. 3.

PLANTS ROUGHLY IN ORDER OF TOLERANCE	PHYSIOLOGICAL CONDITIONS PRESENTED BY		
	STRONGLY ACID & VERY STRONGLY ACID SOILS	RANGE OF MODERATELY ACID SOILS	SLIGHTLY ALK. & SLIGHTLY ACID SOILS
Alfalfa Sweet Clover Asparagus			▓▓▓
Garden Beets Sugar Beets Cauliflower Lettuce		▓▓▓	▓▓▓
Spinach Red Clovers Peas Cabbage Ky. Blue Grass White Clovers Carrots		▓▓▓	▓▓▓
Timothy Barley Wheat Fescue (tall & meadow) Corn Soy Beans Oats Alsike Clover Crimson Clover Tomatoes Vetches Millet Cow Peas Lespedeza Tobacco Rye Buckwheat	▓	▓▓▓	▓▓
Red Top Potatoes (except Bent Grass (creeping) Fescue (red & sheep's)	▓▓	▓▓	
Poverty Grass Blue Berries Cranberries Azalea (native) Rododendron (native)	▓▓▓		

Figure 14:6. Diagram showing the relation of higher plants to the physiological conditions presented by mineral soils of different reactions. Note that the correlations are very broad and are based on pH ranges. The fertility level will have much to do with what the relationship shall be in specific cases. Such a chart is of great value in deciding whether or not to add lime and the rate of application if any.

come one of the commonest routine tests made on soils. Moreover, its determination in competent hands is easy and rapid.

Electrometric method.   The most accurate method of determining soil pH is by means of a pH meter. In this electrometric method the H ion concentration of the soil solution is balanced against a standard hydrogen electrode or an electrode that functions in a similar way. In the hands of a skilled operator the instrument gives very consistent results, but the mechanism is rather complicated. Hence, figures obtained by a person unable properly to check and standardize the apparatus may at times be questionable.

Dye methods.   A second method, very simple and easy but much less accurate than the electrometric, consists in the use of certain *indicators*. (See Fig. 14:7.) Many dyes change color with an increase or decrease of pH, making it possible, within the range of the indicator, to estimate the approximate H ion concentration of a solution. By using a number of dyes, either separately or mixed, a range of pH from 3 to 8 is easily covered. In making such a pH determination on soil, the sample is saturated with the dye and after standing in contact a few minutes a drop of the liquid is run out and its color observed in thin layer. By the use of a suitable color chart the approximate pH may be ascertained. When properly manipulated the indicator method is accurate within about 0.2 of a pH unit.

Limitations of pH values.   Because of the precision with which pH readings can be duplicated electrometrically, it is often assumed that the figure so determined is a very accurate indication of the H ion concentration of the soil solution. As a matter of fact, the interpretation of such data is somewhat uncertain and speculative. The reason is this: the H ion concentration of soil solution, as already emphasized (p. 362 and Fig. 14:1), is markedly heterogeneous. It ranges from a low acidity at the surface of the capillary films to a very high acidity near the colloidal interfaces. Such being the case, the pH figure of a soil as actually measured is only an average value. Furthermore, there is often considerable variation in the pH as one goes from one spot in a given field to another.

In the light of such a situation it might seem peculiar that so much reliance is placed on soil pH. In the first place, it is easily and quickly determined. More important, however, is its susceptibility to certain broad correlations that are of great practical significance (Figs. 14:5 and 14:6). Thus, a great deal may be inferred regarding the physiological condition of a soil from its pH value; much more, in fact, that from any other single analytical datum. Furthermore, the variations in pH value from one local soil area to another in a given field remind us that great accuracy in estimating soil acidity may not be so necessary from a practical point of view.

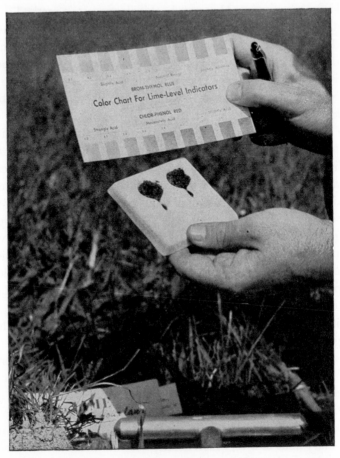

Figure 14:7. The indicator method for determining pH is widely used in the field. It is simple and is accurate enough for most purposes. *(Photo courtesy N. Y. State College of Agriculture, Cornell University.)*

14:12. SOIL ACIDITY PROBLEMS

Other than the maintenance of fertility in general, two distinct procedures are often necessary on acid soils, especially those at intermediate pH values. One is the intensification of the acidity in order to encourage such plants as azaleas and rhododendrons. The other is the application of lime, usually in such amounts as to raise the pH at least to 6.0 or even to 6.5 or 7.0. This so modifies the physiological conditions as to favor alfalfa, sweet clover, red clover, and other lime-loving crops.

Since liming is such an important agricultural feature, its consideration will be reserved for later and fuller discussion (Chap. 15). However, the methods of intensifying the acidity of the soil are briefly discussed in the following section.

14:13. METHODS OF INTENSIFYING SOIL ACIDITY

A reduction of the pH of soils is often desirable for several reasons. For example, this is done to favor such plants as rhododendrons and azaleas, as suggested above, and also to discourage certain diseases, especially the actinomycetes that produce potato scab. In arid regions treatments are sometimes made to reduce the high pH of alkali soils sufficiently to allow common field plants to grow. (See p. 383.)

Acid organic matter. When dealing with ornamental plants mentioned above, acid organic matter may be mixed with the soil already at hand to lower the pH of the latter. Leafmold, pine needles, tanbark, sawdust, and moss peat, if highly acid, are quite satisfactory in preparing such a compost. Farm manure, however, may be alkaline and consequently should be used with caution for the purpose under consideration.

Use of chemicals. When the above methods are not feasible, chemicals may be used. For rhododendrons, azaleas, and other plants that require considerable iron, *ferrous sulfate* [13] is sometimes recommended. This salt by hydrolysis develops sulfuric acid which drastically lowers the pH and liberates some of the iron already present in the soil. At the same time soluble and available iron is being added. Such a chemical thus serves a double purpose in effecting a change in the physiological condition of a soil.

Another material that is even better in some respects is *flowers of sulfur*. This usually undergoes vigorous microbial oxidation in the soil (see p. 139) and under favorable conditions is four or five times more effective pound for pound in developing acidity than is ferrous sulfate. Moreover, it is comparatively inexpensive, easy to obtain, and is a material often used for other purposes on the farm.

No definite recommendation can be made as to the amounts of ferrous sulfate or of sulfur that should be applied, since the buffering of soils and

---

[13] Aluminum sulfate will acidify soil just as satisfactorily as the ferrous sulfate but it carries no iron. Moreover, the aluminum thereby introduced may be toxic to plants that might later occupy the soil.

their original pH are so variable. With composted soils to be used in green-houses, in nurseries, and around ornamental plants, the best way is to make several preliminary treatments using different amounts of the amend-ments with definite increments of the soil. After incubating at optimum temperature and moisture for several weeks, pH determinations may be made and a tentative decision arrived at as to the amounts of ferrous sul-fate or sulfur that probably would give the desired results.

For rhododendrons and azaleas 1 to 2 pounds of sulfur per 100 square feet for each half a pH that a medium textured soil is to be lowered, is perhaps not too much. The dosage must, of course, be varied according to the texture of the soil and its organic content. In any case the sulfur should be well mixed with the surface soil.

Control of potato scab.   Sulfur is also effective in the control of potato scab since the actinomycetes that cause it are discouraged by acid-ity. Ordinarily when the pH is lowered to perhaps 5.3, their virulence is much reduced. In using sulfur to thus increase soil acidity the manage-ment of the land, and especially the rotation, should be such that succeed-ing crops are not unfavorably affected.

For the control of potato scab the amount of sulfur to apply will vary depending on circumstances. The buffering capacity of the soil and the original soil pH will be the determining factors. The results of a given treatment both on the pH and the crop, should be checked and the ap-plications made in succeeding years changed to conform with the influence exerted by the previous dosage.

14:14. REACTION OF ZONAL SOILS OF ARID REGIONS

Arid region zonal soils occur in areas where the rainfall is seldom more than 20 inches yearly and usually is much less. Lack of extensive leaching leaves the base status of these soils high. In fact, a fully and normally de-veloped zonal profile usually carries at some point in its profile (usually in the C horizon) a calcium carbonate accumulatioin greater than that of its parent material. The lower the rainfall the nearer the surface this layer will be. (See Fig. 12:7.)

As a result these soils may have alkaline subsoils and alkaline or neutral surface layers. When enough leaching has occurred to free the solum of calcium carbonate, a mild acidity may then develop in the surface hori-zons. Such a situation exists in the case of the chernozems. The genetic classification of zonal soils of arid regions with a pertinent description of each group, has already been presented (p. 314 and ff.).

14:15. REACTION OF SALINE AND ALKALI SOILS

When the drainage of arid region soils is impeded and the surface evapo-ration becomes excessive, soluble salts tend to accumulate in the surface horizon. Such intrazonal soils are designated as *halomorphic* (see p. 319) and have been classified [14] under three heads: *Saline, Saline-Alkali,* and *Nonsaline-Alkali.*

Saline soils.[15] These soils contain a concentration of neutral soluble salts sufficient to seriously interfere with the growth of most plants. Less than 15 per cent of the cation exchange capacity of these soils is occupied by sodium ions and the pH usually is below 8.5. This is because the soluble salts present are mostly neutral and, due to their domination, there is only a small amount of exchangeable sodium present.

Such soils are included among those designated by Hilgard [16] as *white alkali* soils because a surface incrustation, if present, is light in color (see Fig. 14:8). The excess soluble salts, which are mostly chlorides and sul-fates of sodium, calcium and magnesium, can readily be leached out of these soils with no appreciable rise in pH. This is a very important practical consideration in the management of these soils.

Saline-alkali soils. This group contains appreciable quantities of neutral soluble salts and enough adsorbed Na ions to seriously affect plants. Although more than 15 per cent of the total exchange capacity of these soils is occupied by sodium, their pH, surprisingly enough, is likely to be below 8.5. This is because of the repressive influence of the neutral soluble salts, just as in the case of saline soils described above.

But unlike these soils, leaching will markedly raise the pH of saline-alkali soils.[17] This is because the exchangeable sodium, once the neutral soluble salts are removed, readily hydrolyzes and thereby markedly in-creases the OH ion concentration of the soil solution. In practice this is unfortunate as the now active Na ions disperse the mineral colloids which then develop a tight, impervious soil structure. At the same time sodium toxicity to plants is noticeably augmented.

---

[14] L. A. Richards (ed.), *Diagnosis and Improvement of Saline and Alkali Soils,* U.S. Regional Salinity Lab., 1947.

[15] *Salinization* is the term used in reference to the natural processes that result in the accumulation of neutral soluble salts in soils.

[16] E. W. Hilgard, *Soils* (New York: Macmillan, 1911), p. 441.

[17] This change may not occur, however, if the salts in the saline-alkali soils are mostly those of calcium and magnesium, or if the water used in irrigation contains large amounts of these cations.

Figure 14:8. Upper. A white "alkali" spot in a field of alfalfa under irrigation. Because of upward capillarity and evaporation, salts have been brought to the surface where they have accumulated in amounts toxic to plants. *(U. S. Soil Conservation Service photo.)* Lower. A close-up photo showing the white salt crust on a saline soil from Colorado. The white salts are in contrast with the darker colored soil (left foreground) underneath. (Scale in inches is shown at bottom of photo.)

380

Nonsaline-alkali soils.[18]   These soils do not contain any great amount of neutral soluble salts, the detrimental effects on plants being largely due to the toxicity of the sodium as well as of the OH ions.[19] The exchangeable sodium, which occupies decidedly more than 15 per cent of the total exchange capacity of these soils, is free to hydrolyze, because the concentration of neutral soluble salts is rather low. Consequently, the pH is above 8.5, often rising as high as 10.0. Due to the deflocculating influence of the sodium, such soils usually are in an unsatisfactory physical condition. As already stated, the leaching of a saline-alkali soil will readily change it to a characteristic alkali soil.

Because of the extreme alkalinity resulting from the Na_2CO_3 present, the surface of alkali soils usually is discolored by the dispersed humus carried upward by the capillary water—hence the name *black alkali* is frequently used. These soils are often located in small areas called *slick spots* surrounded by soils that are quite productive.

14:16. GROWTH OF PLANTS ON HALOMORPHIC SOILS [20]

Saline and saline-alkali soils with their relatively low pH (usually less than 8.5) detrimentally influence plants largely because of their high soluble salt concentration. (See Fig. 14:8.) It is common knowledge that when a water solution containing a relatively large amount of dissolved salts is brought into contact with a plant cell it will cause a shrinkage of the protoplasmic lining. This action, called *plasmolysis*, increases with the concentration of the salt solution. The phenomenon is due to the osmotic movement of the water, which passes from the cell towards the more concentrated soil solution. The cell then collapses. The nature of the salt, the species and even the individuality of the plant, as well as other factors, determine the concentration at which the individual succumbs. The adverse physical condition, especially of saline-alkali soils, may be a factor also.

---

[18] *Alkalinization* refers to the natural processes that give rise to soils with an undue accumulation of exchangeable sodium and a very high pH.

[19] The high pH is largely due to the hydrolysis of sodium carbonate which occurs as follows:

$$2\ Na^+ + CO_3^= + 2\ H_2O \rightleftharpoons 2\ Na^+ + 2\ OH^- + H_2CO_3$$

The OH ions resulting give pH values of 10 and above. Also, the sodium complex undergoes hydrolysis as follows:

$$\text{Na}\ \boxed{\text{Micelle}}\ + \text{HOH} \rightleftharpoons \text{H}\ \boxed{\text{Micelle}}\ + Na^+ + OH^-$$

[20] H. E. Hayward and C. H. Wadleigh, "Plant Growth on Saline and Alkali Soils," *Advances in Agronomy*, Vol. 1: 1–35, A. G. Norman (ed.), *op. cit.* This article carries a good bibliography.

Alkali soils, dominated as they are by active sodium, exert a detrimental effect on plants in three ways: (1) caustic influence of the high alkalinity induced by the sodium carbonate and bicarbonate, (2) toxicity of the bicarbonate and other anions, and (3) the adverse effects of the active sodium ions on plant metabolism and nutrition. As already suggested, the removal of the neutral salts from a saline-alkali soil will raise its pH and increase the activity of its adsorbed sodium to the point where it affects plants in the ways already described for alkali soils.

14:17. TOLERANCE OF HIGHER PLANTS TO HALOMORPHIC SOILS

The capacity of higher plants to grow satisfactorily on salty soils depends on a number of interrelated factors. The physiological constitution of the plant, its stage of growth, and its rooting habits certainly are a part of the picture.[21] In respect to the soil we must consider the nature of the various salts, their proportionate amounts, their total concentration, and their distribution in the solum. The structure of the soil and its drainage and aeration are also of moment.

As a result, it is difficult to forecast accurately the tolerance of crops. Only carefully controlled trials will answer this question and even then with no great degree of certainty. Perhaps the best comparative data are those presented by Richards [22] (see Table 14:1), who stipulates that tolerance shall mean the ability to produce fairly satisfactory crop yields.

14:18. MANAGEMENT OF SALINE AND ALKALI SOILS [23]

Ordinarily there are three general ways in which saline and alkali lands may be handled in order to avoid, at least partially, the injurious effects to plants. The first of these is *eradication;* the second is a *conversion* of some of the salts to less injurious forms; while the third may be designated as *control.* In the first two methods an attempt is made actually to eliminate by various means some of the salts or to render them less toxic. In the third, soil-management procedures are employed which keep the salts

---

[21] It is interesting to note that old alfalfa is more tolerant than young alfalfa and that deep rooted legumes show a greater resistance than those with shallow rootage. For the salt tolerance of forage legumes and grasses see L. Bernstein, *Salt Tolerance of Grasses and Forage Legumes,* Agr. Inf. Bul. 194, U.S. Dept. of Agric., 1958.

[22] Richards, *op. cit.*

[23] See D. W. Thorne and H. B. Peterson, *Irrigated Soils* (Philadelphia and Toronto: Blakeston, 1954); and W. P. Kelley, *Alkali Soils, Their Formation Properties & Reclamation* (New York: Reinhold, 1951).

so well distributed throughout the soil solum that there is no toxic concentration within the root zone.

TABLE 14:1

Relative Tolerance of Certain Plants to Salty Soils. The Placings are More or Less Tentative Due to the Number of Complicating Factors Involved

High Tolerance	Medium Tolerance	Low Tolerance
Alkali sacation	Alfalfa	Alsike clover
Bermuda grass	Barley	Apples
Canadian wild rye	Birdsfoot trefoil	Cabbage
Cotton	Carrots	Celery
Date palm	Figs	Ladino clover
Garden pea	Grapes	Lemon
Kale	Lettuce	Orange
Milo	Oats	Peach
Rape	Olives	Pear
Rescue grass	Onions	Peas
Rhodes grass	Rye	Plum
Salt grass	Sweet clover	Potatoes
Sugar beets	Sudan grass	Red clover
Western wheat grass	Tomatoes	White clover

Eradication. Of the methods used to free the soil, at least partially, of excess salts, the commonest are: (1) underdrainage, (2) leaching or flushing, and (3) scraping. A combination of the first two, flooding after tile drains have been installed, is the most thorough and satisfactory. When this method is used in irrigated regions, heavy and repeated applications of water can be made. The salts that become soluble are leached from the solum and are drained off through the tile. The irrigation water used must, of course, be relatively free of silt and salts, especially those containing sodium.

The leaching method works especially well with pervious saline soils whose soluble salts are largely neutral and high in calcium and magnesium. Of course, little exchangeable sodium should be present. On the other hand, merely treating certain alkali and saline-alkali soils with water may intensify their alkalinity because of the removal of the neutral soluble salts. This allows an increase in the per cent sodium saturation, thereby increasing the concentration of OH ions in the soil solution. This may be avoided, as explained below, by converting the toxic sodium carbonate and bicarbonate to sodium sulfate by first treating the soil with heavy applications of gypsum or sulfur. (For reaction see below.) Leaching will then render the soil more satisfactory for crops.

Removal by scraping off the alkali incrustations that have accumulated at the surface is sometimes resorted to. It is never very effective, however, as large quantities of salts still remain in the soil. Land carrying enough alkali to require this procedure is usually so heavily charged that any type of reclamation is more or less unsatisfactory.

Conversion.[24]   The use of gypsum on alkali land, as already suggested, is often recommended for the purpose of changing part of the caustic alkali carbonates into sulfates. Several tons of gypsum an acre are usually necessary. The soil must be kept moist, in order to hasten the reaction, and the gypsum should be cultivated into the surface, not plowed under. The treatment may be supplemented later by a thorough leaching of the soil with irrigation water in order to free it of some of its sodium sulfate. The gypsum reacts with both the Na_2CO_3 and the adsorbed sodium as follows:

$$Na_2CO_3 + CaSO_4 \rightleftharpoons CaCO_3 + Na_2SO_4 \downarrow$$
leachable

$$\begin{matrix} Na \\ Na \end{matrix} \boxed{\text{Micelle}} + CaSO_4 \rightleftharpoons Ca \boxed{\text{Micelle}} + Na_2SO_4 \downarrow$$
leachable

It is also recognized that sulfur can be used to advantage on salty lands, especially where sodium carbonate abounds. The sulfur upon oxidation yields sulfuric acid which not only changes the sodium carbonate to the less harmful sulfate but also tends to reduce the intense alkalinity. The reactions of the sulfuric acid with the compounds containing sodium may be shown as follows:

$$Na_2CO_3 + H_2SO_4 \rightleftharpoons CO_2 + H_2O + Na_2SO_4 \downarrow$$
leachable

$$\begin{matrix} Na \\ Na \end{matrix} \boxed{\text{Micelle}} + H_2SO_4 \rightleftharpoons \begin{matrix} H \\ H \end{matrix} \boxed{\text{Micelle}} + Na_2SO_4 \downarrow$$
leachable

It is to be noted that not only is the sodium carbonate changed to sodium sulfate, a mild neutral salt, but the carbonate radical is entirely eliminated. When gypsum is used, however, the carbonate remains as a calcium salt.

[24] See D. G. Aldrich and W. R. Schooner, *Gypsum and Other Sulfur Materials for Soil Conditioning,* Cal. Agr. Exp. Sta. Circular 403, 1951; and C. A. Bower, *Chemical Amendments for Improving Sodium Soils,* Agr. Inf. Bul. 195, U.S. Dept. of Agric., 1959.

Control. The retardation of evaporation is, of course, an important feature of salty soil control. This will not only save moisture, but also may retard the translocation upward of soluble salts into the root zone. As pointed out earlier, however, there are no inexpensive methods of reducing evaporation from large acreages. Consequently, other control practices must be turned to.

It is needless to say that, where irrigation is practiced, an excess of water should be avoided unless an attempt is being made to free the soil of soluble salts. Frequent light irrigations are often necessary, however, to keep the salts sufficiently dilute to allow normal plant growth.

The timing of irrigation is extremely important on salty soils, particularly during the spring planting season. Since young seedlings are especially sensitive to salts, irrigation often precedes or follows planting to move the salts downward. After the plants are well established, their salt tolerance often is somewhat greater.

The use of salt-resistant crops is another important feature of the successful management of saline and alkali lands. Sugar beets, cotton, sorghum, barley, rye, sweet clover, and alfalfa are especially to be recommended. (See Table 14:1.) Moreover, a temporary alleviation of alkali will allow less-resistant crops to be established. Farm manure is especially useful in such an attempt. A crop, such as alfalfa, once it is growing vigorously, may maintain itself in spite of the salt concentrations that may develop later. The root action of tolerant plants is especially helpful in improving alkali soils which have a poor physical condition.

14:19. CONCLUSION

Although the discussion closes with pertinent suggestions regarding the management of saline and alkali soils, it must not be forgotten that the major theme of this chapter is *soil reaction* or, if you will, soil pH. And it is not difficult to see that as many, or even more, features of practical concern stem from soil reaction as from any other single soil characteristic. Material in the chapters that follow will emphasize this point even more decisively.

Lime and Its Soil-Plant Relationships[1]

CHAPTER 15

Soil acidity and the nutritional conditions that accompany it result from a lack of exchangeable metallic cations. The quantity of these adsorbed cations controls the percentage base saturation and thereby indirectly determines the H ion concentration of the soil solution. Consequently, an increase in soil pH is attained by adding suitable quantities of certain compounds carrying one or more of these necessary metals. This narrows the problem, therefore, to that of choosing the compounds that will most suitably do the job.

The two metallic cations best suited for the alleviation of soil acidity are *calcium* and *magnesium*. They are cheap and plentiful and have favorable effects on the physical condition of soils. Moreover, their carbonates and even their oxides and hydroxides are comparatively mild and easy to handle. In humid region soils calcium and, to a lesser extent, magnesium are the metallic cations that, together with H-ions, normally predominate in the colloidal complexes. (See p. 88.) It is only natural, therefore, that on acid soils attempts are made to increase their concentration by artificial means.

The choice of these two cations, however, only partially solves the problem. The associated anion in the liming compounds must also be considered. For example, calcium and magnesium salts of strong acids are generally unsatisfactory. The reason is simple. When by cation exchange adsorbed hydrogen is replaced by the metallic cations of a salt such as

---

[1] *Soil Sci.*, Vol. 65, No. 1, January 1948, carries a symposium of articles on calcium, as does *Soil Sci.*, Vol. 73, No. 1, January 1952. Many of these articles bear on the phase under consideration.

CaSO₄, a strong acid is liberated in the soil solution. This may be shown as follows:

$$\begin{array}{c} H \\ H \end{array} \boxed{\text{Micelle}} + CaSO_4 \rightleftharpoons Ca \boxed{\text{Micelle}} + 2\ H^+ + SO_4^=$$

Thus, even though the amount of active calcium has been increased, the pH of the soil solution may actually be reduced. Consequently, salts such as gypsum and calcium chloride are seldom recommended as liming materials. They are used only when large amounts of calcium are desired without an increase in pH.

15:1. FORMS OF LIME

With the elimination of salts of strong acids, two satisfactory groups of calcium and magnesium compounds remain. They are (1) the salts of weak acids such as the *carbonates,* and (2) basic compounds such as the *oxides* and *hydroxides.* These compounds of calcium and magnesium are commonly referred to as *agricultural limes* [2] and have the advantage, among other things, of leaving no residue of an objectionable nature in the soil. For example, the direct action of $CaCO_3$ and CaO with soil acids may be shown, perhaps oversimplified, as follows:

$$\begin{array}{c} H \\ H \end{array} \boxed{\text{Micelle}} + CaCO_3 \rightleftharpoons Ca \boxed{\text{Micelle}} + CO_2\uparrow + H_2O$$

$$\begin{array}{c} H \\ H \end{array} \boxed{\text{Micelle}} + CaO \rightleftharpoons Ca \boxed{\text{Micelle}} + H_2O$$

Note that in both cases as the reaction goes to the right there is a neutralization or removal of H ions from the system and an increase in exchangeable calcium. Consequently, an increase in percentage base saturation is effected while at the same time the pH of the soil solution is raised.

As is to be expected, liming materials do not appear on the market as single compounds of magnesium or calcium, nor are they by any means pure. The better grades of the oxides and hydroxides are generally used in the trades, the less pure materials have an outlet as agricultural lime. The

---

[2] Lime from the strictly chemical standpoint refers to one and only one compound —calcium oxide. Agriculturally, however, the term has a broader meaning. Thus used, it includes all compounds of *calcium* and *magnesium* employed in a practical way to raise the pH of soils and to alleviate the nutritional factors associated with soil acidity.

carbonated forms of lime have a number of different sources and vary to a marked degree in purity and fineness.[3]

15:2. OXIDE OF LIME

Commercial oxide of lime is commonly spoken of as *burned lime, quick-lime*, or often simply as the *oxide*. Since it usually is a finely ground powder it commonly is marketed in paper bags. Oxide of lime is quite caustic and often rather disagreeable to handle.

The devices for producing burned lime are various, ranging from small ovens to the large cylindrical kilns of commerce. In any case the general result is the same. The limestone with which the kiln is charged is decomposed by the heat. Carbon dioxide and other gases are driven off, and the impure calcium and magnesium oxides are left behind. The essential reactions that occur when calcium carbonate and dolomite are burned are as follows:

$$CaCO_3 + Heat \longrightarrow CaO + CO_2 \uparrow$$
$$CaMg(CO_3)_2 + Heat \longrightarrow CaO + MgO + 2\ CO_2 \uparrow$$

The purity of burned lime, as it is sold for agricultural purposes, is variable, ranging from 85 to 98 per cent. Perhaps a purity of 95 per cent is a suitable average figure. The impurities of burned lime consist of the original impurities of the limestone, such as chert, clay, and iron compounds, etc.

A number of compounds are present in commercial oxide of lime. Calcium oxide and magnesium oxide are, of course, most prominent. With them are small amounts of the hydroxides since the oxides readily take up water from the air and slake to some extent even when bagged. Also contact with the carbon dioxide of the atmosphere will tend to produce carbonates. Besides these, there are the inert impurities already mentioned.

15:3. HYDROXIDE OF LIME

This form of lime is commonly, and of course improperly, referred to as the *hydrate*. And since it is produced by adding water to burned lime,

---

[3] Certain other compounds of calcium may at some future time be classed as agricultural lime if their use becomes common. For instance, by-product calcium silicates ($CaSiO_3$ and Ca_2SiO_4) have been successfully used in an experimental way. When an excess of this material is applied to soils, detrimental effects to higher plants, often obtained from overdoses of calcium carbonate, are not observed.

See W. H. MacIntire, *et al.*, "Nature and Liming Value of Quenched Calcium Silicate Slag," *Soil Sci.*, 50: 219–32, 1940.

the hydroxides that result are often spoken of as *slaked lime*. The slaking reaction is as follows:

$$CaO + MgO + 2\ H_2O \longrightarrow Ca(OH)_2 + Mg(OH)_2$$

Hydroxide of lime appears on the market as a white powder, highly caustic and not at all pleasant to handle. And like the oxide it requires bagging. Representative samples generally show a purity of perhaps 95 or 96 per cent.

In order to maintain the concentration of this form of lime at a high point, the slaking often is not carried to completion. As a result, considerable amounts of the oxides are likely to remain. Moreover, hydroxide of lime carbonates rather readily.[4] This is likely to be the case if the bag is left open and the air is moist. Besides the impurities, six important lime compounds are usually present: the oxides, the hydroxides, and the carbonates of calcium and magnesium. The hydroxides, of course, greatly predominate.

15:4. CARBONATE OF LIME

A number of lime compounds are sold under the head of commercial carbonate of lime. Of these, pulverized or ground limestone is the most common. There are also bog lime or marl, oyster shells, and precipitated carbonates. Great deposits of marl occur under peat beds (p. 352), and when dredged out, dried, and crushed, make excellent lime. However, the cost usually is too high to allow successful competition with limestone. Also lime carbonates are by-products from certain industries. All of these forms of lime are variable in their content of calcium and magnesium.

The two important compounds carried by limestones are *calcium carbonate* ($CaCO_3$) and *dolomite* [$CaMg(CO_3)_2$]. These occur in varying proportions. When little or no dolomite is present the limestone is spoken of as *calcic*. As the magnesium increases this grades into a *dolomite limestone* and finally, if very little calcium carbonate is present and the stone is almost entirely made up of calcium-magnesium carbonate and impurities, the term *dolomite* is used. Most of the crushed limestone on the market is calcic and dolomitic, although ground dolomite is available in certain localities.

---

[4] The carbonation of calcium and magnesium hydroxides occurs as follows:
$$Ca(OH)_2 + CO_2 \longrightarrow CaCO_3 + H_2O$$
$$Mg(OH)_2 + CO_2 \longrightarrow MgCO_3 + H_2O$$

Ground limestone, which is used to a greater extent than all other forms of lime combined, varies in purity from approximately 75 to 99 per cent. The average purity of the representative crushed limestone may be put at perhaps 94 per cent.

15:5. CHEMICAL GUARANTEE OF LIMES

Since the various forms of lime are sold on the basis of their chemical composition, the commercial guarantees in this respect become a matter of great importance. The caustic forms, that is the oxide and hydroxide, may bear composition guarantees stated in one or more of the following ways—the *conventional oxide content,* the *calcium oxide equivalent,* the *neutralizing power,* and *percentages of calcium and magnesium.* In order to facilitate the explanation and comparison of the various methods of expression, composition figures for commercial burned and hydroxide of lime are drawn together in Table 15:1.

Conventional oxides and CaO equivalent. Since the *oxide* form of expression is so commonly used, this type of guarantee is designated here as the *conventional* method. The *calcium oxide equivalent,* as the term implies, is a statement of the strength of the lime in one figure, namely, CaO. The magnesium oxide is expressed in terms of calcium oxide equivalent and this figure is added to the percentage of calcium oxide present. This may be conveniently done by means of conversion factors.[5] Thus, for the

[5] In order to express one lime in chemically equivalent amounts of another, simply multiply by the appropriate factor as given below:

MgO	to CaO	— 1.389	MgCO₃ to CaCO₃	—	1.186
CaCO₃	to CaO	— .560	MgCO₃ to Mg	—	.288
CaO	to CaCO₃	— 1.786	CaCO₃ to Ca	—	.400
MgCO₃	to CaO	— .664	MgO to Mg	—	.602
	CaO to Ca	— .714			

A thorough student should be able not only to derive the above factors but also to make the conversion without them, namely by the direct use of atomic and molecular weights. For example, we wish to express, say, 1 pound of pure MgO in chemically equivalent pounds of pure CaO. As the following reactions indicate, these two compounds, molecule per molecule, are equal in neutralizing power:

$$CaO + 2 HCl \longrightarrow CaCl_2 + H_2O$$
$$MgO + 2 HCl \longrightarrow MgCl_2 + H_2O$$

But the molecular weight of CaO is 56 (40 + 16) and that of MgO is 40.3 (24.3 + 16). Hence on the basis of weight it takes 56 lbs. of CaO to equal 40.3 lbs. of MgO. And if the pounds of CaO necessary to equal 1 pound of MgO are desired, the proportion would be:

$$40.3 : 56.0 :: 1 : x$$
solving: $40.3 \ x = 56$
$$x = 1.389 \text{ lbs. of CaO necessary to equal 1 lb. of MgO.}$$

Here then is a factor that can be used to express pounds, or tons or per cents, etc., of MgO in chemically equivalent quantities of CaO.

commercial oxide of Table 15:1, 18 per cent of MgO is equivalent to 25 per cent of CaO ($18 \times 1.389 = 25$) and $77 + 25 = 102$, the calcium oxide equivalent. This means that every 100 pounds of the impure burned lime is equivalent in neutralizing capacity to 102 pounds of *pure* calcium oxide.

TABLE 15:1

Composition of a Representative Commercial Oxide and Hydroxide of Lime Expressed in Different Ways

Forms of Lime	Conventional Oxide Content, Percentage	Calcium Oxide Equivalent	Neutraliz- ing Power	Elemental, Percentage
Commercial oxide	CaO = 77 MgO = 18	102.0	182.1	Ca = 55.0 Mg = 10.8
Commercial hydroxide	CaO = 60 MgO = 12	76.7	136.9	Ca = 42.8 Mg = 7.2

Neutralizing power and elemental expression. The *neutralizing power,* as the term is arbitrarily used in respect to lime, is nothing more than a statement of its strength in terms of calcium carbonate—that is, its $CaCO_3$ *equivalent.* Thus, by multiplying by 1.786 in the case above, the calcium oxide equivalent of 102 becomes 182.1, the $CaCO_3$ equivalent. This means that every 100 pounds of the impure burned lime is equivalent in neutralizing capacity to 182.1 pounds of *pure* calcium carbonate.

The *elemental* method of expression, while not so common as the other modes of statement, is required by law in some states. It may readily be calculated from the conventional oxide guarantee. Or, if given alone, the other forms of statement may be derived from it.

Commercial caustic limes practically always carry the conventional oxide guarantee and sometimes the elemental. Thus, the amount of magnesium, as well as calcium, present is indicated. This is an important consideration. In addition, one or even both of the other forms of guarantee may be given. The latter are especially desirable as they show the strength of the lime in one figure, thus making comparisons between different brands easy.

Limestone guarantees. The guarantees on ground limestone differ in two respects from those of the caustic forms of lime. Usually the separate percentages of calcium and magnesium carbonates are given. These are almost always accompanied by the percentage of *total carbonates.*[6] In addition, one or more of the other four modes of guarantee may be used. By way of illustration the six methods of expression are presented in Table 15:2 for a representative ground limestone.

TABLE 15:2

Composition of a Representative Commercial Ground Limestone Expressed in Different Ways

Separate Carbonates, (Per Cent)	Total Carbonates, (Per Cent)	Neutral- izing Power	Conventional Oxide, (Per Cent)	Calcium Oxide Equivalent	Elemental, (Per Cent)
$CaCO_3 = 80$			$CaO = 44.80$		$Ca = 32.00$
	94	96.6		54.10	
$MgCO_3 = 14$			$MgO = 6.70$		$Mg = 4.03$

Total carbonates vs. neutralizing power. The total carbonate method of guarantee has many advocates because it is so simple and requires no chemical explanation. Furthermore, when the total neutralizing figure for a given limestone is higher than the total carbonates, it is usually due to the presence of dolomite in the limestone. Since this mineral reacts with the soil rather slowly (see Fig. 15:1), the advantage from the standpoint of total neutralizing power is questionable unless the lime is very finely ground. Consequently, the total carbonate method of expression is perhaps a truer indication of the comparative field value of limestones.

Those that favor the neutralizing-power method of expression stress its accuracy and the fact that it can be determined very easily and quickly. This is an important consideration in a control laboratory when many samples must be analyzed. Moreover, there is the advertising phase of the controversy. For instance, a dolomitic limestone containing 46 per cent of $CaCO_3$ and 43 per cent of $MgCO_3$ [7] has a *neutralizing power* of 97 but its *total carbonate figure* is only 89. When competition is keen, such a difference may lead to much misunderstanding and controversy.

---

[6] It is well to remember that both of these methods of guarantee are in part conventional since only part of the calcium is present as $CaCO_3$. The remainder, as well as all the magnesium, is carried by the admixed dolomite [$CaMg(CO_3)_2$]. Magnesium carbonate, as such, is usually not present.

[7] This is only a conventional method of expressing the constituents in dolomitic limestone. Actually this material is composed of a mixture of $CaCO_3$ and dolomite [$CaMg(CO_3)_2$]. (See page 389.)

15:6. FINENESS GUARANTEE OF LIMESTONE

The application to the soil of two different liming materials in chemically equivalent quantities does not necessarily mean that equivalent results will be attained. This is especially true if the two materials are both limestones, since the particles contained therein are apt to be quite variable in size as well as hardness. The importance of this is apparent since it is well known that the finer the division of any material the more rapid is likely to be its solution and rate of reaction. The caustic limes usually appear on the market as almost impalpable powders; consequently their fineness is always satisfactory.

Therefore, in order to rate a limestone as to its probable effects in comparison with other limes, a *fineness guarantee* is desirable. This is usually

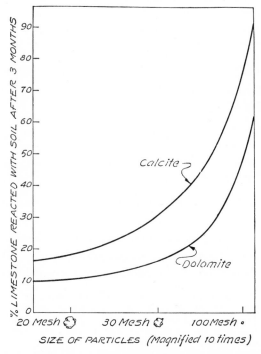

Figure 15:1. The relationship between particle size of calcite and dolomite respectively and the rate of reaction of these minerals with the soil. Note that calcite particles of a given size react more rapidly than do corresponding dolomite particles. The coarse fractions of both minerals neutralize the soil acidity very slowly. *(These data were calculated from C. J. Schollenberger and R. M. Salter. See footnote 9, p. 394.)*

one of the requirements of laws controlling the sale of agricultural limestone. A mechanical analysis is made by the use of screens of different
mesh, a 10-mesh sieve, for example, having ten openings to the linear
inch.[8] The proportion of the limestone that will pass through the various
screens used constitutes the guarantee.

15:7. INTERPRETATION OF A FINENESS GUARANTEE

Before a statement can be made as to the degrees of fineness a limestone
should attain to be satisfactory, some of the experimental work available
on the subject should be considered. White presents the following significant data (Table 15:3) as a result of certain laboratory and greenhouse studies at State College, Pennsylvania.

TABLE 15:3

**A Comparison of Various Grades of Limestone When Applied at the
Same Rates, Pennsylvania Agricultural Experiment Station [a]**

(100-mesh material is taken as 100)

Conditions	100-mesh and Smaller	60–80-mesh	20–40-mesh	8–12-mesh
Solubility in carbonated water	100	57	45	28
Value in correcting acidity	100	57	27	18
Formation of nitrates	100	94	56	12
Plant Growth	100	69	22	5

[a] J. W. White, *The Value of Limestone of Different Degrees of Fineness,* Bulletin
149, Penn. Agr. Exp. Sta., 1917.

These figures show that the finer grades of limestone are much more
rapidly effective. Further data by the same author indicate that, while the
coarser lime is less rapid in its action, it remains in the soil longer and its
influence should be effective for a greater period of years. Other investigators [9] have published results that substantiate the conclusions above. The

[8] The diameter of the individual openings will, of course, be much less than 0.1
of an inch, the exact size depending on the wire used in making the sieve. Usually
the diameter of the openings in inches is a little more than one-half of the quotient
obtained by dividing 1 by the mesh rating. For instance, the openings of a 10-mesh
screen are approximately .07 in. diameter; those of a 50-mesh, .0122 in.; and those
of a 100-mesh screen, approximately .0058 in. Unfortunately there is no standardiza-
tion of the sieves used for grading agricultural limestone.

[9] T. L. Lyon, *Relative Effectiveness of Limestone Particles of Different Sizes,* Bulletin
531, Cornell Univ. Agr. Exp. Sta., 1931. See also C. J. Schollenberger and R. M. Salter,
"A Chart for Evaluating Agricultural Limestone," *Jour. Amer. Soc. Agron.,* 35: 955–
66, 1943. And F. L. Davis, "Effect of Fineness of Agricultural Lime upon Crop Response," *Agron. Jour.,* 43: 251–55, 1951.

proportionate responses are somewhat different, however. This is to be expected, as limestones of different hardness applied to various soil types are sure to respond rather diversely.

Fine limestone. Everything considered, a pulverized limestone, *all of which will pass a 10-mesh screen, and at least 50 per cent of which will pass a 100-mesh sieve,* should give excellent results and yet be cheap enough to encourage its use. Such a lime is sufficiently pulverized to rate as a *fine* limestone.

Nevertheless, many limes are finer than this, 50 or 60 per cent sometimes passing a 200-mesh screen. However, because of the cost of grinding the stone to a very fine condition and the rapidity with which such material disappears from the soil, a medium ground lime such as specified above, seems to be a more desirable commercial product. Such material has enough of the finer particles to give quick results and yet a sufficient amount of the coarser fragments to make it last over the period of the rotation.

A limestone which does not approximate the fineness designated above should be discounted to the extent to which it falls short. It may be necessary, for example, to consider 3,000 pounds of one limestone as equal to 1 ton of another, even though their chemical analyses are the same. Considerable judgment in the interpretation of fineness guarantee is necessary in order that such an adjustment be correctly made. Much limestone that falls below the standard set above is now being used because, as a by-product, it is very cheap. When the amounts put on the land are properly adjusted, as good results may be expected from the coarser limes as from the finer limestones and the effects should last considerably longer.

15:8. CHANGES OF LIME ADDED TO THE SOIL

In considering the changes that lime undergoes when added to the soil two things must always be kept in mind: (1) that the calcium and magnesium compounds applied undergo solution under the influence of a variable partial pressure of carbon dioxide; [10] and (2) that an acid colloidal complex will adsorb considerable amounts of calcium and magnesium ions.

Reaction with CO_2. When lime, whether the oxide, hydroxide, or the carbonate, is applied to an acid soil, the movement, as solution occurs, is toward the bicarbonate form. This is because the partial carbon dioxide pressure, usually several hundred times greater than that of the atmos-

---

[10] For a discussion of this phase see R. Bradfield, "Calcium of the Soil: 1. Physico-Chemical Relations," *Proc. Soil Sci. Soc. Amer.,* 6: 8–15, 1941.

pheric air, generally is intense enough to prevent the existence of the hydroxide or even the carbonate. The reactions, written only for the purely calcium limes, are as follows:

$$CaO + H_2O \longrightarrow Ca(OH)_2$$
$$Ca(OH)_2 + 2\ H_2CO_3 \longrightarrow Ca(HCO_3)_2 + 2\ H_2O$$
$$CaCO_3 + H_2CO_3 \longrightarrow Ca(HCO_3)_2$$

Reaction with soil colloids. This, however, represents only the solution of the lime in carbonated water. The soil situation is not so simple as these reactions might lead one to assume. This is because the soil colloidal matter continually upsets the equilibrium tendencies by adsorbing the ions of calcium and magnesium. These ions may be taken from the soil solution proper or directly from the solid phase if the contact is sufficiently close. The adsorption in respect to calcium may be indicated as follows:

$$\frac{H}{H}\ \boxed{\text{Micelle}}\ +\ Ca(OH)_2 \rightleftharpoons Ca\ \boxed{\text{Micelle}}\ +\ 2\ H_2O$$

$$\frac{H}{H}\ \boxed{\text{Micelle}}\ +\ \underset{\text{(in solution)}}{Ca(HCO_3)_2} \rightleftharpoons Ca\ \boxed{\text{Micelle}}\ +\ 2\ H_2O + 2\ CO_2\uparrow$$

$$\frac{H}{H}\ \boxed{\text{Micelle}}\ +\ \underset{\text{(solid phase)}}{CaCO_3} \rightleftharpoons Ca\ \boxed{\text{Micelle}}\ +\ H_2O + CO_2\uparrow$$

As the above reactions of limestone proceed carbon dioxide is freely evolved. In addition, the adsorption of the calcium and magnesium raises the percentage base saturation of the colloidal complex and the pH of the soil solution is pushed up correspondingly. (See p. 359.)

Distribution of Ca and Mg in limed soil. Calcium and magnesium, if supplied by a limestone of average fineness, will exist in the soil, at least for a time, in three forms: (1) as solid calcium and calcium-magnesium carbonates; (2) as exchangeable bases adsorbed by the colloidal matter; and (3) as dissociated cations in the soil solution mostly in association with bicarbonate ions. When the calcium and calcium-magnesium carbonates have all dissolved, the system becomes somewhat simpler, involving only the exchangeable cations and those in soil solution.

Depletion of Ca and Mg. As time goes on the particles of the added lime carbonates gradually disappear and the colloidal complex loses part of its bases. This is effected by H ions generated by carbonic and other acids. In this way the so-called reserve lime, both carbonate and adsorbed, is gradually fed into the soil solution by cation exchange, there to be used in many different ways. The mechanism of these losses is fully explained on page 90.

As the soluble calcium and magnesium compounds are removed the percentage base saturation and pH are gradually reduced and eventually another application of lime is necessary. This, then, is the type of cycle through which much of the calcium and magnesium added to arable soils swings in humid regions.

15:9. LOSS OF LIME FROM ARABLE SOILS

Calcium and magnesium are lost from soils in three ways: (1) by erosion, (2) by crop removal, and (3) by leaching. Since these three types of lime loss have already been discussed and evaluated in Chapter 9, it is a simple matter to draw such data together in tabular form (Table 15:4).

TABLE 15:4

Lime Losses from Soil in Pounds per Acre per Year

Manner of Removal	*Calcium*		*Magnesium*	
	CaO	$CaCO_3$	MgO	$MgCO_3$
By erosion, Missouri experiments, 4 per cent slope	120	214	48	100
By the average crop of a standard rotation	35	62	25	52
By leaching from a representative silt loam	125	223	30	63
Total		499		215

Although the values cited cannot be used as representing losses from soils in general, they are quite significant when used comparatively.

The data for erosion removals are for a silt loam in Missouri, cropped to a rotation of corn, wheat, and clover. (See Table 9:8.) The acre annual removal by crops was calculated for a standard and representative rotation assuming reasonable yields. (See Table 9:5.) The leaching losses are for a postulated representative silt loam under a rainfall of perhaps 36 to 40 inches and cropped to a standard farm rotation. (See Table 9:5.) All data are in pounds per acre per year expressed in the conventional *oxide* form and also in the more practical terms of *calcium* and *magnesium carbonates*.

The greater loss of calcium than magnesium, no doubt, is due to the fact that the soil colloidal matter almost always carries a much larger amount of the former in an exchangeable condition. And, since the average lime supplies several times more calcium than magnesium, this loss ratio will in general be maintained and even accentuated in arable lands as liming proceeds.

This does not mean, however, that the magnesium in lime is of minor importance. Far from it. In fact, judging from the figures of Table 15:4, there should always be at least one third as much magnesium as calcium in the lime applied in order to proportionately meet the outgo of the two constituents. Other things being equal, it is generally wise to select a magnesium-containing limestone.

The figures quoted in the table above indicate that 500 to 600 pounds of limestone per acre per year may be required to meet the loss from cropped soils in humid regions. This amounts to perhaps 1 to 1.5 tons of carbonate of lime during the period of the average rotation depending upon the kind of soil and other factors. Such a conclusion justifies the attention that is paid to lime in any scheme of fertility management in areas of medium to heavy rainfall.

15:10. THE EFFECTS OF LIME ON THE SOIL

It has already been emphasized that the changes of lime in the soil are many and complicated. Therefore, the discussion that follows must of necessity, rather than choice, be more or less general in nature. The better known effects of liming will be considered under three heads: (1) physical, (2) chemical, and (3) biological.

Physical effects. In heavy soils there is always a tendency for the fine particles to become too closely associated. Such a condition interferes with air and water movement and, therefore, granulation is highly desirable. A satisfactory crumb structure is somewhat encouraged in an acid soil by the addition of any form of lime, although the influence is largely indirect. For example, the effects of lime upon biotic forces are paramount, especially those that have to do with the decomposition of the soil organic matter and the synthesis of humus. The genesis of the latter as well as its persistence greatly encourages granulation. (See p. 59.) In this respect the stimulating effect of lime on deep rooted plants, especially legumes, should not be ignored.

Chemical effects. If a soil at pH of 5.0 is limed to a more suitable pH value (say 6.5) a number of significant chemical changes occur. Many of these were stressed in Chapter 14 and will be merely outlined here to re-emphasize their importance. For example:

1. The concentration of H ions will decrease.
2. The concentration of OH ions will increase.
3. The solubility of iron, aluminum, and manganese will decline.
4. The availability of phosphates and molybdates will be augmented.
5. The exchangeable calcium and magnesium will increase.
6. The percentage base saturation will increase.
7. The availability of potassium may be increased or decreased depending on conditions.

Of the specific chemical effects of lime mentioned, the reduction in acidity is one commonly uppermost in the popular mind. However, the indirect effects on nutrient availability and on the toxicity of certain elements are probably more important. Liming of acid soils enhances the availability and plant uptake of elements such as molybdenum, phosphorus, calcium, and magnesium. At the same time, it drastically reduces the concentration of iron, aluminum, and manganese which under very acid conditions are apt to be present in toxic quantities.

Biological effects. Lime stimulates the general-purpose, heterotrophic soil organisms, thereby increasing the activity of the organic matter and nitrogen of an acid soil. The rate of the turnover of these constituents often is more important than the actual amounts present. This stimulation of enzymic processes not only favors the formation of humus but also encourages the elimination of certain organic intermediate products that might be toxic to higher plants.

Most of the favorable soil organisms, as well as some of the unfavorable ones such as those that produce potato scab, are encouraged by liming. Aminization, ammonification, and sulfur oxidation are markedly speeded up by increasing the pH. The bacteria that fix nitrogen from the air, both nonsymbiotically and in the nodules of legumes, are especially stimulated by the application of lime.

Nitrification, a biological phenomenon of great importance, requires the presence of metallic cations. When lime is inadequate, this desirable transformation will not proceed rapidly. In fact, the successful growth of most soil microorganisms so definitely depends upon lime that satisfactory biological activities cannot be expected if soils fall below a given calcium and magnesium level.

15:11. CROP RESPONSE TO LIMING

The biological effects of lime will now be extended to include higher plants, obviously a consideration of great practical concern. Figure 14:6 specifies in a general way the lime levels at which various plants seem to grow most satisfactorily, thereby indicating whether or not a particular crop is likely to be benefited by liming. Of the lime-loving plants, alfalfa, sweet clover, red clover, asparagus, cauliflower and lettuce are representative. However, a surprisingly large proportion of our crop plants is quite tolerant to the conditions presented by moderately acid soils. Such plants respond to lime, if at all, more or less indirectly due to its stimulating influence upon the legume preceding them in the rotation. And as a further examination of Figure 14:6 will show, some plants, such as cranberries and native azaleas, grow much better when the content of exchangeable calcium and magnesium of soils is exceedingly low. The chart under consideration is worthy of careful study.

Reasons for response. When plants are benefited by lime, a number of possible reasons may be suggested. These are listed as follows: (1) direct nutritive or regulatory action of the calcium and magnesium; (2) removal or neutralization of toxic compounds of either an organic or inorganic nature; (3) retardation of plant diseases; (4) an increased availability chemically of plant nutrients; and (5) an encouragement of microorganic activities favorable in a nutritive way. Since several of these factors undoubtedly function concurrently, crop response to liming is a complicated phenomenon and only the broadest conclusions may be drawn.

The growth of a number of plants is definitely retarded by liming, prominent among which are cranberries, blueberries, watermelons, laurel, and certain species of azaleas and rhododendrons. It is, therefore, advantageous not only to know the condition of the soil but also to understand the influence of lime on the crop to be grown. Lime is too often used as a cure-all, little attention being paid to the widely differing responses exhibited by various crops.

15:12. OVERLIMING [11]

This brings us to the question of *overliming*, that is, the addition of lime until the pH of the soil is above that required for optimum plant growth

[11] See J. Q. Lynd and L. M. Turk, "Overliming Injury on an Acid Sandy Soil," *Jour. Amer. Soc. Agron.*, 40: 205–15, 1948. See also E. R. Purvis and O. W. Davidson, "Review of the Relation of Calcium to Availability and Absorption of Certain Trace Elements by Plants," *Soil Sci.*, 65: 111–16, 1948.

on the soil in question. Under such conditions many crops that ordinarily respond to lime are detrimentally affected, especially during the first season following the application. With heavy soils and when farmers can afford to apply only moderate amounts of lime, the danger is negligible. But on sandy soils, low in organic matter and therefore lightly buffered, it is easy to injure certain crops even with a relatively moderate application of lime.

The detrimental influences of excess lime have been already mentioned. (See p. 369.) Consequently, they are merely outlined here for convenience:

1. Deficiencies of available iron, manganese, copper, or zinc may be induced.
2. Phosphate availability may decrease due to the formation of complex and insoluble calcium phosphates.
3. The absorption of phosphorus by plants and especially its metabolic use may be interfered with.
4. The uptake and utilization of boron may be hindered.
5. The drastic change in pH may, in itself, be detrimental.

With so many possibilities and with such complex, biocolloidal interrelations to deal with, it is easy to see why overliming injuries in many cases have not been satisfactorily explained.

15:13. PRACTICAL PROBLEMS RESPECTING LIME

The use of lime in a practical way raises three questions. If the first is answered in the affirmative, the other two present themselves in logical sequence. The three questions are: (1) Shall lime be applied? (2) Which form shall be used? (3) What shall be the rate of application? These queries will be considered in order.

15:14. SHALL LIME BE APPLIED?

The old idea respecting lime was that of a *cure-all*—that there would be no harm in trying it; and perhaps it might be beneficial. Such an attitude should now be a thing of the past as it may lead to a waste of money and in some cases to overliming. The use of lime must be based on measured soil acidity and on crop requirements.

Soil pH and crops to be grown. In coming to a decision as to the desirability of applying lime, the chemical condition of the soil itself should be examined. For this a pH determination commonly is made either by means of a glass electrode and potentiometer or by the less accurate indicator-dye method (p. 375). Representative subsoil as well as surface samples should be examined. The pH is correlated fairly closely with percentage base saturation and is an indicator of the probable activity of the calcium, magnesium, and other elements in the soil. Besides it is very easily and quickly determined. Here are two reasons why this test is one of the most popular and significant determinations that is now available for soil diagnosis.

Before a recommendation can be made, however, the lime needs in general of the crop or crops to be grown should be considered. The final decision rests upon the proper coordination of these two types of information. A grouping of crops such as that shown on page 374 (Fig. 14:6) will greatly aid in deciding whether or not to lime.

15:15. FORM OF LIME TO APPLY [12]

On the basis of the ideas already presented, it is evident that five major factors should be considered in deciding on a specific brand of lime to apply. These factors are as follows:

1. Chemical guarantees of the limes under consideration.
2. Cost per ton applied to the land.
3. Rate of reaction with soil.
4. Fineness of the limestone.
5. Miscellaneous considerations (handling, storage, bag, or bulk, etc.).

Guarantee and cost relations.   By a purely arithmetical calculation based on factors 1 and 2 above, the cost of equivalent amounts of lime as applied to the land can be determined. These factors will show which lime will furnish the greatest amount of neutralizing power in total for every dollar expended.

For instance, the *neutralizing power* ($CaCO_3$ equivalent) of two limes, a hydroxide and a ground limestone, are guaranteed at 135 and 95 respectively. The cost of applying a ton of each to the land (all charges, including trucking and spreading) for purposes of calculation will be considered to be $15.00 in the case of the hydrate and $8.00 for the carbonate. Obviously, it will require only 95/135 or 0.7 of a ton of the hydroxide to equal 1 ton of the carbonate. The cost of equivalent amounts of neutralizing power, based on 1 ton of limestone, will therefore be $10.50 for the hydroxide of lime and $8.00 for the limestone. Unless a rapid rate of reaction

[12] It is well to remark at the outset that more than 95 per cent of the agricultural lime used in the United States is ground limestone, principally because it is cheaper than other forms. Handling and storage also are factors.

were desired, the advantage in this case would definitely be with the limestone.

Rate of reaction with soil. Burned and hydrated limes react with the soil much more rapidly than do the carbonate forms. For this reason, these caustic materials may be preferred where immediate reaction with the soil is required. In time, however, this initial advantage is nullified due to the inevitable carbonation of the caustic forms of lime.

In comparing carbonate containing materials, it should be remembered that highly dolomitic limestones generally react more slowly with the soil than do those which are highly calcic. This difference is due to the comparatively slow rate of reaction of dolomite, which is supplied along with calcite in dolomitic limestones. (See Fig. 15:1.) When rapid rate of reaction is not a factor, however, dolomitic limestone is often preferred due to the fact that significant quantities of magnesium are supplied by this material. Soils treated with highly calcic limestone have been known, over a period of two or three rotations, to develop a magnesium deficiency even though the pH was maintained near 7.

The fineness of the limestone under consideration is important especially if the material is high in dolomite. If it is not sufficiently pulverized to rate as a so-called *fine* lime (see rule on p. 395), allowance must be made for the lack of rapid acting material by increasing the rate of application.

Miscellaneous factors. There are several miscellaneous factors that at times may be important. The handling of the caustic limes, even when bagged, is somewhat more disagreeable than working with limestone. The necessity for storage also comes in, since sometimes it is desirable to carry lime from one season to another. The limestone has the advantage here, as it does not change in storage, if kept dry, as do the others.

The question of purchasing the lime, especially the limestone, in bags or in bulk, has become increasingly important in recent years. Spreading limestone in bulk by truck has greatly reduced the handling costs. (See Fig. 15:2.) This method, however, tends to limit the choice as to when the material may be applied, since wet or plowed fields cannot be serviced by heavy machinery. The decision as to what method to use should not be finally approved, however, until the nature of the soil and the probable response of the crops have again been reviewed.

15:16. AMOUNTS OF LIME TO APPLY

It is well to emphasize at the outset that all recommendations as to the amounts of lime to apply are only estimates. It is impossible to decide with accuracy and certainty. Too many factors are involved, among the more important being that of buffering. It must always be remembered that we are dealing with a colloidal complex, the buffering of which we are never quite sure of.

Moreover, the objective of the lime addition is to rectify properly the very indefinite nutritional condition of the soil. We are never quite certain what amounts of calcium and magnesium will accomplish this or just what pH should be temporarily established.

A situation that adds to the difficulty of deciding how much lime to apply is the practice usually of adding lime only once in a rotation. Hence, the rate of application must be stepped up sufficiently to insure enough active lime during this period. This requires good judgment and experience.

In arriving at a practical decision, a number of factors should be considered. The principal ones are as follows:

1. Soil
   - Surface
     - pH [13]
     - Texture and structure
     - Amount of organic matter
   - Subsoil: pH, texture, and structure
2. Crops to be grown
3. Length of the rotation
4. Kind of lime used and its chemical composition
5. Fineness of the limestone
6. Experience

Soil characteristics. The pH test is invaluable in making decisions as it gives some idea as to the percentage base saturation of the soil and how acute is the need for lime. The texture and organic matter also are important since they are indicative of the adsorptive capacity of the soil and the strength of buffering. Naturally the higher the buffer capacity of a soil the greater must be the amount of lime applied in order to attain a satisfactory activity of calcium and magnesium and a given change in pH.

The subsoil also should be tested for pH and examined as to texture and structure. A subsoil pH markedly above or below that of the furrow-slice may justify a reduction or an increase, as the case may be, in the acre-rate of lime application. Advice as to the cropping of any soil should not be given without a knowledge of subsoil conditions.

---

[13] Other chemical tests, such as the determination of cation exchange capacity, are sometimes made and are of some practical value in deciding how much lime to apply. See M. Peech and R. Bradfield, "Chemical Methods for Estimating Lime Needs of Soils," *Soil Sci.*, 65: 35–55, 1948. This paper carries an extended bibliography.

Other considerations. The other factors listed above have already been discussed. Besides, their importance is self-evident. As to the kinds of lime, the three forms in respect to their effects on the soil are roughly in the ratio of 1 ton of representative finely ground limestone to 0.7 of a ton of commercial hydroxide to a little over 0.5 of a ton of representative oxide. The fineness of limestone is as important as chemical composition. The experience factor has been listed to emphasize the wisdom of taking advantage of lime knowledge wherever it may be found.

Suggested amounts. In ordinary practice it is seldom economical to apply more than 3 to 4 tons of finely ground limestone to the acre of mineral soil at any one time, unless it is very acid and the promise for increased crop yield exceptionally good. The data cited in Table 15:5, while more or

TABLE 15:5

Suggested Total Amounts of Finely Ground Limestone That Should be
Applied per Acre-furrow-slice of Mineral Soil for
Red Clover in Rotation [a]

	Limestone, Pounds per Acre	
Need for Lime		
	Sandy Loam	*Silt Loam*
Moderate	1500–2000	2500–3500
High	2500–3500	5000–6000

[a] In calculating these rates, the assumption is made that the amounts suggested will be used as *initial* applications. After the pH of the soil has been raised to the desired level, smaller *maintenance* rates may be satisfactory.

less suggestive, serve in a general way as guides in practical liming operations for a four- or five-year rotation with average mineral soils. It is assumed that a crop with a medium lime requirement is the principal legume of the rotation. The recommendations are in terms of finely ground limestone. If the lime is coarser than the minimum already quoted (see p. 395), or if an oxide or hydroxide is used, due allowance should be made. If alfalfa or sweet clover are to be grown, the amounts should be increased by perhaps 1,000 pounds per acre in the case of the sandy loam and 2,000 for the silt loam.

15:17. METHODS OF APPLYING LIME AND ITS PLACE IN THE ROTATION

As already suggested, the activity of lime is greatly encouraged by contact. Hence, the more thoroughly it is mixed with the soil, the greater will be the number of active centers and the more rapid and effective will be the treatment.

Methods of application. To obtain this quick action, lime is best applied to plowed land and worked into the soil as the seedbed is prepared. It should be mixed thoroughly with the surface half of the furrow-slice. Top-dressing with lime and leaving it on the surface is seldom recommended except on permanent meadows and pastures.

However, it is often much more convenient and in the long run just as effective to apply the lime on the surface and plow it under. The spreading is usually done in the fall on sod land that is to be turned later that autumn or the next spring. This practice provides a longer interval during which lime may be applied and usually results, in the case of a sod, in a minimum of soil packing if heavy machinery is used. It also makes possible the bulk-spreading of lime, using large trucks. This is becoming increasingly popular. (See Fig. 15:2.)

Figure 15:2. The bulk application of limestone by trucks specially equipped is becoming more and more common. Because of the weight of such machinery much limestone is applied to sod land and plowed under. In some cases this same method is used to spread commercial fertilizers. (See p. 499.) *(Photo courtesy George Serviss, Grange League Federation.)*

The time of year at which lime is applied is immaterial, the system of farming, the type of rotation, and related considerations being the deciding factors. Winter application may even be practiced.

Equipment used. A lime distributor should be used, especially if the amount to be applied is at all large. A manure spreader can be utilized and even an endgate seeder may be pressed into service. Small amounts of lime may be distributed by means of the fertilizer attachment on a grain drill. Several types of distributors are available for the bulk spreading of limestone. The evenness of distribution is as important as the amount of lime used and should by no means be neglected.

The addition of small amounts of limestone, say 300 to 500 pounds an acre, often gives remarkable results, when drilled in with the crop that is being seeded. Even though the lime is not mixed thoroughly with the soil and there is little change in the pH of furrow-slice as a whole, the influence on the crop may be very favorable. Apparently the lime in this case is functioning more as a fertilizer and as a means of rectifying conditions within the crop and at its root-soil interfaces rather than as an amendment for the whole furrow-slice.

Place in rotation. A discussion of the application of lime is never complete without some consideration being given to the place in the rotation at which the liming is best done. The rule is to apply the lime with or ahead of the crop that gives the most satisfactory response. Thus, in a rotation of corn, oats, fall wheat, and two years of alfalfa and timothy, the lime is often applied when the wheat is seeded in the fall. It can then be spread on the plowed ground and worked in as the seedbed is prepared. Its effect is thus especially favorable on the new legume seeding made in the wheat.

However, application to plowed land may result in some compaction of the soil if heavy machinery is used and certainly more power is necessary than for a soil in sod. For that reason spreading on sod land is often favored. In practice, the place of lime in the rotation is often determined, in part at least, by expediency, since the vital consideration is, after all, the application of lime regularly and in conjunction with a suitable rotation of some kind.

15:18. LIME AND SOIL-FERTILITY MANAGEMENT

The influence of successively liming a soil over a period of years may tend to raise or lower its fertility, according to the system of management that accompanies the applications of the lime. The use of lime alone may increase crop yields for a few years. Chemical reactions will be encouraged, soil organisms will be stimulated, and more nutrients will become available for crop use. Such stimulation, however, will soon wane and, if nothing is returned to the land, its productivity must ultimately drop back to even a lower level than before the lime applications began.

This being the case, farm manures, crop residues and legumes should be utilized to the fullest extent in connection with the lime. To help this combination keep up the fertility, fertilizers carrying nitrogen and potash as well as phosphates should be resorted to. Trace elements may be required in addition, especially boron. Lime improperly used exhausts the soil, but when rationally supplemented, it becomes one of the most important factors in the maintenance of the fertility and the productivity of acid soils.

The Nitrogen
Economy of Soils

CHAPTER 16

Of the various plant nutrients, nitrogen probably has been subjected to the greatest amount of study and even yet is receiving much attention. And there are very good reasons. The amount in the soil is small, while the quantity withdrawn annually by crops is comparatively large. At times the soil nitrogen is too readily soluble and is lost in drainage; at times it suffers volatilization; at other times it is definitely unavailable to higher plants. Moreover, its effects on plants usually are very marked and rapid. Thus, overapplications sometimes occur which may be harmful. All in all, nitrogen is a potent nutrient element that should not only be conserved, but also carefully regulated.

16:1. THE INFLUENCE OF NITROGEN ON PLANT DEVELOPMENT [1]

Favorable effects. Of the three elements usually applied in commercial fertilizers, nitrogen seems to have the quickest and most pronounced effect. It tends primarily to encourage aboveground vegetative growth and to impart to the leaves a deep green color. With cereals it increases the plumpness of the grains and their percentage of protein. With all plants nitrogen is a regulator in that it governs to a considerable degree the utilization of potassium, phosphorus, and other constituents. Moreover, its application tends to produce succulence, a quality particularly desirable in certain crops such as lettuce and radishes.

[1] Good discussions of the effects of the various nutrients on plant growth are given by E. J. Russell, *Soil Conditions and Plant Growth* (New York: Longmans, Green, 1949). Also see D. N. Prianishnikov, *Nitrogen in the Life of Plants,* translation by S. A. Wilde, Kramer Business Service, Inc., Madison, Wis., 1950.

Plants receiving insufficient nitrogen are stunted in growth and possess restricted root systems. The leaves turn yellow or yellowish-green and tend to drop off. The addition of available nitrogen will cause a remarkable change, indicative of the unusual activity of this element within the plant.

Oversupply detrimental.   Because of the immediate effect on plants of the application of available nitrogen compounds, one may be led to recommend higher applications than are necessary. Such a suggestion is unfortunate, since nitrogen is expensive and is easily lost from the soil. Of the three fertilizer constituents, it is the only one which, when added somewhat in excess, will result in harmful effects on certain crops. Very dark green, soft, and sappy leaves are an indication of an oversupply of nitrogen. The possible and important detrimental effects of this element may be listed as follows:

1. Nitrogen may *delay maturation* by encouraging excessive vegetative growth, which remains green beyond the normal time of ripening.
2. It may *weaken the straw* and encourage *lodging* in grain.
3. Nitrogen may *lower quality*. This is especially noticeable in certain grains and fruits, such as barley and peaches.
4. It may on occasion *decrease resistance* to *disease*.

It must not be inferred, however, that all plants are detrimentally affected by large amounts of nitrogen. Many crops such as the grasses, lettuce, radishes, and the like should have plenty of this element for their best and most normal development. With such crops the detrimental effects cited above are not to be expected unless exceedingly large quantities of nitrogen are applied. Nitrogenous fertilizers may be used freely in such cases, the cost of the materials in respect to the value of the crop increases being the major consideration.

16:2. THE NITROGEN CYCLE [2]

In all soils there is a very considerable intake and outgo of nitrogen in the course of a year, accompanied by many complex transformations. Some of these changes may be controlled more or less by man, while others are beyond his command. This interlocking succession of largely biochemical reactions, constitutes what is known as the *nitrogen cycle*. (See Fig. 16:1.) It has attracted scientific study for years and its practical significance is beyond question.

[2] For an over-all and well-documented consideration of soil nitrogen, see L. E. Ensminger and R. W. Pearson, "Soil Nitrogen," *Advances in Agronomy,* 2: 81–111, 1950.

The nitrogen income of arable soils is derived from such materials as crop residues, green manures, farm manure, commercial fertilizers, and ammonium and nitrate salts brought down by precipitation. In addition, there is the fixation of atmospheric nitrogen accomplished by certain microorganisms. The outgo is due to crop removal, to drainage, to erosion, and to loss in a gaseous condition both elemental and as ammonia.

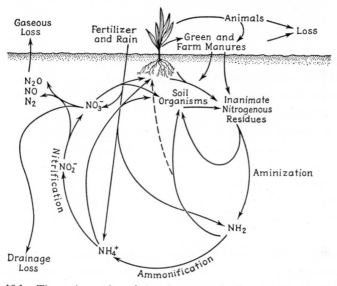

Figure 16:1. The main portion of the nitrogen cycle. In tracing the transfers, it is well to begin with the nitrogenous organic residues.

Much of the nitrogen added to the soil undergoes many transformations before it is removed. The nitrogen in organic combination is subjected to especially complex changes. Proteins are converted into various decomposition products and finally some of the nitrogen appears in the nitrate form. Even then it is allowed no rest, as it is either appropriated by microorganisms and higher plants, or is removed in drainage, or is lost by volatilization. And so the cyclic transfer goes on and on. The mobility of nitrogen is remarkable, rivaling carbon in its ease of movement.

16:3. NITROGEN TRANSFORMATIONS IN SOILS [3]— AMINIZATION

The proteins and allied compounds, which largely constitute the nitrogenous matter commonly added to soil, are of little value directly to higher

[3] The amount of nitrogen in mineral soils and its relationship to the soil organic matter is dealt with on page 150 and ff.

plants. They can be readily used, however, by the heterogeneous soil or-ganisms, both plant and animal. As a result of the enzymic digestion in-duced by these organisms, such compounds readily break down into amino compounds such as proteoses, peptones, and finally to amino acids. Hence, the process is spoken of as *aminization*. This transformation may be indi-cated more or less graphically as follows:

$$\begin{matrix} \text{Proteins and} \\ \text{near-proteins} \end{matrix} + \begin{matrix} \text{Enzymic} \\ \text{digestion} \end{matrix} \longrightarrow \begin{matrix} \text{Complex amino} \\ \text{compounds} \end{matrix} + CO_2 + E + \begin{matrix} \text{Other} \\ \text{products} \end{matrix}$$

Soil organisms of many kinds acquire energy (E) by this type of diges-tion and also utilize some of the nitrogen as the enzymic processes take place. At the same time carbon dioxide is freely evolved as the amino com-pounds and other products emerge.

Fate of amino nitrogen. As the digestion takes place, the nitrogen involved may go in one of two directions. It may be synthesized into the cell contents of soil organisms and again become a part of the protein-aceous complex of the soil, or it may be changed to simpler products, eventually appearing in the ammonium form. The enzymic process that gives rise to the latter form of nitrogen is called *ammonification* (Fig. 16:1).

Microorganisms, particularly those of a heterotrophic nature, when in need of nitrogen seem to use amino forms very readily. But while higher plants may possibly directly employ amino nitrogen, such an appropriation occurs so sparingly as to merit here no more than passing notice.

16:4. AMMONIFICATION

As already indicated, the same organisms, in general, that facilitate aminization also promote ammonification. In so doing, they tap ready sources of energy as well as appropriate some of the nitrogen involved. The enzymic process may be indicated as follows.[4]

$$\underset{\substack{\text{Amino} \\ \text{combination}}}{R\text{-}NH_2} + HOH \xrightarrow[\text{Hydrolysis}]{\text{Enzymic}} R\text{-}OH + NH_3 + \text{Energy}$$

$$2\ NH_3 + H_2CO_3 \longrightarrow (NH_4)_2CO_3 \rightleftharpoons 2\ NH_4{}^+ + CO_3{}^=$$

Ammonification seems to proceed to the best advantage in well-drained aerated soils with plenty of basic cations present. It will take place to some

---

[4] R represents large organic complexes with which NH_2 is associated in amino compounds.

extent under almost any condition, however, due to the great number of different organisms capable of accomplishing such a change. This is one of the advantages of a general-purpose flora and fauna.

Utilization of ammonium compounds. The fate of the ammoniacal nitrogen (as shown in Fig. 16:1) is four-fold. *First,* considerable amounts are appropriated by some of the ammonifiers themselves or by other soil organisms capable of using this type of compound. Mycorrhizal fungi (see page 118), no doubt, are able to absorb ammoniacal nitrogen and pass it on in some form to their host.

Second, higher plants are able to use this form of nitrogen, often very readily indeed. Young plants of almost all kinds are especially capable in this respect, although they seem to grow better if some nitrate nitrogen is also available. Azaleas, laurel, and other plants that require a low-lime soil are additional cases in point. Still other plants, such as lowland rice, for example, even prefer ammoniacal nitrogen instead of the nitrate.

Third, NH_4 ions are subject to fixation by some of the clay minerals.[5] This ion is about the same size as that of potassium and is subject to retention by the same minerals which fix the K ion. (See p. 455.) Illite and related clays have a significant NH_4-fixing capacity. In this fixed form, the nitrogen is not subject to rapid oxidation, although in time it may become available.

Finally, when plant and animal synthesis temporarily is satisfied the remaining ammonium nitrogen may go in a third direction. It is readily oxidized by certain special-purpose forms of bacteria that use it, not only as a source of nitrogen, but also as a source of energy. Thus, one arrives at a much-talked-of and perhaps comparatively over emphasized phase of biochemistry—*nitrification.* It is so named because its end product is nitrate nitrogen.

16:5. NITRIFICATION

Nitrification is a process of enzymic oxidation brought about by certain special-purpose bacteria. It seems to take place in two coordinated steps, two distinct groups of bacteria being involved. As shown below, the first step is the production of nitrous acid by one group of bacteria, apparently followed immediately by its oxidation to the nitrate form by another. (See

---

[5] As much as 50 per cent of the total nitrogen present in the C horizon of certain illite-containing soils has been found to be in the "fixed" ammonia form. See F. J. Stevenson, *et al.,* "Further Evidence for Naturally Occurring Fixed Ammonium in Soils," *Soil Sci.,* 85: 42–6, 1958.

Fig. 16:2 for this organism.) The enzymic changes are represented very simply as follows [6]:

$$2\ NH_4^+ + 3\ O_2 \xrightarrow[\text{Oxidation}]{\text{Enzymic}} 2\ NO_2^- + 2\ H_2O + 4\ H^+ + \text{Energy}$$

$$2\ NO_2^- + O_2 \xrightarrow[\text{Oxidation}]{\text{Enzymic}} 2\ NO_3^- + \text{Energy}$$

Under most conditions favoring the two reactions, the second transformation is thought to follow so closely on the first as to preclude any great accumulation of the nitrite. This is fortunate, as this ion in any concentration is toxic to higher plants. In very alkaline soils there is some evidence that the second reaction may be delayed until after the NH₄ ion concentration is reduced to a relatively low level. This may result in nitrite accumulation of sufficient magnitude to adversely affect plant growth.

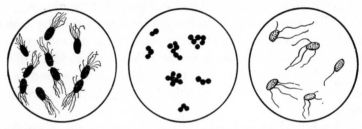

Figure 16:2. Some soil organisms especially important in the nitrogen cycle. Left to right, *Azotobacter*, nitrate bacteria, and nodule organisms of alfalfa.

Organisms concerned. The organisms in this case are all special purpose and autotrophic (see p. 122), in contrast to the general purpose and heterotrophic organisms concerned with aminization and ammonification. They obtain most of their energy by the oxidation of inorganic compounds. Like higher plants, they acquire carbon from carbon dioxide, at the same time respiring quantities of this gas.

Collectively, the nitrifying organisms are called nitrobacteria. Of these the *Nitrosomonas* are concerned in the conversion of ammonia into nitrites. The organisms having to do with the oxidation of nitrites to nitrates are generally designated as *Nitrobacter*. In common usage these two groups of bacteria are simply spoken as *nitrite* and *nitrate* organisms.

It is necessary to remark in this connection that other soil organisms probably are able to produce nitrate by-products. It is also possible that

---

[6] The enzymic oxidations involved in nitrification are exceedingly complex. Hence, this simple method of representation may be somewhat misleading.

photochemical oxidation may take place in tropical soils. How extensive such forms of nitrification are cannot be stated. Apparently, however, the bilateral oxidation already sketched (reaction on p. 414) is the most important in a practical way.

Rate of nitrification. Under ideal temperature, soil, and moisture conditions, nitrification occurs at a very rapid rate. Daily rates of from 6 to 22 pounds of nitrogen per 2 million pounds of soil have been found when 100 pounds of nitrogen in the ammonium form were added.[7] Much higher rates occurred when a larger application of ammonium compounds was made. Obviously, under ideal conditions the nitrifying organisms can supply nitrates at a rate which more than meets the needs of crop plants.

16:6. SOIL CONDITIONS AFFECTING NITRIFICATION

The nitrifying bacteria are extremely sensitive to their environment, much more so than the heterotrophic aminizing and ammonifying organisms. As a result, nitrification is a weak link of the nitrogen cycle. Consequently, soil conditions that influence the vigor of nitrification deserve practical consideration. They are: (1) aeration, (2) temperature, (3) moisture, (4) active lime, (5) fertilizer salts, and (6) the nitrogen-carbon ratio.

Aeration.[8] Since nitrification is a process of oxidation, any procedure that increases the aeration of the soil should, up to a certain point, encourage it. Plowing and cultivation, especially if granulation is not impaired, are recognized means of promoting nitrification.

Temperature. The temperature most favorable for the process of nitrification is from 80 to 90° F. At a temperature of 125° F. nitrification practically ceases. At freezing or below, nitrification will not take place, but at about 35 to 40° F. it begins and slowly increases in intensity until the optimum temperature is reached. The lateness with which nitrification attains its full vigor in the spring is well known, application of nitrogen being used to offset the delay.

Moisture. The rate with which nitrification proceeds in a soil is governed to a marked extent by the water content, the process being retarded by both very low and very high moisture conditions. In practice, it is safe to assume that the optimum moisture as recognized for higher plants

---

[7] See F. E. Broadbent and K. B. Tyler, "Nitrification of Ammoniacal Fertilizers in Some California Soils," *Hilgardia,* 27: 247–67, 1957.

[8] See F. M. Amer and W. V. Bartholomew, "Influence of Oxygen Concentration in Soil Air on Nitrification," *Soil Sci.,* 71: 215–20, 1951.

is also optimum for nitrification. One reservation, however, must be made. Nitrification will progress appreciably at moisture contents at or even below the wilting coefficient for higher plants.

Active lime. It is a very common observation that lime stimulates nitrification in soils. Apparently, the process of oxidation requires an abundance of exchangeable bases. This accounts in part for the feeble nitrification in acid mineral soils and the seeming sensitiveness of the organisms to a low pH. As a matter of fact, however, acidity itself within reasonable limits seems to have little influence on nitrification when adequate bases are present. This is especially true of peat soils. At pH values even below 5 these soils may show remarkable accumulations of nitrates. (See p. 350.)

Fertilizers. Small amounts of many kinds of salts, even those of the trace elements, stimulate nitrification. A reasonable balance of N, P, and K has been found to be helpful. Apparently, the stimulation of the organisms is much the same as is that of higher plants.

Applications of large quantities of ammonium nitrogen to strongly alkaline soils have been found to depress the second step in the nitrification reaction.[9] Apparently the ammonia is toxic to the nitrobacter under these conditions, but does not affect adversely the nitrosomonas. Consequently, nitrite accumulation may occur in toxic quantities when ammonium containing compounds are added to soils very high in pH. Similarly, on such soils adverse effects may result from a compound such as urea which supplies NH_4 ions in the soil by hydrolysis.

Carbon-nitrogen ratio. The significance of the carbon-nitrogen ratio has already been rather fully considered (p. 147) so that the explanation here may be brief. Carbohydrates, whatever their source, readily supply energy to the general-purpose organisms of the soil, and, under favorable conditions, a tremendous multiplication of this rough-and-ready group is initiated. As a result, all of the inorganic nitrogen that is available in the soil is quickly converted to organic forms in microbial tissue. Nitrification is thus more or less at a standstill, because of a lack of ammoniacal nitrogen, this also having been swept up by the decay organisms. Thus, a competition with higher plants for nitrogen is initiated, often of a most serious nature.

After the carbonaceous matter has partially decomposed so that energizing material is no longer abundant, nitrogen assimilation slows down and by-product ammonium compounds appear in the soil. Conditions may now become favorable for nitrification, and nitrates may again accumu-

[9] See Broadbent and Tyler, *op. cit.*

late. Thus, the carbon-nitrogen ratio, through its selective influence on soil microorganisms, exerts a powerful control on nitrification and the presence of nitrate nitrogen in the soil. (See Fig. 6:4.)

16:7. THE FATE OF NITRATE NITROGEN

The nitrate nitrogen of the soil whether added in fertilizers or formed by nitrification may go in four directions (see Fig. 16:1). It may (1) be used by microorganisms, and (2) by higher plants, it may (3) be lost in drainage, and it may (4) escape from the nitrogen cycle in a volatile condition.

Use by soil organisms and plants. The assimilation of nitrate nitrogen by soil organisms and higher plants has already been dealt with, and only a few words more are necessary thereto. So voracious is the microorganic flora at times that it competes seriously with higher plants. It is probable that a large proportion of the nitrate formed during the year is appropriated by soil organisms. Higher plants thus not only feed on by-product nitrogen, but they must also be satisfied with what is left by the general-purpose soil flora and fauna. Nevertheless, field crops remove from 60 to more than 100 pounds of nitrogen yearly per acre.

Leaching and volatilization. The amount of nitrate nitrogen found in *drainage water,* the third avenue of loss, is not usually very great, especially if the soil carries a crop. It is evident from data already quoted (pp. 216 and ff) that perhaps the average annual removal of nitrogen from a representative humid-region mineral soil by leaching is in the order of 5 or 6 pounds an acre. Compared to the removal by crop plants, this loss is moderate. With bare soils, however, the withdrawal by leaching is much greater.

Under certain conditions, especially those of poor drainage and aeration, it seems probable that nitrate compounds in the soil may be *reduced*—their nitrogen, at least in part, escaping in gaseous form. The various phases of reduction will be considered in the next section.

16:8. THE VOLATILIZATION OF SOIL NITROGEN [10]

The conditions under which the volatilization of soil nitrogen occurs are not well understood, but most authorities agree that this loss is greatly en-

[10] See J. Wijler and C. C. Delwiche, "Investigations on the Denitrifying Process in Soils," *Plant and Soil,* 5: 155–69, 1954.

couraged by poor drainage and lack of aeration. The maintenance of the soil in a bare condition and the presence of excessive amounts of mobile nitrogenous compounds may also be important factors. The meager data available in respect to such volatilization indicate that this form of loss is of considerable magnitude even from well-managed cropped soils.

Reduction by organisms. The biochemical reduction of nitrate nitrogen to gaseous compounds is thought to be the principal type of volatilization. The microorganisms involved seem to be the general-purpose heterotrophic forms that under favorable conditions promote aminization and ammonification. However, under inadequate aeration [11] at least some of them seem to readily abstract oxygen from nitrates and their reduced products. The trend of the reaction may be tentatively represented as follows:

$$2\ HNO_3 \xrightarrow{-2[O]} 2\ HNO_2 \begin{array}{c} \xrightarrow{-2[O]} H_2N_2O_2 \text{ (hyponitrite)} \begin{array}{c} \xrightarrow{+2[H]} 2\ H_2O + N_2 \text{ (Elemental N)} \\ \rightleftharpoons N_2O + H_2O \text{ (nitrous oxide)} \end{array} \\ \xrightarrow{-[O]} 2\ NO + H_2O \text{ (nitric oxide)} \end{array}$$

nitrates   nitrites

Apparently under most soil conditions nitrous oxide (N_2O) is the gas lost in largest quantities. Soil pH may influence the nature of the compounds lost, values above 7 favoring the loss of elemental N and values below 6 increasing the loss due to nitric oxide (NO).

Chemical reduction. There is another way [12] by which nitrogen may possibly be lost in the gaseous form. For instance, nitrites in a slightly acid solution will evolve gaseous nitrogen when brought in contact with certain ammonium salts, with simple amines, such as urea, and even with non-nitrogenous sulfur compounds and carbohydrates. The following reaction is suggestive of what may occur to urea.

$$2\ HNO_2 + CO(NH_2)_2 \longrightarrow CO_2\uparrow + 3\ H_2O + 2\ N_2\uparrow$$
Nitrite   Urea

[11] F. J. Jones, "Loss of Elemental Nitrogen from Soils under Anaerobic Conditions," *Soil Sci.,* 70: 193–96, 1951.

[12] J. K. Wilson, "Soil Algae as Reducers of Nitrate to Nitrite," *Proc. Soil Sci. Soc. Amer.,* 6: 196, 1941; and *Nitrous Acid and the Loss of Nitrogen,* Cornell Univ. Agr. Exp. Sta., Memoir 253: 1–36, 1943. For a more conservative stand consult F. E. Allison, and J. Doetsch, "Nitrogen Gas Production by the Reaction of Nitrites with Amino Acids in Slightly Acidic Media," *Proc. Soil Sci. Soc. Amer.,* 15: 163–66, 1950.

It is well to note that the type of volatilization pictured above is strictly chemical and does not require adverse soil conditions. Its practical importance, of course, will depend upon the amount of nitrogen that thereby escapes from the soil. Most investigators do not credit this mechanism with large nitrogenous losses.

Quantity of N volatilized. Since gaseous nitrogen is unavailable to higher plants, any extensive reduction, no matter what the mechanism may be, undoubtedly is a serious drain on the nitrogen cycle. Lysimeter studies [13] have indicated that perhaps 20 per cent of the nitrogen added to soils in the form of fertilizers, manures, etc., is not accounted for by crop removal and drainage. This is presumably lost by volatilization.

Unpublished results from the Cornell lysimeters covering a period of 15 years showed a loss of nitrogen of from 40 to 45 pounds an acre a year unaccounted for. The soil studied was a well-drained sandy loam cropped to vegetables and fertilized either with nitrate of soda or sulfate of ammonia.

Such losses are not confined to humid-region soils as studies of Utah soils indicate.[14] At least one half of the total loss of nitrogen from cropped soils as compared to virgin land was not accounted for by leaching, erosion, and crop removal. Volatilization must have been active.

In recent years, attention has been called to the fact that volatilization losses may be greater than those cited, especially when large quantities of fertilizer are applied. Nitrates have been reduced even under conditions of apparently good drainage. Volatilization is likely of greater consequence than has been supposed in the past. It is certainly of greater magnitude than that commonly lost in drainage from cropped soils. (See p. 216.) The only suggestions that can be made at present for the control of volatilization are to keep a crop on the land as much as possible, provide for adequate drainage and tilth, and avoid an excess at any one time of active nitrogeneous compounds in the soil.

16:9. MAJOR DIVISIONS OF THE NITROGEN CYCLE [15]

The discussion so far has concerned itself with that part of the nitrogen cycle dealing with nitrogen already in the soil or plant. (See Fig. 16:1.) It is to be noted that two general types of enzymic activities are current

---

[13] See F. E. Allison, "The Enigma of Soil Nitrogen Balance Sheets," *Advances in Agronomy,* 7: 213–50, 1955.

[14] A. F. Bracken and J. E. Greaves, "Losses of Nitrogen and Organic Matter from Dry-land soils," *Soil Sci.,* 51: 1–15, 1941.

[15] See Allison, *op. cit.*

therein: (1) synthetic or building-up procedures, and (2) breakdown and simplifying processes such as aminization, ammonification, nitrification, and reduction. At any one time most of the soil nitrogen is involved in the synthetic processes, a very small proportion appearing in the ammoniacal, nitrite, and nitrate forms. This is fortunate, as the loss of much nitrogen by drainage and volatilization is thus avoided. Most people do not realize the importance of this situation or of the fact that higher plants are by-product feeders, living on the nitrogen left over from the metabolism of the soil fauna and flora.

The part of the nitrogen cycle, yet to be considered, concerns itself with the acquisition by the soil of nitrogen from various sources. Four ways of addition are recognized in arable soils: (1) nitrogen fixation by legume bacteria; (2) free fixation or azofication; (3) additions in rain water and snow; and (4) application of nitrogen in fertilizers, farm manure, and green manures. They will be considered in order.

16:10. FIXATION OF ATMOSPHERIC NITROGEN BY NODULE BACTERIA [16]

It has been recognized for centuries that certain crops such as the clovers, alfalfa, peas, beans, and others, improve the soil in some way, making it possible to grow larger yields of cereals after these plants have occupied the land. Within the last century the benefit has been traced to the fixation of nitrogen through the agency of bacteria contained in nodules on the roots of certain host plants. The specific plants so affected belong, with a few exceptions,[17] to the family of legumes.

Nodule formation. The legume organisms live in the root nodules, take free nitrogen from the soil air, and synthesize it into complex forms. The nodules evidently are the result of an irritation of the root surface, much as a gall is caused to develop on a leaf or on a branch of a tree by an insect. The entrance of the organisms normally is effected through the root hairs. The infection tube ultimately extends the entire length of the root hair and into the cortex cells of the rootlets, where the growth of the

---

[16] The literature on the fixation of nitrogen by microorganisms is exceedingly copious. One may best begin with S. A. Waksman, *Soil Microbiology* (Baltimore: Williams and Wilkins, 1932). Also see A. G. Norman, "Recent Advances in Soil Microbiology," *Proc. Soil Sci. Soc. Amer.*, 11: 9–15, 1946; and F. E. Clark, "Soil Microorganisms and Plant Roots," *Advances in Agronomy*, 1: 242–82, 1949.

[17] Alnus and a few other nonlegumes carry root nodules similar to those of legumes. For proof that nitrogen is fixed by such associations, see G. Bond, "An Isotopic Study of the Fixation of Nitrogen Associated with Nodulated Plants of *Alnus, Myrica* and *Hippophae*," *Jour. Exptl. Botany*, 6: 303–11, 1955.

tubercle starts and where the fixation of nitrogen occurs. (See Figs. 16:2 and 16:3.)

Figure 16:3. Nodules on the roots of legumes. Left to right, red clover, alfalfa, and field peas. Although the nitrogen fixing bacteria are segregated in the nodules, they apparently freely use the juices of the host plant as a source of energy. The nitrogen fixed may go in three directions—(1) appropriated by the host, (2) used by non-legumes growing in close association, and (3) left in the soil when the nodules slough off and decompose.

How the plant absorbs this nitrogen after it has been secured by the bacteria is not well understood; nor is it known in exactly what form the nitrogen is at first fixed, although amino and amide forms very soon appear.[18] It seems likely that some of the nitrogen compounds produced within the bacterial cells are diffused through the cell wall and absorbed by the host plant.

Organisms involved. Since the plants are able to use some of this nitrogen fixed by the microbes, the relationship thus established is often spoken of as *symbiotic*. The organism is a *rhizobium* and there are a number of strains, depending on the host plants. They may, therefore, be classified according to the host as *Rhizobium meliloti* for those of alfalfa and sweet clover, *Rhizobium trifolii* for the clovers, *Rhizobium japonicum* for soybeans, and so on. As a group, they are often referred to as the *nodule* or *legume organisms* instead of by the more technical terms.

The organisms from one species of legumes are not necessarily well adapted to the ready production of effective nodules on other leguminous

[18] This is a complex and highly controversial question. See A. I. Virtanen, "Mechanism of Symbiotic Nitrogen Fixation by Leguminous Plants," *Proc. Soil Sci. Soc. Amer.*, 4: 221–22, 1939; and P. W. Wilson, *The Biochemistry of Symbiotic Nitrogen Fixation* (Madison: University of Wisconsin Press, 1940).

species. Certain cross-inoculations are successful in practice, however. For instance, the organisms seem to be readily interchangeable within the clovers, the vetches, and the beans. Those from sweet clover and bur clover will inoculate alfalfa, while the bacteria may be transferred from vetch to field pea or from cowpea to velvet bean.[19] The part played by the plant is doubtless to furnish the carbohydrates that supply energy to the nitrogen-assimilating bacteria.

A partial listing of the groups within which cross inoculation may easily be made follows:

Group 1. (Alfalfa group) Alfalfa, bur clovers, white, yellow and hubam sweet clovers, fenugreek, yellow trefoil, and others.

Group 2. (Clover group) Mammoth and red clover, alsike clover, crimson clover, hop clover, white clover, zigzag clover, landino clover, and others.

Group 3. (Cowpea group) Lespedezas, acacia, kudzu, cowpea, peanut, partridge pea, jack bean, velvet bean, lima bean, etc.

Group 4. (Pea and vetch group) Garden pea, sweet pea, horse bean, lentil, Canada field pea, hairy vetch, common vetch, purple vetch, etc.

Group 5. (Soybean group) All varieties of soybeans.

Group 6. (Bean group) Garden bean (numerous varieties), pinto bean, and scarlet runner.

Group 7. (Lupine group) Lupine, serradella, blue lupine, yellow lupine, and white lupine.

The effect of inoculation. The influence of inoculation upon the crop yield and percentage of nitrogen in the legume is very striking. Data bearing upon the latter phase are shown in Table 16:1. Analyses are given

TABLE 16:1

Effect of Inoculation with the Legume Organisms on the Nitrogen Content of Sweet Clover and Alfalfa [a]

(Calculated as percentages based on dry matter)

Soil Treatment	Sweet Clover		Alfalfa	
	Tops	*Roots*	*Tops*	*Roots*
Inoculated	2.29	2.01	2.56	2.14
Not inoculated	1.37	0.88	1.51	0.71

[a] A. C. Arny and R. W. Thatcher, "The Effect of Different Methods of Inoculation on the Yield and Protein Content of Alfalfa and Sweet Clover," *Jour. Amer. Soc. Agron.*, 9: 127–37, 1917.

[19] L. W. Erdman, *Legume Innoculation: What it is—What it does*, Farmers Bulletin 2003, U.S. Dept. of. Agric., 1959.

for both the tops and roots of sweet clover and alfalfa grown on soil inoculated and not inoculated. The soil originally was not known to carry the legume organisms.

16:11. AMOUNT OF NITROGEN FIXED BY NODULE BACTERIA

The amount of nitrogen fixed by the legume bacteria depends on many factors. The condition of the soil, especially as to aeration, drainage, moisture, and the amount of active calcium, are of prime importance. The sensitivity of legumes to soil acidity is largely attributed to the failure of nodule bacteria to function under these conditions. Many soils are in such a condition as to harbor only a meager, nonvirulent flora of legume bacteria. Even when the above factors are favorable, a large amount of readily available nitrogen in the soil will discourage nodulation and thereby reduce fixation. (See Fig. 16:4.)

Figure 16:4. The influence of added inorganic nitrogen on the total nitrogen in clover plants, the proportion supplied by the fertilizer and that fixed by the clover. Increasing the rate of nitrogen application decreased the amount of nitrogen fixed by the clover. (From T. W. Walker, *et al.,* "Fate of Labeled Nitrate and Ammonium Nitrogen When Applied to Grass and Clover Grown Separately and Together," *Soil Sci.,* 81: 339–52, 1956.)

Molybdenum is known to be essential for the process of nitrogen fixation. Although needed in minute quantities only, this micronutrient is apparently required for the enzymatic reaction by means of which nitrogen is fixed. Some investigators believe that much of the favorable response of certain legumes to lime may be due indirectly to increased availability of molybdenum associated with liming.

Some legume field crops, such as alfalfa and sweet clover, facilitate a fixation of especially large amounts of nitrogen. The clovers are less effective, while some legumes can be credited with but a scanty acquisition. Lyon and Bizzell [20] in a ten-years' experiment at Ithaca, New York, report the following magnitude of fixation in pounds per acre per year:

Alfalfa	251	Soybeans	105
Sweet Clover	168	Hairy Vetch	68
Red Clover	151	Field Beans	58
Alsike Clover	141	Field Peas	48

A fixation ranging from 188 to 260 pounds per acre per year was recorded by Collison [21] at Geneva, New York, for alfalfa. Perhaps for an average crop of alfalfa, 200 to 250 pounds of nitrogen an acre would be a conservative figure for the first year and possibly for the second also. The corresponding estimate for red clover might well be 100 to 150 pounds per acre.

16:12. FATE OF THE NITROGEN FIXED BY LEGUME BACTERIA

The nitrogen fixed by the nodule organisms may go in three directions. *First,* it may be used by the host plant, the latter benefiting greatly by the symbiosis. *Second,* the nitrogen may pass into the soil itself, either by excretion or more probably by the sloughing off of the roots and especially of their nodules. The crop in association with the legume may thereby benefit. This influence is a matter of common observation. The more vigorous development of timothy or bluegrass in association with clover than when grown alone is a well-known example.

Third, when a legume sod is turned under, some of the nitrogen becomes available to the succeeding crop. Because of the narrow carbon-nitrogen ratio of such residues their nitrogen may swing through the nitrogen cycle with remarkable ease and may quickly appear in the ammoniacal and nitrate forms.

[20] T. L. Lyon and J. A. Bizzell, "A Comparison of Several Legumes with Respect to Nitrogen Accretion," *Jour. Amer. Soc. Agron.,* 26: 651–56, 1934.

[21] R. C. Collison; H. C. Beattie; and J. D. Harlan, *Lysimeter Investigations. III. Mineral and Water Relations and Final Nitrogen Balance in Legume and Nonlegume Crop Rotations for a Period of 16 Years,* Bulletin 212, N. Y. State Agr. Exp. Sta., 1933. For further data regarding amounts of nitrogen fixed by the various legume organisms, see E. B. Fred; I. L. Baldwin; and Elizabth McCoy, *Root Nodule Bacteria and Leguminous Plants,* Madison, Wis., 1932, p. 218.

16:13. DO LEGUMES ALWAYS INCREASE THE SOIL NITROGEN?

With respect to the fate of the nitrogen fixed by legumes, some people assume that legumes always leave the soil on which they have been growing definitely richer in nitrogen. As a matter of fact, the result is likely to be just the opposite, especially when the soil already is high in nitrogen or the crop is harvested and removed from the land. Beans and peas in particular are likely to leave the land depleted since they support a low nitrogen fixation. Moreover, their roots often are partially removed in harvesting.

Losses noted. Swanson [22] determined total nitrogen in the soil of a considerable number of fields in Kansas that had grown alfalfa continuously for twenty or thirty years, at the same time analyzing soil from contiguous land in native sod. In most cases, the alfalfa soil was lower in nitrogen than the sod. This tendency for legumes actually to lower instead of raise the total nitrogen has been substantiated for New York soils by carefully controlled lysimeter experiments with alfalfa and clover.[23]

Even the turning under of the entire legume crop will not always increase the nitrogen of the soil. Mooers [24] conducted experiments for ten years in which wheat, followed by cowpeas, was grown annually. On one set of plots the cowpea vines were plowed under each year, and on the other set they were removed. The surface 8 inches of soil into which the vines were plowed under lost 288 pounds of nitrogen to the acre during the experiment. However, where the vines were removed before plowing the loss was 388 pounds. It would seem that, in spite of the fixation of nitrogen that may have occurred, the influence of the wheat and other sources of loss were such as to reduce the nitrogen content of the soil.

Increase possible. However, it is possible that soils may gain some nitrogen if leguminous crops are plowed under especially on soils originally low in nitrogen. On eroded areas, and on areas badly depleted by poor soil and crop management, legumes can be expected to increase nitrogen and organic matter contents. When grown in combination with grasses, legumes are especially effective in rehabilating such soils. For crops other than legumes, supplemental nitrogen from fertilizers will be needed to obtain normal crop yields and to help supply the needed organic matter.

[22] C. O. Swanson, "The Effect of Prolonged Growing Alfalfa on the Nitrogen Content of the Soil," *Jour. Amer. Soc. Agron.,* 9: 305–14, 1917.

[23] Collison; Beattie; and Harlan, *op. cit.*

[24] C. A. Mooers, *Effects of Liming and Green Manuring on Crop Yields and on Soil Supplies of Nitrogen and Humus,* Bulletin 135, Tenn. Agr. Exp. Sta., 1926.

Legumes—nitrogen savers. It is evident, therefore, that the influence of legumes on the amount of nitrogen in the soil is uncertain. When the total soil nitrogen is high, legumes may reduce the nitrogen level, especially if the crop is removed from the land. Even when the aboveground parts are plowed under, there may still be a decrease. Some accretion is likely if the nitrogen level of the soil to begin with is low.

In general, however, the net draft of legumes on the soil nitrogen is less than that of nonlegumes, and as a consequence, their use is to be encouraged in a rotation where the maintenance of soil nitrogen is important. Legumes are usually so economical in their use of soil nitrogen that a high protein crop may often be harvested with little depletion of the land in respect to this element. Thus, they are nitrogen *savers*. This is an important fertility axiom.

16:14. FIXATION OF ATMOSPHERIC NITROGEN BY AZOFICATION

Soils may acquire a part of their nitrogen supply independently of higher plants, fertilizers, and rainfall. There exist in soils certain microorganisms, using the organic matter as a source of energy, that are able to obtain elemental nitrogen from the soil air. This nitrogen is incorporated in the bodies of these organisms and is left in the form of proteins and related compounds upon their death. The process is called *azofication*, because a major part of the fixation is ascribed to the *Azotobacter* group of bacteria. Since these organisms use the soil organic matter as a source of energy and are not directly associated with higher plants, as are the legume bacteria, the transformation is often spoken of as *nonsymbiotic* or *free fixation*.

Specific organisms involved. Although several different groups of bacteria, blue-green algae,[25] and perhaps fungi are able to acquire atmospheric nitrogen nonsymbiotically, the major fixation in the representative soil apparently is brought about by two groups of heterotrophic bacteria. One of these is the aerobic *Azotobacter* already mentioned. (See Fig. 16:2.) The other is an anaerobic, or perhaps a facultative, bacterium called *Clostridium pastorianum*. Because of low oxygen at the soil interfaces, conditions favorable for the latter organism, are present in most

---

[25] Nitrogen fixation in rice paddies has been attributed to blue-green algae and apparently the quantities fixed are of much practical importance. Nitrogen fixation by these and other organisms is discussed by G. E. Fogg, "Nitrogen Fixation by Photosynthetic Organisms," *Ann. Rev. of Pl. Physiol.*, 7: 51–70, 1956.

soils, even when in the best of tilth. Consequently, these two groups of bacteria probably work side by side in the fixation of the nitrogen of the soil air.

It is not to be assumed that the *Azotobacter* and *Clostridium pastorianum* acquire all of their nitrogen from atmospheric sources. Since less energy is required for the acquisition of ammoniacal and nitrate nitrogen, these forms are probably readily used. In fact, in a soil high in such available nitrogen, it is doubtful whether a great deal of free fixation takes place.

Factors influencing azofication. Highly carbonaceous organic matter, since it supplies energy readily, greatly encourages azofication. Sod land presents almost ideal conditions for azofication since it contains a large supply of organic matter with a wide carbon-nitrogen ratio, and it is likely to be low in nitrate nitrogen.

Azotobacter are notably sensitive to active calcium and, unless a fair amount of bases is present, the fixation is slow. In this respect, azofication resembles nitrification. In mineral soils the free fixation of nitrogen often begins to lag noticeably at pH 5.6 and at pH values below 5.0 becomes more or less negligible. The maintenance of the pH of mineral soils above 6.0 or even 6.5 by judicious liming is recommended. Such is not the case, however, with peat soils, since they ordinarily contain suitable amounts of active lime even at relatively high H ion concentrations. (See p. 352.)

16:15. AMOUNT OF NITROGEN FIXED BY AZOFICATION

It is difficult to determine accurately the exact amount of nitrogen fixed by azofication in soils because of the other processes involving nitrogen that are taking place simultaneously. Estimates which have been made, however, indicate that considerable quantities of nitrogen are fixed annually in this manner. For example, long-time experiments in England [26] and in New York [27] indicate that 40 to 45 pounds of nitrogen per acre per year may be fixed by nonsymbiotic organisms. In these experiments carbonaceous plant residues were returned to the soil. One would expect azofication to have been at a maximum under these conditions. In the New York experiments nonsymbiotic fixation was reduced more than half by removing the crop residues.

[26] A. D. Hall, *Book of the Rothamsted Experiments* (New York: Dutton, 1905), p. 139.
[27] T. L. Lyon and B. D. Wilson, *Some Relations of Green-manures to the Nitrogen of a Soil,* Memoir 115, Cornell Univ. Agr. Exp. Sta., 1928.

Research with isotopic forms of nitrogen have shown wide variations in the amount of nitrogen fixed by azofication.[28] The range in values found is from a few pounds to perhaps 60 pounds per acre per year. In most cases, evidence indicates that one would not expect more than about 25 pounds of nitrogen to be added in this manner, and that the amount may be much less.

Azofication vs. volatilization.   Under conditions wherein little fertilizer nitrogen is applied, it has been suggested that azofication gains and volatilization losses may balance each other. As a rough approximation this is probably correct. The growing use of considerable quantities of fertilizers undoubtedly modifies this situation. The presence of fertilizer nitrates, for example, would tend to reduce azofication but would likely increase opportunities for volatilization. This fact emphasizes the interrelations of various factors influencing the nitrogen cycle. It also cautions one against sweeping generalizations concerning the magnitude of gains or losses of nitrogen.

16:16. THE ADDITION OF NITROGEN TO SOIL IN PRECIPITATION—MAGNITUDE

Nitrogen occurring in rain and snow generally is in the nitrate and ammoniacal forms and, consequently, is readily available to plants. The amounts thus brought down are variable, usually fluctuating markedly with season and location. It is well known that the additions are greater in the tropics than in humid-temperate regions and larger in the latter than under semiarid climates. In Table 16:2 will be found some of the more important data regarding the amounts of nitrogen thus added to the soil in various parts of the world. It will be noted that the figures are, for the most part, from temperate regions.

Apparently the ammoniacal nitrogen added to the soil in precipitation is, at least in temperate regions, always larger in amount than that in the nitrate form. It is also noticeable that, while the nitrate nitrogen is about the same for most locations, the ammonium form shows wide variations. Considering the figures as a whole, it seems safe to suggest that under a humid-temperate climate, an average of about 4½ pounds of ammoniacal and 1½ pounds of nitrate nitrogen fall on every acre of land yearly in rain and snow. Allowing for some loss in runoff, perhaps 5 pounds of nitrogen an acre actually enter the soil each year. This annual acquisition of nitro-

---

[28] For a review of this subject see C. C. Delwiche and J. Wijler, "Nonsymbiotic Nitrogen Fixation in Soils," *Plant and Soil,* 7: 113–29, 1956.

gen in a readily available form to each acre of land affords some aid in the maintenance of soil fertility, as it is equivalent to about 31 pounds of commercial nitrate of soda.

TABLE 16:2

Amounts of Nitrogen Brought Down in Precipitation [a]

Location	Years of Record	Rainfall in Inches	Pounds per Acre per Year	
			Ammoniacal Nitrogen	Nitrate Nitrogen
Harpenden, England	28	28.8	2.64	1.33
Garford, England	3	26.9	6.43	1.93
Flahult, Sweden	1	32.5	3.32	1.30
Groningen, Holland	...	27.6	4.54	1.46
Bloemfontein and Durban, South Africa	2	...	4.02	1.39
Ottawa, Canada	10	23.4	4.42	2.16
Ithaca, New York	11	29.5	3.65	0.69

[a] These data were obtained from a number of sources, see T. L. Lyon; H. O. Buckman; and N. C. Brady, *The Nature and Properties of Soils* (New York: Macmillan, 1952), p. 467.

16:17. REACTIONS OF NITROGEN FERTILIZERS

Nitrogen applied in fertilizers undergoes the same kinds of reactions as does nitrogen released by biochemical processes from plant residues. Most of the fertilizer nitrogen will be present in one or more of three forms: (1) nitrate, (2) ammonia, and (3) urea. The fate of each of these forms has already been discussed briefly. Thus, urea nitrogen is subject to ammonification, nitrification, and utilization by microbes and higher plants. Ammonium fertilizers can likewise be oxidized to nitrates or they can be utilized without change. And nitrate salts can be lost by volatilization or leaching or they can be absorbed by plants or microorganisms.

High concentrations. There is one important fact that should be remembered when dealing with the reaction of fertilizer nitrogen: The added fertilizer salts will almost invariably be localized and in higher concentrations than one would expect to find in unfertilized soils. For this reason, the usual reactions are sometimes subject to modification. A few examples will be cited.

When anhydrous ammonia, ammonium-containing salts, or even urea are added to highly alkaline soils there is a possibility of some nitrogen loss in the form of free ammonia. Also, under these conditions, the nitrification process is inhibited, only the first step preceding normally. Nitrites may thus accumulate in this situation until essentially all the ammonium form has been oxidized. Only then will the second step, that of nitrate formation, take place at normal speed.

The addition of large amounts of nitrate-containing fertilizers may effect the processes of azofication and volatilization. In general, azofication is depressed by adequate mineral nitrogen. Volatilization, on the other hand, is often encouraged by abundant nitrates. Heavy nitrate fertilization would thus tend to reduce the amount of nitrogen remaining in the soil as a net result of these two processes.

In most soil situations the effects of higher localized concentrations of fertilizer materials on nitrogen transformations are not serious. Except for a few situations such as these cited, we can assume that fertilizer nitrogen will be changed in soils in a manner very similar to that of nitrogen released by biological transformations.

16:18. PRACTICAL MANAGEMENT OF SOIL NITROGEN

The problem of nitrogen control is twofold: (1) the maintenance of an adequate supply in the soil; and (2) the regulation of the turnover in such a way as to assure a ready availability at such times as to meet crop demands. To begin with, let us draw up a rough balance sheet which will show, at least in a general way, how great the nitrogen deficit is likely to be.

Nitrogen balance sheet. It has been suggested for a representative humid-region soil that azofication approximately offsets the possible losses of nitrogen by volatilization (p. 428). It has also been tentatively assumed that rain-and-snow acquisition equals in general leaching removals (see above). Therefore, the nitrogen in the harvested crops plus that carried away by erosion approximately represents the yearly deficit. Considering the former as perhaps 75 pounds an acre a year, and the latter as possibly 25 pounds for lands having a moderate slope (see Table 9:8), it seems that in a general way 100 pounds, more or less, of nitrogen an acre will be required annually to effect a balance. Such figures should be used guardedly, as they are more or less hypothetical and are designed merely to give a general concept of the problem.

Meeting the deficit. In practice, nitrogen deficits are met in four ways—crop residues, farm manure, legumes, and commercial fertilizers.

On dairy farms and beef ranches much of the deficit will be met by the first three methods, fertilizers being used as a supplementary source. On most other types of farms, fertilizers will play a more significant role. Where vegetables and other crops with high nutrient requirements are grown, the nitrogen deficit will be met almost entirely with commercial fertilizers.

Turnover regulations. By all odds, the more difficult of the two general problems of nitrogen control is the regulation of this element after it enters the soil. Availability at the proper time and in suitable amounts, with a minimum of loss, is the ideal. Even where commercial fertilizers are used to supply much of the nitrogen, maintaining an adequate, but not excess, quantity of available nitrogen is not an easy task.

Since soils under any given climate tend to assume what may be called a *normal* or *equilibrium content* of nitrogen under ordinary methods of cropping and manuring, any attempt to raise the nitrogen content to a point materially higher than this normal will be attended by an unnecessary waste due to drainage and other losses. It would appear to be good practice, therefore, to maintain only a moderate nitrogen level in a soil. At the same time, the nitrogen should be kept suitably active by the use of legumes and other organic materials with a narrow C:N ratio, and by the applications of lime and commercial fertilizers.

This is essentially the recommendation already made for soil organic matter (p. 159), and it is known to be both economical and effective. In short, the practical problem is to supply adequate nitrogen to the soil, to keep it mobile, and at the same time to protect it from excessive losses due to leaching, volatilization, and erosion.

The Supply and Availability of Phosphorus and Potassium

CHAPTER 17

Considerable nitrogen can be added to soils through biochemical fixation brought about by microorganisms. If the proper legume is chosen, for example, the organisms will often fix this element from the air in quantities sufficient to temporarily increase the nitrogen already present. With other nutrient elements such as phosphorus and potassium, however, we have no such microbial aid. Consequently, other sources must be depended upon to meet the demands of plants.

There are at least four main sources of phosphorus and potassium from which we can draw in meeting these demands: (1) commercial fertilizer; (2) barnyard manures; (3) plant residues, including green manures; and (4) native compounds of these elements, both organic and inorganic, already present in the soil. Since the first three sources are to be considered in later chapters, our attention at present will be focused on the ways and means of utilizing the body of the soil as source of these mineral elements. We will begin with phosphorus.

17:1. IMPORTANCE OF PHOSPHORUS

With the possible exception of nitrogen, no other element has been as critical in the growth of plants in the field as has phosphorus. A lack of this element is doubly serious, since it may prevent other nutrients from being acquired by plants. For example, prior to the extensive usage of commercial fertilizers most of our soil nitrogen was indirectly dependent upon the supply of phosphorus. This was due to the vital influence of the latter

432

element on legume growth. Today the demand for phosphorus by nitrogen yielding legumes is still universally recognized.

The need of plants for phosphorus has been especially considered in the formulation of commercial fertilizers. This element, in the form of super-phosphate, was the first to be supplied as a manufactured product. Until fairly recently the amount of "phosphoric acid" in mixed fertilizers almost invariably exceeded that of nitrogen or potash. Even today the total tonnage of phosphorus, expressed as P_2O_5, exceeds that of any other fertilizer element sold in this country.

17:2. INFLUENCE OF PHOSPHORUS ON PLANTS

It is difficult to state in detail the functions of phosphorus in the economy of even the simplest plants. Only the more important functions will need be considered here. Phosphorus makes its contribution through its favorable effect on the following:

1. Cell division and fat and albumin formation.
2. Flowering and fruiting, including seed formation.
3. Crop maturation, thus counteracting the effects of excess nitrogen applications.
4. Root development, particularly of the lateral and fibrous rootlets.
5. Strength of straw in cereal crops, thus helping to prevent lodging.
6. Crop quality, especially of forages and of vegetables.
7. Resistance to certain diseases.

17:3. THE PHOSPHORUS PROBLEM

Although the amount of total phosphorus in an average mineral soil compares favorably with that of nitrogen, it is much lower than potassium, calcium, or magnesium. (See Table 2:3.) Of even greater importance, however, is the fact that most of the phosphorus present in soils is currently unavailable to plants. Also when soluble sources of this element are supplied to soils in the form of fertilizers, their phosphorus is often "fixed" or rendered unavailable even under the most ideal field conditions. (See p. 439.)

Fertilizer practices in many areas exemplify very well the problem of phosphorus availability. As already emphasized, the tonnage of phosphorus supplying materials used as fertilizers definitely exceeds that of nitrogen or potassium carriers. The removal of phosphorus from soils by crops, however, is low compared to that of nitrogen and potassium, often being only $\frac{1}{3}$ or $\frac{1}{4}$ that of the latter elements. The necessity for high fertilizer dosage when relatively small quantities of phosphorus are being removed from soils indicates that much of the added phosphates become unavailable to growing plants.

The influence of this situation on fertilizer practice is clearly shown when we consider the additions of fertilizer phosphorus in comparison with crop removal. In the eastern part of the United States, more phosphorus is being added to our crops each year than is being removed when the crops are harvested. (See Fig. 17:1.) In some states, additions of this element to croplands are three to four times as great as its removal. Since phosphorus is lost only sparingly by leaching, the inefficiency of utilization of phosphate fertilizers is obvious.

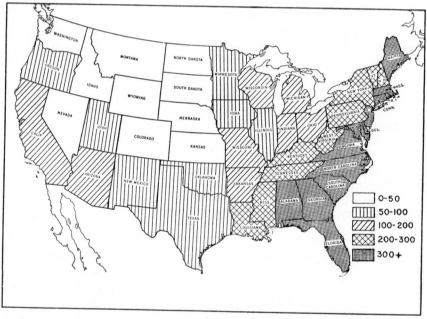

Figure 17:1. Phosphorus applied in fertilizers as percentage of that removed in crops harvested in 1957. Obviously the store of phosphorus in some soils is rapidly being built up. (Data calculated from crop estimates and fertilizer consumption figures.)

Briefly then, the over-all phosphorus problem is threefold: (1) a small total amount present in soils; (2) the unavailability of such native phosphorus; and (3) a marked "fixation" of added soluble phosphates. Since crop removal of phosphorus is relatively low and world phosphate supplies are huge, problem (1), that of supplying sufficient total phosphorus, is not serious. Increasing the availability of native soil phosphorus and the retardation of fixation or reversion of added phosphates are, therefore, the problems of greatest importance. These two phases will be discussed following a brief review of the phosphorus compounds present in soils.

17:4. PHOSPHORUS COMPOUNDS IN SOILS [1]

Both inorganic and organic forms of phosphorus occur in soils and both are important to plants as sources of this element. There is a serious lack of information, however, on the relative amounts of these two forms in different soils. Data available from Oregon, Iowa, and Arizona (Table 17:1) give some idea of their relative proportions. Despite the variation which occurs, it is evident that a consideration of soil phosphorus would not be complete unless some attention were given to both forms. (See Fig. 17:6.)

TABLE 17:1

The Total Phosphorus Content in Parts per Million of Soils from Three States and the Percentage of the Total Phosphorus in the Organic Form

Soils	No. of Samples	Total P ppm	Organic Fraction %
Western Oregon Soils [a]			
Hill soils	4	357	65.9
Old valley—filling soils	4	1479	29.4
Recent valley soils	3	848	25.6
Iowa Soils [b]			
Prairie soils	2	613	41.6
Gray-brown podzolic soils	2	574	37.3
Planosols	2	495	52.7
Arizona Soils			
Surface soils	19	703	36.0
Subsoils	5	125	34.0

[a] From B. R. Bertramson and R. E. Stephenson, "Comparative Efficiency of Organic Phosphorus and of Superphosphate in the Nutrition of Plants," *Soil Sci.*, 53: 215–26, 1942.
[b] Iowa data from R. W. Pearson and R. W. Simonson, "Organic Phosphorus in Seven Iowa Profiles: Distribution and Amounts as Compared to Organic Carbon and Nitrogen," *Proc. Soil Sci. Soc. Amer.*, 4: 162–67, 1939. Arizona data from W. H. Fuller and W. T. McGeorge, "Phosphates in Calcareous Arizona Soils, II. Organic Phosphorus Content," *Soil Sci.*, 71: 45–50, 1951.

[1] For a review of compounds of phosphorus, especially the organic fraction, see W. H. Pierre, "The Phosphorus Cycle and Soil Fertility," *Jour. Amer. Soc. Agron.*, 40: 1–14, 1948 and J. M. Bremmer, "A Review of Recent Work on Soil Organic Matter," Part I, *Jour. of Soil Science,* 2: 67–82, 1951.

Inorganic compounds.   Most inorganic phosphorus compounds in soils fall into one of two groups: (1) those containing *calcium* and (2) those containing *iron* and *aluminum*. The calcium compounds of most importance are listed in Table 17:2. Fluorapatite, the most insoluble and

TABLE 17:2

Inorganic Calcium Compounds of Phosphorus Often Found in Soils

Compound	Formula		
Fluor-apatite	$3\ Ca_3(PO_4)_2 \cdot CaF_2$		
Carbonate-apatite	$3\ Ca_3(PO_4)_2 \cdot CaCO_3$		
Hydroxy-apatite	$3\ Ca_3(PO_4)_2 \cdot Ca(OH)_2$	Solubility	increases
Oxy-apatite	$3\ Ca_3(PO_4)_2 \cdot CaO$		
Tricalcium phosphate	$Ca_3(PO_4)_2$		
Dicalcium phosphate	$CaHPO_4$		
Monocalcium phosphate	$Ca(H_2PO_4)_2$		

unavailable of the group, usually is an original mineral. It is found in even the more weathered soils, especially in their lower horizons. This fact is an indication of the extreme insolubility and consequent unavailability of the phosphorus contained therein. The simpler compounds of calcium such as mono- and dicalcium phosphate are readily available for plant growth. Except on recently fertilized soils, however, these compounds are present in extremely small quantities only, since they easily revert to the more insoluble forms.

Much less is known of the exact constitution of the iron and aluminum phosphates contained in soils. The compounds involved are probably hydroxy-phosphates such as dufrenite, wavellite, strengite, variscite,[2] etc. These compounds are most stable in acid soils and are extremely insoluble.

Many investigators have shown that phosphates react with certain iron or aluminum silicate minerals such as kaolinite. There is some uncertainty, however, as to the exact form in which this phosphorus is held in the soil. Most evidence indicates that it too is probably fixed as iron or aluminum phosphates such as those described in the preceding paragraph.

Organic phosphorus compounds.   There has been relatively less work done on the organic phosphorus compounds in soils, in spite of the fact that this fraction in some cases comprises more than half of the total soil phosphorus. One of the reasons for lack of information on these com-

[2] S. C. Chang and M. L. Jackson, "Fractionation of Soil Phosphorus," *Soil Science,* 84: 133–44, 1957.

pounds is the fact that they apparently are exceedingly complex. The meager data available, however, indicate that the three main groups of organic phosphorus compounds found in plants are also present in soils.[3] These are: (1) phytin and phytin derivatives, (2) nucleic acids, and (3) phospholipids. There are likely other organic phosphorus compounds present in soils; some investigators doubt that those listed account for all the organic phosphorus.

17:5. FACTORS THAT CONTROL THE AVAILABILITY OF INORGANIC SOIL PHOSPHORUS [4]

The availability of inorganic phosphorus is largely determined by the following factors: (1) soil pH; (2) soluble iron, aluminum, and manganese; (3) presence of iron, aluminum, and manganese containing minerals; (4) available calcium; (5) amount and decomposition of organic matter; and (6) activities of microorganisms. The first four of these factors are interrelated since their effects are largely dependent upon soil acidity.

17:6. pH AND PHOSPHATE IONS

It will be remembered from Chapter 14 (p. 369) that the availability of phosphorus to plants is determined to no small degree by the ionic form of this element. The ionic form in turn is determined by the pH of the solution in which the ion is found. Thus, in highly acid solutions only the H_2PO_4 ions are present. If the pH is increased, first the HPO_4 ions and finally PO_4 ions dominate. This situation is shown by means of the following equations:

$$H_2PO_4^- \underset{\text{(Very Acid Solutions)}}{\overset{+OH^-}{\rightleftharpoons}} H_2O + HPO^=_4 \underset{\text{(Very Alkaline Solutions)}}{\overset{+OH^-}{\rightleftharpoons}} H_2O + PO^{\equiv}_4$$

It should be remembered that at intermediate pH levels two of the phosphate ions may be present simultaneously. Thus, in solutions at pH 6.0 both H_2PO_4 and HPO_4 ions are found.

[3] See Pierre, *op. cit.*, and C. A. Bower, "Separation and Identification of Phytin and Its Derivatives from Soils," *Soil Sci.*, 59: 277–85, 1945.

Phytin is a calcium-magnesium salt of inositol phosphoric acid and is rather widely distributed in plants, especially in the seeds. Nucleic acids are found in both plants and animals and are even more complex than is phytin. They are apparently polymeric combinations of phosphoric acid, carbohydrates, and bases such as pyrimidine and purine.

[4] The subject of phosphorus availability has been reviewed by L. A. Dean, "Fixation of Soil Phosphorus," *Advances in Agronomy*, I: 391–411, 1949. Also see A. Weld, "The Retention of Phosphate by Soil, A Review," *Jour. of Soil Sci.*, 1: 221–38, 1950.

In general, the H_2PO_4 ion is considered somewhat more available to plants than is the HPO_4 ion. In soils, however, this relationship is complicated by the presence or absence of other compounds or ions. For example, the presence of soluble iron and aluminum under very acid conditions, or calcium at high pH values, will markedly affect the availability of the phosphorus. One can readily see, therefore, that the effect of soil pH on phosphorous availability is determined in no small degree by the various cations present. We will first discuss the effect of these ions in acid soils.

17:7. INORGANIC PHOSPHORUS AVAILABILITY IN ACID SOILS (SEE FIG. 17:2.)

Let us assume that we are working with either a nutrient solution or an organic soil very low in inorganic matter. Assume also that these media are acid in reaction but that they are low in iron, aluminum and manganese. The H_2PO_4 ions, which would dominate under these conditions would be readily available for plant growth. Normal phosphate absorption by plants would be expected so long as the pH was not too low.

Precipitation by Fe, Al and Mn ions. If the same degree of acidity should exist in a normal mineral soil, however, quite different results would be expected. Some soluble iron, aluminum, and manganese are usually found in strongly acid mineral soils. Reaction with the H_2PO_4 ions would immediately occur, rendering the phosphorus insoluble and also unavailable for plant growth.

The chemical reactions occurring between the soluble iron and aluminum and the H_2PO_4 ions probably result in the formation of so-called hydroxy-phosphates. This may be represented as follows, using the aluminum cation as an example: [5]

$$Al^{+++} + H_2PO_4^- + 2\ H_2O \Longleftrightarrow 2\ H^+ + Al(OH)_2H_2PO_4$$

Soluble   Insoluble

In most strongly acid soils the concentration of the Fe and Al ions greatly exceeds that of the H_2PO_4 ions. Consequently, the above reaction moves to the right forming the insoluble phosphate. This leaves only minute quantities of the H_2PO_4 ion immediately available for plants under these conditions.

---

[5] See C. V. Cole and M. L. Jackson, "Solubility Equilibrium Constant of Dihydroxy Aluminum Dihydrogen Phosphate Relating to a Mechanism of Phosphate Fixation in Soils," *Proc. Soil Sci. Soc. Amer.*, 15: 84–9, 1950.

Fixation by hydrous oxides. It should be emphasized that the H_2PO_4 ion reacts not only with the soluble iron, aluminum, and manganese but also with insoluble hydrous oxides of these elements such as limonite and goethite. In fact, the actual quantity of phosphorus fixed by these minerals in acid soils quite likely exceeds that due to chemical precipitation by the soluble Fe, Al, and Mn cations. (See Fig. 17:2.)

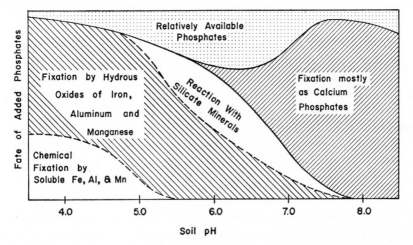

Figure 17:2. Diagram showing the inorganic fixation of added phosphates at various soil pH values. Average conditions are postulated and it is not to be inferred that any particular soil would have exactly the above distribution. The actual proportion remaining in an available form will depend upon contact with the soil, time for reaction, and other factors. It should be kept in mind that some of the added phosphorus may be changed to an organic form in which it would be temporarily unavailable.

The compounds formed as a result of fixation by iron and aluminum oxides are likely to be hydroxyl-phosphates just as in the case of chemical precipitation described above.[6] Their formation can be illustrated by means of the following equation, if we represent the hydrous oxide of aluminum as aluminum hydroxide:

$$Al \underset{\diagdown \ OH}{\overset{\diagup \ OH}{\underset{\gets}{\longleftarrow}}} OH + H_2PO_4^- \rightleftharpoons Al \underset{\diagdown \ H_2PO_4}{\overset{\diagup \ OH}{\underset{\gets}{\longleftarrow}}} OH + OH^-$$

Soluble   Insoluble

By means of this and similar reactions the formation of several basic-phosphate minerals, containing either iron or aluminum or both, is thought

[6] J. A. Kittrick and M. L. Jackson, "Electron-microscope Observations of the Reaction of Phosphate with Minerals, Leading to a Unified Theory of Phosphate Fixation in Soils," *Soil Science*, 7: 81–90, 1956.

to occur. Since several such compounds are possible, fixation of phosphorus by this mechanism probably takes place over a relatively wide pH range. Also the large quantities of hydrous iron and aluminum oxides present in most soils make possible the fixation of tremendous amounts of phosphorus in total by this means.

Thus, as both of the above equations show, the acid condition which would make possible the presence of the readily available H_2PO_4 ion in mineral soils at the same time results in conditions conducive to the vigorous *fixation* or precipitation of the phosphorus by iron, aluminum, and manganese compounds. (See Fig. 17:2.)

Fixation by silicate clays.   A third means of fixation of phosphorus under moderately acid conditions involves silicate minerals such as kaolinite, montmorillonite, and illite. Although there is some doubt as to the actual mechanisms involved, the over-all effect is essentially the same as when phosphorus is fixed by simpler iron and aluminum compounds. Some workers [7] visualize the fixation of phosphates by silicate minerals as a surface reaction between exposed OH-groups on the mineral crystal and the H_2PO_4 ions. Other investigators [8] have evidence that aluminum and iron ions are removed from the edges of the silicate crystals forming hydroxyphosphates of the same general formula as those already discussed. This type of reaction might be expressed as follows:

$$[Al] + H_2PO_4^- + 2\ H_2O \Longleftrightarrow 2\ H^+ + Al(OH)_2H_2PO_4$$

In
silicate crystal   Insoluble

Thus, even though phosphates react with different ions and compounds in acid soils, apparently the same insoluble iron and aluminum compounds are formed in each case. Major differences from soil to soil are probably due to differences in rate of phosphate precipitation and in the surface area of the phosphates once reaction has occurred. This will receive attention later.

Anion exchange.   Part of the phosphate which has reacted with iron and aluminum compounds and with silicate clays is subject to replacement by other anions such as the hydroxyl ion. Such replacement has been called

[7] See P. R. Stout, "Alterations in the Crystal Structure of Clay Minerals as a Result of Phosphate Fixation," *Proc. Soil Sci. Soc. Amer.*, 4: 177–82, 1939; and L. A. Dean and E. J. Rubins, "Anion Exchange in Soils: I. Exchangeable Phosphorus and the Anion-exchange Capacity," *Soil Sci.*, 63: 377–87, 1947.

[8] Apparently the predominance of evidence supports this concept. See J. B. Hemwall, "The Role of Soil Clay Minerals in Phosphorus Fixation," *Soil Science*, 83: 101–08, 1957.

anion exchange. It may be illustrated by a reverse of the reaction on page 438. Thus,

$$Al(OH)_2H_2PO_4 + OH^- \rightleftharpoons Al(OH)_3 + H_2PO_4^-$$

One anion (OH) has been exchanged for another (H_2PO_4). This reaction shows how anion exchange can take place and illustrates the importance of liming in helping maintain a higher level of available phosphates.

17:8. INORGANIC PHOSPHORUS AVAILABILITY AT HIGH pH VALUES (SEE FIG. 17:2)

In alkaline soils, phosphate precipitation is caused mostly by calcium compounds. Such soils are plentifully supplied with exchangeable calcium and in most cases with $CaCO_3$. Available phosphates will react with both the Ca ion and its carbonate. As an illustration, let us assume that concentrated superphosphate is added to a calcareous soil. The reactions would be as follows:

$$\underset{\text{(Soluble)}}{Ca(H_2PO_4)_2} + \underset{\text{(Adsorbed)}}{2\ Ca^{++}} \rightleftharpoons \underset{\text{(Insoluble)}}{Ca_3(PO_4)_2} + 4\ H^+$$

$$\underset{\text{(Soluble)}}{Ca(H_2PO_4)_2} + 2\ CaCO_3 \rightleftharpoons \underset{\text{(Insoluble)}}{Ca_3(PO_4)_2} + 2\ CO_2\uparrow + 2\ H_2O$$

Although the $Ca_3(PO_4)_2$ thus formed is quite insoluble, it may be converted in the soil to even more insoluble compounds. The hydroxy-, oxy-, carbonate- or even fluor-apatite compounds, may be formed if conditions are favorable and if sufficient time is allowed. (See Table 17:2.)

This type of reversion may occur in soils of the eastern United States which have been heavily limed. It is much more serious, however, in western soils due to the widespread presence of excess $CaCO_3$. The problem of utilizing phosphates in alkaline soils of the arid West is thus fully as serious as it is on highly acid soils in the East.

17:9. pH FOR MAXIMUM INORGANIC PHOSPHORUS AVAILABILITY

With insolubility of phosphorus occurring at both extremes of the soil pH range (see Fig. 17:2) the question arises as to the range in soil reaction in which minimum fixation occurs. The basic iron and aluminum phosphates have a minimum solubility around pH 3 to 4. At higher pH values some of the phosphorus is released and the fixing capacity is somewhat reduced. Even at pH 6.5, however, much of the phosphorus is still probably chemically combined with iron and aluminum. As the pH approaches 6 precipitation as calcium compounds begins and at pH 6.5 the formation of insoluble calcium salts is a factor in rendering the phosphorus unavailable. Above pH 7.0 even more insoluble compounds such as apatites are formed.

These facts seem to indicate that maximum phosphate availability to plants is obtained when the soil pH is maintained in the range from 6.0 to 7.0. (See Fig. 17:2.) Even in this range, however, the fact should be emphasized that phosphate availability may still be very low and that added soluble phosphates are readily fixed by soils. The low recovery (perhaps 10 to 30 per cent) by plants of added phosphates in a given season is partially due to this fixation.

17:10. AVAILABILITY AND SURFACE AREA OF PHOSPHATES

Inorganic phosphate availability is determined primarily by two factors: (1) the nature of the phosphorus compounds present in soils; and (2) the surface area of these compounds. The first of these factors has been considered in the preceding section. We shall discuss briefly the second factor, that of surface area.

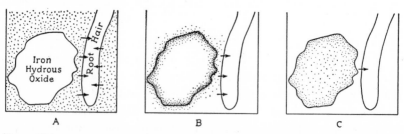

Figure 17:3. Diagrams showing how relatively soluble phosphates are rendered unavailable by compounds such as hydrous oxide. (A) The situation just after application of a soluble phosphate. The root hair and the crystal is surrounded by soluble phosphates. Within a very short time (B) most of the soluble phosphate has reacted with the surface of the iron oxide crystal. The phosphorus is still fairly readily available to the plant roots since most of it is located at the surface of the particle where exudates from the plant can encourage exchange. In time (C) the phosphorus penetrates the crystal and only a small portion is found near the surface. Under these conditions its availability is low.

When soluble phosphates are added to soils two kinds of compounds form immediately: (1) fresh precipitates of Ca, or Fe and Al phosphates; and (2) similar compounds formed on the surfaces of either $CaCO_3$ or Fe and Al oxide particles. In each case, the total surface area of the phosphate is high and consequently the availability of the phosphorus contained therein is reasonably rapid. Thus, even though the water soluble phosphorus in superphosphate may be precipitated in the soil in a matter of a few days, the freshly precipitated compounds will release much of their phosphorus to growing plants.

Effects of aging. With time, changes take place in the reaction products of soluble phosphates and soils. These changes generally result in a reduction in surface area of the phosphates and a similar reduction in their availability. An increase in the crystal size of precipitated phosphates occurs in time. This decreases their surface area. Also, there is a penetration of the phosphorus held by $CaCO_3$ and Fe or Al oxide particles into the particle itself. (See Fig. 17:3.) This leaves less of the phosphorus near the surface where it can be made available to growing plants. By these processes of aging, phosphate availability is reduced. Thus, the supply of available phosphorus to plants is determined not only by the kinds of compounds which form, but by their surface areas as well. (See Fig. 17:4.)

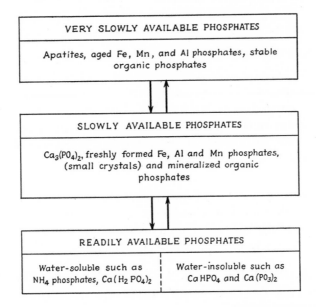

Figure 17:4. Diagram showing the classification of phosphate compounds in three major groups. Fertilizer phosphates are generally in the "readily available phosphate" group but are quickly converted to the slowly available forms. These can be utilized by plants at first but upon aging they are rendered less available and are then classed as very slowly available. At any one time perhaps 80–90 per cent of the soil phosphorus is in "very slowly available" forms. Most of the remainder is in the slowly available form since perhaps less than one per cent would be expected to be readily available.

17:11. PHOSPHORUS FIXING POWER OF SOILS

In light of the above discussion it is interesting to note the actual quantity of phosphorus which soils are capable of fixing. Data from three New Jersey soils presented in Table 17:3 emphasize the tremendous power of

TABLE 17:3

The Phosphorus Adsorbing Power of Three New Jersey Soils Limed and Unlimed Expressed as Pounds of 20 Per Cent Superphosphate per Acre-Furrow-Slice [a]

Soil	*Treatment*	*pH*	*P-fixing Power, Lbs.* *20% Super/A.F.S.*
Sassafras	No lime	3.6	28,400
Sassafras	lime	6.5	13,916
Collington	No lime	3.2	93,720
Collington	lime	6.5	50,268
Dutchess	No lime	3.8	68,728
Dutchess	lime	6.5	44,020

[a] From S. J. Toth and F. E. Bear, "Phosphorus-Adsorbing Capacities of Some New Jersey Soils," *Soil Sci.,* 64: 199–211, 1947.

certain soils in this respect. For example, to satisfy the phosphorus fixing power of the unlimed Collington soil nearly 47 tons of superphosphate containing 20 per cent P_2O_5 would be required. Although liming definitely reduced the fixing capacity, the quantity of phosphorus fixed even on the limed soils is enormous. Thus, over 25 tons of superphosphate would be required to completely satisfy the phosphorus fixing power of the limed Collington soil.

One Coastal Plain soil was reported [9] to have a phosphate fixing capacity of 125 tons of 20 per cent superphosphate per acre-furrow-slice. Although such values are somewhat higher than usual because of the nature and amounts of the iron and aluminum compounds in the soils, they do not overemphasize the problem of phosphate fixation.

17:12. THE INFLUENCE OF SOIL ORGANISMS AND ORGANIC MATTER ON THE AVAILABILITY OF INORGANIC PHOSPHORUS

In addition to pH and related factors, organic matter and microorganisms strikingly affect inorganic phosphorus availability. Just as was the case

[9] F. E. Bear and S. J. Toth, "Phosphate Fixation in Soil and Its Practical Control," *Ind. and Eng. Chem.,* 34: 49–52, 1942.

with nitrogen, the rapid decomposition of organic matter and consequent high microbial population results in the *temporary* tying up of inorganic phosphates in microbial tissue.

Moreover, products of organic decay, such as organic acids and humus, are thought to be effective in forming complexes with iron and aluminum compounds. This engagement of iron and aluminum reduces inorganic phosphate fixation to a remarkable degree. The exact importance of this effect has not as yet been completely ascertained. The ability of humus and lignin to reduce phosphate fixation, however, is shown in Figure 17:5. Both materials were effective in releasing phosphorus after it had been fixed as basic iron phosphate. Thus, organic decomposition products undoubtedly play an important role in inorganic phosphorus availability.

Figure 17:5. The effect of added organic materials on the release of phosphorus previously fixed by iron compounds. Both humus and lignin are effective, the humus to the greater degree. These results suggest that mineral fixation of phosphorus may be lower in soils comparatively high in organic matter. (After Swenson, Cole and Sieling.)

17:13. THE AVAILABILITY OF ORGANIC PHOSPHORUS

Only meager information has been obtained on the factors affecting the availability to higher plants of organic phosphorus compounds. It has been established, however, that both *phytin* and *nucleic acids* can be utilized as sources of phosphorus.[10] Apparently the phytin is absorbed directly by the plants, while the nucleic acids probably are broken down by enzymes at the root surfaces and the phosphorus is absorbed in either the organic or inorganic form. In spite of the readiness with which these compounds may be assimilated, however, plants commonly suffer from phosphorus deficiency even in the presence of considerable quantities of organic forms of this element. Just as with the inorganic phosphates the problem is one of availability.

[10] H. T. Rogers; R. W. Pearson; and W. H. Pierre, "Absorption of Organic Phosphorus by Corn and Tomato Plants and the Mineralizing Action of Exo-enzyme Systems of Growing Roots," *Proc. Soil Sci. Soc. Amer.*, 5: 285–91, 1941.

Phytin behaves in the soil much as do the inorganic phosphates,[11] forming iron, aluminum and calcium phytates. In acid soils the phytin is rendered insoluble and thus unavailable because of reaction with iron and aluminum. Under alkaline conditions calcium phytate is precipitated and the phosphorus carried is likewise rendered unavailable.

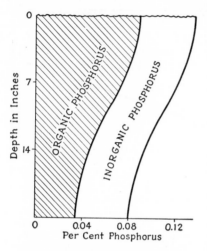

Figure 17:6. The distribution of organic and inorganic phosphorus with soil depth. Note that about ¾ the total phosphorus was in the organic form in the surface layer (0–7″) of these soils, while about half was in this form in the subsoil. (Average of 22 grassland soils calculated from T. W. Walker, and A. F. R. Adams, "Studies of Soil Organic Matter: I. Influence of Phosphorus Content of Parent Materials on Accumulations of Carbon, Nitrogen, Sulfur, and Organic Phosphorus in Grassland Soils," *Soil Sci.* 85: 307–18, 1958.)

The fixation of nucleic acids involves an entirely different mechanism, but the end result—low phosphorus availability—is the same. Apparently nucleic acids are strongly adsorbed by clays, especially montmorillonite. This adsorption is particularly pronounced under acid conditions and results in a marked decrease in the rate of decomposition of the nucleic acids. Consequently, the available phosphorus supply from this source is low, especially in acid soils which contain appreciable amounts of montmorillonite.

The judicious application of lime to acid soils is thus fully as important in organic phosphorus nutrition as it is in rendering inorganic compounds available. Whether we are dealing with inorganic soil phosphates, added fertilizers, or organic materials, the importance of lime as a controlling factor in phosphate availability is clearly evident.

17:14. PRACTICAL CONTROL OF PHOSPHORUS AVAILABILITY

From a practical standpoint the phosphorus utilization picture is not too encouraging. The inefficient utilization of applied phosphates by plants has long been known. The experimental use of radioactive phosphorus ma-

[11] For a discussion of the factors affecting the availability of organic phosphorus compounds, see C. A. Bower, *Studies on the Forms and Availability of Soil Organic Phosphorus,* Iowa Agr. Exp. Sta. Res. Bul. 362, Aug. 1949.

terials has recently emphasized this point even more thoroughly.[12] By adding fertilizers containing traceable phosphorus it has been possible to determine the proportion of the applied phosphates absorbed during the year of application.

The results of experiments on corn, soybeans, and potatoes are shown in Table 17:4. Even though on some soils marked responses were obtained

TABLE 17:4

The Recovery of Applied Fertilizer Phosphates During the First Crop Year [a]

Soil	Crop	Percentage of Fertilizer Phosphorus Recovered the First Year
Bladen	Corn	11.8
Bladen	Potatoes	7.6
Bladen	Soybeans	18.2
Webster	Corn	6.5
Clarion	Corn	3.4

[a] Bladen data calculated from B. A. Krantz; W. L. Nelson; C. D. Welch; and N. S. Hall, "A Comparison of Phosphorus Utilization by Crops," *Soil Sci.*, 68: 171–78, 1949. The other data are from G. Stanford and L. B. Nelson, "Utilization of Phosphorus as Affected by Placement: I. Corn in Iowa," *Soil Sci.*, 68: 129–36, 1949.

from the addition of phosphate fertilizers, the efficiency of phosphorus utilization was very low. Apparently maximum yields were obtained only by supplying much more phosphorus than the plants absorbed in a given season.

Liming and placement of fertilizers. The small amount of control that can be exerted over phosphate availability seems to be associated with *liming, fertilizer placement* and *organic matter maintenance*. By holding the pH of soils between 6.0 and 7.0 the phosphate fixation can be kept at a minimum. (See Figs. 14:5 and 17:2.) In order to prevent rapid reaction of phosphate fertilizers with the soil these materials are commonly placed in localized bands. In addition phosphatic fertilizers are quite often pelleted or aggregated to retard still more their contact with the soil. The effective utilization of phosphorus in combination with barnyard manure is evidence of the importance of organic matter in increasing the availability of this element.

In spite of the above precautions a major portion of the added phos-

[12] The entire August 1949 issue of *Soil Science* (Vol. 68: 113–202) is devoted to reports of field experiments which were designed to give information on the efficiency of phosphorus utilization.

phates still reverts to less available forms (see Fig. 17:1). It should be remembered, however, that the reverted phosphorus is not lost from the soil and through the years undoubtedly is slowly available to growing plants. This becomes an important factor especially in soils which have been heavily phosphated for years.

17:15. POTASSIUM—THE THIRD "FERTILIZER" ELEMENT

The history of fertilizer usage in the United States shows that nitrogen and phosphorus received most of the attention when commercial fertilizers first appeared on the market. Although the role played by potassium in plant nutrition has long been known, the importance of potash fertilization has received full recognition only in comparatively recent years.

The reasons that a widespread deficiency of this element did not develop until recently are at least twofold. Firstly, the supply of available potassium originally was so high in most soils that it took many years of cropping for a serious depletion to appear. Secondly, even though the potassium in certain soils may have been insufficient for optimum crop yields, production was much more drastically limited by a lack of nitrogen and phosphorus. With an increased usage of fertilizers carrying these latter elements, crop yields have been correspondingly increased. As a consequence, the draft on soil potassium has been greatly augmented. This, coupled with considerable loss by leaching, has enhanced the demand for potassium to the point that its usage in commercial fertilizers now exceeds that of nitrogen and rivals that of phosphorus.

17:16. EFFECTS OF POTASSIUM ON PLANT GROWTH [13]

The presence of adequate available potassium in the soil has much to do with the general tone and vigor of the plants grown. Moreover, by increasing crop resistance to certain diseases and by encouraging the root system, potassium tends to counteract the ill effects of too much nitrogen. In delaying maturity potassium works against undue ripening influences of phosphorus. In a general way, it exerts a balancing effect on both nitrogen and phosphorus, and consequently is especially important in a mixed fertilizer.

Potassium is essential for starch formation and the translocation of sugars. It is necessary in the development of chlorophyll, although it does

---

[13] Sodium has been found to partially take the place of potassium in the nutrition of certain plants. When there is a deficiency of potash, the native sodium of the soil, or that added in such fertilizers as nitrate of soda, may be very useful.

not, like magnesium, enter prominently into its molecular structure. This element is important to cereals in grain formation, giving plump heavy kernels. Abundant available potassium also is absolutely necessary for tuber development. Consequently, the percentage of this element usually is comparatively high in mixed fertilizers recommended for potatoes. In fact, all root crops respond to liberal applications of potassium. As with phosphorus, it may be present in large quantities in the soil and yet exert no harmful effect on the crop.

The leaves of crops suffering from a potassium deficiency [14] appear dry and scorched at the edges, while the surfaces are irregularly chlorotic. With such plants as red and alsike clover, alfalfa, and sweet clover, these symptoms are preceded by the appearance of small dots arranged more or less regularly around the edges of the leaves. As a result of such deterioration photosynthesis is much impaired and the synthesis of starch practically brought to a standstill.

17:17. THE POTASSIUM PROBLEM

Availability of potassium. In contrast to the situation as regards phosphorus, most mineral soils, except those of a sandy nature, are comparatively high in *total* potassium. In fact, the total quantity of this element is generally greater than that of any other major nutrient element. Amounts as great as 40,000 to 60,000 pounds of K_2O per acre-furrow-slice are not at all uncommon. (See p. 22.) Yet the quantity of potassium held in an easily exchangeable condition at any one time often is very small. Most of this element is held rigidly as part of the primary minerals or is fixed in forms that are at best only moderately available to plants. Also competition by microorganisms for this element contributes at least temporarily to its unavailability to higher plants.[15] Thus, the situation in respect to potassium utilization parallels that of phosphorus and nitrogen in at least one respect. A very large proportion of all three of these elements in the soil is insoluble and relatively unavailable to growing plants.

Leaching losses. Unlike the situation in respect to nitrogen and particularly phosphorus, however, much potassium is lost by leaching. An

[14] For the deficiency symptoms of potassium, see *Potash Deficiency Symptoms,* distributed by The American Potash Institute, Washington, D. C., 1937. See also *Hunger Signs in Crops,* American Society of Agronomy and the National Fertilizer Association, Washington, D. C., 1949; and *If They Could Speak,* Chilean Nitrate Educational Bureau, New York, 1941.

[15] H. Jenny and E. R. Shade, "The Potassium-lime Problem in Soils," *Jour. Amer. Soc. Agron,* 26: 162–70, 1934.

examination of the drainage water from mineral soils on which rather liberal fertilizer applications have been made will usually show considerable quantities of potash. In extreme cases, the magnitude of this loss may approach that of potash removal by the crop. For example, heavily fertilized sandy soils on which crops such as vegetables or tobacco are grown may suffer serious losses by leaching. Even on a representative humid region soil receiving only moderate rates of fertilizer, the annual loss of potash by leaching is usually about 20 pounds per acre. (See Table 9:5.)

Crop removal. The third phase of the potassium problem concerns the concentration of this element in plants, or in other words, its removal by growing crops. Under ordinary field conditions and with an adequate nutrient supply, potassium removal by crops is high, often being 3 to 4 times that of phosphorus and equaling that of nitrogen. The removal of 75 to 100 pounds K_2O per acre by a 16-ton silage corn crop is not at all unusual. Moreover, this situation is made even more critical by the fact that plants tend to take up soluble potassium far in excess of their needs if sufficiently large quantities are present. This tendency is termed *luxury consumption* since the excess potassium absorbed apparently does not increase crop yields to any extent.

Examples of luxury consumption. The principles involved in luxury consumption are shown by the graph of Figure 17:7. For many crops

Figure 17:7. A schematic diagram showing the general relationship between the potassium content of plants and the available soil potassium. If excess quantities of potash fertilizers are applied to a soil, the plants will absorb potassium in excess of that required for optimum yields. This luxury consumption may be wasteful, especially if the crops are completely removed from the soil.

there is a more or less direct relationship between the available potassium in the soil and the removal of this element by plants. The available potassium would, of course, include both that added and that already present. A certain amount of this element is needed for optimum yields and this is termed *required potassium*. All potassium above this critical level is considered as a *luxury,* the removal of which is decidedly wasteful.

Under field conditions luxury consumption becomes particularly serious. For example, to save labor a person may be tempted to supply potassium (1) only once in a 3 or 4 year rotation, or (2) during the first year of a 3 or 4 year perennial hay crop. Much of the potassium thus added is likely to be wastefully absorbed by the first crop of the rotation sequence, or in the case of the hay, even in the first cutting. Consequently, little of the added potassium would remain for subsequent crops.

In summary then the problem of potassium economy in its most general terms is at least threefold: (1) a very large proportion of this element at a given time is relatively unavailable to higher plants; (2) due to the solubility of its available forms, it is subject to wasteful leaching losses; and (3) the removal of this element by crop plants is high, especially when luxury quantities of this element are supplied. With these ideas as a background let us now consider the various forms of potassium in soils and their availabilities.

17:18. FORMS AND AVAILABILITY OF POTASSIUM IN SOILS

For convenience of study, the various forms of potassium in soils can be classified on the basis of availability in three general groups: (1) *unavailable;* (2) *readily available;* and (3) *slowly available.* Although most of the soil potassium is in the first of these three forms, from an immediate practical standpoint the latter two are undoubtedly of greater significance.

The relationship among these three general categories is shown diagramatically in Figure 17:8. Equilibrium tendencies presented therein are of vital practical importance, especially when we are dealing with the slowly and readily available forms. A slow change from one form to another can and does occur. This makes possible a fixation and conservation of added soluble potassium and a subsequent slow release of this element when the readily available supply is reduced.

Relatively unavailable forms. By far the greatest part (perhaps 90 to 98 per cent) of all soil potassium in a mineral soil is in relatively unavailable forms. (See Fig. 17:8.) The compounds containing most of this form of potassium are the feldspars and the micas. These minerals are quite resistant to weathering and probably supply relatively insignificant quantities of potassium during a given growing season.[16] However, their

---

[16] See E. R. Graham and H. C. Turley, "Soil Development and Plant Nutrition III. The Transfer of Potassium from the Nonavailable Form as Reflected by the Growth and Composition of Soybeans," *Proc. Soil Sci. Soc. Amer.,* 12: 332–35, 1947.

accumulative contribution from year to year to the over-all available potassium in the soil undoubtedly is of considerable importance. Potassium is gradually released to more available forms through the action of solvents such as carbonated water. Also, the presence of acid clay is of some significance in the breakdown of these primary minerals with the subsequent release of potassium and other bases. (See p. 269.)

Figure 17:8. Diagram showing the relative proportions of the total soil potassium in unavailable, slowly available, and readily available forms respectively. Only 1 to 2 per cent is rated as readily available. Of this, approximately 90 per cent is exchangeable and only 10 per cent appears in the soil solution at any time.

Even higher values (11 to 18 per cent) have been obtained for so-called nonexchangeable colloid potassium. See L. K. Wood, and E. E. DeTurk, "The Absorption of Potassium in Soils in Nonreplaceable Forms," *Proc. Soil Sci. Soc. Amer.*, 5:152–61, 1940.

The figures quoted are modified from O. J. Attoe and E. Truog, "Exchangeable and Acid Soluble Potassium as Regards Availability and Reciprocal Relationships," *Proc. Soil Sci. Soc. Amer.*, 10:81–6, 1945.

Readily available forms.   The readily available potassium constitutes only about 1 or 2 per cent of the total amount of this element in an average mineral soil. It exists in soils in two forms: (1) potassium in the soil solution, and (2) exchangeable potassium adsorbed on the soil colloidal surfaces. Although most of this available potassium is in the exchangeable form (approximately 90 per cent), soil solution potassium is somewhat more readily absorbed by higher plants and is, of course, subject to considerable leaching loss. (See p. 218.)

As represented in Figure 17:8, these two forms of readily available potassium are in dynamic equilibrium. Such a situation is extremely important from a practical standpoint. To begin with, absorption of soil solution potassium by plants results in a temporary disruption of the equilibrium. Then, to restore the balance, some of the exchangeable potassium immediately moves into the soil solution until the equilibrium is again established. On the other hand, when water soluble fertilizers are added just the reverse of the above adjustment occurs.

It is not to be inferred from this, however, that it is necessary for an element to be in the soil solution before absorption by plants can take place. Direct absorption from the colloidal surfaces is also thought to occur (see p. 37) and undoubtedly this plays a vital role in the nutrition of many plants.

Slowly available forms. Under certain soil conditions the potassium of such fertilizers as muriate of potash not only becomes adsorbed as described above but also may become definitely "fixed" by certain soil colloids. Potassium in this form cannot be replaced by ordinary exchange methods and consequently is referred to as *nonexchangeable* potassium. As such, this element is not readily available to higher plants. This form is in equilibrium, however, with the available forms and consequently acts as an extremely important reservoir of slowly available potassium. The entire equilibrium may be represented as follows.[17] (See Fig. 17:8.)

$$\text{Nonexchangeable K} \rightleftharpoons \text{Exchangeable K} \rightleftharpoons \text{Soil solution K}$$

The importance of the adjustment shown above to practical agriculture should not be overlooked. It is of special value in the conservation of added potassium. For example, most potash-containing fertilizers are added at planting time and are usually applied in localized bands. Immediately upon dissolving, a large proportion of the soluble (soil solution) potassium becomes attached to the colloids. As a result, the above equilibria shift to the left and some exchangeable ions are converted to the nonexchangeable form. Although this renders more potassium at least temporarily unavailable, the over-all effect apparently is beneficial. In this form the potassium is not subject to leaching and thus a significant conservation is attained. Also, since the fixed potassium is slowly reconverted to the available forms later, it is by no means completely lost to growing plants.

Release of fixed potassium. The above reaction is perhaps of even greater practical importance in another way. The quantity of nonexchangeable or "fixed" potassium in some soils is quite large. (See legend

[17] M. Peech and R. Bradfield, "The Effect of Lime and Magnesia on the Soil Potassium and on the Absorption of Potassium by Plants," *Soil Sci.,* 55: 37–48, 1943.

of Figure 17:8.) The fixed potassium in such soils is continually released to the exchangeable form in amounts large enough to be of great practical importance. For example, Bray and DeTurk [18] found a release of as much as 288 pounds of potassium per acre from an Illinois soil in a 6-month period. Other similar results have been observed. The data in Table 17:5

TABLE 17:5

Potassium Removal by Very Intensive Cropping and the Amount of This Element Coming from the Nonexchangeable Form

Soil	Total K Used by Crops (Lbs./A)	Percentage of the K Coming from Nonexchangeable Form
Wisconsin soils: [a]		
Carrington silt loam	119	75
Spencer silt loam	59	80
Plainfield sand	88	25
Mississippi soils: [b]		
Robinsonville f.s.l.	108	33
Houston clay	57	47
Ruston sandy loam	42	24

[a] Average of six consecutive cuttings of Ladino clover, from C. E. Evans and O. J. Attoe, "Potassium Supplying Power of Virgin and Cropped Soils," *Soil Sci.,* 66: 323–34, 1948.

[b] Average of eight consecutive crops of millet, from L. E. Gholston and C. D. Hoover, "The Release of Exchangeable and Nonexchangeable Potassium from Several Mississippi and Alabama Soils upon Continuous Cropping," *Proc. Soil Sci. Soc. Amer.,* 13: 116–21, 1948.

give an idea of the magnitude of the release of nonexchangeable potassium from certain soils. In several cases cited the potassium removed by crops was largely supplied from nonexchangeable forms.

17:19. FACTORS AFFECTING POTASSIUM FIXATION IN SOILS [19]

Although the exact mechanism or mechanisms that govern potassium fixation and release are not clearly understood, it is definitely known that

[18] R. H. Bray, and E. E. DeTurk, "The Release of Potassium from Nonreplaceable Forms in Illinois Soils," *Proc. Soil Sci. Soc. Amer.,* 3: 101–06, 1939.

[19] See A. K. Levine and J. S. Joffe, "Fixation of Potassium in Relation of Exchange Capacity of Soils. V. Mechanism of Fixation," *Soil Sci.,* 53: 407–16, 1947. See also G. Stanford, "Fixation of Potassium in Soils Under Moist Conditions and on Drying in Relation to Type of Clay Mineral," *Proc. Soil Sci. Soc. Amer.,* 12: 167–71, 1947; and J. I. Wear and J. L. White, "Potassium Fixing in Clay Minerals as Related to Crystal Structure," *Soil Sci.,* 71: 1–14, 1951.

several soil conditions markedly influence the amounts fixed. Among the factors are: (1) the nature of the soil colloids; (2) wetting and drying; (3) freezing and thawing; and (4) the presence of excess lime. These will be considered briefly in turn.

The effects of colloids, moisture and temperature.   The ability of the various soil colloids to fix potassium varies widely. For example, kaolinite and soils in which this clay mineral is dominant fix little potassium. On the other hand, clays of the 2:1 type such as montmorillonite and illite fix potassium very readily and in large amounts.

The mechanism for potash fixation is probably not the same for all minerals. Montmorillonite and similar minerals, for example, apparently fix this element appreciably only upon drying. This has been explained [20] by assuming an entrapment of potassium ions between the contracting structural units (see Fig. 4:5) as the soil dries. Some release of the ions thus held occurs upon rewetting, but the liberation is rather slow.

Under moist conditions fixation is apparently due to micaceous minerals such as illite. The exact manner by which potassium is changed in these minerals from an exchangeable to a fixed, nonexchangeable cation is not known. However, it is quite possible that the potassium migrates into the interior of colloidal crystals, and there becomes an integral part of the lattice structure.

Alternate freezing and thawing has been shown to result in the release of fixed potassium under certain conditions.[21] Although the practical importance of this is recognized, the mechanism by means of which it occurs is not as yet understood.

Influence of lime.   Applications of lime often result in an increase in the potassium fixing power of soils.[22] Under normal liming conditions this may be more beneficial than detrimental due to the conservation of the potassium so affected. Thus, potassium in well limed soils is not as likely to be leached out as drastically as is that in acid soils. This is illustrated by data in Table 17:6.

The sandy soil studied was limed to increase the base saturation from 28 to 72 per cent. When 6.2 inches of water were percolated through the original soil (28 per cent base saturation), about 70 per cent of the exchangeable potassium was removed. The limed sample (72 per cent base

[20] J. B. Page and L. D. Baver, "Ionic Size in Relation to Fixation of Cations by Colloidal Clay," *Proc. Soil Sci. Soc. Amer.,* 4: 150–55, 1940.

[21] L. O. Fine; T. A. Bailey; and E. Truog, "Availability of Fixed Potassium as Influenced by Freezing and Thawing," *Proc. Soil Sci. Soc. Amer.,* 5: 183–90, 1940.

[22] The effect of lime on potash fixation was reviewed by Peech and Bradfield, *op. cit.*

saturation) when similarly treated sustained a potassium loss of only 16 per cent. The effect of lime in preventing potash loss undoubtedly is of considerable practical importance in many cases.

TABLE 17:6

The Effect of Percentage Base Saturation on the Leaching Losses of Exchangeable Potassium from a Creedmore Coarse Sandy Loam [a]

Soil pH	Base Saturation (%)	Exchangeable Potassium Loss by Leaching (% of Total)
4.83	28	70
5.30	40	49
5.63	50	26
7.03	72	16

[a] From L. D. Baver, "Practical Applications of Potassium Interrelationships in Soils and Plants," *Soil Sci.,* 55: 121–26, 1943.

There are conditions, however, under which the effects of lime on the availability of potash are so drastic as to become quite undesirable.[23] For example, in certain soils potassium deficiency is apparently due to the presence of excess calcium carbonate. The unavailability of potassium in such soils is thought to be due in some way to lime induced fixation.

17:20. TWO PRACTICAL IMPLICATIONS IN RESPECT TO POTASSIUM

Frequency of application.   One very important suggestion that is evident from the facts thus far considered is that frequent light applications of potassium are usually superior to heavier and less frequent ones. Such a conclusion is reasonable when we consider the luxury consumption by crops, the ease with which this element is lost by leaching, and the fact that excess potassium is subject to fixation. Although the latter phenomenon has definite conserving features, these are in most cases entirely outweighed by the disadvantages of leaching and luxury consumption.

The K supplying power of soils.   A second very important suggestion of practical significance is that full advantage should be taken of the potash supplying power of soils. The idea that each pound of potassium removed by plants or through leaching must be returned in fertilizers may not always be correct. In some soils the large quantities of moderately available

[23] See H. Allaway and W. H. Pierre, "Availability, Fixation and Liberation of Potassium in High-lime Soils," *Jour. Amer. Soc. Agron.,* 31: 940–53, 1939.

forms already present can be utilized. Where slowly available forms are not found in significant quantities, however, supplementary additions are frequently necessary. Moreover, the importance of lime in reducing leaching losses of potassium should not be overlooked as a means of effectively utilizing the power of soils to furnish this element.

In this chapter and the one preceding, the factors affecting the supplies of nitrogen, phosphorus, and potassium available to growing plants have been considered. We have dealt mostly with those reactions taking place within the soil which determine in part the amounts of these elements that plants have at their disposal. We are now ready to discuss means of supplementing the natural supply of these elements. Let us begin by considering commercial fertilizers, our main outside source of these and other nutrient constituents.

The

Micronutrient Elements

CHAPTER 18

Of the sixteen elements known to be essential for plant and micro-organism growth, seven are required in such small quantities that they are called *micronutrients* or trace elements. These are iron, manganese, zinc, copper, boron, molybdenum, and chlorine. Other elements such as silicon, vanadium, and sodium appear to be helpful for the growth of certain species. Still others such as cobalt, iodine, and fluorine have been shown to be essential for animal growth, but are apparently not required by plants. As better techniques of experimentation are developed and as purer salts are made available, it is likely that these or other elements may be added to the list of essential nutrients.

Micronutrients have become of more widespread concern during the past fifteen years than was the case earlier. The following have likely attributed to this situation: (1) crop removal of the trace elements have in some cases lowered their concentration in the soil below that required for normal growth; (2) improved crop varieties and macronutrient fertilizer practices have greatly increased the level of crop production and thereby the micronutrient removal; (3) the trend toward high analysis fertilizers has tended to eliminate the use of impure salts which formerly contained some micronutrients; and (4) man's increased knowledge of plant nutrition has helped in the diagnosis of trace element deficiencies which heretofore may have gone unnoticed. Demands for efficiency of crop production will undoubtedly continue to encourage attention to these elements.

18:1. DEFICIENCY VS. TOXICITY

One common characteristic of all the micronutrients is that they are required in very small amounts. Also, they are all harmful when the available

458

forms are present in the soil in large quantities. Thus the range of concentration of these elements in which plants will grow satisfactorily is not too great. Molybdenum, for example, may be beneficial if added at rates as little as ½ to 1 *ounce* per acre, while applications of 3 or 4 pounds of available molybdenum per acre may be toxic to most plants. Even those quantities present under natural soil conditions are in some cases excessive for normal crop growth. Although somewhat larger amounts of the other micronutrients are required and can be tolerated by plants, control of the quantities added, especially in maintaining nutrient balance, is absolutely essential.

18:2. ROLE OF THE MICRONUTRIENTS [1]

As might be expected, the specific role of the various micronutrients in plant and microbial growth processes is not well understood. The meager information available, however, suggests that several trace elements are effective through certain *enzyme systems*. For example, copper, iron, and molybdenum are capable of acting as "electron carriers" in enzyme systems which bring about oxidation-reduction reactions in plants. Apparently such reactions, essential to plant development and reproduction, will not take place in the absence of these micronutrients. Zinc and manganese also function in enzyme systems which are necessary for important reactions in plant metabolism.

Molybdenum and manganese have been found to be essential for certain nitrogen transformations in microorganisms as well as in plants. Molybdenum is thought to be essential for the process of nitrogen fixation, both symbiotic and nonsymbiotic. It must be present in plants if nitrates are to be metabolized into amino acids and proteins. In each case molybdenum apparently is an essential part of the respective enzyme system which facilitates the nitrogen change.

Zinc is thought to be concerned in the formation of some growth hormones and in the reproduction process of certain plants. Copper is involved in respiration and in the utilization of iron. A boron deficiency decreases the rate of water absorption and of translocation of sugars in plants—and iron is essential for the synthesis of proteins contained in the chloroplasts. It is obvious that the place of the trace elements in plant metabolism is a complicated one. As research uncovers new facts the role of these micro-

[1] See A. Nason, "The Functions of Metals in Enzyme Systems," *Soil Sci.,* 85: 63–78, 1958; and H. G. Gauch, "Mineral Nutrition of Plants," *Ann. Rev. of Pl. Phys.,* 8: 31–64, 1957.

nutrients will be more fully understood and undoubtedly more adequately appreciated.

18:3. SOURCE OF MICRONUTRIENTS [2]

Parent materials tend to influence, in a practical way, the micronutrient contents of soils, perhaps even more so than that of the macronutrients. Deficiencies of trace elements can frequently be related to low contents of the micronutrients in the parent rocks or transported parent material. Similarly, toxic quantities are commonly related to abnormally large amounts in the soil-forming rocks and minerals.

As might be expected, the scant data available indicate that sources of the seven micronutrients vary markedly from area to area. Also, because of the extremely small quantities of some of these elements present in soils and in rocks, little is known about the specific compounds in which they are found. Except for iron and manganese, which are present in many soils in large total quantities, widespread accurate analyses for micronutrients in soils and rocks have not been made. (See Table 18:1.) For these reasons only generalizations can be drawn concerning micronutrient sources.

All of the micronutrients have been found in varying quantities in igneous rocks. Two of them, iron and manganese, have prominent structural positions in certain of the original silicate minerals. Others may also occupy structural positions as minor replacements for the major constituents of silicate minerals.

As mineral decomposition and soil formation occur, the mineral forms of the micronutrients are changed, just as was the case for macronutrients. Oxides, and, in some cases, sulfides of elements such as Fe, Mn, and Zn are formed. (See Table 18:1.) Secondary silicates, including the clay minerals, may contain considerable quantities of iron and manganese. The micronutrient cations that are released as weathering occurs are subject to colloidal adsorption just as are the Ca or H ions. Anions such as the borate and molybdate may suffer adsorption or reaction in soils similar to that of the phosphates. Chlorine, which is by far the most soluble of the group, is added to soils in considerable quantities each year through rain water. Its incidental addition in fertilizers and in other ways helps prevent the deficiency of chlorine under field conditions.

Organic matter is an important secondary source of some of the trace elements. In uncultivated profiles there is a somewhat greater concentra-

[2] See R. L. Mitchell, "Trace Elements," in F. E. Bear (ed.), *Chemistry of the Soil* (New York: Reinhold, 1955), Chap. 9.

tion of micronutrients in the surface soil, much of it presumably in the organic fraction. Although the elements thus held are not always readily available to plants, their release through decomposition is undoubtedly an important fertility factor.

TABLE 18:1

Major Natural Sources of the Seven Micronutrients and their
Suggested Contents in a Representative Humid-region Surface Soil [a]

Element	Major Forms in Nature	Suggested Analysis of a Surface Soil [b] (p.p.m.)
1. Iron	oxides, sulfides, and silicates	25,000
2. Manganese	oxides, silicates, and sulfides	2,500
3. Zinc	sulfides, oxides, and silicates	100
4. Copper	sulfides, hydroxy-carbonates	50
5. Boron	boro-silicates, borates	50
6. Molybdenum	sulfides, molybdates	2
7. Chlorine	chlorides	50

[a] For a comprehensive discussion of the geochemistry of these and other elements see V. M. Goldschmidt, *Geochemistry* (London: Clarendon Press, 1954).

[b] Analysis of a given soil would likely give values severalfold higher or lower than those listed. Consequently these more or less average figures should be used with caution.

18:4. GENERAL CONDITIONS CONDUCIVE TO MICRONUTRIENT DEFICIENCY [3]

Micronutrients are most apt to limit crop growth under the following conditions: (1) highly leached acid sandy soils; (2) muck soils; (3) soils very high in pH; and (4) soils which have been very intensively cropped and heavily fertilized with macronutrients only.

Strongly leached acid sandy soils are low in micronutrients for the same reasons that they are deficient in most of the macronutrients: (1) their

[3] See A. A. Nikitin, "Technological Aspects of Trace Element Usage," *Adv. in Agron.,* 6: 182–97, 1954.

parent materials were originally deficient in the elements; and (2) acid leaching has removed much of the small quantity of micronutrients originally present. In the case of molybdenum, acid soil conditions also have a marked depressing effect on availability.

The micronutrient contents of organic soils are dependent upon the extent of the washing or leaching of these elements into the bog area as the deposits formed. In most cases, this rate of movement was too slow to give deposits which are as high in micronutrients as are the surrounding mineral soils. Intensive cropping of muck soils also accentuates trace element deficiencies. Much of the harvested crops, especially vegetables, are removed from the land. Eventually the micro- as well as macronutrients must be supplied in the form of fertilizers if good crop yields are to be maintained. Intensive cropping of heavily fertilized mineral soils can also hasten the onset of micronutrient shortage, especially if the soils are coarse in texture.

The soil pH and calcium content have a marked influence on the availability of all the micronutrients except chlorine. Under very acid conditions, molybdenum is rendered unavailable, while at high pH values all the cations are unfavorably affected. Overliming can bring about a deficiency of iron, manganese, zinc, copper, and even boron. Such conditions occur in nature in many of the calcareous soils of the west.

18:5. FACTORS INFLUENCING THE AVAILABILITY OF THE MICRONUTRIENT CATIONS [4]

Each of the four micronutrient cations (Fe, Mn, Zn, and Cu) are influenced in a characteristic way by their soil environment. However, certain soil factors tend to have the same general effects on the availability of all of them. These factors will be given consideration first.

Soil pH. The micronutrient cations are most soluble and available under acid conditions. In very acid soils there is a relative abundance of the ions of Fe, Mn, Zn, and Cu. In fact, under these conditions the concentrations of one or more of these elements is often sufficiently high to be toxic to common plants. As pointed out in Chapter 15 (p. 399), one of the primary reasons for liming acid soils is to reduce the concentration of these ions.

As the pH is increased, the ionic forms of the micronutrient cations are

---

[4] For a review of the use of radioactive techniques in studying these problems, see D. W. Thorne and H. H. Wiebe, "Solubility and Plant Utilization of Micronutrients," a Chapter in C. L. Comar (ed.), *Atomic Energy and Agriculture*, The Amer. Assoc. Adv. of Sci., Washington, D.C. 1957, pp. 49–69.

changed to the hydroxides or oxides. An example might be shown as follows, using the ferrous ion as typical of the group:

$$Fe^{++} + 2\ OH^- \longrightarrow Fe(OH)_2$$

(Soluble)   (Insoluble)

All of the hydroxides of the trace element cations are insoluble, some more so than others. The exact pH at which precipitation occurs varies from element to element and even between oxidation states of a given element. In any case, however, the principle is the same—at low pH values the solubility of micronutrient cations is at a maximum and as the pH is raised, their solubility and availability to plants decrease. The desirability of maintaining an intermediate soil pH is obvious.

Zinc fixation at high pH values is favored by a second phenomenon only indirectly related to soil pH. Particles of lime, particularly if they contain dolomite as well as calcite, strongly adsorb the zinc ions. It is likely that zinc may react with the magnesium-containing lime, replacing the Mg ion in the mineral framework.

Oxidation state and pH. Three of the trace element cations are found in soils in more than one valence state. These are iron, manganese, and copper. The lower-valence states are encouraged by conditions of low oxygen supply and relatively higher moisture level. They are responsible for the subdued subsoil colors, grays and blues, in contrast to the bright reds, browns, and yellows of well-drained mineral soils.

The changes from one valent state to another are in most cases brought about by microorganisms and organic matter. In some cases the organisms may obtain their energy directly from the inorganic reaction. For example, the oxidation of manganese from the two valent manganous form (Mn^{++}) to MnO_2 can be carried on by certain bacteria and fungi. (See Fig. 18:1.) In other cases, organic compounds formed by the microbes may be responsible for the oxidation or reduction. In general, high pH values favor oxidation while acid conditions are more conducive to reduction.

The oxidized states of Fe, Mn, and Cu are generally much less soluble at pH values common in soils than are the reduced states. The hydroxides (or hydrous oxides) of these high-valent forms precipitate at lower pH values and are extremely insoluble. For example, the hydroxide of trivalent ferric iron precipitates at pH values near 3.0 while ferrous hydroxide does not precipitate until a pH of 6.0 or higher is reached.

The interaction of soil acidity and aeration in determining micronutrient availability is of great practical importance. Very acid soils that are somewhat poorly drained often supply toxic quantities of iron and manganese. Such toxicity is less apt to occur under well-drained conditions.

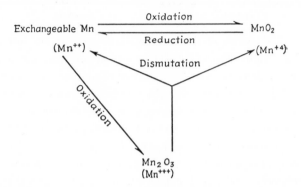

Figure 18:1. The relationship among the various forms of manganese in soils. Exchangeable Mn^{++} is available to plants but is subject to oxidation by microorganisms to the trivalent form (Mn_2O_3) or to the more insoluble 4 valent form (MnO_2). The Mn_2O_3 can be changed (dismutation) into Mn^{++} and MnO_2. High pH and good oxidation conditions encourage formation of MnO_2 and low manganese availability. (Modified from H. G. Dion, and P. J. G. Mann, *Jour. Agr. Sci.,* 36: 239–45, 1946.)

At the high end of the soil pH range, good drainage and aeration often have the opposite effect. Well-oxidized, calcareous soils are sometimes deficient in available iron or manganese even though there are adequate total quantities of these trace elements present. The hydroxides of the high-valent forms of these elements are too insoluble to supply the ions needed for plant growth. (See Fig. 18:1.)

Other inorganic reactions. The application of large quantities of phosphate fertilizers can adversely affect the supply of some of the micronutrients. The uptake of both iron and zinc may be reduced in the presence of excess phosphates. From a practical standpoint, phosphate fertilizers should be used in only those quantities that are required for good plant growth.

Lime-induced chlorosis (iron deficiency) in fruit trees has been found to be encouraged by the presence of the bicarbonate ion. The chlorosis apparently results from iron deficiency on soils with high pH. In some way the bicarbonate ion interferes with iron metabolism.

Zinc, manganese, and iron ions are found as integral elements in certain silicate clays, especially of the 2 to 1 type. Depending on conditions, these ions may be released from the clays or they may be fixed by them.

Since the total quantities of iron and manganese in a soil are sufficiently large, the fixation of these elements by clays is apparently of little significance. Zinc fixation is somewhat more serious, however, since the total amount of this element in soils is usually quite small. (See Table 18:1.)

Organic combinations. Each of the four micronutrient cations may be held in organic combination. Microorganisms also assimilate them as they are apparently required for many microbial transformations. The organic compounds in which these trace elements are combined undoubtedly vary considerably, but they include proteins, amino acids, and constituents of humus and acids such as citric and tartaric. Among the most important, are the so-called *organic complexes* which are a combination of the metallic cation and certain organic groups. These complexes may protect the micronutrients from certain harmful reactions such as the precipitation of iron by phosphates and vice versa. (See p. 370.) On the other hand, complex formation may reduce micronutrient availability below that necessary for normal plant needs.

On soils high in organic matter, complex formation by copper is thought to be responsible for the deficiency of this element.[5] For example, copper appears to be bound very tightly by the organic matter in certain muck soils. Regular applications of copper-containing salts may be necessary for the normal production of vegetables on these high-organic-containing soils. Zinc deficiencies have also been attributed to reaction with organic matter. Advantage has been taken of the complex-forming tendencies of manganese, copper, zinc, and especially iron in the development of synthetic compounds called *chelates*. These compounds can be used to supply selected micronutrients in forms which protect the cations from some harmful inorganic reactions in soils. At the same time, the chelated nutrients can be utilized by growing plants. Chelates will be dealt with in the next section.

18:6. CHELATES [6]

Chelate is a term derived from a Greek word meaning "claw." As this term indicates, the chelates have a marked tendency to hold tightly certain cations that are attracted to them. Furthermore they tend to protect these cations, oftentimes to the benefit of growing plants.

---

[5] See W. Reuther, "Copper and Soil Fertility," *The Yearbook of Agric. (Soils)*, U.S. Dept. of Agric., 1957, pp. 128–35.

[6] See A. Wallace (ed.), *Symposium on the Use of Metal Chelates in Plant Nutrition* (Palo Alto, Calif.: The National Press, 1956).

A chelate is an organic compound which combines with and protects certain metallic cations including iron, manganese, zinc, and copper. The cation-chelate combinations make complex ring structures and the metals so bound essentially lose their usual ionic characteristics. (See Fig. 18:2.) They are less apt to take part in reactions with other soil constituents, which may be an advantage. For example, chelated metals remain in solution at much higher pH values than do the inorganic ionic forms. The protected cations are not so subject to precipitation as insoluble hydroxides.

Figure 18:2. The structural formula for a common iron chelate, ferric ethylenediaminetetraacetic acid (Fe-EDTA). The iron is protected and yet can be utilized by many plants.

Specific examples can be cited which show the protective action of chelating compounds. As pointed out in Section 18:5, inorganic iron salts added to a calcareous soil are precipitated and rendered unavailable for plant growth. If ferric sulfate were added, the reaction would occur as follows, assuming the hydroxyl ions to come from the soil solution:

$$Fe^{+++} + 3\ OH^- \rightleftharpoons Fe(OH)_3$$
$$\text{(Soluble)} \qquad\qquad\qquad \text{(Insoluble)}$$

As the equilibrium arrows indicate, most of the ferric ion would be changed to the insoluble form.

If, instead of the sulfate salt of iron, an iron chelate were used, the ferric ion would be protected from precipitation. As shown in Figure 18:2, the iron is part of a complex combination which supplies very few ferric ions. Consequently, there would be little opportunity for the above reaction to take place except where the soil pH is very high. One would expect the chelate to be a better source of iron than an inorganic salt where there is danger of reaction between the metallic cation (Fe^{+++}) and soil constituents.

Although chelated metals are protected against soil reactions, these forms of the micronutrients are apparently assimilated fairly readily by growing plants. Thus, so long as the nutrients remain in these combinations they are considered as being in the available form.

Stability of chelates. The use of chelates to supply iron is quite successful so long as the soil pH is not too high. Application can be made to the soil or as a spray to the foliage. With some of the other nutrients, however, less consistent advantage has been shown for the chelates over other nutrient compounds. This may be due to the fact that for most of the chelates, iron is attracted more strongly by the organic compound than are the other micronutrients. Thus, if a zinc-containing chelate is added to a soil which has significant quantities of available iron the following reaction may occur:

$$\text{Zn chelate} + \text{Fe}^{++} \rightleftharpoons \text{Fe chelate} + \text{Zn}^{++}$$

The iron chelate is more stable than its zinc counterpart, which explains the tendency of the reaction to go to the right. The released Zn ion is subject to reaction with the soil the same as is zinc from an inorganic salt such as $ZnSO_4$. It is obvious that the added metal-chelate combination must be stable within the soil if it is to have any lasting advantage.

It should not be inferred that only iron chelates are effective. The chelates of other micronutrients including zinc, manganese, and copper have been used successfully to supply these nutrients. Apparently, replacement by iron in the soil is sufficiently slow to permit absorption by plants of the added trace element. Also, since spray applications are often used to supply zinc and manganese, the possibility of reaction of these elements with iron in the soil can be eliminated.

The use of chelates in the United States is substantial, approximately one million pounds being sold in 1954 for agricultural purposes.[7] More than half of this was used in meeting micronutrient deficiencies of citrus in Florida. Although chelates may not replace the more conventional methods of supplying most micronutrients, they do offer some possibilities in special cases. Agricultural and chemical research shall likely continue to increase the opportunities for their use.

18:7. FACTORS INFLUENCING THE AVAILABILITY OF THE MICRONUTRIENT ANIONS

Unlike the cations needed in trace quantities by plants, the anions seem to have relatively little in common. Chlorine, molybdenum, and boron are

[7] See Wallace, *op. cit.*

quite different chemically so that one would expect little similarity in their reaction in soils.

Chlorine. Chlorine has only recently been found to be essential for plant growth, in spite of the fact that it is used in larger quantities by most crop plants than any of the micronutrients except iron. Two reasons account for man's failure to recognize the essentiality of this nutrient earlier: (1) the wide occurrence of chlorine as an impurity in salts used for research work; and (2) the annual additions to soil of significant quantities of chlorine through precipitation.

Most of the chlorine in soils is in the form of simple, soluble chloride salts such as KCl. The chloride ions are not adsorbed by negatively charged clays and as a result are subject to movement with the water, both upward and downward in the profile. In humid regions, one would expect little chlorine to remain in the soil since it would be leached out. In semiarid and arid regions, a somewhat higher concentration might be expected, the amount reaching the point of salt toxicity in some of the poorly drained saline soils. In most well-drained areas, however, one would not expect a high chlorine content in the surface of arid-region soils.

Except under conditions where toxic quantities of chlorine are found in soils, there are apparently no common situations under field conditions which reduce the availability and utilization of this element. Accretions of chlorine from the atmosphere are believed to be in sufficient quantities to meet crop needs. Salt spray alongside ocean beaches evaporates, leaving NaCl dust which moves into the atmosphere to be returned later, dissolved in snow and rain. The amount added to the soil in this way varies tremendously, depending on the distance from the salty body of water and other factors.[8] It is likely that a figure of about 10 pounds per acre per year is the minimum that can be expected in most situations. An average figure of perhaps 20 pounds would be more representative of the amount added. In any case, this form of accretion plus that commonly added as an incidental component of commercial fertilizers should largely prevent a field deficiency of chlorine.

Boron. The availability and utilization of boron is determined to a considerable extent by pH. Boron is most soluble under acid conditions. It apparently occurs in acid soils, in part at least, as boric acid (H_3BO_3) which is readily available to plants. In quite acid sandy soils, soluble boron fertilizers may be leached downward with comparative ease. Apparently, the element is not fixed under these conditions. In heavier soils, especially if they are not too acid, this rapid leaching does not occur.

[8] See V. M. Goldschmidt, *Geochemistry* (London: Clarendon Press, 1954), p. 592.

At higher pH values, boron is less available. This may be due to lime-induced fixation of this element by clay and other minerals since the calcium and sodium borates are reasonably soluble. In any case, overliming can, and often does, result in a deficiency of boron.

Boron is held in organic combinations from which it may be released for crop use. The content of this nutrient in the topsoil is generally higher than that in the subsoil. This may in part account for the noticeably greater boron deficiency in periods of dry weather. Apparently, during drouth periods plants roots are forced to exploit only the lower soil horizons where the boron content is quite low. When the rains come, plant roots again can absorb boron from the topsoil where its concentration is highest.

Figure 18:3. The effect of pH on the adsorption of molybdenum by an Australian soil. A given quantity of molybdenum was shaken with samples of soil at different pH values and the amount of Mo in solution was determined. (From Jones, L. H. P., "The Solubility of Molybdenum in Simplified Systems and Aqueous Soil Suspension," *Jour. Soil Sci.,* 8: 313–27, 1957.)

Molybdenum. Soil conditions affect the availability of molybdenum much the same as they do that of phosphorus. For example, molybdenum is quite unavailable in strongly acid soils. (See Fig. 18:3.) Under these conditions, this element apparently reacts with soil minerals such as the silicates, and iron and aluminum compounds. The fixed molybdate ion ($MoO_4^{\equiv}$) can be replaced by phosphates through anion exchange, indicating that the same soil compounds may be involved in molybdenum and phosphate fixation.

The liming of acid soils will usually increase the availability of molybdenum. The effect is so striking that some researchers, especially those in Australia and New Zealand,[9] argue that the primary reason for liming very acid soils is to supply molybdenum. Furthermore, in some instances, an ounce or so of molybdenum added to acid soils has given about the same increase in the yield of legumes as has the application of several tons of lime. Although these general results have not been consistently verified by

[9] See T. W. Walker, *et al.,* "The Effects and Interractions of Molybdenum, Lime, and Phosphate Treatments on the Yield and Composition of White Clover Grown on Acid, Molybdenum Responsive Soil," *Plant and Soil,* 6: 201–20, 1955.

experiments in the United States, research has pointed to specific acid soil areas where economical responses can be obtained from molybdenum applications.

The utilization of phosphate by plants seems to favor that of molybdenum and vice versa. For this reason, molybdate salts are often applied along with superphosphate to molybdenum-deficient soils. This practice apparently encourages the uptake of both elements and is, of course, a convenient way to add the extremely small quantities of molybdenum required.

A second common anion, the sulfate, seems to have an effect on molybdenum absorption opposite to that of phosphorus. Sulfate has been found to reduce molybdenum uptake, although the specific mechanisms for this antagonism is not yet known.

18:8. NEED FOR NUTRIENT BALANCE [10]

Nutrient balance among the trace elements is essential and is perhaps even more difficult to maintain than is that for the macronutrients. Some of the plant enzyme systems which are dependent upon micronutrients require more than one element. For example, both manganese and molybdenum are needed for the assimilation of nitrates by plants.[11] The mutually beneficial effects of phosphates and molybdenum have already been discussed. Apparently, for some plants zinc and phosphorus are needed for optimum utilization of manganese. The utilization of boron and calcium is dependent upon the proper balance between these two nutrients. A similar relationship exists between potassium and copper, and between potassium and iron in the production of good quality potatoes. Copper utilization is favored by adequate manganese which in some plants is assimilated only if zinc is present in sufficient amounts. Of course, the effects of these and other nutrients will depend upon the specific plant being grown, but the complexity of the situation is seen from the examples cited.

Antagonism.   Some enzymatic and other biochemical reactions re-requiring a given micronutrient may be "poisoned" by the presence of a second trace element in toxic quantities. Examples of known antagonistic effects of elements on the absorption of micronutrients are as follows:

---

[10] See Gauch, *op. cit.*, and Nikitin, *op. cit.*

[11] See E. G. Mulder and F. C. Gerretsen, "Soil Manganese in Relation to Plant Growth," *Adv. in Agron.*, 4: 221–77, 1952.

1. Excess copper or sulfate may adversely affect the utilization of molybdenum.
2. Iron deficiency is encouraged by an excess of zinc, manganese, and copper.
3. Excess phosphate may encourage a deficiency of zinc, iron, and copper.
4. Heavy nitrogen fertilization intensifies copper deficiency.
5. Excess sodium or potassium may adversely affect manganese uptake.
6. Excess lime reduces boron uptake.
7. Iron, copper, and zinc may reduce the absorption of manganese.

Some of the antagonistic effects listed above may be taken advantage of in reducing toxicities of certain of the micronutrients. For example, copper toxicity of citrus groves, caused by residual copper from insecticide sprays, may be reduced by adding iron and phosphate fertilizers. Sulfur additions to calcareous soils containing toxic quantities of soluble molybdenum may reduce the availability and hence the toxicity of the latter element.

These examples of nutrient interractions, both beneficial and detrimental, emphasize the highly complicated nature of the biological transformations in which micronutrients are involved. Luckily, the total acreage is small wherein unfavorable nutrient balances require special micronutrient treatment. This acreage is increasing, however, as man makes more intensive use of the soil and the crops grown thereon.

18:9. SOIL MANAGEMENT AND MICRONUTRIENT NEEDS

The needs for each of the micronutrients are just as specific as are those for the macronutrients. Because of the interractions just cited, they may be even more so. It is obvious, therefore, that any generalizations with respect to management practices involving all the trace elements should be used with caution. The advice of the expert should be sought in any specific case. He will be acquainted with the particular problem and will be prepared to suggest a solution. And he can point out the necessary precautions to prevent toxicities.

A review of factors determining micronutrient availability gives a clue as to how management practices might help keep these elements available at optimum levels. *First,* in ascertaining the cause of plant abnormalities one should keep in mind the conditions wherein micronutrient deficiencies or toxicities are apt to occur. Sandy soils, mucks, and soils having very high or very low pH values would be suspect. Areas of intensive cropping and heavy macronutrient fertilization may be deficient in the micronutrients.

Second, in thinking of remedies for a known deficiency or toxicity, soil pH changes should be considered. In very acid soils, one might expect

Figure 18:4. Areas in which copper, iron molybdenum, and zinc deficiencies occur as revealed by limited growth or other symptoms of nutritional troubles in specific crops. The general areas shown are actually intermittent in character. (Courtesy K. C. Beeson, U. S. Plant Soil Nutrition Laboratory)

toxicities of iron and manganese and deficiencies of phosphorus and molybdenum. These can be corrected by liming and by appropriate fertilizer additions. Calcareous alkaline soils may have deficiencies of iron, manganese, zinc, and copper, and in a few cases, a toxicity of molybdenum. The use of acid-forming fertilizers or of sulfur may be resorted to in lowering the soil pH. High organic matter additions may not be desirable under these conditions since they encourage the oxidation of iron and manganese to the higher-valent and more insoluble forms.

No specific statement can be made concerning the pH value most suitable for all the elements. However, medium-textured soils generally supply adequate quantities of micronutrients when the soil pH is held between 6 and 7. In sandy soils, a somewhat more acid reaction may be justified since therein the total quantity of micronutrients is low, and even at pH 6.0 some deficiencies may occur.

Third, drainage and moisture control can influence micronutrient solubility in soils. Improving the drainage of acid soils will encourage the formation of the oxidized forms of iron and manganese. These are less soluble and, under acid conditions, less toxic than are the reduced forms.

Moisture control at high pH values can have the opposite effect. High moisture levels maintained by irrigation may result in the chemical reduction of high-valent compounds, the oxides of which are extremely insoluble. Flooding a soil will favor the reduced forms which are more available to growing plants.

The *fourth,* and perhaps the most common procedure is to add chemical nutrients to correct the deficiency or even toxicity. In some areas, this procedure has been used successfully for many years. Onion producers on the muck lands of some of the Northern states have added copper sulfate as a regular component of their fertilizer for many years. Citrus growers in California and especially Florida have supplied zinc as a spray for as many as twenty years and have used other micronutrients in their fertilizers for a like period of time. In wide areas throughout the country, boron is added as a regular component of fertilizer for alfalfa. It is also used for certain crops having high requirements for this element such as beets and celery.

Marked differences in crop needs for micronutrients make fertilization a problem where rotations are being followed. On general crop farms, vegetables are sometimes grown in rotation with small grains and forages. If the boron fertilization is adequate for a vegetable crop such as red beets or even for alfalfa, the small grain crop grown in the rotation is apt to show toxicity damage. Such a situation occurs commonly in western New York. These facts emphasize the need for specificity in determining crop nutrient requirements and for care in meeting these needs. (See Table 18:2.)

TABLE 18:2

Common Micronutrient Fertilizer Rates for Soil Application and Some Plants Having a High Requirement for these Nutrients

Micronutrient	Common Range in Fertilizer Rates [a] (lbs/acre)	Crops Having a High Requirement
1. Iron	15–50 lbs.	Blueberries, cranberries, rhododendron, peaches, grapes, nut trees.
2. Manganese	15–30 lbs.	Oats, beans, soybeans, onions, potatoes, citrus
3. Zinc	5–50 lbs.	Citrus and fruit trees, soybeans, corn, beans
4. Copper	2–50 lbs.	Citrus and fruit trees, onions, small grains
5. Boron	5–30 lbs.	Alfalfa, clovers, sugar beets, cauliflower, celery, apples and other fruits
6. Molybdenum	1 oz.–2 lbs.	Alfalfa, sweet clover, cauliflower, broccoli, celery

[a] These rates are in terms of the elements which are applied to the soil as soluble salts. Foliage-spray applications which are commonly made for zinc, manganese, molybdenum, and others, would, of course, be made at much smaller rates.

Macronutrient deficiencies are more universally apparent than are those of the trace elements. For many years, applications of fertilizers containing nitrogen, phosphorus, and potash have been a means of supplying small quantities of the micronutrients. Superphosphate, for example, may contain up to about 20 parts per million of boron. Chilean nitrate of soda supplies small quantities of several of the trace elements. These and other fertilizers will receive our attention in the chapter which follows.

Fertilizers and
Fertilizer Management

CHAPTER 19

While the use of animal excrement on cultivated soils was common as far back as agricultural records can be traced, mineral salts have been systematically and extensively employed for the encouragement of crop growth hardly more than one hundred years. They are now an economic necessity on many soils. Any inorganic salt, such as ammonium nitrate, or an organic substance, such as fish scrap, purchased and applied to the soil to promote crop development is considered to be a commercial fertilizer.[1]

19:1. THE FERTILIZER ELEMENTS

There are at least thirteen essential nutrient elements that plants obtain from the soil. Two of these, calcium and magnesium, are applied as lime in regions where they are deficient. Although not usually rated as a fertilizer, lime does exert a profound nutritive effect. Sulfur is present in several commercial fertilizers and its influence is considered important. It is not critical nutritionally except in certain localities, however, and consequently receives only secondary attention as a fertilizer. This leaves three elements other than the micronutrients—*nitrogen, phosphorus,* and *potassium.* And since they are so commonly applied in commercial fertilizers they are often referred to as *the fertilizer elements.*

19:2. THE NUTRIENT BALANCE

Before taking up a discussion of the various fertilizing materials, one point should be emphasized most emphatically. The three fertilizer elements, when properly used, not only tend to check, balance, support, and supplement one another but the other nutrient elements as well. These rela-

[1] H. Collings, *Commercial Fertilizers* (Philadelphia: Blakiston, 1947).

475

tionships are very important in fertilizer practice since they have much to do with the economy and effectiveness of fertilizers.

Ideally, the elements added should so supplement the nutrients already in the soil as to present to the plant just the correct proportion of available nitrogen, phosphorus, and potassium. At the same time the amounts and availability of the other essential elements should be ideal. In short, the fertility balance as a whole should be such as to produce a large and normal crop growth.

In practice, however, such an ideal is difficult to attain. The soil is always more or less an unknown quality as to the seasonal availability of its constituents. Moreover, it is difficult to forecast the reactions that will occur when the fertilizer contacts the soil. The influence of calcium, magnesium, manganese, iron, aluminum, and other elements upon the effectiveness of a fertilizer is always problematical.

19:3. THREE GROUPS OF FERTILIZER MATERIALS

The emphasis which has been placed on the three nutrient elements leads directly to a very simple grouping of the fertilizer materials. On the basis of the elements supplied, they automatically fall into three groups: (1) those that supply nitrogen; (2) those serving as a source of available phosphoric acid; and (3) those carrying water-soluble potash.

The classification, however, is not so simple as this grouping would imply, as several fertilizer materials carry two of the elements of nutrition. As examples of this overlapping, potassium nitrate and ammoniated superphosphate may be cited. The situation will be fully apparent when the fertilizer tables presented later are examined and the compounding of mixed goods considered.

Because of the lack of space it will only be possible to discuss each of the three groups in a general way, listing the various fertilizers of each, and mentioning the outstanding characteristics of the more important. Fortunately, detailed descriptions of the various fertilizers and their properties are available in published form if the reader cares to go further than these pages will carry him.

If the reader is already familiar with the individual fertilizer materials or does not wish to consider them at this point, he may omit sections 19:4 to 19:8 inclusive and continue the question of fertilizers and fertilizer practice with section 19:9 (p. 487).

19:4. NITROGEN CARRIERS—TWO GROUPS

Often referred to as *ammoniates,* nitrogen fertilizers may be divided for convenience into two groups: (1) *organic* and (2) *inorganic.* These groups are so different both as to source and chemical and physical properties that they are best discussed separately. Let us begin first with the organic ammoniates.

19:5. ORGANIC NITROGEN CARRIERS

The organic fertilizers, among which are garbage tankage, fish scrap, castor pomace, and cocoa meal (see Table 19:1), must undergo aminization, ammonification,

TABLE 19:1

Organic Nitrogen Carriers

Fertilizer	Source	Per Cent Nitrogen
Dried blood	Packing house	8 to 12
Animal tankage	Packing house	5 to 10 (3 to 13% P_2O_5)
Meat meal	Packing house	10 to 11 (1 to 5% P_2O_5)
Garbage tankage	Steam-treated garbage, grease removed	2 to 4 (some P_2O_5 and K_2O)
Process tankage	Waste treated with acid under steam	6 to 10 (some P_2O_5)
Sewage sludge	Sludge dried and ground	5 to 6 (variable amounts of P_2O_5 and K_2O)
Dried fish scrap	Cannery waste and non-edible fish	6 to 10 (4 to 8% P_2O_5)
Cottonseed meal	Ground cake after removal of oil	6 to 9 (2 to 3% P_2O_5 and 1 to 2% K_2O)
Linseed meal	Ground cake after removal of oil	4 to 5 (1.5% P_2O_5 and 1.5% K_2O)
Tobacco stems	Waste tobacco, midribs and stems	1.5 to 3.5 (4 to 9% K_2O)
Castor meal	Ground cake after removal of oil	5 to 7 (about 2% P_2O_5 and 1% K_2O)
Cocoa-cake meal	Ground cake refuse	3.5 to 4.5 (some P_2O_5 and K_2O)

and nitrification before their nitrogen becomes fully available to higher plants. As a result, they are not so quickly effective as nitrate of soda, ammonium nitrate or sulfate of ammonia, and do not produce a suitable crop response unless the soil is warm. Their action, however, is mild and natural.

Organic fertilizers are used in many cases because they tend to liberate their nitrogen gradually throughout the season. Also they aid in maintaining a good physical condition in any fertilizer mixture of which they may be a part. This conditioning influence is important as it assures a ready drillability of the mixture. Mixed fertilizers sometime contain from 200 to 300 pounds per ton of some organic material for this reason.

The main objection to the organic ammoniates is the cost of the nitrogen carried, which is three to five times as much as that supplied as nitrate of soda, sulfate of ammonia, or other inorganics. Some of the organic ammoniates listed in Table 19:1 are too expensive for general use.

19:6. INORGANIC NITROGEN CARRIERS

General consideration.   There are many inorganic carriers which are used to supply nitrogen in mixed fertilizers. The most important of these, together with their compositions and sources, are listed in Table 19:2. Fortunately, there is a wide range in the nitrogen contents of these materials—from 3 per cent in ammoniated

TABLE 19:2

Inorganic Nitrogen Carriers

Fertilizer	Chemical Form	Source	Approximate Per Cent Nitrogen
1. Sodium nitrate	$NaNO_3$	Chile saltpetre and synthetic	16
2. Ammonium sulfate	$(NH_4)_2SO_4$	By-product from coke and gas, and also synthetic	21
3. Ammonium nitrate [a]	NH_4NO_3	Synthetic	33
4. "Cal-nitro" and "A.N.L."	NH_4NO_3 & dolomite	"	20
5. Urea [b]	$CO(NH_2)_2$	"	42–45
6. Calcium cyanamid [c]	$CaCN_2$	"	22
7. Anhydrous ammonia [d]	Liquid NH_3	"	82
8. Ammonia liquor	Dilute NH_4OH	"	20–25
9. Nitrogen solutions	NH_4NO_3 in NH_4OH or Urea in NH_4OH	"	27–53
10. Ammo-phos [e]	$NH_4H_2PO_4$ and other ammonium salts	"	11 (48% P_2O_5)
11. Diammonium phosphate	$(NH_4)_2HPO_4$	"	21 (53% P_2O_5)

[a] Deliquescence controlled by surface coating materials or by mixing with dolomite, as in the case of "Cal-nitro" and "A.N.L." (trade names).

[b] The commercial compound is treated with a finely ground drier to control deliquescence.

[c] This fertilizer contains over 25 per cent $Ca(OH)_2$ and about 13 per cent carbon besides other ingredients such as $CaCO_3$, CaS, etc. The total amount of calcium expressed as CaO is approximately 53 per cent.

[d] The cheapest form of nitrogen for fertilizer use now available.

[e] Manufactured by treating ammonia with phosphoric acid

$$NH_3 + H_3PO_4 \longrightarrow NH_4H_2PO_4$$

superphosphate to 82 per cent in anhydrous ammonia. Also, several chemical forms are represented, including ammonium and nitrate compounds as well as materials such as urea and cyanamid. Both of the latter upon hydrolysis in the soil yield NH_4 ions which can be taken up by plants or can be oxidized to nitrates. Although all the materials listed are used as nitrogen carriers, the ammonium and nitrate containing compounds are employed most widely.

The materials listed in Table 19:2 have one thing in common—they can all be produced synthetically starting with atmospheric nitrogen. This fact has far reaching significance, especially in respect to future nitrogen utilization. In the first place, it means that the quantity of nitrogen available to produce these compounds is limited only by the quantity present in the atmosphere.

Secondly, synthetic methods of supplying nitrogen have played a significant role in reducing the cost of this element, historically so much more expensive than either potassium or phosphorus. In addition, synthetic processes have yielded a wide variety of materials in large enough quantities to make their usage practical. Such a variety was not possible when natural deposits alone were depended upon.

As a result of these and other features, synthetic nitrogen carriers are assuming more and more importance. Considerably more than two thirds of the fertilizer nitrogen used in the United States today is carried by synthetics. Their methods of manufacture are worthy of brief consideration.

Ammonia and its solutions. Perhaps the most important of the synthetic processes is that in which ammonia gas is formed from the elements hydrogen and nitrogen. This may be represented as follows:

$$N_2 + 3\ H_2 \longrightarrow 2\ NH_3$$

This reaction is extremely important since it yields a compound which is at the present time the least expensive of any listed in Table 19:2. Of equal importance is the fact that this is the first step in the formation of many other synthetic compounds.

The ammonia gas formed in the above reaction is utilized in at least three ways. Firstly, it may be liquefied under pressure yielding anhydrous ammonia. (See Table 19:2.) This material is employed in the production of ammoniated superphosphate and mixed fertilizers, in addition to being used as a separate material for direct application. (See p. 500.) Secondly, ammonia gas may be dissolved in water yielding NH_4OH. This is often used alone (ammonia liquor) or more frequently as a solvent for other nitrogen carriers such as NH_4NO_3 and urea, to give the so-called "nitrogen solutions" (Figure 19:1). In recent years these solutions have become increasingly popular and now furnish a high proportion of the nitrogen in commercial fertilizers. The factor which limits their usage in even larger quantities is the tendency of these materials to depress phosphate availability.[2]

A third very important use of ammonia gas is in the manufacture of other inorganic nitrogen fertilizer materials. The reactions by means of which some fertilizer compounds are produced synthetically from ammonia are shown diagramatically in Figure 19:1. A careful study of this diagram will be very helpful in establishing the

---

[2] Both anhydrous ammonia and the "nitrogen solutions" reduce the availability of phosphorus in fertilizers if too large quantities of these materials are used. The effect of adding too much of the nitrogen compounds is to bring about reversion of the phosphorus to $Ca_8(PO_4)_2$, in which form it is not considered easily available to plants.

relationship between ammonia and the materials derived synthetically from it. These substances will be considered briefly.

Figure 19:1. Diagram showing how various fertilizer materials may be synthesized from ammonia. This gas is obtained as a by-product of coke manufacture and, in even larger quantities, by direct synthesis from elemental nitrogen and hydrogen. In recent years, NH_3 and the other synthetic materials shown above have supplied most of our fertilizer nitrogen.

Sulfate of ammonia. Sulfate of ammonia is produced synthetically as shown in Figure 19:1.[3] This material has long been one of the most important nitrogen carriers, especially in the manufacture of mixed fertilizers. Its nitrogen is somewhat cheaper than that carried by nitrate of soda, and consequently it has been used extensively as a top dressing material. Under favorable conditions the NH_4 ions nitrify readily, thus increasing the ease of nitrogen utilization. Its use is most satisfactory on soils well supplied with lime.

Sodium and ammonium nitrates. Nitric acid, the manufacture of which is possible from oxidized ammonia, is used in making both ammonium and sodium nitrates. Ammonium nitrate which has the advantages of supplying both NH_4 and NO_3 ions, has been employed in increasing quantities in the past few years. When used as a separate material, this salt is best supplied in the form of pellets which are suitably coated or otherwise treated to reduce its deliquescence. It must always be remembered that this fertilizer is a hazard in case of fire because of its explosive properties. The percentage of nitrogen in ammonium nitrate carriers ranges from 20 per cent for "Cal-nitro" and "A.N.L." to perhaps 33 per cent for the higher grades of ammonium nitrate (Table 19:2).

In addition to the synthetic source mentioned above, sodium nitrate is obtained as a natural product, saltpetre, from salt beds in Chile. In fact, before the coming of synthetics, Chilean nitrate of soda represented essentially the sole source of this compound.

[3] Much of the NH_3 used in the production of $(NH_4)_2SO_4$ is a by-product of coke manufacture. Sulfate of ammonia obtained from this source is termed "by-product" in contrast to the "synthetic" cited in Figure 18:1.

Sodium nitrate has long been one of the main inorganic sources of commercial nitrogen and still continues popular. It supplies nitrogen in a form that immediately stimulates many crops even if the soil is cold. Hence, it is extremely valuable early in the spring and as a side-dressing later in the season.

Other synthetic nitrogen carriers. Another promising synthetic is urea, a fertilizer containing almost three times as much nitrogen as nitrate of soda. It readily undergoes hydrolysis in the soil, producing ammonium carbonate.[4] Thus, the immediate effect of this fertilizer is towards alkalinity although its residual influence tends to lower soil pH. The ammonium carbonate produced is ideal for rapid nitrification, especially if exchangeable bases are present in adequate amounts. Urea thus ultimately presents both NH_4 ions and NO_3 ions for plant absorption. Its one serious objection, high deliquescence, has been largely overcome by coating its particles with dry powders.

Calcium cyanamid, another synthetic product of some importance, has two objections as a fertilizer. When used to top-dress crops it may cause injury to the foliage if not carefully applied. This is less likely to occur if the pelleted, rather than the powdered form is used. In the soil its nitrogen changes rather readily to ammonium carbonate but there are certain temporary intermediate products that may be harmful to crops.

Of the synthetics carrying phosphorus in addition to nitrogen, the ammonium phosphates are perhaps most important. Both mono- and diammonium phosphates are available. These compounds are made from phosphoric acid and ammonia. (See Fig. 19:1.) Since their phosphorus as well as their nitrogen is water soluble these compounds are in demand where a high degree of water solubility is required.

Nitraphosphates. By acidulating rock phosphate with nitric rather than sulfuric or phosphoric acids, fertilizers containing so-called nitraphosphates are formed. They are apparently as effective as other materials in supplying nitrogen but are used primarily in the manufacture of complete fertilizers.

19:7. PHOSPHATIC FERTILIZER MATERIALS

Superphosphate. The principal phosphorus fertilizer material at the present time is superphosphate. (See Table 19:3.) The ordinary grades (16 to 21 per cent available P_2O_5) are made by treating raw rock phosphate with suitable amounts of sulfuric acid. (See Fig. 19:2.) A large proportion of the phosphorus is thus changed to the primary phosphate form $(Ca(H_2PO_4)_2)$ although some is left in the secondary condition $(CaHPO_4)$.[5] Much of the superphosphate now used is this ordinary

---

[4] $CO(NH_2)_2 + 2 H_2O \longrightarrow (NH_4)_2CO_3$

[5] Representing the complex raw rock by the simple formula $Ca_3(PO_4)_2$, the following conventional reactions may be used to show the changes that occur during the manufacture of ordinary 16 to 21 per cent superphosphate.

$$Ca_3(PO_4)_2 + 2 H_2SO_4 \longrightarrow Ca(H_2PO_4)_2 + 2 CaSO_4 + \text{impurities}$$
(Insoluble)   (Water Soluble)

The acid is never added in amounts capable of completing this reaction. Consequently, some secondary phosphate—$CaHPO_4$, spoken of as *citrate soluble phosphoric acid,* is produced.

$$Ca_3(PO_4)_2 + H_2SO_4 \longrightarrow 2 CaHPO_4 + CaSO_4 + \text{impurities}$$
(Insoluble)

grade, which consists of about 31 per cent phosphates, 50 per cent gypsum, and 19 percent impurities of various kinds. The total *phosphorus* to the hundred weight is rather low, ranging from 7 to 9 pounds, while the sulfur and calcium amount to about 12 and 18 pounds respectively.

The high-analysis treble superphosphates contains 40 to 47 per cent available P_2O_5. It differs from the ordinary type principally in that it contains more phosphorus and no gypsum.[6] This material is becoming more and more widely used since higher analysis fertilizers have become accepted.

TABLE 19:3

Phosphorous Carriers

Fertilizer	Chemical Form	Source	Approximate Percentage of Available P_2O_5
Superphosphates	$Ca(H_2PO_4)_2$ and $CaHPO_4$	Made from rock phosphate	16–50
Ammoniated superphosphate	$\begin{cases} NH_4H_2PO_4 \\ CaHPO_4 \\ Ca_3(PO_4)_2 \\ (NH_4)_2SO_4 \end{cases}$	Synthesized	16–18 (3–4% N)
Ammo-phos	$NH_4H_2PO_4$ mostly	Synthesized	48 (11% N)
Diammonium phosphate	$(NH_4)_2HPO_4$	Synthesized	53 (21% N)
Basic slag [a]	$(CaO)_5 \cdot P_2O_5 \cdot SiO_2$	Steel slag	15–25
Bone black	$Ca_3(PO_4)_2$	Refining refuse	32–35
Raw bone meal	$Ca_3(PO_4)_2$	Packing house	20–25
Steamed bone meal [b]	$Ca_3(PO_4)_2$	Packing house	23–30
Rock phosphate	Fluor- and Chlor-apatites	Ground rock	25–30
Calcium metaphosphate	$Ca(PO_3)_2$	Synthesized [c]	62–63
Phosphoric acid	H_3PO_4	Synthesized	54
Superphosphoric acid	H_3PO_4 and $H_4P_2O_7$	Synthesized	76

[a] The formula of this fertilizer is very uncertain. Basic slag is intensely alkaline because of the presence of large amounts of the hydroxide and carbonate of lime.

[b] The steamed bone meal is cooked under pressure and the fat and oil removed. The bone is left open and porous.

[c] Synthesized from rock phosphate or limestone and P_2O_5:

$$Ca_3(PO_4)_2 + 2\ P_2O_5 \longrightarrow 3\ Ca(PO_3)_2 + \text{impurities, or}$$
$$CaCO_3 + P_2O_5 \longrightarrow Ca(PO_3)_2 + CO_2 + \text{impurities.}$$

[6] The *treble* superphosphate is synthesized by treating a high grade phosphate rock with phosphoric acid:

$$Ca_3(PO_4)_2 + 4\ H_3PO_4 \longrightarrow 3\ Ca(H_2PO_4)_2 + \text{impurities}$$

Of the two superphosphates, the ordinary grade (16 to 21 per cent available P_2O_5) is by far the most commonly used. And since much of it goes into mixed fertilizers or is ammoniated, the finely ground, rather than the granulated materials are in demand. The former gives more uniform mixtures, and does not segregate when handled as does the granulated. Moreover, it is contacted more readily by the ammonia when ammoniated superphosphate is made. But when superphosphate is to be applied separately to the soil or is used to reinforce farm manure (p. 519) the well granulated type is preferable. This form does not revert as rapidly in the soil as do the finer grades and in addition is more pleasant to handle.

Figure 19:2. Diagram showing how several important phosphate fertilizers are manufactured. (This diagram is modified from one supplied the authors by Mr. Travis Hignett, Tennessee Valley Authority.)

Since superphosphate gives a very acid reaction when tested with indicators, it is generally supposed that it must increase the acidity of soils to which it is added. As a matter of fact, it has practically no effect within the ordinary pH range. But at a low pH superphosphate tends to reduce acidity, while at a pH of 7.5 to 8.5 the modification is in the other direction. The slight influence of this fertilizer on soil reaction probably is due to the vigorous reversion that occurs as soon as it contacts the soil.

Ammoniated phosphates.   Ammoniated superphosphate contains from 3 to 4 per cent of nitrogen and 16 to 18 per cent of phosphoric acid. It affords a chance of easily changing ammonia to a suitable fertilizer form, at the same time improving the physical qualities of the superphosphate itself. It is usually made by treating superphosphate with ammonia liquor or nitrogen solutions.

Ammo-phos, which may analyze 11 per cent of nitrogen and 48 per cent of phosphoric acid, is also an economical fertilizer when a higher analysis is required. Diammonium phosphate is a more recently developed material containing up to 21 per cent N and 53 per cent P_2O_5. It should be very valuable on soils with high potassium-supplying power where both nitrogen and phosphorus are needed.

Basic slag and bone meal.   Basic slag, while commonly used in Europe, is on the market only to a limited extent in the United States. Because of the alkalinity and the rather ready availability of its phosphoric acid, it is a very desirable phosphatic fertilizer. It seems to be especially effective on acid soils apparently because of its high content of calcium hydroxide.

Bone meal is an expensive form of phosphoric acid. Moreover, it is rather slowly available in the soil. Bone meal can be applied in large amounts and yet produce no detrimental influence on crop growth. This is not so likely to be the case, of course, with some of the more readily soluble phosphatic fertilizers.

Rock phosphate.　　Raw rock phosphate, due to its insolubility, must be finely ground in order that it may react at all readily when applied to the soil. Its availability is markedly increased by the presence of decaying organic matter. For that reason it is often recommended as a reinforcement for farm manure, liberal amounts being used. Ordinarily it should not be applied alone unless the soil is rather well supplied with active organic matter.

Rock phosphate is the least available of the phosphatic fertilizers already mentioned, the order being: ammonium phosphates and superphosphate, basic slag, bone meal, and raw rock. Although its chemical formula is given conventionally as $Ca_3(PO_4)_2$, rock phosphate is much more complicated than this formula would suggest. It apparently approaches the fluorapatite ($3\ Ca_3(PO_4)_2 \cdot CaF_2$) in its molecular make-up. (See p. 436.) This, no doubt, accounts in part for its slow availability.

Considerable discussion at one time arose regarding the relative merits of superphosphate and raw rock phosphate. Thorne,[7] after a critical review of the field experiments where these two materials were compared, came to the conclusion that superphosphate is generally somewhat superior. He found that, while raw rock may be employed with profit on land materially deficient in phosphorus, superphosphate has generally proved the more effective and the more economical carrier of phosphoric acid for crops.

These conclusions, which are amply corroborated by other investigators, do not imply that raw rock phosphate is never equal or superior to superphosphate, nor that raw rock may not have a place as a fertilizer on many farms especially those near the phosphate fields. To a soil rich in organic matter it may be added to advantage. It is especially useful in reinforcing farm manure, seemingly being about as effective under such conditions as is superphosphate. However, the trend in fertilizer manufacture seems to be such that raw rock phosphate will continue to be used largely as a source of phosphorus for the manufacture of other and more soluble forms.

High analysis phosphates.　　Mention should be made of two very high analysis phosphate fertilizers not as yet in general use—calcium metaphosphate [$Ca(PO_3)_2$—62 to 63 per cent available P_2O_5] and superphosphoric acid (76 per cent P_2O_5). (See Table 19:3.) Both are more or less in the experimental stage but hold great promise as they seem to be as effective, when used in equivalent amounts, as superphosphate. Their concentrations make them extremely attractive when transportation is a factor.

The $Ca(PO_3)_2$, commonly called *meta-phos*, may be made by treating either phosphate rock or limestone with phosphorus pentoxide. (Table 19:3, note 00.) The highly concentrated P_2O_5 can be produced at the mine, shipped to a point where

[7] C. E. Thorne, *Raw Phosphate Rock as a Fertilizer*, Bul. 305, Ohio Agr. Exp. Sta., 1916. See also F. C. Bauer, *et al.*, *Effects of Soil Treatment on Soil Productivity*, Bul. 516: 124–30, Ill. Agr. Exp. Sta., 1945.

limestone is cheaply available, and the meta-phos manufactured in the territory where it is to be used. Transportation costs are thus cut to a minimum.

Superphosphoric acid, a new synthetic product, is the highest phosphorus-containing material used in fertilizer manufacture today. (Table 19:3.) Its P_2O_5 content is 76 per cent. This liquid can be used in the manufacture of other liquid fertilizers, or to make a high analysis superphosphate (54 per cent P_2O_5). It is not widely used as yet but offers much promise.

Classification of phosphate fertilizers. For purposes of evaluation and sale the various phosphorus compounds that are present in phosphatic fertilizers are classified in an arbitrary yet rather satisfactory way in Table 19:4.

TABLE 19:4

Fertilizer Classification of Phosphates

1. *Water-solube*	$Ca(H_2PO_4)_2$ $NH_4H_2PO_4$ K phosphate	*Available* phosphoric acid [a]
2. *Citrate-solube* In 15 per cent neutral ammonium citrate—$CaHPO_4$ In 2 per cent solution of citric acid —phosphate of basic slag		
3. *Insoluble* Phosphate of bone and raw phosphate rock		*Unavailable* phosphoric acid [a]

[a] The various fertilizers studied are grouped as follows:
Available—superphosphate (all grades), ammoniated superphosphate, ammo-phos, basic slag, mono-calcium phosphate, meta-phos and dicalcium phosphate.
Mostly unavailable—rock phosphate and bone meal.

It is well to note that the classification of the phosphates is in some degree artificial as well as arbitrary. For instance, *available* phosphates, because of the reversion that occurs, are not strictly available once they contact the soil. The term *available* really refers to those phosphates that readily stimulate plant growth. Those phosphates that are less effective are rated as currently *unavailable,* yet in the soil they may eventually supply a certain amount of phosphorus to crops.

Suppose in the case of ordinary superphosphate that the guarantee is 20 per cent available P_2O_5. The term available phosphoric acid is here used in the sense explained above and includes both the water solube $Ca(H_2PO_4)_2$ and the citrate soluble $CaHPO_4$. With ammo-phos (11 per cent total nitrogen and 48 per cent available P_2O_5) the available phosphoric acid is carried by the water-soluble $NH_4H_2PO_4$. Since phosphate fertilizers are guaranteed in the terms set forth above, it is absolutely necessary that a person be familiar with the distinctions noted. Otherwise, a correct interpretation of a guarantee is impossible.

19:8. FERTILIZER MATERIALS CARRYING POTASSIUM

One of the largest known deposits of potassium salts occurs in Germany, where there are extensive beds varying from 50 to 150 feet in thickness, lying under an area stretching from the Harz Mountains to the Elbe River. It is known as the Strassfurt deposits. Crude potash salts occur in other sections of Germany, in France, in the United States, in Canada, and elsewhere.

While potash deposits are found in other parts of the world, the French, German, and American mines are the ones operating most extensively. The First World War stimulated considerable investigation regarding possible sources of potash, especially in the United States. Domestic underground deposits and saline brines now furnish most of the potash used in America.

Kainit and manure salts(see Table 19:5) are the most common of the crude

TABLE 19:5

Potash Fertilizer Materials

Fertilizer	Chemical Form	Percentage of K_2O
Potassium chloride [a]	KCl	48–60
Potassium sulfate	K_2SO_4	48–50
Sulfate of potash-magnesia [b]	Double salt of K and Mg	25–30
Manure salts	KCl mostly	20–30
Kainit	KCl mostly	12–16
Potassium nitrate	KNO_3	44 (and 13% N)
Wood ashes	K_2CO_3 largely	3–7 (and 1–2% P_2O_5)
Tobacco stems	Organic	4–9 (and 2–4% N)

[a] All of these fertilizers contain other potash salts than those listed.
[b] Contains 25 per cent of $MgSO_4$ and some chlorine.

potash sources. The high grade chloride and sulfate of potash originally imported from Germany and France are their refined equivalents. The potassium chloride, now used so extensively in the United States, comes mostly from underground deposits, saline brines, and old lake beds found in this country.

All potash salts used as fertilizers are water-soluble and are therefore rated as readily available. Unlike nitrogen salts, most potassium fertilizers, even if employed in large amounts, have little or no effect on the soil pH. Some discrimination is made, however, against potassium chloride (muriate) in respect to potatoes and especially tobacco since large dosages are considered to lower the quality. Hence, when large amounts of potash are to be applied for the latter crop, the major part usually is preferred in the sulfate form.

Potassium-magnesium sulfate, although rather low in potash, has attained considerable usage in parts of this country where magnesium is likely to be deficient.

In some respects it is a more desirable source of magnesia than is dolomitic limestone or dolomite.

Tobacco stems, as well as other potassium-carrying organics, are used in making mixed goods (see p. 490) and are important as a filler and drier. In some parts of the country wood ashes are sometimes obtainable. They carry their potassium largely in the carbonate form, a combination especially desirable for certain crops. The amount of lime added with wood ashes is usually large and on an acid soil may have a considerable influence.

19:9. SULFUR IN SOIL FERTILIZATION [8]

In examining the sulfur problem in humid regions it will be found that for a representative farm soil the total loss of sulfur (erosion, leaching, and crop removal combined) perhaps falls within the range of 20 to 30 pounds an acre yearly. (See Tables 9:5 and 9:8.) This deficiency is met in several ways.

Consider first the addition of sulfur in rain and snow. The amount depends, of course, upon location, ranging from 2 or 3 pounds of combined sulfur an acre a year to perhaps over 100 pounds near industrial centers. Since the influence of industrial centers is extremely local, it is hardly safe in general to assume that this source will fully meet the deficit (20 to 30 pounds yearly per acre) already set up.

In general and dairying farming the problem is taken care of in a more or less automatic way. In practical soil management sulfur is returned to the soil in green manures, crop residues, and farm manures. Commercial fertilizers, such as superphosphate, ammonium sulfate, and potassium sulfate contain considerable amounts of sulfur and are now commonly used. An application to the acre of 10 tons of farm manure reinforced with 500 pounds of ordinary superphosphate adds well over 100 pounds of sulfur. This alone, once during the rotation, would go far toward meeting any deficit.

There is another angle to the sulfur problem that until a few years ago escaped attention—the probability that the soil, and perhaps to a lesser degree higher plants, absorb sulfur dioxide from the atmosphere. Workers [9] who advanced the idea substantiate their suggestions rather conclusively. The magnitude of this absorption, which, bear in mind, is exclusive of the sulfur added in precipitation, probably is in excess of that brought down by rain, snow, and dust. Bertramson places it at 27 pounds an acre a year

---

[8] *Soil Science*, Vol. 70, No. 1, July 1950, carries a sulfur symposium of nine well-documented papers which cover most of the phases relating to sulfur as a fertilizer.

[9] F. J. Alway; A. W. Marsh; and W. J. Methley, "Sufficiency of Atmospheric Sulfur for Maximum Crop Yields," *Proc. Soil Sci. Soc. Amer.*, 2: 229–38, 1937.

for Indiana soils.[10] Here, then, is another automatic addition, a further insurance against a sulfur deficiency. And incidentally it furnishes a second reason why crops requiring large amounts of sulfur, such as alfalfa, can be grown successfully on land receiving no artificial applications of this element.

In the light of the information available, it seems that the sulfur situation is not comparable with, nor so serious as that of phosphorus. With certain soils in eastern Washington and Oregon, in Minnesota, and in California, sulfur in some form undoubtedly must be added artificially, especially in the growing of alfalfa and sweet clover. However, under ordinary conditions, if the normal residues produced on the farm are utilized, there seems little reason for sulfur being a limiting factor in soil productivity, especially if fertilizers carrying sulfur are used.

19:10. MICRONUTRIENTS

Micronutrient additions to fertilizers must be much more carefully controlled than is the case for the macronutrients. The difference between the amount of a given micronutrient present when deficiency occurs and when there is a toxicity is extremely small. Consequently, micronutrients should be added only when one is certain they are needed and when the amount required is known.

When a trace-element deficiency is to be corrected, especially if the case is urgent, a salt of the lacking nutrient often is added separately to the soil. (See Table 19:6.) Copper, manganese, iron, and zinc generally are usually supplied as the sulfate while boron is applied as borax. Molybdenum is added as sodium molybdate. Iron and in some cases zinc may be supplied as a chelate. (See p. 465.) Iron, manganese, and zinc are sometimes sprayed in small quantities on the leaves rather than being applied directly to the soil. So called "fritted" silicate compounds of boron, manganese, iron, and zinc may also be used to supply these nutrients.

The rate of application should be carefully regulated as an overdose can cause severe injury. For instance, 50 pounds of borax an acre are nearing the maximum for the average soil when its pH is near 7. A few ounces of molybdenum is often all that is required. Much, of course, depends upon the crop grown. In case of doubt as to the amounts to apply, expert advice should be sought.

In some cases trace elements, especially boron, are placed in ordinary

[10] B. R. Bertramson, *et al.*, "Sulfur Studies of Indiana Soils and Crops," *Soil Sci.*, 70: 27–41, 1950.

commercial fertilizers and their presence therein stated in the guarantee. A stock mixture is compounded using some organic ammoniate as a base to which is added the desired trace-element salts. A few pounds of this mix-

TABLE 19:6

Salts of Micronutrients Commonly Used in Fertilizers [a]

Compound	Formula	Nutrient Content
Copper sulfate	$CuSO_4$	25–35% Cu
Basic copper sulfate	$CuSO_4 \cdot 3Cu(OH)_2$	13–53% Cu
Copper carbonate (basic)	$CuCO_3 \cdot Cu(OH)_2$	57% Cu
Zinc sulfate	$ZnSO_4$	23–35% Zn
Zinc sulfate (basic)	$ZnSO_4 \cdot 4Zn(OH)_2$	55% Zn
Manganese sulfate	$MnSO_4$	23% Mn
Manganese sulfate (basic)	$2MnSO_4 \cdot MnO$	40–49% Mn
Sodium borate	$Na_2B_4O_7$	34–44% B_2O_3
Ferrous sulfate	$FeSO_4$	20% Fe
Ferric sulfate	$Fe_2(SO_4)_3$	17% Fe
Sodium molybdate	Na_2MoO_4	37–39% Mo

[a] Modified from A. A. Nikitin, "Technological Aspects of Trace Elements Usage," *Adv. in Agron.,* 6: 183–97, 1954.

ture are included in each ton of the fertilizer. The idea, of course, is to insure against a possible deficiency of the trace elements. One objection to such a practice is that not enough of any one trace element may be added to the soil to adequately meet a real deficiency should it occur. Furthermore, the amount of trace element applied varies with the dosage of the commercial fertilizer. Trace elements usually require a more careful regulation than can be attained in this way.

That the fertilization with trace elements is of great practical importance cannot be denied. Plant malnutritions, due to such deficiencies, are becoming more and more apparent. All kinds of plants are affected. The last few years, has seen a tremendous development of this phase of fertility regulation.

19:11. MIXED FERTILIZERS

For years, fertilizer manufacturers have placed on the market mixtures of materials which contain at least two of the so-called "fertilizer elements," and usually all three. The former are designated as *incomplete* fertilizers while the latter are spoken as *complete*. In either case materials such as those discussed in previous sections are mixed in proper proportions to furnish the desired amount of the nutrient elements. For example, an ammonia solution, superphosphate, muriate of potash and a small amount of an organic such as castor pomace might be used if a complete fertilizer is desired.

Physical condition.   In addition to supplying nitrogen, phosphorus, and potassium in desired proportions, however, a commercial fertilizer should have certain other properties. Of utmost importance in this regard is the *physical condition* of the mixed goods. The fertilizer should be drillable when first purchased and should remain in this condition after storage. Mixtures of certain materials cannot be used because of their tendency to "set up" or harden. Of the fertilizer materials commonly found in mixed goods, ammonium and sodium nitrates, sulfate of ammonia and potassium chloride are most likely to develop unsatisfactory physical conditions. Improperly cured superphosphate may also give trouble. The extreme deliquescence of some of the salts, especially ammonium nitrate, tends to make mixed fertilizers sticky and thus reduce the drillability.

Methods of insuring free flowage.   The free flowing condition of a mixed fertilizer is maintained by two important procedures: (1) Moisture resistant bags are commonly used in distribution; and (2) certain moisture absorbing materials are usually included in the fertilizer mix. In the latter case, organic ammoniates such as castor pomace, tobacco stems and dried poultry manure are especially valuable. Dolomitic limestone used to counteract the acid developing tendencies of certain fertilizers also acts as a conditioner. The manufacturer is as careful regarding the drillability of his product as he is in respect to the maintenance of its guaranteed analysis. Many complete fertilizers carry as much as 300 lbs. a ton of materials that will help insure a suitable physical condition.

Another method of encouraging the free flowing of fertilizers is that of granulating the goods after mixing. Separate materials such as sodium and ammonium nitrates have been pelleted for several years to prevent caking. In recent years the granulation of small but steadily increasing amounts of mixed fertilizers has taken place in this country.

In addition to having free flowing properties, granulated fertilizers present certain other advantages. For example, they are less disagreeable to handle since they are comparatively free of small dustlike particles. The granulation also prevents the fertilizer from being carried by the wind and retards its reaction with the soil.

19:12. EFFECT OF MIXED FERTILIZERS ON SOIL pH

Acid-forming fertilizers.   Most complete fertilizers, unless specially treated, tend to develop an acid residue in soils. This is mainly due to the influence of certain of the nitrogen carriers, especially those of an ammoniacal nature. The major effect of NH_4 ions is exerted when they are nitrified. Upon oxidation the ammonium compounds tend to increase acidity as shown by the following reaction:

$$NH_4^+ + 2\ O_2 \longrightarrow 2H^+ + NO_3^- + H_2O$$

Two other effects of NH_4 ions are important, but to a lesser extent, in decreasing soil pH. For example, when ammonium sulfate is added to a soil, some of the NH_4 ions are readily adsorbed by the soil colloidal matter replacing equivalent quantities of other cations. If metallic cations are displaced their loss by leaching is encouraged. This ultimately may result in a lowering of soil pH. On the other hand, if H ions are displaced sulfuric acid appears in the soil solution. A similar development of sulfuric acid occurs if higher plants or microorganisms use the ammonium radical of the fertilizer to a greater extent than they do the sulfate.

In addition to ammonium compounds, materials such as urea and some of the organics, which upon hydrolysis yield ammonium ions, are potential sources of acidity. The phosphorus and potash fertilizers commonly used have little effect upon soil pH unless they also contain nitrogen.

Nonacid-forming fertilizers.   For many years no particular attention was paid to this acid-forming tendency of certain fertilizer materials. For instance, the average mixed fertilizer sold in the United States in 1933 had an acidity equivalent per ton of about 150 pounds of calcium carbonate.[11] Although this has been reduced to some extent, the average mixed fertilizer is still rather acid in effect.[12]

In many instances, however, this acid forming tendency is completely counteracted by adding dolomitic limestone to the mixture. Such fertilizers are termed *neutral* or *nonacid-forming* and exert little residual effect on soil pH. Data are available in respect to nitrogen fertilizers that make it

[11] A. L. Mehring and A. J. Peterson, "The Equivalent Physiological Acidity or Basicity of American Fertilizers," *Jour. Assoc. Official Agr. Chemists,* 17: 95–100, 1934.
[12] A. L. Mehring, "Fertilizers for Special Use," a chapter in *Amer. Soc. Agron. Monograph* No. 3, 1952.

rather easy to calculate the approximate amount of dolomitic limestone necessary in any particular case.[13]

19:13. THE FERTILIZER GUARANTEE

Every fertilizing material, whether it is a single carrier or a complete ready-to-apply mixture, must carry a guarantee as to its content of nutrient elements. The exact form is generally determined by the state in which the fertilizer is offered for sale. The *total nitrogen* is usually expressed in its *elemental form* (N). The phosphorus is quoted in terms of *available phosphoric acid* (P_2O_5), while the potassium is stated as *water soluble potash* (K_2O).

The guarantee of a simple fertilizer, such as sulfate of ammonia, is easy to interpret, since the name and the composition of the material is printed on the bag or tag. When the amount of the nutrient element carried is noted, the purity of the fertilizer can usually be ascertained if a person is at all familiar with the compounds present. For instance, if the material is nitrate of soda containing 16 per cent total nitrogen, it is apparent that the fertilizer is high-grade, since *chemically pure* sodium nitrate contains only slightly more than 16 per cent nitrogen.

The interpretation of an analysis of a complete fertilizer is almost as easy. The simplest form of guarantee is a mere statement of the relative amounts of N, P_2O_5, and K_2O. Thus, a 5–10–10 fertilizer contains 5 per cent *total nitrogen,* 10 per cent *available phosphoric acid,* and 10 per cent *water-soluble potash.* In some states, figures as to *water-soluble nitrogen, water-insoluble nitrogen,* and *available insoluble nitrogen* are required by law.

An *open formula* guarantee is used by some companies. Such a guarantee not only gives the usual chemical analysis but also a list of the various ingredients, their composition, and the pounds of each in a ton of the mix-

---

[13] See W. H. Pierre, "Determination of Equivalent Acidity and Basicity of Fertilizers," *Analy. Ed., Ind. and Eng. Chem.,* 5: 229–34, 1933.

It is, of course, very difficult to determine the exact potential acidity of a given fertilizer. The approximate acidifying capacity of a few materials are cited below. The values are in terms of pounds $CaCO_3$ per 20 pounds N supplied by the fertilizer.

Ammonium sulfate	107	Ammonium nitrate	36
Ammo-phos	100	Cottonseed meal	29
Anhydrous ammonia	36	Castor pomace	18
Urea	36	High grade tankage	15

The basicity in the same terms for certain fertilizers is as below:

Nitrate of soda	36	Tobacco stems	86
Calcium cyanamid	57	Cocoa meal	12

ture. Such a type of guarantee is given below (Table 19:7) for a 5–10–10 *neutral* fertilizer.

TABLE 19:7

An Open Formula Guarantee of an 8–16–16 (Nonacid-forming) Fertilizer

Pounds of Ingredients per Ton	*Total N lbs.*	*Available P_2O_5 lbs.*	*Soluble K_2O lbs.*
300 lbs. nitrogen solution	120		
100 lbs. sulfate of ammonia	20		
100 lbs. diammonium phosphate	20	52	
300 lbs. treble superphosphate		135	
666 lbs. superphosphate		133	
534 lbs. muriate of potash			320
2,000 lbs. 8–16–16	160	320	320

Commercial fertilizers are sometimes grouped according to their nutrient *ratio*. For instance, a 5–10–10, a 6–12–12, a 10–20–20, and a 15–30–30 all have a 1–2–2 ratio. These fertilizers should give essentially the same results when suitably applied in equivalent amounts. Thus, 1,000 lbs. of 10–20–20 furnishes the same amounts of N, P_2O_5 and K_2O as does a ton of 5–10–10.

This grouping according to ratios is valuable when several analyses are offered and the comparative costs become the deciding factor as to which should be purchased. Moreover, fertilizer recommendations are sometimes made on the basis of the ratio, the particular analysis being decided on later.

19:14. FERTILIZER INSPECTION AND CONTROL

So many opportunities are open for fraud, either as to availability or the actual quantities of ingredients present, that laws controlling the sale of fertilizers are necessary. These laws apply not only to the ready-mixed goods but to the separate carriers as well. Such regulations protect not only the public but also the reliable fertilizer companies, since goods of unknown value are kept off the market.

Certain provisions are more or less common to the various state fertilizer laws in this country. In general, there is a license fee or tonnage tax on all fertilizers selling for a certain price or over. In addition, the manufacturer must print the following data on the bag or on an authorized tag:

1. Number of net pounds of fertilizer to a package.
2. Name, brand, or trade-mark.
3. Chemical composition guaranteed.
4. Potential acidity in terms of lbs. of $CaCO_3$ per ton.
5. Name and address of manufacturer.

An example of how this information often appears on the fertilizer bag is shown in Figure 19:3.

Figure 19:3. A fertilizer bag on which is printed the information commonly required by law in most states. Note the acid-forming tendency of this particular fertilizer.

For the enforcement of such laws, the various states usually provide adequate machinery. The inspection and analyses may be in the hands of an agency such as the state department of agriculture, the agricultural experiment station, or the state chemist's office. In any case, inspectors are provided who take samples of the fertilizers on the market throughout the state. These samples are analyzed in order to ascertain whether the goods are up to the guarantee. The expense of the inspection and control of fertilizers is usually defrayed by a license fee or a tonnage tax.

If a fertilizer falls below the guarantee—allowing, of course, for any variation permitted by law—the manufacturer is subject to prosecution in the state courts.

A more effective check on fraudulent guarantees, however, is in publicity. The state law usually provides for the publication each year of a bulletin containing the "guaranteed" and "found" analyses of all brands inspected. This has proved to be very effective in preventing fraud. It protects not only the fertilizer user but also the manufacturer, as his guarantees thus receive an official sanction. The "found" analysis of most fertilizers is generally up to or more often above the guarantee.

19:15. FERTILIZER ECONOMY

High vs. low analyses. Whether buying mixed fertilizers or the various separate carriers, such as nitrate of soda, sulfate of ammonia, and the like, it is always important to obtain high-analysis goods. Price data indicate that the higher the grade, especially of a mixed fertilizer, the greater is the amount of the various nutrients obtained for every dollar expended. This is a price rule well worth remembering. It holds because the overhead is about the same for every ton of fertilizer, regardless of the amount of nutrients that it contains. Concentration, therefore, reduces the overhead per unit of nutrient carried. This is shown graphically in Figure 19:4. Obviously, from the standpoint of economy, an 8–16–16 fertilizer furnishes more nutrients *per dollar* than a 4–8–8 or a 5–10–10.

Figure 19:4. Relative farm costs of nutrients in fertilizer of different concentrations. Note that the same amount of *nutrients* is supplied by the indicated quantities of each fertilizer. These nutrients are furnished more cheaply by the higher analysis goods, mainly because of the lower handling costs.

In the past, certain disadvantages of high analysis fertilizers have somewhat hampered their increased usage. For example, the equipment used to place the fertilizer in the soil was too crude to satisfactorily distribute the smaller amounts of the more concentrated materials. Also, when improperly placed, the more concentrated goods often resulted in injury to young seedlings. Modern fertilizer placement machinery, however, has largely overcome these difficulties. Hence, the savings which result from the use of higher analysis materials seem to far outweigh any associated disadvantages that may now exist.

Relative costs of N, P₂O₅ and K₂O.   Another price factor to remember in purchasing fertilizers is the relative costs of nitrogen, phosphoric acid, and potash. Nitrogen has generally been more expensive than the other two constituents. This price differential has been somewhat reduced, however, due to the production of synthetic nitrogen carriers. Until recent years phosphoric acid was the least expensive of the three constituents. Since the Second World War, however, the cost of potash has been somewhat less than phosphoric acid. These facts should be kept in mind, especially when comparing the costs of fertilizers having different ratios.

Purchase of separate materials.   In many instances a saving can be effected by purchasing the separate materials and applying them to the soil. Superphosphate is often applied alone for all sorts of crops. Nitrate of soda, sulfate of ammonia, and similar nitrogenous fertilizers are employed to advantage in orchards, as top-dressings on meadows and pastures, and as a side-dressing in vegetable production and the growing of such field crops as cotton. When farm manure is available, the use of superphosphate with lime and manure in a legume rotation is generally desirable. The separate fertilizers may thus be effectively applied without the necessity of mixing and some saving thereby effected.

Home mixing fertilizers.   In the past considerable amounts of the mixed fertilizer used in this country were prepared by *home mixing,* that is, on the farm. The various materials were purchased separately and the compounding was done by the farmer himself. Labor was then cheap compared to the cost of the ready mixed goods and a considerable saving was thus possible.

At the present time, however, it is doubtful whether such savings are still possible by home mixing. In the first place, it is difficult to purchase the separate materials at reasonable prices, especially in small amounts. This is particularly discouraging to the individual farmer who does not need materials in amounts as large as a carload lot. On the other hand, if his operations are large enough to allow him to use fertilizer by the carload, he can often buy the manufactured mixed goods at a price considerably lower than that quoted for ton lots.

Another disadvantage of home mixing is the difficulty of obtaining the most economic materials. For example, liquid ammonia, now the cheapest source of our most expensive major nutrient (nitrogen), cannot be used conveniently in home mixing because of the difficulties of handling. Also, proper conditioners are not too easily obtained and may be too expensive. And finally, it is often difficult to thoroughly mix the separate ingredients because of a lack of adequate equipment. These disadvantages discourage home mixing, especially when labor costs are high.

19:16. THE MOVEMENT OF FERTILIZER SALTS IN THE SOIL

To fully understand the reasons for some of the specific methods of applying fertilizers (see next section), the movement of fertilizer salts within the soil should be reviewed. As previously pointed out, phosphorus compounds tend to move but little, except in the more sandy soils. (See p. 216.) Consequently, for maximum effectiveness this element should be placed in the zone of root development. Surface applications, unless worked into the soil, do not supply the deeper roots with phosphorus. Also, due to phosphorus immobility, the total quantity of this element necessary for a given season can be applied at one time without fear of loss by leaching.

On the other hand, potassium, and to an even greater extent, nitrogen, tend to move from their zones of placement. This movement is largely *vertical,* the salts moving up or down depending upon the direction of water movement. These translocations greatly influence the time and method of applying nitrogen and potassium. For example, it is often undesirable to supply nitrogen all in one annual application because of the leaching hazard. This tendency for the downward movement of nitrates is taken advantage of, however, in subsequent *top-dressings* where this fertilizer is applied on the surface of the ground. Water movement in the latter case is depended upon to carry the dissolved nitrate salts down to the plant roots.

The movement of nitrogen, and, to a lesser degree, potassium, must be considered in the *placement* of the fertilizer with respect to the seed. If the fertilizer salts are located in a band directly under the seeds, the upward movement of nitrates and some of the potassium salts by capillary water often results in injury to the stand. Rain immediately after planting followed by a long dry spell encourages such damage to seedlings. Placing the fertilizer immediately above the seed or on the soil surface also may result in injury especially to row crops. The possibility of such injuries should be kept in mind in reading the following section.

19:17. METHODS OF APPLYING SOLID FERTILIZERS [14]

Much emphasis is placed on the selection of the correct fertilizer ratio and on the adequate and economical amounts of the various fertilizers to be used. However the method of application is equally as important and must not be overlooked. A fertilizer should be placed in the soil in such a position that it will serve the plant to the best advantage. This involves not only different zones of placement but also the time of the year the fertilizer is to be applied. The methods of application will be discussed on the basis of the crops to be fertilized.

Row crops. Cultivated crops such as corn, cotton, and potatoes are usually fertilized in the *hill* or the *row*, part or all of the fertilizer being applied at the time of planting. If placed in the hill the fertilizer may be deposited slightly below and on one side, or better, on both sides of the seed. When applied to the row, the fertilizer usually is laid in as a narrow *band*, on one or both sides of the row, 2 or 3 inches away and a little below the seed level. (See Fig. 19:5.)

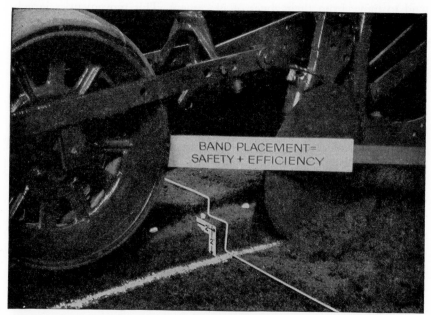

Figure 19:5. The best fertilizer placement for row crops is to the side and slightly below the seed. This eliminates the danger of fertilizer "burn" and concentrates the nutrients near the seed. *(Photo courtesy W. L. Nelson, American Potash Institute.)*

[14] See "Methods of Applying Fertilizer," Recommendations of the National Joint Committee on Fertilizer Application, Published as Pamphlet No. 149 by the National Fertilizer Association, November 1948.

When the amount of fertilizer is large, it is often wise to broadcast part and thoroughly work it into the soil before the planting is done. In some cases the crop is side-dressed with an additional amount of fertilizer later in the season. This practice involves placing the fertilizer along the side of the row at a time most satisfactory to the crop. This requires experience and good judgment.

Vegetables.   Vegetables are fertilized much the same as are other row crops. However, larger total amounts are usually applied and side-dressing is common, especially with a nitrogen fertilizer such as nitrate of soda. This is done after the crop is well started and is in addition to the regular fertilization. When the fertilizer is applied around the hill, as with such crops as melons, the treatment is called a *spot-application.*

Small grains.   With small grains and similar crops the drill is equipped with a fertilizer distributor, the fertilizer entering the soil more or less in contact with the seed. As long as the fertilizer is low in analysis and the amount applied does not exceed 300 or 400 pounds per acre, germination injury is not serious. Higher rates, especially of high analysis fertilizers, may result in serious injury if the seed and fertilizer are placed together. The more modern grain drills are equipped to place the fertilizer alongside the seed rather than in contact with it.

Pastures and meadows.   With meadows, pastures, and lawns, it is advisable to fertilize the soil well at the time of seeding. The fertilizer may be applied with the seed, or better, broadcasted, and worked thoroughly into the soil as the seedbed is prepared. The latter method is preferable, especially if the fertilization is heavy. During succeeding years it may be necessary to top-dress such crops with a suitable fertilizer mixture. This requires care. The amount of fertilizer applied and the time of treatment should be so regulated as to avoid injury to the foliage and to the root crowns of the plants.

Trees.   Orchard trees usually are treated individually, the fertilizer being applied around each tree within the spread of the branches but beginning several feet from the trunk. The fertilizer is worked into the soil as much as possible. When the orchard cover-crop needs fertilization, it is treated separately, the fertilizer being drilled in at the time of seeding or broadcast later.

Ornamental trees are often fertilized by what is called the *perforation* method. Numerous small holes are dug around each tree, within the outer half of the branch-spread zone and extending well into the upper subsoil. Into these holes, which are afterward filled up, is placed a suitable amount of an appropriate fertilizer. This method of application places the nutrients within the root zone and avoids an undesirable stimulation of the grass that may be growing around ornamental trees.

Plow-sole fertilization. Larger quantities of fertilizer are often required than can be safely applied in bands at planting time. One method used to supply the extra fertilizer is that of plowing under and thereby placing part of the application on the *plow sole* before the crop is planted. This type of application is probably most widely used as a supplementary measure rather than to replace the customary methods. Adverse weather conditions may seriously reduce the effectiveness of this procedure, however.

19:18. THE APPLICATION OF LIQUID FERTILIZERS [15]

The use of liquid materials as a means of fertilization is assuming considerable importance in certain areas of this country. Three primary methods of applying liquid fertilizers have been used: (1) direct application to the soil; (2) application in irrigation water; and (3) the spraying of plants with suitable fertilizer solutions.

Direct application to soil. The practice of making direct applications of anhydrous ammonia and nitrogen solutions to soils is rapidly increasing throughout the United States. Special equipment is necessary which takes advantage of the pressure of the liquid ammonia to force the material into the soil. Little plant injury or wastage of ammonia occurs if the material is applied about four inches below the seed.[16] This method allows the direct utilization of the cheapest nitrogen source as now available.

In addition to liquid nitrogen materials, liquid fertilizers containing N, P, and K are in use in some areas of the United States. Although somewhat lower in analysis than the better solid mixtures, these liquids can be loaded, transported, and applied with the use of little labor. Apparently, crop response is as good as is the case with solids.

In irrigation water. In the West, particularly in California and Arizona, there is some application of liquid fertilizers in irrigation waters. Liquid ammonia, phosphoric acid, and even complete fertilizers are allowed to dissolve in the irrigation stream. The nutrients are thus carried into the soil in solution. This requires no added application costs and allows the utilization of relatively inexpensive nitrogen carriers. Increased usage

---

[15] For a review of this subject, see Mehring, "Fertilizers for Special Uses," *op. cit.*

[16] For a discussion of this method, see W. B. Andrews; F. E. Edwards; and J. S. Hammons, *Ammonia as a Source of Nitrogen,* Miss. Agr. Exp. Sta. Bul. 451, 1958.

of these materials attest the growing popularity of the irrigation method of application.

Applied as spray on leaves. The direct application of micronutrients of urea to plants as a spray shows some promise.[17] This type of fertilization is unique. Nor does it involve any extra procedures or machinery since the fertilizer is applied simultaneously with the insecticides. Apple trees seem to respond especially well to urea as much of the nitrogen is absorbed by the leaves. Moreover, that which drips or is washed off is by no means lost for it falls on the soil from which it may later be absorbed by plants.

19:19. FACTORS INFLUENCING THE KIND AND AMOUNT OF FERTILIZERS TO APPLY

The agricultural value of a fertilizer is necessarily uncertain, since a material so easily subject to change is placed in contact with two wide variables, *the soil* and *the crop*. Soil conditions are constantly fluctuating, not only from year to year but progressively throughout the season. The kind and the amount of the fertilizer applied should, as nearly as possible, meet these changes.

Also, the soil and the added fertilizer *react* with each other often very vigorously both chemically and biologically. The reversion of phosphoric acid is an example of the first while the microbial decomposition of the organic ammoniates illustrates the latter. The result may be an increase or, more often, a decrease in the effectiveness of the fertilizer application. Due allowance should be made for these reactions when deciding on the kind and amount of fertilizer to apply.

Again there is *the weather* which has a tremendous effect on the soil, upon the crop, and upon the fertilizer applied. If there is either an excess or deficiency of moisture, full efficiency of the fertilizer cannot be expected. In fact, any factor which may tend to limit plant growth will necessarily reduce fertilizer efficiency, and consequently the crop response to fertilization. It is only when other factors are not limiting that the amounts of fertilizers can be estimated with any degree of certainty.

In spite of the complexity of the situation, however, certain *guides* can be used in deciding the kind and amounts of fertilizers to be applied. The following are especially pertinent:

[17] D. H. Palmiter, *Soil and Foliage Applications of Nitrogen for Apple Scab Control,* N. Y. Agr. Exp. Sta., Farm Res., reprint 156, 1950.

1. Kind of crop to be grown $\begin{cases} \text{economic value} \\ \text{nutrient removal} \\ \text{absorbing ability} \end{cases}$

2. Chemical condition of the soil in respect to $\begin{cases} \text{total nutrients} \\ \text{available nutrients} \end{cases}$

3. Physical state of the soil, especially as to $\begin{cases} \text{moisture content} \\ \text{aeration} \end{cases}$

The last of these factors in most cases has an indirect effect on fertilizer usage and has been discussed sufficiently elsewhere (p. 199 and 252). Consequently, only the first two will be considered in the following sections.

19:20. KIND OF CROP TO BE FERTILIZED

Crops of high economic value such as vegetables justify larger fertilizer expenditures per pound of response obtained. Consequently, for these crops complete fertilizers are used in rather large amounts. As much as 2,000 pounds of analyses such as 8–16–16 are often recommended.

With crops having a low economic value per acre, much lower rates of fertilizer application are generally advisable. The extra yields obtained by applying large amounts of fertilizer are not usually sufficient, especially with such crops as pastures and meadows, to pay for the additional plant nutrients used.

It must always be remembered that the very highest yields obtainable under fertilizer stimulation are not always the ones that give the best return on the money invested. In other words, the law of diminishing returns is a factor in fertilizer practice regardless of the crop being grown. Therefore, the application of moderate amounts of fertilizer is to be urged for all soils until the maximum paying quantity that may be applied for any given crop is approximately ascertained.

If the nutrient removal by a given crop is high, fertilizer applications are usually increased to compensate for this loss. The extra fertilizer may be applied directly to the particular crop under consideration or to some preceding and more responsive crop in the rotation. It should not be implied that in all cases an attempt should be made to return nutrients in amounts equivalent to those that have been removed. Advantage should be taken, particularly with respect to potash, of the nutrient supplying power of the soil. This source is usually insufficient, however, and extra fertilizer additions must be made. In fact, due to the vigorous reaction of phosphorus with soils, additions of this element in considerable excess of the amounts removed by crops and in other ways are usually economically sound.

Tremendous differences exist in the ability of plants to absorb nutrients from a given soil. For example, Lespedesa and peanuts, both of which are legumes, can readily absorb adequate potassium under much lower soil potash levels than can alfalfa or soybeans. Consequently, responses to additions of potassium usually are much greater with the latter two crops. Obviously, crop characteristics deserve very careful study.

19:21. CHEMICAL CONDITION OF THE SOIL— TOTAL VS. PARTIAL ANALYSES [18]

In adequately dealing with the problem of the kind and quantity of fertilizer to add to any particular soil, it is necessary to know, what nutrient element or elements are deficient. At first thought this might appear to be a very simple proposition. Chemistry has to its credit so many wonderful accomplishments that it would seem mere routine to analyze the soil for the various nutrient elements and immediately detect the constituents limiting crop growth.

As will appear later, however, this is asking rather too much unless the chemical data are extensively supplemented by information from other sources. No phase of soil science has received so much popular recognition as has chemical analysis; nor has any other *technical soil procedure* been so generally overrated in the minds of the general public. Nevertheless, certain of these tests (especially the "quick tests") are of considerable value when properly run and when interpreted by competent specialists who have information of a practical nature at their command.

Two general types of chemical analyses are commonly made in respect to the constituents present in soils—*total* and *partial*. In a *total analysis* the entire amount of any particular constituent present in the soil is determined, regardless of its form of combination and its availability. Such data are of great value in studying soil formation and other phases of soil science. Ordinarily, however, they give little if any information on the availability of the essential elements to plants. If this information is to be obtained, analyses suitable for measuring only the available portion of a given nutrient constituent must be employed. Such analyses are called *partial* since only a portion of the total quantity of a soil constituent is determined.

[18] M. Peech, *et al., Methods of Soil Analysis for Soil Fertility Investigations,* Cir. 757, U.S. Dept. of Agriculture, 1947.

For plant tissue tests in respect to soil deficiencies, see J. Q. Lynd, *et al.,* "Nutrient Deficiencies Diagnosed with Foliar Analyses and Plant Tissue Tests," *Agron. Jour.,* 42: 402–07, 1950. A number of articles bearing on tissue testing are cited.

19:22. TESTS FOR AVAILABLE SOIL NUTRIENTS— QUICK TESTS

Many procedures for the *partial analyses* of soils have been developed during the past half century. In general, these procedures attempt to extract from the soil amounts of certain fertility elements comparable to those removed by plants. The large number of extracting solutions which have been employed in trying to measure nutrient availability is mute testimony of the difficulties involved. The extraction solutions employed have varied from strong acids such as H_2SO_4 to weak solutions of CO_2 in water. Buffered salt solutions such as sodium or ammonium acetate are the extracting agents now most commonly used.

Quick tests—general consideration. The group of tests most extensively used for nutrient availability are the so-called *rapid* or *quick tests*.[19] As the name implies, the individual determinations are quickly made, a properly equipped laboratory being able to handle thousands of samples a year. Since these tests are the only ones having practical possibilities for widespread usage, their limitations as well as their merits will be critically reviewed.

A weak extracting solution such as buffered sodium acetate is generally employed in rapid tests and only a few minutes are allowed for the extraction. Most of the nutrients removed are those rather loosely held by the colloidal complex. The test for a given constituent may be reported either in general terms, such as *low, medium,* or *high,* or more specifically, in pounds per acre. The constituents most commonly tested for are phosphorus, potassium, calcium, and magnesium while aluminum, iron, and manganese are frequently included.

Limitations of quick tests. With this general description as a background, we are in a position to consider the specific *limitations* and *merits* of rapid tests. Perhaps the first limitation is the difficulty of properly *sampling soils* in the *field.* Generally only a very small sample is taken, per-

[19] C. A. Spurway, *Soil Testing—A Practical System of Soil Fertility Diagnosis,* Technical Bulletin 132, 2nd rev., Mich. Agr. Exp. Sta., 1938.

R. H. Bray, *Rapid Tests for Measuring and Differentiating Between the Adsorbed and Acid-Soluble Forms of Phosphate in Soils,* Mimeograph Pamphlet A. G. 1028, Ill. Agr. Exp. Sta., 1942 and *Directions for Modified Tests for Replaceable Potassium in Soils,* Mimeograph Pamphlet A. G. 1033, Ill. Agr. Exp. Sta., 1942.

M. Peech and L. English, "Rapid Microchemical Soil Tests," *Soil Sci.,* 57: 167–95, 1944.

H. A. Lunt, *et al., The Morgan Soil Testing System,* Bul. 541, Conn. Agr. Exp. Sta., 1950.

haps a pint or so from an area of land often several acres in size. The chances of error, especially if only a few borings are made, are quite high. In general, at least 15 to 20 borings are suggested for each sample in order to increase the probability that a representative portion of the soil has been obtained.

A second limitation of these tests is the fact that their chemical procedures are somewhat *arbitrary*. It is essentially impossible to extract from a soil sample in a few minutes the amount of a nutrient, or even a constant proportion thereof, that a plant will absorb from that soil in the field during the entire growing season. To make matters worse, serious *technical difficulties* are sometimes encountered in accurately determining the amounts of the several nutrients even after they are extracted. This emphasizes the importance of good scientific equipment as well as technical knowledge and skill in making rapid tests.

Perhaps the biggest hurdle to overcome in the successful employment of

Figure 19:6. A satisfactory interpretation of a quick test analysis of a soil cannot be made without certain pertinent field data. The record sheet above suggests the items that are most helpful to the expert in making a fertility recommendation. (*Modified from a form used by the Ohio Agr. Exp. Sta.*)

quick tests is the *interpretation* of the chemical data obtained. Since the results are arbitrary they must be correlated with crop responses before reliable fertilizer recommendations can be made. Even then the recommendations must be made in light of a practical knowledge of the crop to be grown, the characteristics of the soil under study and other environmental conditions. Two soils testing exactly the same in respect to a given constituent have been found to respond quite differently in terms of crop yields to identical fertilizer treatments in the field.

Trained personnel should make and interpret tests. Obviously, it is unwise to place any particular confidence in fertilizer recommendations when the tests are made and interpreted by an amateur. Not only might the novice make inaccurate determinations but he is sure to lack the knowledge and judgment necessary for a rational interpretation in terms of fertilizer needs.

Obviously the interpretation of quick test data is best accomplished by experienced and technically trained men, who fully understand the scientific principles underlying the common field procedures. Although the rapid tests themselves are made by specially trained analysts and not usually by the soil and crop specialists, the latter fully understand the interpretation and limitations of the chemical data furnished them.

As already suggested, it is essential that a person have considerable related information in order to make the proper use of quick test data. Examples of supplementary data desirable are shown by the sample information sheet in Figure 19:6. This supplementary information may be as helpful as the actual test results in making fertilizer recommendations.

Merits of rapid tests. It must not be inferred from the preceding discussion that the limitations of rapid tests outweigh their advantages. In fact, when the precautions already cited are observed, rapid tests are an invaluable tool in making fertilizer recommendations. Moreover, these tests will become of even greater importance in so far as they are correlated with the results of field fertilizer experiments. Such field trials undoubtedly will be expanded to keep pace with the increasing use of the rapid tests.

19:23. THE BROADER ASPECTS OF FERTILIZER PRACTICE

It is obvious that fertilizer practice involves many intricate details regarding soils, crops, and fertilizers. In fact, the interrelations of these three are so complicated and far reaching that a practical grasp of the situation requires years of experience. The unavoidable lack of exactness in fertilizer decisions should ever be kept in mind.

Leaving the details and viewing the situation in a broad way, it seems to be well established that any fertilizer scheme should provide phosphoric acid and potash in amounts sufficient to balance the nitrogen, since this element is so active and subject to such ready loss from the soil. A plan that calls for an abundance of minerals is a sound one if it does not unduly waste nutrients by fixation or by leaching. Such a plan, coupled with a heavy fertilization of the money crop, does not, however, constitute all that is deemed fundamental in a rational system of soil fertilization.

Not only must the soil, the crop, and the fertilizer receive careful study, but the crop rotation employed and its management should be considered in addition. Obviously, also the fertilizer applications must be correlated with the use of farm manure, crop residues, green manure, trace elements, and lime. Moreover, the residues of previous fertilizer additions must not be forgotten. In short, fertilizer practice is only a phase, but a very important one, of the fertility management of soils.

Farm Manure
and Green Manure

CHAPTER 20

Farm manure is one of the most important agricultural by-products. By its utilization part of the unused portion of the crop may enter the soil, there to exert an influence far greater than its nutrient content would lead one to expect. The world has already entered an era in which the prevention of agricultural waste is becoming necessary. Therefore, up-to-date farm management demands a more careful handling, as well as a wiser utilization of the manure produced on the farm.

20:1. THE CHEMICAL COMPOSITION OF FARM MANURE [1]

The term *farm manure* is employed in reference to the refuse from all animals of the farm, although as a general rule the bulk of the manure which ultimately finds its way back to the land is produced by cattle. This is supplemented to a greater or less extent by manure from horses, hogs, sheep, and poultry.

Farm manure consists of two original components, the *solid* and the *liquid,* in about the ratio of 3 to 1. On the average, a little more than *one half the nitrogen,* almost *all of the phosphoric acid,* and about *two fifths of the potash* are found in the solid manure. (See Fig. 20:1.) Nevertheless, this apparent advantage of the solid manure is offset by the ready availability of the constituents carried by the urine, giving the latter about

---

[1] For analyses of farm manure, see:

L. L. Van Slyke, *Fertilizers and Crop Production* (New York: Orange Judd, 1932), pp. 216–26.

C. E. Thorne, *Farm Manures* (New York: Orange Judd, 1941), pp. 89–93.

A. F. Gustafson, "Farm Manure—Its Production, Management and Use," Extension Bul. 642, Cornell Univ. Agr. Exp. Sta., 1944.

A. F. Gustafson, "Poultry Manures," War Emergency Bul. 117, Cornell Univ. Agr. Exp. Sta., 1944.

an equal agricultural value with the solid excrement. Such figures are suggestive of the care that should be taken of the liquid manure.

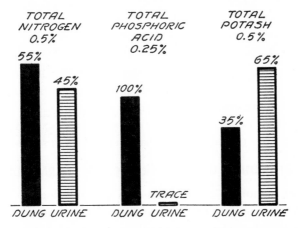

Figure 20:1. Diagram showing the distribution of nitrogen, phosphoric acid, and potash between the solid and liquid portions of average farm manure.

While extended data are available as to the chemical composition of the liquid and solid portions of the excreta from the various farm animals,[2] it is extremely difficult to quote reliable average figures on mixed farm manure as it ordinarily is applied to the land. This is because a number of variable factors enter in which may radically change the amounts and proportions of nitrogen, phosphoric acid, and potash present. The more important of these factors are: (1) kind of animal; (2) age, condition, and individuality of animals; (3) food consumed; (4) litter used; and

[2] The composition of fresh animal-excrement [a]

	Excrement, percentage	Percentage of			
		H₂O	N	P₂O₅	K₂O
Horse	Solid 80	75	0.55	0.30	0.40
	Urine, 20	90	1.35	Trace	1.25
	Whole manure	78	0.70	0.25	0.55
Cow	Solid, 70	85	0.40	0.20	0.10
	Urine, 30	92	1.00	Trace	1.35
	Whole manure	86	0.60	0.15	0.45
Sheep	Solid, 67	60	0.75	0.50	0.45
	Urine, 33	85	1.35	0.05	2.10
	Whole manure	68	0.95	0.35	1.00
Swine	Solid, 60	80	0.55	0.50	0.40
	Urine, 40	97	0.40	0.10	0.45
	Whole manure	87	0.50	0.35	0.40
Hens	Whole manure	55	1.00	0.80	0.40

[a] L. L. Van Slyke, *op. cit.*, p. 218.

(5) the handling and storage which the manure receives before it is spread on the land.

In spite of the marked variability of farm manure, representative composition figures will be ventured. For purposes of calculation and discussion, average farm manure ready for field application will be considered as containing *0.5 per cent of nitrogen, 0.25 per cent of phosphoric acid,* and *0.5 per cent of potash.* The tentative nature of such figures, however, must always be kept in mind. Besides nitrogen, phosphorus, and potassium, farm manure contains calcium, magnesium, sulfur, and probably all of the trace elements. The latter are in some cases extremely important in the maintenance of a balanced nutrient condition in soils so treated.

20:2. OUTSTANDING CHARACTERISTICS OF FARM MANURE [3]

As a farm manure is essentially a fertilizer, it is logical to contrast it with the ready-mixed commercial fertilizers on the market. In such a comparison, six characteristics are outstanding: (1) the moist condition of manure; (2) its variability; (3) its low analysis; (4) its unbalanced nutrient condition; (5) the residual influence exerted by farm manure; and (6) its rapid fermentative processes.

Moisture and variability. Of the above characteristics the first two may be disposed of quickly. The variability of farm manure has already been sufficiently emphasized since it is a condition ordinarily to be expected. As to the moisture, whether in fresh or well-rotted manure, the amount may vary from 50 to 80 per cent depending on conditions.

Low analysis. Since representative farm manure is considered to contain 0.5 per cent of nitrogen, 0.25 per cent of phosphoric acid, and 0.5 per cent of potash, a ton of this material supplies only 10, 5, and 10 pounds of total nitrogen, phosphoric acid, and potash respectively. It is without doubt a low-analysis material when compared to the commercial fertilizers commonly on the market, such as an 8–16–16 for instance, which

---

[3] Data as to the amounts of manure likely to be produced by the different classes of farm animals are often useful in fertility calculations.

Tons of Manure Produced Annually by Farm Animals per 1,000 Pounds Live Weight [a]

Animal	Weight of Excrement	Weight of Bedding	Total Weight
Horse	9.00	3.0	12.00
Cow	13.50	1.5	15.00
Pig	15.25	3.0	18.25
Sheep	6.25	3.5	9.75
Steer	7.50	1.5	9.00
Hen	4.75	—	4.75

[a] L. L. Van Slyke, *op. cit.,* p. 287.

supplies 160, 320, and 320 pounds per ton respectively of these three constituents.

It must not be assumed, however, that the amounts of the three fertilizer elements added to an acre of land in an ordinary application of farm manure are correspondingly small. Because of the large acre applications of this fertilizer (10, 15, or even 20 tons an acre) the quantities of the nutrient elements added are comparatively large. For example, 10 tons of representative farm manure will supply in total about 100 pounds of nitrogen, 50 pounds of phosphoric acid, and 100 pounds of potash.

In such a comparison, however, it is well to remember that only a part of the nutrient constituents of farm manure is readily available. In general, only about *one half of the nitrogen, one sixth of the phosphoric acid,* and a little more than *one half of the potash* are readily available (during the first season) to plants. On the basis of readily available nutrients 1 ton of average farm manure supplies approximately 5 pounds of N, 1 pound of P_2O_5, and 5 pounds of K_2O.

Nutrients unbalanced. The phosphoric acid of most mineral soils is not only low but rather unavailable. Moreover, the phosphorus added in fertilizers is adsorbed rather strongly by the soil complex and is likely to become partly inactive. As a consequence, it seems necessary for a complete fertilizer to carry as much or even more phosphoric acid than nitrogen or even potash. The ratio of a ready-mixed complete commercial fertilizer in respect to these three constituents ($N-P_2O_5-K_2O$) ordinarily is seldom less than 1–1–1 or 1–2–1, while in some cases the ratio is as high as 1–3–1.

Farm manure with an availability ratio of 5–1–5 is obviously too low in phosphoric acid to be fully effective and is considered as unbalanced for that reason. It is often advisable, especially when the farm manure is used for cereal crops, to correct this condition by reinforcing it with suitable amounts of superphosphate or some other phosphatic fertilizer. (See p. 519.)

Residual effects. The length of time through which the effects of an application of farm manure may be detected in crop growth is surprising. Hall [4] cites data from the Rothamsted experiments in which the effects of eight yearly acre applications of 14 tons each were apparent forty years after the last treatment. This, of course, is an extreme case. Ordinarily, profitable increases may be obtained from manure only for three or four years after the treatment.

[4] A. D. Hall, *Fertilizers and Manures* (New York: Dutton, 1928), p. 234.

The sixth outstanding characteristic of farm manure, its fermentative and decay activities, will be considered in the following section.

20:3. THE FERMENTATION OF MANURE [5]

In the process of digestion, the food of animals becomes more or less decomposed. This condition comes about partly because of the digestive processes themselves and partly from the concurrent bacterial action that takes place. Consequently, the fresh excrement consists of decayed or partially decayed plant materials. This is more or less intimately mixed with litter and the whole mass is moistened with the urine carrying considerable quantities of soluble compounds of nitrogen, potassium, and other nutrients. Moreover, the whole mass is teeming with bacteria and other organisms.

Aerobic fermentation.   When manure is first produced, it is usually somewhat loose, especially if considerable litter is present. The first microbial changes are, therefore, likely to be largely aerobic in nature. These transformations usually are rapid and are accompanied by considerable heat.

The simple nitrogenous compounds are influenced first, although the more complicated constituents are by no means unaffected. Carbon dioxide is given off in large quantities. The urea of the urine is readily influenced by aerobic activities and quickly undergoes hydrolysis. The ammonium carbonate which results is unstable and promptly produces ammonia. The odor of this gas in horse stables gives evidence of such a change.

$$CO(NH_2)_2 + 2\ H_2O \longrightarrow (NH_4)_2CO_3$$

$$(NH_4)_2CO_3 \longrightarrow 2\ NH_3\uparrow + CO_2\uparrow + H_2O$$

If conditions are favorable for nitrification, and such is likely to be the case, nitrates may appear in abundance. Since such compounds of nitrogen are very soluble and subject to but little adsorption, serious leaching losses may occur. Hence, in the earlier and better aerated decomposition stages, farm manure may be depleted of its nitrogen in two forms—ammoniacal and nitrate.

Anaerobic decay.   In a manure the gaseous oxygen is gradually used up while carbon dioxide is released. The decay now changes from aerobic to anaerobic, it becomes slower, and the temperature tends to fall. New

---

[5] For discussions concerning the decomposition of manure, see S. A. Waksman, *Principles of Soil Microbiology* (Baltimore: Williams and Wilkins, 1932), Chap. 25.

organisms may now function, although many of those active under aerobic conditions probably continue to be effective. The products become changed to a considerable degree. Carbon dioxide, of course, is still evolved in large amounts, but instead of ammonia being formed, the nitrogenous matter is converted, at least in part, into the usual putrefactive products.

Reduction in bulk. Because of the great loss of carbon dioxide and water during these decay processes, there is a considerable reduction in the bulk of the manure. Fresh excrement readily loses from 20 to 40 per cent in bulk by partial rotting and perhaps 50 per cent as it becomes more thoroughly decomposed. It is often argued that, if the manure is properly stored, this rapid loss of carbon dioxide and water should raise the percentage amounts of the fertilizer elements present. This may be true for potash and phosphoric acid. But in practice the losses in handling due to leaching and fermentation sometimes are so pronounced as to place well-rotted manure at a disadvantage as far as its total supply of plant nutrients is concerned. This is especially likely to be the case in respect to nitrogen which is subject to losses by both volatilization and leaching.

Well-decayed vs. fresh manure. In many cases, however, well-rotted manure [6] is more desirable than the fresh material. This is especially true if the fresh manure is strawy. The addition of straw to a soil may widen its carbon-nitrogen ratio and reduce as well as prevent the formation of nitrate nitrogen (p. 147). Strawy manure apparently tends to produce the same effect and a crop immediately following its application, may show nitrogen starvation. Under such conditions the well-decayed product is more desirable. When manure is used as a top-dressing, as is sometimes the case with fall wheat and other crops, well-rotted material should always be applied if possible. In trucking and vegetable gardening, well-decomposed manure is generally preferred. Such is also the case with home gardens, flower beds, lawns, and greenhouses. *Composting*, which is largely a biological process, is often resorted to, especially in the latter cases, farm manure being used in building up the compost pile. Because of its high organic content and the influence of its nitrogen and microorganisms, manure is especially valuable for such purposes.

---

[6] A change of a biological nature which takes place if the manure dries out too much is *fire-fanging*. Many people consider this to be due to actual combustion, as the manure is very light in weight and has every appearance of being burned. This condition, however, is produced by fungi and the dry and dusty appearance of the manure is due to the mycelia, which penetrate in all directions and use up the valuable constituents. Manure thus affected is of little value either as a fertilizer or as a soil amendment.

A compost is commonly made of alternate layers of manure and the vegetable matter that is to be decayed. Layers of sod or of soil high in organic matter may also be introduced to advantage. The manure supplies especially active decay organisms which, in the presence of nitrogen, cause a rapid and effective humification. The foundation of such a compost is usually soil, and the pile is preferably capped with earth.

The mass should be kept moist in order to reduce the loss of ammonia and elemental nitrogen and to encourage vigorous bacterial action. Superphosphate is often added to balance up the mixture and make it more effective. A nitrogen fertilizer may also be employed with profit as well as ground limestone.

20:4. NUTRIENT LOSSES DURING MANURIAL PRODUCTION

A certain amount of every crop is lost before it is consumed by animals. Such loss is usually small on most farms, especially when compared to the nutrients retained by the livestock. Attention is therefore particularly directed toward those losses sustained by the food as it undergoes normal digestion, and is about to be voided.

As might be expected, the data bearing on this phase is variable, since so much depends on the age, conditions, individuality, and class of animal, and the character of the food. As a generalization and for purposes of calculation, it may be considered that *three fourths of the nitrogen, four fifths of the phosphorus, nine tenths of the potash,* and *one half of the organic matter* are recovered in the voided excrement. This means losses of about 25, 20, 10, and 50 per cent respectively for these constituents. (See Fig. 20:2.)

20:5. LOSSES DURING THE HANDLING AND STORAGE OF FARM MANURE

Since approximately one half of the nitrogen and three fifths of the potash of average farm manure are in a soluble condition, the possibility of loss by leaching is usually great, even though the manure is not exposed to especially heavy rainfall. In addition, decomposition, both of an aerobic and anaerobic nature, will cause a rapid waste of nitrogen in the ammonium, nitrate, and elemental forms. Packing and moistening the manure in the pile will change the decay from aerobic to anaerobic, thus reducing somewhat the waste of gaseous nitrogen while encouraging the simplification of the manurial constituents. Tight floors in the stables and impervious bottoms under the manure pile should considerably diminish leaching losses.

While the figures are extremely variable, it is probable that *one half* of the *nitrogen, potash,* and *organic matter* and at least *one third* of the *phosphoric acid* of farm manure are lost even under fairly careful methods of storage. On farms where manure remains outside for several months, the losses will, of course, be higher. Thus, at least one half of the nutrient constituents of the manure may often be wasted. This represents considerably over one half of the fertilizer value, since the elements removed are those most readily available to plants.

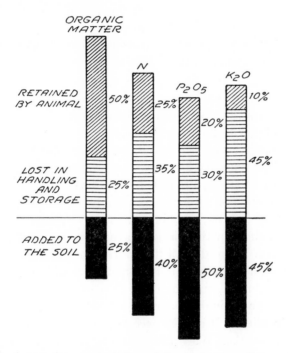

Figure 20:2. A tentative representation of the proportion of the organic matter, nitrogen, phosphoric acid, and potash originally present in the feed (1) retained by the animals, (2) lost in handling and storage of the manure, and (3) applied to the soil.

Considering the losses which the food sustains during digestion and the waste of the manure in handling and storage, it cannot be expected that more than *25 per cent of the organic matter, 40 per cent of the nitrogen, 50 per cent of the phosphoric acid,* and *45 per cent of the potash* of the original crop as removed from the land will, under ordinary conditions, reach the soil. (See Fig. 20:2.) This is a fairly conservative estimate.

20:6. PRACTICAL HANDLING AND STORAGE OF FARM MANURE

Reducing liquid losses. Considerable loss of manurial constituents occurs in the stable, due to leaching. Therefore, the first care is to the bedding, which should be chosen for its absorptive properties, its cost, and its capacity to keep animals clean.

Coordinated with this are the floors, which should be tight so that the free liquid will be held in contact with the absorbing materials. Preservation in stalls with tight floors has been for years a common method of handling farm manure in England. The trampling of the animals and the continued addition of litter as the manure accumulates aid in the preservation.

Apply directly to the field. When it is possible to haul the manure directly to the field, this practice is to be advised. This system saves time and labor, and very largely obviates leaching losses since the soluble portions of the manure are carried directly into the soil. Such a practice, however, will not prevent some losses by volatilization.

It should not be assumed that daily spreading will always result in the greatest conservation of nutrients. For example, consider the areas where, during the winter months, manure is spread on frozen ground or on snow over frozen ground. In the spring the snow melts and the water often runs off the land before the soil thaws. This melt water carries much of the soluble potash and nitrogen of the manure with it, especially on land that is quite sloping. As much as about 25 per cent of the potash supplied in manure may be lost in this manner.[7]

Storage in piles. It is often necessary to store manure outside, fully exposed to the weather. When this is the case, certain precautions should be observed. In the first place, the pile should be located on level ground far enough from the eaves of any building so that it receives no extra water in times of storm. (See Fig. 20:3.) The sides of the heap should be steep enough to shed water readily, while the depth of the pile should be such as to allow little leaching even after heavy storms. The earth under the manure may be slightly dished in order to prevent loss of excess water. If

[7] See A. R. Midgley and D. E. Dunklee, *Fertility Runoff Losses from Manure Spread during the Winter,* Bul. 523, Vt. Agr. Exp. Sta., 1945.

possible, the soil of the depression should be puddled, or better, covered with cement.

Figure 20:3. Millions of dollars worth of nutrients are lost annually by the careless handling of farm manure. Scenes such as the above are all too common.

Manure pits. Some European farmers have constructed manure pits of concrete. These pits are usually rectangular in shape with a shed covering. One or even both ends may be open to facilitate the removal of the manure. In such a structure, leaching is prevented by the solid bottom while the roof allows a better control of moisture conditions. By keeping the manure carefully piled and well moistened, decomposition may proceed with a minimum waste. Large losses of nitrogen and especially of carbon (as CO_2), however, will still take place.

Covered barnyards. Another method of storage is in covered barnyards or in sheds where animals are fed and bedded. The floor of such a structure should be more or less impervious. The manure is kept thoroughly packed as well as damp by the animals. This is a common method of handling manure in the fattening of steers in the Middle West and elsewhere and allows a minimum loss.

It is evident from this consideration that well-protected and carefully preserved manure will be higher in available plant nutrients than that carelessly handled. Since hauling directly to the field affords less chance of loss by leaching and fermentation, this mode of handling should be adopted wherever feasible. If storage must be resorted to, the precautions already suggested should be observed insofar as possible.

20:7. ECONOMIC UTILIZATION OF FARM MANURE

Method and rate of application. In the application of manure to the land, the same general principles observed in the use of any fertilizer should be kept in mind. Of these, fineness of division and evenness of distribution are of prime importance. The efficiency of the manure may be raised considerably thereby.

A third important factor is the rate of application. Since the supply of manure is often limited in diversified farming, it is usually better, especially with field crops, to decrease the amounts at each spreading and cover a greater acreage. Thus, instead of adding 20 tons to the acre, 10 tons may be applied and twice the acreage covered. Applications can then be made oftener and a larger and quicker net return realized for each ton of manure.

Not only is there a greater crop yield per ton from the smaller applications but a greater recovery of the manurial fertility in the crops may also result. Ohio experiments [8] show that, in the first rotation after the manure is applied, a 25 to 30 per cent higher recovery may be expected from an 8-ton treatment to the acre than from a 16-ton application.

Manure spreader. Evenness of application and fineness of division are greatly facilitated by the use of a manure spreader. This also makes possible the uniform application of small amounts of manure, even as low as 5 or 6 tons to the acre. It is impossible, of course, to spread such small amounts by hand and obtain an even distribution.

Surface application vs. plowing under. Whether manure should be plowed under or not depends largely on the crop on which it is used. On meadows and pastures it is spread as a top-dressing. With certain other crops, however, it is commonly plowed under. This is particularly necessary if the manure is long, coarse, and not well rotted. If manure is fine and well decomposed, it may be harrowed into the surface soil as is sometimes done with wheat. Obviously, the method of application employed will depend on the crop, the soil, and the condition of the manure.

[8] C. E. Thorne, *et al., Plans and Summary Tables of the Experiments at the Central Farm,* Circular 120, Ohio Agr. Exp. Sta., 108, 1912.

C:N ratio. In the utilization of farm manure it is well to remember that its addition to the soil in large amounts may widen the carbon-nitrogen ratio. This is likely to be the case if the manure is unusually strawy. The delay in plant growth that is sometimes observed from the use of strawy manure may be due to the reduction of nitrate accumulation induced by the high carbon content of the materials added. If such is likely to be the case, a sufficient interval should elapse between the application of the manure and the planting of the crop in order that nitrification may again be active.

20:8. REINFORCEMENT OF FARM MANURE

Reasons for reinforcement. As already explained, average farm manure contains about five times more readily available nitrogen and potash respectively than active phosphoric acid. (See p. 511.) It is thus badly unbalanced. In comparison with a complete commercial fertilizer, there should be at least five times more available phosphoric acid in the manure than is usually present to be sure that its nitrogen and potassium are properly balanced. Hence, in order to obtain the most economical results with manure, liberal applications of phosphorus should be used in the rotation in connection with it. Sometimes, however, part of the phosphatic fertilizer is mixed with the manure before it is applied to the land. This is the practice that is spoken of as *reinforcement*.

Rate of phosphate additions. The amount of phosphatic fertilizers that should be added to a ton of farm manure depends on the acre-rate of application of the latter. Ordinarily from 500 to 600 pounds of 16 to 20 per cent superphosphate or its equivalent are applied to the acre in this way during the course of a field crop rotation. Thus, if 10 tons of manure are spread on an acre, each ton should be reinforced with 50 or 60 pounds of ordinary superphosphate. If 15 tons of manure are applied an acre, the reinforcement may be at the rate of 35 to 40 pounds of superphosphate a ton. If raw rock phosphate is used instead, it generally is applied at double the rate of superphosphate because of the less ready availability of the rock.

If the superphosphate is added each day in the stable in the case of dairy cows, 2 pounds per cow will amount to a reinforcement of about 50 pounds to the ton of manure. With this as a gauge any desired rate of superphosphate application to the land may be decided on, provided, of course, the tons of manure that are to go on each acre of land are known in advance. Thus, if the rate of manuring is to be 10 tons, 2 pounds of superphosphate daily per cow would mean the application of 500 pounds of superphosphate to each acre of land receiving the manure.

20:9. CROPS THAT RESPOND TO FARM MANURE

Since manure is available in limited amounts on the average farm and as mineral fertilizers give good results on grass and legumes, it is often considered judicious to reserve most of the manure for other crops of the rotation. This is especially the case when a feed crop such as corn or such cash crops as cabbage, tobacco, cotton, or potatoes are grown.

The top-dressing of the meadows with farm manure is allowable, especially with a new seeding or when the sod is soon to be plowed under for a cultivated crop. When the soil is acid and lime cannot be applied, it is practically necessary to top-dress the new seeding in order to insure a good stand of clover. Manure thus takes the place of lime, in a way, and strengthens and protects the crop. In many communities a large proportion of the farm manure is applied to the meadows, no doubt for the reasons just suggested.

The value of manure in orchards should not be overlooked, especially on sandy soils, as the maintenance of organic matter as well as nitrogen is a vital factor in orchard practice. In most cases, however, the fertility of an orchard soil can be maintained adequately by means of leguminous cover-crops and a nitrogenous commercial fertilizer, thus releasing what farm manure there is for use in the regular field rotation or for vegetables.

With trucking, garden, and greenhouse crops, the applications of large amounts of manure when obtainable have always proved advisable. As a matter of fact, manure when correctly handled, has shown itself one of the best fertilizers for intensive operations. This is due not only to the nutrients carried by the manure, but to the large quantities of easily decomposed organic matter that are at the same time introduced. As large amounts of highly phosphatic fertilizers usually accompany or follow the manure in such cases, direct reinforcing is unnecessary.

20:10. FARM MANURE AND THE MAINTENANCE OF SOIL FERTILITY

The value of farm manure is determined not only by the organic matter it furnishes but especially by the quantity of nitrogen that it supplies. The nitrogen, when released by microbial activity, is used as a nutrient by higher plants. In addition, it makes possible the maintenance of a higher soil organic matter level than would otherwise be the case. Thus, even though farm manure no doubt has a very considerable influence on the physical and biological properties of the soil, it must be considered particularly as a nitrogen fertilizer and to a lesser degree one of potash also.

Viewed in this light the question immediately arises: Can the fertility problems of the representative general or dairy farm be solved by the use of farm manure even if it should be reinforced adequately with superphosphate? The answer, of course, is "No," especially if a more or less permanent fertility system is in operation. There are several reasons for such an answer.

In the first place, hardly one half of the nitrogen, potash, and phosphoric acid removed from the soil by the crops fed to animals is returned to the land in farm manure. (See Fig. 20:2.) And, of course, not all crops are used for animal food. Thus, the utilization of farm manure alone would obviously result in a gradual reduction of soil fertility unless other sources of nutrients were resorted to. Reinforcement with superphosphate would only delay the evil hour. It is only when farm manure is properly coordinated with lime, commercial fertilizers, and legumes as well as with good tillage, weed elimination, and soil-water and erosion control, that the fullest benefits from this valuable farm by-product are to be realized.

20:11. GREEN MANURES—DEFINED

From time immemorial the turning under of a green crop to better the condition of the soil has been a common agricultural practice. Records show that the use of beans, vetches, and lupines for such a purpose was well understood by the Romans, who probably borrowed the idea from other nations. The art was lost in Europe to a great extent during the Middle Ages, but was revived again as the modern era was approached.

This practice of turning into the soil undecomposed green plant tissue is referred to as *green-manuring*. Material so added, if the soil is in a proper condition and well managed, brings about a number of favorable effects and may aid materially in maintaining or raising the crop-producing capacity of a soil.

20:12. THE BENEFITS OF GREEN-MANURING

Supplies organic matter. The influence exerted by green-manuring which is generally mentioned first relates to the organic supply of the soil.

When there is a shortage of farm manure, the practice becomes of special importance since roots and other crop residues may not be adequate to maintain the humus content of the land.

Addition of nitrogen. The plowing under of a green manure not only adds organic carbon to the soil but also returns soil nitrogen. The amount of nitrogen may be large or small, depending on conditions. If the crop turned under is a legume and the nodule organisms have been active, the store of soil nitrogen may be thereby increased. The organic matter content is also augmented since the amount of soil humus finally formed is determined to a considerable degree by the amount of organic nitrogen present (see p. 149).

Biochemical benefits. The organic material added in green manures also acts as a food for soil organisms, and tends to stimulate biological changes sometimes to a marked degree.[9] Such biochemical action is of special consequence in the production of carbon dioxide, ammonium, nitrates, and perhaps other simple compounds. The response of the general-purpose flora of the soil and of the *Azotobacter* to carbonaceous and nitrogenous materials is well known. Even in peat soils, made up largely of organic matter, organisms may be definitely activated by the turning under of a green-manuring crop.

Conservation and availability of nutrients. A growing green-manuring crop exerts a conserving influence on the nutrients of the soil since it takes up soluble constituents that might otherwise be lost in drainage or by erosion. In this respect it functions as a *cover-crop*.[10] The presence of a green manure crop on the soil at a time when it might otherwise be bare is highly desirable.

The increased availability of the inorganic constituents of the soil is a phase that should not be forgotten in this connection. Jensen [11] found that the addition of 3 per cent of green manure to the soil raised the solubility of lime and phosphoric acid 30 to 100 per cent. This was over and above the mineral constituents which came directly from the decomposing green

[9] For the activating influence of green manures, see R. D. Lewis and J. H. Hunter, "The Nitrogen, Organic Carbon, and pH of Southeastern Coastal Plain Soils as Influenced by Green-manuring Crops," *Jour. Amer. Soc. Agron.*, 32: 586–601, 1940.

[10] A *cover-crop* is one planted for the purpose of covering or protecting the soil at certain times of year, especially from erosion hazards.

A *catch-crop* is one that follows the main crop. It must be rapid in growth as it can occupy the soil only a relatively short time. Both a cover-crop and a catch-crop may, on occasion, be used as a green manure.

[11] C. A. Jensen, "Effect of Decomposing Organic Matter on the Solubility of Certain Inorganic Constituents of the Soil," *Jour. Agr. Res.*, 9: 253–68, May 1917.

crop. Potassium, magnesium, and iron may also be markedly influenced in the same manner.

20:13. INFLUENCE OF LEGUMINOUS GREEN MANURES ON SOIL NITROGEN

When a nonlegume is turned under as a green manure, nitrogen originally in the soil is merely returned in an organic form. There is no gain. But if a legume is so utilized, there is a possibility of increasing temporarily the soil nitrogen to the extent of the symbiotic fixation. Since an increase in the organic nitrogen of the soil means an increase in fertility as well as a possible rise in humus, the probable magnitude of the fixation is worthy of some attention.

Amounts of nitrogen fixed.   Data have already been cited (p. 424) which indicate that the nodule organisms of a vigorous crop of alfalfa might fix above 200 pounds of nitrogen an acre. Comparable figures for red clover are perhaps 100 to 150 pounds an acre. Soybeans compare rather well with red clover but hairy vetch and field beans ordinarily will acquire from the air only a half or a third as much nitrogen. If these crops are turned under, the soil, of course, gains in organic nitrogen to the extent of the microbial fixation. For instance, a ton of dry red clover contains from 40 to 50 pounds of nitrogen. If a green-manuring crop equivalent to 2 tons of such dry substance an acre should be turned under, there would be a gain in soil nitrogen of 80 to 100 pounds.

Increase in humus.   Assuming the latter figure and a carbon-nitrogen ratio of 12 to 1, this amount of organic nitrogen should support an increase in humus of perhaps 1,800 pounds if it were all used in this way. Concurrently, of course, there is the stimulation of soil organisms of all kinds. This activation, common to all green manures when properly used, is especially charactertistic of those of a leguminous nature.

20:14. THE DESIRABLE CHARACTERISTICS OF A GREEN MANURE

An ideal green-manuring crop should possess three major characteristics: (1) rapid growth; (2) abundant and succulent tops; and (3) the ability to grow well on poor soils. The more rapid the growth, the greater the chance of fitting such a crop into the rotation and of using it economically as a means of soil improvement. Abundant tops and roots are, of course, a necessary feature. And as already suggested, the higher the moisture content of the green manure the more rapid is the decay and the more quickly are benefits obtained. As the need of organic matter is especially urgent on poor land, a hardy crop has great advantages.

When other conditions are equal, it is better to make use of a leguminous green manure in preference to a nonleguminous one, because of the nitrogen gained by the soil and the organic activity it promotes. A little additional nitrogen is sometimes of tremendous importance.

However, it is often difficult to obtain a catch of some legumes and they may be so valuable as animal feed, that it is poor management to turn the stand under. Again, the seeds of many legumes are expensive, almost prohibiting the use of such crops as green manures. Moreover, some legumes do not fit into the common rotations in such a way as to be turned under conveniently as a green manure.

20:15. PLANTS SUITABLE AS GREEN MANURES

Some of the plants utilized in the various parts of the United States as green manures are listed in Table 20:1. Their value, of course, depends

TABLE 20:1

List of Possible Green-manuring Crops

Legumes		Nonlegumes	
Southern Section Especially	*Wide Range*	*Wide Range in Most Cases*	
Crimson clover	Alfalfa	Rye	Ryegrass
Bur clover	Red clover	Oats	Sudan grass
Lespedeza	Sweet clover	Barley	Mustard
Crotalaria	Soy bean	Millet	Rape
Smooth vetch	Canadian field	Buckwheat	Weeds
Austrian winter	pea	Wheat	Winter oats and
pea	Cowpea		barley

in part on climate, some of those mentioned being unsuited to northern regions and vice versa.

The growing of two crops together for green-manuring purposes is sometimes recommended. If properly chosen in respect to growth habits, climatic adaptation, and soil requirements, the advantages are noteworthy. Not only can larger amounts of green material be produced but also, if one of the crops is a legume, nitrogen fixation may be taken advantage of. Also one crop may offer physical support to the other, a factor of no mean importance when dealing with plants that tend to lodge.

Oats and peas, and rye and vetch are excellent examples of such green-manure combinations. The two nonlegumes in these cases are highly desirable because of their rapid, abundant, and succulent growth and because they may be accommodated to almost any rotation. These nonlegumes are hardy and will start under adverse weather conditions and in a poorly prepared seedbed. They are thus extremely valuable on poor soils. Moreover, their influence is notably enhanced by sowing a legume with them. In any case the mixtures should be plowed under when at mid-growth or soon after, as at that time their carbon-nitrogen ratio is comparatively narrow.

20:16. THE PRACTICAL UTILIZATION OF GREEN MANURES

The turning under of green crops must be judicious in order that the soil may not be clogged with too much undecayed matter. Once or twice in a rotation is usually enough for such treatments. Good drainage should always be assured as aeration is of vital importance in the proper decay of plant residues in the soil.

In regions of low rainfall. In regions where rainfall is scanty, great caution must be observed in the use of green manures. The available moisture that should go to the succeeding crop may be used by the green manure itself or in the processes of decay, and the soil left light and open. In the drier portions of the United States, it is doubtful whether green manures are of any real value because of this.

Conditions at time of turning. It is generally best to turn green crops under when their succulence is near the maximum and yet at a time when suitable tops have been produced. With most green manure this occurs at about or a little beyond the half-mature stage. The content of lignin and other compounds which may resist microbial attack is still low. Moreover, the carbon-nitrogen ratio of the green manure is comparatively narrow at this time.

Again, the succulence encourages a rapid and more or less satisfactory decay, with the maximum production of humus and other products. The plowing should be done, if possible, at a season when a plentiful supply of rain occurs. The effectiveness of this type of manuring is thereby much enhanced as the moisture conditions are such as to insure a rapid and effective decomposition.

Whether to fall- or spring-plow a green-manuring crop is of practical concern and is decided largely by such factors as climate, the nature of the soil, and the crop used. Fall plowing seems to be of some advantage in the northern states as measured by nitrate accumulations during the following summer. The reverse seems to be true farther south where the winters are milder and shorter and where the spring and summer seasons are longer. Whether the soil is sandy or clayey must also be considered.

Rotation considerations. Whether or not a crop can be used advantageously as a green manure often is determined by the character of the rotation. In the northern states, due to the shorter season, it is often somewhat of a problem whether a green manure may be introduced without seriously interfering with the regular crops of the rotation. Not only is the period for the growth of the green manure very short, but the time interval between the turning under of the green substance and the planting of the next crop is often inadequate. In our southern states this disadvantage is not encountered to such an extent, since the season is much longer and the rotation less likely to offer interference.

20:17. GREEN-MANURING AND THE MAINTENANCE OF SOIL FERTILITY

It cannot be emphasized too strongly that green manuring is only one of the several practices that may be employed in an attempt to maintain, or partially maintain, the fertility of arable lands. Moreover, it usually is the last of the various method so employed to be resorted to. Crop residues, especially roots, and farm manure under ordinary conditions supply most of the organic matter found in mineral arable soils, and if the nitrogen level is high, these should suffice as far as organic matter maintenance is concerned. Whether or not green manures are used should depend in part on the adequacy of these sources of plant tissue. The plowing under of green plants, therefore, may be considered as a supplementary measure, very important in some cases but ordinarily not so essential in the general fertility scheme as are certain other practices.

The Fertility Management
of Mineral Soils

CHAPTER 21

While most of the fundamental facts and conceptions regarding the nature and properties of soils and their plant relationships have been presented, they have not been adequately correlated in a practical way. It seems desirable at this point, therefore, to interrelate these facts and ideas in such a manner as to establish a general scheme of fertility management flexible enough to meet any situation.

The maintenance of soil fertility at a satisfactory level while at the same time producing profitable crops is an intricate problem. It is related to and depends upon many variable factors not strictly of a fertility nature. These factors definitely govern the scope of the various fertility problems and are in turn affected by soil fertility maintenance. Consequently, the *over-all soil management* requirements must be discussed briefly before narrowing our attention to the problems of soil fertility.

21:1. THE FIVE MAJOR FEATURES OF GOOD SOIL MANAGEMENT

In outlining a good system of soil management five major features usually are cited. Of these *good tilth* deserves first consideration. (See p. 65.) This means a suitable condition of the soil physically and implies in addition a satisfactory regulation of soil moisture and soil air. The proper maintenance of soil humus and the encouragement thereby of granulation are the first requisites of tilth. Plowing and cultivation should loosen the soil with a minimum of soil aggregate destruction. These operations should be properly timed, especially with respect to soil moisture. Good tilth also is a primary factor in erosion control and in a broad way is related to crop

527

rotation. A good rotation should preserve or perhaps even enhance soil aggregation.[1]

The *control of weeds*, a second major factor in soil management, is also closely associated with good tilth. At certain times during the growing season tillage is practiced almost wholly for the control of weeds. Some weeds, however, such as mustard, quack grass and bindweed, cannot be discouraged effectively by cultivation, and other means must be employed. Of these, herbicide sprays seem most effective. (See p. 205.) Weeds, by using moisture and nutrients that otherwise might go to the crop, undoubtedly are one of the most serious problems that confront many farmers.

The control of *plant diseases* and *insect pests* is in certain cases a phase of soil management. Many insects and disease organisms pass a part, or the whole, of their life cycle in the soil. The handling of the soil may greatly affect their virulence. The time of plowing the land, the order of the crops grown, the intervals between the successive crops, the burning of residues, and the addition of chemicals are illustrative of the relation of soil management to insect and disease control. The fall plowing of the land to reduce cutworm activity and the burning or plowing under of cornstalks to suppress the corn-borer organisms are specific examples. The addition of sulfur to lower the pH in potato-scab control and the use of hydroxide of lime to make the soil alkaline in the suppression of the club root disease of cabbage may also be cited.

A *proper sequence of crops* is also in part a feature of soil management since the rotation employed greatly influences the soil physically, chemically, and biologically. For instance, sod crops tend to conserve nitrogen, encourage humus accumulation, and promote granulation. Cultivated crops, on the other hand, encourage organic decay and increase the losses of nutrients in drainage. Whether a crop is a legume or a nonlegume is an important consideration. Again, erosion control is in part a question of crop selection. In short, no system of soil management is complete until a suitable rotation has been decided upon. The role of crop rotation in soil fertility maintenance will be discussed later. (See p. 542.)

---

[1] Experiments on Marshall silt loam at Clarinda, Iowa, show that soil aggregation in 1949, after an eight-year comparison of continuous corn with a rotation of corn-oats-meadow, was about twice as high on the latter set of plots. Moreover there was a positive correlation between corn yields and degree of granulation.

C. H. M. Van Bavel and F. W. Schaller, "Soil Aggregation, Organic Matter, and Yields in a Long-Time Experiment as Affected by Crop Management," *Proc. Soil Sci. Soc. Amer.*, 15: 399–408, 1950.

A good system of soil management should, above all, provide an adequate supply of *available plant nutrients*. This is the fifth major requisite. If the fertility of the soil is high, the situation is comparatively simple. The good tilth and adequate aeration and moisture control already emphasized should make it possible for plants to absorb the nutrients in proper amounts. That is, in a fertile soil chemical and biological processes are so regulated and encouraged as to supply sufficient quantities of nitrogen, phosphoric acid, potash, lime, and other constituents necessary for satisfactory crop growth.

But on the other hand, if any one of these essential elements is lacking, it must be added. As most land soon requires such additions, the maintenance of a well balanced fertility has become a most important and widespread problem in the management of soils, particularly in humid regions. Even in arid regions perhaps the only feature holding a priority rating is water supply.

21:2. NUTRIENT GAINS AND LOSSES AS THEY INFLUENCE FERTILITY MANAGEMENT

All the elements essential for the growth of plants are involved in the fertility management of a soil. Supplying each of these elements entails problems which are unique and which often differ markedly from the supply problems of the others. One basic principle is essentially the same, however, for all of these constituents; *the maintenance of optimum amounts of the nutrient elements can be realized only by keeping a favorable equilibrium between gains and losses.* Here, again, excesses as well as deficiencies must be considered. Also, the gains and losses refer directly only to those forms of a given element which are readily *available* for plant growth. For example, the solution of phosphorus from insoluble minerals is just as valid a gain as is the phosphorus supplied by fertilizers. Conversely, the reversion of added phosphates to insoluble forms is an actual loss of available phosphorus, even if only a temporary one. (See Fig. 21:3.)

21:3. FERTILITY MANAGEMENT IN OUTLINE

The major features that must be looked to in the successful management of soil fertility are seven in number. When properly co-ordinated they may be considered as a *system* of fertility maintenance. They are listed below with some of the means by which they are effectively attained in practice.

1. Adequate supply of nitrogen from
   - Crop residues
   - Farm manure
   - Legumes
     - Regular crop
     - Green manure
   - Rain and snow
   - Nitrogen fertilizers

2. Addition of soil organic matter by means of
   - Crop residues
   - Farm manure
   - Green manure
     - Legume
     - Nonlegume

3. Application of lime if necessary
   - Calcic or dolomitic limestone is most commonly used.

4. Addition of phosphorus
   - Superphosphate or other phosphatic fertilizers

5. Provision for available potassium by means of
   - Farm manure
   - Crop residues
   - Potash fertilizers

6. Sulfur deficiencies are met with
   - Flowers of sulfur or gypsum or superphosphate
   - Sulfur compounds carried in rain and snow

7. Application of trace elements
   - As separate salts or in mixtures

21:4. THE NITROGEN DEFICIT—HOW MET

The relationship between the gains and loss in available soil nitrogen is shown in Figure 20:1. A few generalizations on expected gains and losses should be helpful in studying this diagram. For example, with field crop rotations, it has been shown that nitrogen losses by leaching and volatilization are approximately offset by rainfall and azofication additions. This leaves the removal of nitrogen by crops and erosion as the two major deficits to be met. The combined losses from arable soils probably amount to at least 75 or 100 pounds of nitrogen per acre yearly. Let us review briefly the most effective means of meeting this deficit.

Crop residues—legumes. The return to the soil of plant materials, including roots and tops, is an important, but often overlooked, source of nitrogen. The plant tissues thus returned may be by-product crop residues remaining after the harvest or they may be green manure crops grown specifically to conserve or add nitrogen. In either case the probability of actually adding to the available soil nitrogen supply is greatly increased if the crop is a legume. A crop of red clover, sweet clover or vetch, for example, may contain from 100 to 150 pounds of nitrogen an acre, much of which is fixed by microorganisms associated with their roots.

Figure 21:1. Diagram showing the major gains and losses of *available* soil nitrogen. The width of the arrows indicates roughly the magnitude of the losses and the addition often encountered. It should be emphasized that the diagram represents average conditions only and that much variability is to be expected in the actual and relative quantities of nitrogen involved.

Farm manure. Another method used on many farms to return nitrogen is that of applying barnyard manure. This by-product carries approximately 10 pounds of nitrogen to the ton and is too valuable to be neglected. Assuming a 10-ton application an acre once in a five-year rotation, the return to land so treated would amount to 20 pounds of nitrogen an acre yearly. While by no means meeting the nitrogen deficit, farm manure narrows it considerably.

Nitrogen from humus and commercial fertilizers. The methods of supplying available nitrogen so far considered generally fall short of replacing the annual losses of this element from soils. Much of this deficiency has been met in the past by the release of nitrogen from decaying soil organic matter. The rate of release from this form apparently was sufficiently rapid when virgin soils were first cultivated to meet crop demands. In time, however, the soil organic matter became reduced in most cases to the point where the rate of nitrogen release from this source was insufficient to obtain maximum crop yields. Consequently, commercial fertilizers were turned to in an effort to maintain a satisfactory supply of available nitrogen. Today such materials not only supplement the other methods of supplying this element, but in many cases they furnish a major supply. In the future, such sources probably will become even more important.

21:5. THE MAINTENANCE OF ACTIVE SOIL ORGANIC MATTER

The nitrogen control of organic matter. Soil humus accumulation is essentially a nitrogen problem, since the nitrogen of the soil organic matter exerts a marked control on the amount of humus that results. This is because of the relatively constant organic matter-nitrogen ratio. Under ordinary conditions in humid region cultivated soils, the humus attains a ratio of roughly 20 to 1 with the nitrogen present. The greater the amount of organic nitrogen, the higher will be the organic level maintained in mineral soils. The various means of supplying nitrogen cited above thus become doubly significant in practical agriculture.

Organic matter level. As to the amount of humus that should be maintained in any particular soil, a statement made on page 159 can well be repeated. "Since the rate at which carbon is lost from the soil increases very rapidly as the organic content is raised, the maintenance of the humus at a high level is not only difficult but also expensive. It is, therefore, unwise to hold the organic matter above a level consistent with crop yields that pay best. Just what this level should be will depend on climatic environments, soil conditions, the particular crops grown and their sequence." (See also Fig. 6:10.)

Activity of organic matter. The activity of the soil organic matter is usually even more important than the actual amount of this constituent present. Many productive soils possess much less nitrogen and organic matter than those in the same community whose crop yields are considerably lower. The analysis of the Ontario loam, a soil of high productivity, and that of the Volusia salt loam, naturally a rather poor soil, well illustrate this point (Table 21:1).

A major difference between these two soils is the amount of active lime which governs in part the effectiveness both of the nitrogen and the organic matter. The poor drainage of the Volusia is also a vital factor. In spite of the larger amounts of nitrogen and humus in the Volusia silt loam, their turnover, due to the inadequate supply of lime and the slow drainage, is too sluggish to meet the needs of most crops. Other unfavorable physiological conditions no doubt grow out of the lack of lime and poor aeration.

TABLE 21:1

Percentage Composition of Ontario Loam and Volusia Silt Loam as Sampled in New York (The Figures Are Averages of Twelve Analyses in Each Case) [a]

Constituents in Total	Ontario Loam	Volusia Silt Loam
Organic matter (N x 20)	3.20	5.00
Nitrogen (N)	0.16	0.25
Phosphoric acid (P₂O₅)	0.11	0.16
Potash (K₂O)	1.98	2.16
Magnesia (MgO)	0.74	0.80
Lime (CaO)	1.04	0.40
Sulfur trioxide (SO₃)	0.14	0.19

[a] J. A. Bizzell, *Chemical Composition of New York Soils,* Bulletin 513, Cornell Univ. Agr. Exp. Sta., 1930.

21:6. THE IMPORTANCE OF CALCIUM AND MAGNESIUM

The major means by which available calcium and magnesium are increased or decreased in soils are shown diagramatically in Figure 21:2. In contrast to the situation in respect to nitrogen, the content of these elements in plants is comparatively low. Consequently, their loss through crop removal as well as their addition through crop residues and farm manure are correspondingly small.

Fertilizer and soil mineral sources. Although the contents of these two elements in mixed fertilizers are not usually guaranteed, they are often furnished in significant quantities in these materials. For example, calcium is an important constituent of such fertilizers as superphosphate, rock phosphate and calcium cyanamid. Magnesium may be added in special fertilizers as sulfate of magnesia or in the dolomite commonly carried by non-acid-forming fertilizers. One would also expect small quantities of available calcium and magnesium to be released by the continuous but slow weathering of certain complex soil minerals.

Leaching and erosion losses vs. liming. Although the changes in available calcium and magnesium cited above are important, a very large proportion of the turnover of these elements is concerned with two other major phases. These are (1) losses of these constituents through leaching and erosion, and (2) their addition in various liming materials.

The combined losses of these nutrients through erosion and leaching often are as great as 500 pounds of CaCO₃ equivalent per acre each year.

This drain is worthy of consideration because of the deficiencies of calcium and magnesium which it may cause. Even more important, however, are the indirect effects of such losses on soil properties, such as per cent base saturation, pH, biological activity, and nutrient availability. Thus, liming practices are used to maintain a favorable physiological condition as well as for nutritional reasons.

Figure 21:2. A schematic representation showing the important ways by which *available* calcium and magnesium are supplied to and removed from soils. The major losses are through leaching and erosion. These are largely replaced by lime and fertilizer applications. Additions in the latter form are much higher than is generally realized due to the large quantities of calcium contained in superphosphates.

It should by all means be remembered that lime is not to be used carelessly as a cure-all but is to be applied judiciously. Too much lime or lime for the wrong crop may be just as bad as the failure to enlist its benefits when they are possible. Chemical tests, especially a determination of soil pH, are indispensable in making lime decisions. The choice of lime to be used should also be carefully made, especially where magnesium deficiencies are suspected.

21:7. THE MAINTENANCE OF AVAILABLE PHOSPHORUS

The maintenance of an available supply of phosphorus is perhaps even more difficult than that of nitrogen or organic matter. A glance at the diagram in Figure 21:3 verifies this fact. This diagram also shows that the factors affecting the quantity of available phosphorus in soils differ markedly from those concerned with the other nutrients. The removal of phosphorus by growing plants is small compared to that of the other so-called "fertilizer" elements, nitrogen and potassium. Consequently, the loss of this element through crop removal is not excessive nor is the return of phosphorus in crop residues of major importance. Because of the relative insolubility of soil phosphorus compounds, the leaching of this element is essentially nil. Erosion losses are also small, especially when compared to those of potassium, calcium, and magnesium.

Figure 21:3. A drawing showing how the *available* phosphorus level in a soil is depleted and replenished. Note that the two main features are the addition of phosphate fertilizers and the fixation of this element in insoluble forms. It should be remembered that the amount of available phosphorus in the soil at any one time is relatively small, especially when compared to that of calcium, magnesium, and potassium. For the availability of soil phosphorus, see Figure 17:1 on page 434.

A twofold program. Maintaining sufficient available phosphorus in a soil thus largely narrows down to a twofold program: (1) the addition of phosphorus containing fertilizers; and (2) the regulation in some degree of the fixation in the soil of both the added and the native phosphates. For many years phosphatic fertilizers have been a standard and effective recommendation. There are only a few soils which do not give or have not given a crop response to available phosphorus applications. Today commercial fertilizers thus supply most of the phosphorus available to crop plants.

Unfortunately, most of the added phosphates do not long remain in an available form. Depending on the soil pH, they are converted to either iron and aluminum compounds (in acid soils) or calcium compounds (in neutral and alkaline soils). In either case much of the phosphorus is fixed in the form of insoluble minerals from which this element is released very slowly. (See Fig. 17:2.) Judicious liming practices which will maintain intermediate pH values (6.0 to 7.0) result in a minimum of phosphorus fixation in the above forms and consequently promote maximum availability to plants. The regulation of soil pH is thus a phase of phosphate management that must not be neglected. (See Fig. 14:5.)

21:8. ADEQUATE AVAILABLE POTASSIUM

Mineral soils, other than those of a markedly sandy nature, contain large stores of potassium. The potash figure for the representative mineral soil is approximately 40,000 pounds to the acre-furrow-slice, not to mention the vast stores of this constituent in the subsoil root zone. In spite of this fact, however, at any one time only a few hundred pounds per acre of available potassium at most are found in an average soil. Obviously, the potash problem of the average soil is not a question of totals but of availability.

Potassium losses and gains. The problem of maintaining soil potassium is outlined diagramatically in Figure 21:4. As was the case for

Figure 21:4. Gains and losses in *available* soil potassium under average field conditions. The approximate magnitude of the changes is represented by the width of the arrows. For any specific case the actual amounts of potassium added or lost undoubtedly may vary considerably from the above representation.

As was the case with nitrogen and phosphorus, it is well to note the increasing importance of commercial fertilizers in meeting crop demands. Also, it should be pointed out that the fixation and release by potash-bearing minerals will be much greater if soils contain appreciable quantities of minerals such as illite, a clay that is especially high in total and exchangeable potash. For the various forms of potassium in soils and their relative magnitude and relationships, see Figure 17:8 on page 452.

each of the nutrients so far discussed, certain features of the problem are different from those of any other element. Crop removal of potash generally exceeds that of the other essential elements with the possible exception of nitrogen. Annual losses from plant removal as great as 100 pounds K_2O per acre are not uncommon, particularly if the crop is a legume and is cut several times for hay. As you might expect, therefore, the return of crop residues and manures is very important in maintaining soil potash. As an example, ten tons of average barnyard manure supply about 100 pounds of potash, fully equal to the amount of nitrogen thus supplied.

The annual losses of available potassium by leaching and erosion greatly exceed those of nitrogen and phosphorus. They are generally not as great, however, as the corresponding losses of available calcium and magnesium. The available potassium depletion by erosion assumes considerable importance when we consider that *total* potassium removal in this manner generally exceeds that of any other major nutrient element. The loss of potential sources of available potassium (soil minerals) cannot but eventually be serious.

Increasing use of potash fertilizers. In the past, potash added in the form of fertilizers has been considered largely as a supplement to that returned in crop residues and that obtained from the slowly available forms of potassium carried by soil minerals. This is still the case on many soils high in slowly available potassium.

On other soils, however, fertilizer potash is now depended upon to supply most of that needed for crop production. This is especially true in cash crop areas and in regions where sandy soils are prominent. Even in some heavier soils, the release of potassium from mineral form is much too slow to support maximum plant yields. Consequently, increased usage of commercial potash must be expected if yields are to be increased or even maintained.[2]

21:9. SULFUR DEFICIENCY

Although sulfur is mentioned specifically in the scheme of fertility management presented on page 530, this nutrient usually is taken care of more or less incidentally by the type of soil management in vogue and may not need special attention. Considerable sulfur is added to arable soils in crop residues, green manures, and farm manure, the latter carrying perhaps 5 or 10 pounds a ton. Besides this, appreciable amounts often are added by

---

[2] A 6–12–12 is now considered as a sort of general purpose fertilizer rather than the 5–10–5 so popular several years ago. This shift in preference is good evidence of the growing importance of potash in soil fertilization.

rain and snow, the quantity ranging from a few pounds an acre annually to as much perhaps as 100 pounds in extreme cases. Another automatic addition is that absorbed from the atmosphere by the soil. (See page 487.) This is thought at times to equal the amount brought down by rain and snow.

Moreover, such fertilizers as sulfate of ammonia, sulfate of potash, and ordinary superphosphate carry appreciable amounts of sulfur. Since the latter fertilizer is approximately one-half gypsum, 100 pounds will supply about 12 pounds of combined sulfur, enough for an acre of the average crop. In the light of such figures, it would seem that soil sulfur, except in certain cases, is not likely to be an element that calls for an unusual amount of attention. Routine fertility practices in most cases should automatically take care of this constituent.

21:10. THE TRACE ELEMENTS

Trace-element fertilization is a phrase of soil management that is destined to great development. The reason is obvious. Our fertility efforts for years have had to do largely with nitrogen, phosphorus, potassium, and lime. In many cases constant cropping with such an unbalanced replacement has gradually exhausted the small amounts of available copper, zinc, manganese, and boron below the current needs especially of certain crops. At present, plant malnutrition due to trace-element deficiencies is becoming apparent in localized areas wherever crops have been grown for any great length of time. This is especially true in eastern and central United States.

Already crop specialists are familiar with the symptoms of trace-element deficiencies [3] and, as time goes on, the growers themselves will learn them for the relatively small number of crops with which they, individually, are concerned. The fertilizer salts that commonly are used have already been considered (p. 488) and gradually the rates of application will be standardized for individual crops and particular soil types.

It is especially important to note here that no fertility diagnosis is now complete without a consideration of the trace elements. So long as even one is deficient, the crop will be unable to make adequate use of the other nutrients no matter how liberally the latter are supplied or how favorable environmental conditions may be. A nutrient ration can be just as seriously

[3] For literature dealing with trace element deficiencies, see *Hunger Signs in Crops,* American Society of Agronomy and the National Fertilizer Association, Washington, D. C., 1949.

unbalanced because of the lack of a mere trace of zinc or boron as from a deficiency of nitrogen or potash.

21:11. THE FLEXIBILITY AND INTERLOCKING OF FERTILITY PHASES

The proper coordination of the various fertility phases described above may, for want of a better term, be referred to as a *system*. The objective is, of course, the maintenance of soil fertility at a satisfactory economic level. Since the various phases may or may not all be applied in any given case, the *flexibility* of the system is apparent.

Another feature of the system worthy of particular attention is the influence of its various phases on the effectiveness of the others, that is—*interlocking* effects. For instance, the amount and activity of the organic nitrogen determines the quantity of humus that can be maintained in a soil. Conversely, organic matter decay influences the mobility and availability of the nitrogen. Thus, the control of the one constituent cannot be attained without almost equal consideration of the other.

Lime also affects the other phases of the system in a very decided way. Through its influence on the soil microorganisms, it has much to do with the activity of the organic matter and the availability of the nitrogen. In fact, the vigor with which carbon and nitrogen revolve in their respective cycles is determined in large degree by calcium and other bases. Also the addition of lime undoubtedly at times liberates potash directly and by speeding up organic decay a decided indirect influence is exerted.

The importance of lime in respect to pH adjustment and the efficiency of superphosphate is widely recognized (p. 398). Conversely, the potassium and phosphorus by their nutritional effects upon microorganisms and higher plants not only render the application of lime to soils more efficient but also beneficially influence the activity of nitrogen and organic matter.

Although less clearly understood, the trace elements are just as definitely interdependent as are the other phases. Thus, the proper interlocking of all of these features means, in general terms, a well-balanced physiological condition within the soil. This ideal, unfortunately, is seldom fully realized in practice.

21:12. A TEST OF THE SYSTEM

Whatever the combination of fertility factors utilized, their effectiveness can only be proved by actual field tests covering a long period. While much data are available in this respect, certain experiments at the Ohio Agricultural Experiment Station are especially interesting because they employ every means of fertility maintenance except the use of complete commercial fertilizers. (See Table 21:2.)

TABLE 21:2

Crop Yields on a Set of Plots at the Ohio Agricultural Experiment Station, Average of Twenty-six Years. (The full treatment consisted of crop residues, legumes, lime, farm manure, and superphosphate. The rotation was corn, wheat, and clover) [a]

Treatment	Average Crop Yield per Acre		
	Corn, Bushels	Wheat, Bushels	Clover Hay, Tons
1. Full treatment	66.2	28.4	2.34
2. Lacking superphosphate	58.9	23.3	1.95
3. Lacking farm manure and superphosphate	36.8	14.2	1.46

[a] C. G. Williams, *The Maintenance of Soil Fertility,* Bulletin 381, Ohio Agr. Exp. Sta., 325, 1924.

Under conditions of good tillage and drainage, corn, wheat, and clover were grown in the order indicated for twenty-six years, enough plots being used to allow a crop of each to be harvested every year. Lime was added, usually just before the corn was planted. In the full treatment the corn received farm manure at the rate of 8 tons to the acre reinforced with 320 pounds of superphosphate.

The essentials of the system applied to the first group of this series of plats were: crop residues, farm manure, lime, legumes as a crop in a suitable rotation, and superphosphate. Trace elements apparently were not lacking and the soil potash in this particular case was apparently adequate. Ultimately, however, potassium and even the trace elements will probably become deficient and a complete fertilizer will be required. In the second group of plots noted, superphosphate was excluded, while in the third group both superphosphate and farm manure were withheld.

The deductions from the data presented are so obvious as to need little explanation. Lime not only exerted a favorably and cumulative influence on this soil but also greatly encouraged the clover. The legume, of course, tended to increase or at least maintain the yields of the other crops of the rotation. The average crop yields of the plats receiving the full treatment were over 12 per cent greater during the last half of the period than during the first half. It is difficult to escape the conclusion that such a system may maintain the productivity of certain soils for a considerable number of years.

In spite of the apparent soundness of the above deductions, a word of warning is in order. The fact that crop yields are rising does not necessarily mean that the basic capacity of soils to produce also is going up or even is unimpaired. There is some evidence that the inherent productiveness of many field soils has been on the down grade. That this may be the trend in some cases is shown by Figure 21:5 which pictures the situation in Ohio [4]

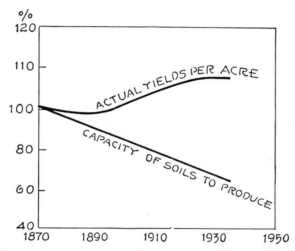

Figure 21:5. Trends in Ohio since 1870 as pictured by R. M. Salter, R. D. Lewis, and J. A. Slipher, "Our Heritage the Soil," Extension Bul. 175, Ohio Agr. Exp. Sta., 1941.

Note that while the inherent capacity of Ohio soils to produce has dropped sharply, actual crop yields have even increased. Apparently new techniques, improved varieties of crops, new lands, tile drainage, and other factors have so far counterbalanced fertility depletion and land exploitations. Sound soil management practices are needed if the soil's capacity to produce is to be maintained.

from 1870 to 1935. During this period, the basic capacity of Ohio field soils to produce was apparently decreased. In recent years, increased fertilizer use and other practices may have reversed this downward trend in soil productivity. In any case, these data emphasize the need for a sound fertility program if we are to maintain productive soils.

[4] R. M. Salter; R. D. Lewis; and J. A. Slipher, *Our Heritage the Soil,* Extension Bul. 175, Ohio Agr. Exp. Sta., 1941.

21:13. CROP ROTATION—AN IMPORTANT FERTILITY FACTOR

While the importance of crop residues, farm manure, green manure, legumes, lime, commercial fertilizers, and tillage is fully recognized, few persons realize the benefits that are derived from a suitable crop rotation. The oversight apparently occurs because the average farmer usually has no means of gauging the benefits of alternating his crops, while the influence of farm manure or of commercial fertilizer is generally clearly apparent.

A study of the long-continued field experiments in the United States and in England has brought out some exceedingly important facts regarding the benefits of a good rotation.[5] The more important may be stated as follows:

1. Rotation of crops when practiced with and without fertilizers averaged 75 per cent as effective as the fertilizers in increasing crop yields and 90 per cent as effective when the comparisons were limited to corn, oats, and wheat. In maintaining the productive power of soils in respect to these three crops, the rotation was in general at least 90 per cent as effective as the fertilizers.
2. The benefits of crop rotations did not impair those received from manure and commercial fertilizers. In other words, the effects from the rotations were more or less distinct and did not in any sense take the place of or render unnecessary the use of farm manure or fertilizers.
3. Excluding such crops as clover, timothy, and cowpeas, the average effectiveness of rotations was practically 20 per cent higher on soils that had been limed than those left acid.
4. On soils long under cultivation, the best results were possible only when a crop rotation containing a legume, and receiving farm manure and commercial fertilizers, was used.

For more specific figures respecting the benefits derived from a suitable rotation of crops, reference may again be made to data of the Ohio Agricultural Experiment Station. In this experiment corn, oats, and wheat were grown separately and continuously on the same land for thirty years, receiving each year farm manure at the rate of 5 tons to the acre. At the same time these crops were grown in a five-year rotation of corn, oats, wheat, and two years of clover and timothy. The rotation received 16 tons of manure every five years divided between the corn and wheat. Since this would average only 3⅕ tons of manure yearly, it is obvious that the rotated crops were not favored as to artificial fertilization in comparison with those grown continuously. The yield data are set forth in Table 21:3.

[5] W. W. Weir, *A Study of the Value of Crop Rotation in Relation to Soil Productivity*, Bulletin 1377, U.S. Dept. of Agric., 1926.

TABLE 21:3

The Comparative Influence of Continuous Culture and Rotation Cropping
upon Yield—Ohio Agricultural Experiment Station,
Average of Thirty Years [a]

	Crop Yields in Bushels per Acre		
Treatment	*Corn*	*Oats*	*Wheat*
Continuous culture	33.8	37.8	19.4
Rotation cropping	51.3	43.7	23.5

[a] C. G. Williams, *The Maintenance of Soil Fertility*, Bulletin 381, Ohio Agr. Exp. Sta., 296–311, 1924.

The results are so striking that little comment is necessary except to suggest that crops grown in sequence probably utilize the soil nutrients more economically than those in continuous culture, and that the rotated crops without a doubt were greatly benefited by the clover. This legume not only acquires nitrogen from the air, if suitably nodulated, but its residues activate the soil constituents as well.

21:14. FERTILITY GENERALIZATION (Before reading this section examine Figure 21:6 and carefully read its legend.)

The system so briefly outlined in the preceding pages is merely a group of practices that are designed, when properly correlated, to maintain, or partially maintain, the fertility and productivity of mineral soils. In some cases all of the features are put into operation, in other cases only a few are employed.

In general and dairy farming the utilization of crop residues, farm manure, legumes, and superphosphate is one of the simplest combinations that can be made of the various fertility factors. Lime may or may not be necessary, while on occasion green manures will be helpful. Because of the rapidity with which potassium deficiencies are now appearing, especially in humid region soils, complete commercial fertilizers are being used more and more frequently. Moreover, trace element deficiencies will need increased attention as time goes on. And whatever may be the fertility combination, its efficiency will be enhanced by a suitable rotation of crops.

With intensive vegetable production the main reliance is usually placed upon complete fertilizers in liberal amounts. With certain other crops an adequate supply of nitrogen and the maintenance of the soil organic matter at present may be the only serious considerations. This is the case with apple production on the medium and heavier types of soil. Again, for still other crops such as tobacco and potatoes, potash and phosphoric acid as well as nitrogen are of particular concern.

Figure 21:6. This lush landscape bespeaks a fertile and productive soil. That the owners hope to keep it so is indicated by the strip cropping and the presence of legumes in a rotation that provides abundant organic residues.

If the other fertility factors are as well taken care of, crop yields will not decline. They may even increase. That trace element deficiencies may sometime appear is probable but an alert county agricultural agent, or even the farmer himself, may anticipate this before crop production is seriously affected. (*U. S. Soil Conservation Service photo.*)

Satisfactory soil productivity is the ultimate objective of soil utilization. The scheme used is a coordination of certain practices and manipulations that are designed to best attain this objective. Sound soil fertility management is, therefore, a practical application of edaphological principles and consequently calls for a thorough knowledge of the nature and properties of soils and their relationship to higher plants.

Index

545